Alcohol, Science and Society

Alcohol, Science and Society

Twenty-nine Lectures with Discussions
as Given at the Yale Summer School
of Alcohol Studies

86099

New Haven
QUARTERLY JOURNAL OF STUDIES ON ALCOHOL

Lecturers

DWIGHT ANDERSON, LL.B.
Director of Public Relations, Medical Society of the State of New York.

SELDEN D. BACON, PH.D.
Assistant Professor of Sociology, Yale University.

REV. ROLAND H. BAINTON, PH.D.
Professor of Ecclesiastical History, Yale University.

EDWARD G. BAIRD, JUR.SC.D.
Research Associate (Associate Professor), Law, Applied Physiology, Yale University.

SYBIL M. BAKER
General Secretary, Family Department, Brookline Friendly Society.

RALPH S. BANAY, M.D.
Lecturer in Criminal Psychopathology, College of Physicians and Surgeons, Columbia University.

DONALD S. BERRY, PH.D.
Director, Traffic and Transportation Division, National Safety Council.

JOHN DOLLARD, PH.D.
Research Associate (Professor), Social Anthropology, Yale University.

EDWARD B. DUNFORD, LL.D.
Attorney at Law, Washington, D.C.

ROBERT FLEMING, M.D.
Instructor in Psychiatry, Harvard University Medical School.

LEON A. GREENBERG, PH.D.
Assistant Professor, Applied Physiology, Yale University.

HOWARD W. HAGGARD, M.D.
Director (Professor), Laboratory of Applied Physiology, Yale University.

DONALD HORTON, PH.D.
Assistant in Anthropology, Yale University.

E. M. JELLINEK, SC.D.
Research Associate (Professor), Applied Physiology, Yale University; Director, Summer School of Alcohol Studies.

NORMAN JOLLIFFE, M.D.
Associate Professor of Medicine, New York University College of Medicine.

BENSON Y. LANDIS, PH.D.
Lecturer (Economics), Applied Physiology, Yale University; Associate Secretary, Department of Research and Education, Federal Council of Churches.

CARNEY LANDIS, PH.D.
Associate Professor of Abnormal Psychology, Columbia University.

REV. FRANCIS W. MCPEEK
Executive Director, Department of Social Welfare, Federation of Churches, Washington, D.C.

HON. WILLIAM M. MALTBIE, LL.D., D.C.L.
Chief Justice, Supreme Court, State of Connecticut.

REV. A. J. MURPHY, PH.D.
 Director, Catholic Charities Bureau, Cleveland.
REV. OTIS R. RICE, PH.D.
 Religious Director, St. Luke's Hospital, New York.
ANNE ROE, PH.D.
 Research Assistant (Assistant Professor), Psychology, Applied Physiology, Yale University.
HARRY S. WARNER, PH.B.
 Editor, The International Student.
W. W.
 Cofounder, Alcoholics Anonymous.

Acknowledgment is made to the lecturers who permitted the publication of their lectures from transcription and to all students, named and unnamed, who took part in the discussions.

Contents

Foreword

THE problem of alcoholism has come into increasing prominence during the last hundred years. This prominence has resulted not from an increase in alcoholism, but from the growth of a sense of social responsibility. This humanitarian interest and this prominence heighten the demands for constructive solutions of this problem.

The problem of alcoholism is today not only one of important magnitude but also one that is especially complicated by the fact that the great majority of those who use alcoholic beverages do not become alcoholics. Our citizens, although concerned by the problem, do not support sympathetically any sweeping nihilistic solution which deprives them of the use of alcoholic beverages in moderation.

Many solutions of the problem of the excessive use of such beverages—of alcoholism—have been suggested. Most have been short lived; none has given a practical solution. The failures have been due to no lack of vigor in the attacks but mainly to the fact that the attacks have been centered chiefly on single factors of the problem as if each were the problem as a whole. Only distortion and not solution results from medical, social, legal, educational or religious panaceas.

The problem of alcoholism has medical, social, legal, educational and religious factors. But each is no more than a factor. The problem is the sum of its factors integrated in their proper relations. This statement does not imply that study of the social or legal or any other aspect is without benefit toward solution of the problem. Quite the contrary; it is only thus that solution can be approached. Such study, however, becomes impractical, indeed obstructive, when the student fails to see the relation of the factor to the problem as a whole. The first step toward solution of the problem is definition—the demonstration of the problem in its totality and the factors in their integration.

The Yale Summer School of Alcohol Studies originated as an attempt toward such definition. It was undertaken as an experiment in social education. One problem, that of alcoholism, was dealt with exclusively and intensively from all important aspects. The purpose was to put before the students, most of whom were professional social workers, ministers, temperance educators and school and college teachers, the facts and the theories in their integration.

The School is a project of the Laboratory of Applied Physiology of Yale University. The activities of the School are under the direction of Professor E. M. Jellinek of that Laboratory. The first session was held in 1943 and 80 students were selected from a large list of applicants; in the Session of 1944, it was possible to enroll 147 students. The course extends over 4 weeks of intensive activity with formal lectures followed by discussions from the floor, seminar and group discussions and some demonstrations.

Of the 33 general lectures given in 1944 by men from various institutions, distinguished in their respective fields, 29 were selected for publication. Both lectures and discussions were recorded and transcribed. No attempt has been made to edit the lectures to read as chapters in a book; they are lectures. The discussions have been edited to the extent only of deleting questions which were repetitious or which were not pertinent to the subject under discussion, and shortening those which were garrulous.

Each lecture represents the ideas and beliefs of the individual lecturer. No source material is given with the lectures; that was provided for the students in the seminar and discussion groups.

The 29 lectures which form the text of this book, and which will be described in the introductory lecture, are not offered as any solution to the problem of alcoholism. They are not intended as such. They are offered as the soundest, independent, nontechnical statements now available on certain medical, social, legal and religious aspects of the problem of alcoholism for the student or general reader who wishes a broad and integrated understanding of this problem. The student of sociological education may, in addition, find interest in the pedagogic experiment of which these lectures form a part.

HOWARD W. HAGGARD

Director, Laboratory of Applied Physiology
Yale University

Lecture 1

Introduction to the Curriculum

E. M. Jellinek

THIS is the second year of the School devoted to the scientific study of the problems of alcohol. The first year was one in which we of the faculty learned quite as much, I am sure, as the students. They may have learned something about alcohol; we definitely learned much about pedagogy in this educational venture.

Last year we plunged straight into the lecture course. In my capacity as chairman—as interlocutor—at these lectures, I soon found that the students were not oriented in the scope of the curriculum. On the first day I was asked why there were no lectures on "why men drink"; actually, many of the later lectures dealt with this question. Several students inquired why there were to be so many lectures on personality but none on the social factors involved in the problems of alcoholism, although, as a matter of fact, several sociological lectures were scheduled. In the discussion periods following the first few lectures many questions were asked which had no connection with the subject matter of the lecture just given. It was apparent that the interrogators were afraid that no opportunity would arise to present these questions in a relevant context. Thus, for instance, during the discussion of the metabolism of alcohol, someone asked the lecturer whether it was not true that the Roman Empire fell when the Romans began to drink heavily. The question was asked at that time because the interrogator thought that no lecture was provided in which a historical question could be cogently presented.

Since we had given each student a schedule of lectures, I could not at first see how such lack of orientation had come about. When I began to think about it, however, I realized that the fault was with us and not with the students. They had been given a list of lecture titles which did not and could not convey much to them concerning the full content and scope of the lectures. Hence I decided on this introductory lecture, which should orient you in the entire curriculum.

To begin with, you may note in your schedules that only a few of the lectures deal with physiological topics. The fact that a physiological laboratory should lay so little stress on its own field in this course is highly significant. It will be illuminating to know how this came about.

The quaint old Yale building which houses the Laboratory of Applied Physiology has a great past. It was once the residence of Mr. Sheffield, after whom the Sheffield Scientific School is named. Later, it became a physiological laboratory in which, under Dr. Russell Chittenden, physiological chemistry was started in America. Dr. Chittenden was one of the key men of the famous Committee of Fifty which, in the 1890's, surveyed the literature on alcohol and undertook some original social surveys and some original experiments.

In 1923 the building became the home of the Laboratory of Applied Physiology, first under the directorship of Dr. Yandell Henderson and, on his retirement in 1938, under that of Dr. Howard W. Haggard. About 1930 Dr. Haggard and his associates began an intensive experimental program on the physiology of alcohol. In the course of time these experiments yielded valuable information on the metabolism of alcohol and particularly on factors which modify its absorption and oxidation. The findings contributed to the understanding of the effects of alcohol and, in a practical way, they contributed to a rational treatment of acute alcoholic intoxication. While the value of such experimental studies must be recognized, it must also be recognized—and I know that Dr. Haggard recognized it particularly keenly—that they contribute only indirectly to the understanding of the question of how inebriety arises. Nor have such studies yielded any tools which could be applied to the prevention of inebriety. The same may be said of the physiological investigations in all laboratories of America and Europe.

Dr. Haggard came more and more to the conclusion that by itself physiology could not contribute essentially to the solution of the alcohol problem, but that this goal could be achieved only through an integration of the researches from many branches of science. As a first step he founded the QUARTERLY JOURNAL OF STUDIES ON ALCOHOL, which opened its pages to the objective discussion of alcohol problems ranging from chemistry to taxation.

The second step was the organization of a unit in which representatives of sociology, psychiatry, internal medicine, psychology, economics, law and statistics would cooperate on alcohol researches and their practical applications in education and therapy. This program supplements the physiological investigations of the Laboratory and includes both the Yale Plan Clinics for the rehabilitation of inebriates and this Summer School. The School can thus be best understood when it is viewed as a part of our total activities, which I shall describe briefly.

INTEGRATED RESEARCH

We are attacking a complex problem and it is not possible to carry out research on a complex problem as a whole, but only on its component parts. Nevertheless, it is possible to devise the individual projects in a manner which will not reduce them to arbitrary abstractions but permit of resynthesis.

The statement that the problem of alcoholism cannot be solved by statutes alone, but that it requires broad social measures, economic readjustments, and education of the individual and of society as well as rehabilitation of the inebriates, does not mean that it is sufficient to carry out all of these various activities simultaneously, but rather that these measures must be brought into a definite relation to one another. What I mean by integration may be illustrated by a homely example.

I have before me a recipe for chicken à la king. This recipe calls for certain amounts of butter, fresh mushrooms, salt, flour, milk or chicken stock, chicken cut in pieces, pimentos, and pepper. Can you imagine the lumpy atrocity which would result if I were to dump all these ingredients into a bowl, mix them up and cook them in a pan? Actually, in order to achieve an integration of these elements into chicken à la king, I must first melt the butter, add the mushrooms, cover the pan and let it cook about 5 minutes. When this has been completed, according to the recipe, I should dredge the contents with flour—whatever dredging might mean—add the seasonings and liquid and let that simmer, and lastly, add the chicken and pimentos. And then I really get chicken à la king. You see that in this procedure, these various ingredients, the butter, flour, milk, and so on, have all been brought into proper relation to each other. The integration of the elements of a problem proceeds on the same general principles. There is no sense in a large variety of researches if they are not brought into a definite system of correlation.

As to the description of our research set-up, I can give an idea here of our general approach and illustrate it from one or two fields. These illustrations will show, among other features, how far the program has extended beyond the physiological studies from which it was an outgrowth.

Among other activities, we have legal research. I shall not give you the details of the legal researches, particularly since you will hear about them from Professor Baird, but for exemplification I should like to touch on the principles that guide us in them, for they are the principles which also guide us in our other studies—social, economic, psychological, physiological and even clinical.

In his book, *Liquor Control*, G. E. Catlin says, "This question [that is, legal control] has usually been approached neither from the side of the empirical test of the social results of learning by doing, nor from the side of research into the permanent physiological, psychological, and social causes of the problem but from the side of abstract principle." It is this abstract principle from which we wish to emancipate ourselves in legal research without losing sight of the fact that legislative action cannot be divorced from legal thought. We wish to analyze to what extent existing or past statutes are rooted in social factors, to what extent statutes aim at what society expects of them and believes to be their goal. We want to test the effectiveness of statutes in terms of indexes of inebriety, such as death from alcoholism, alcoholic mental disorders, and related manifestations. We want to analyze the reasons of success and failure of identical statutes in different localities. We want to test the dependence of successes and failures upon the way the statutes are handled and upon the social factors prevailing in the locality. We want to uncover those social factors which tend to weaken and those which tend to reinforce the law in action.

The objects of our sociological and psychological researches blend, to a considerable extent, with the objects of our legal research. We are investigating not merely inebriety, but that complex of which inebriety is an aspect. We are interested in the function of alcohol in society, that is, in the uses to which society puts it, consciously or unconsciously. We must know what abstinence, moderate and immoderate use of alcoholic beverages signify to society or groups of society in terms of prestige, fellowship, need for the occasional relaxation of certain social rules, as well as in terms of rightly or wrongly attributed virtues and dangers. If the handling of the problem of alcoholism is to be based on knowledge, we must know to what extent and by what means society utilizes the effects on the one hand and attempts to control them on the other hand. And we must study the anomalies of action and of attitude which may arise from the possible conflict of these two opposing trends.

These objectives are to be achieved through carefully designed field surveys such as those being conducted by Dr. Bacon on drinking habits in New Haven and our geographically more scattered survey of the experiences of ministers with individual problems of alcoholism. The extreme form of inebriety is the objective of our study of alcoholic derelicts. Knowledge on the extreme form of the use of alcoholic beverages, namely inebriety, is only one of our objects. We go into all phases of the use of beverage alcohol, whether excessive or not. Briefly, we are studying drinking as a folkway.

The sociological researches are supplemented by investigations into the economic origins and economic consequences of inebriety. Increasing and decreasing expenditures on alcoholic beverages in relation to the national income and to total consumer outlay may reflect what might be called the moods of society. The organization of supply and modes of distribution are factors which play a part in the ups and downs of consumption.

The psychological investigations tend to determine the actions and reactions of personalities in this complex of social and economic stimulation and inhibition. Past psychological research was primarily interested in the range of the psychological effects of alcohol. Our researches are more concerned with motivation. Not only the motivations of the drinker but the motivations of the abstainer, too, receive due attention. Some of our psychological projects are of a formal nature and others are byproducts of clinical observations at the Yale Plan Clinics for the rehabilitation of alcoholics.

I have mentioned here only a few of our many projects and none in the fields of medicine, physiology and bibliography, but these few are sufficient to illustrate the trend of our researches. All our studies aim at finding those facts which show the way toward the prevention of inebriety.

The Meaning of Scientific Study

The nature of all our researches is the reflection of a trend which is becoming, of late, more and more evident in all branches of science. The scientist is discovering his social responsibility and society is discovering the utility of specialized knowledge. The scientist is coming out of his seclusion and entering into the reality of life as it is lived. It is a consequence of the awakening of social responsibility that scientists must make their findings available and understandable to a wide public and not to their professional colleagues only. It has been a curse that in the past there has been a lag of 40 to 60 years between the findings of research and the knowledge of the public. Scientists have wrung their hands in despair that the public was using obsolete facts and obsolete ideas which to them had become practically mythology. It had never occurred to these scientists that if any recrimination was called for, it should have been self-recrimination.

The realization that scientific knowledge must be put to work, that it must take part in the practical solution of social issues, has led to the creation of this School. Its aim is to make the most recent findings of science available to the general public. The best way of accomplishing this is to communicate such knowledge as we have to those who, in their daily activities, come into contact with the general public more intimately than we do here, and who are qualified to process the knowledge which we impart to them for the purpose of general consumption.

That the scientific approach to the alcohol problem may be valuable was only an assumption on our part. The School is a test of this assumption. In the opening lecture of the first session of this School I said:

To those who have doubts about the value of the scientific approach in this particular field I must say that to a certain extent my colleagues and I must share their doubts. Where science is concerned, the scientist cannot believe in untested propositions, and this proposition has not been tested. The scientist may form an hypothesis, but an hypothesis is only a belief. In a sense this School will be a test of the applicability of scientific thought to the problems of alcohol. Because of the composition of the student body of this School it should be an excellent testing ground.

Judging by the attitude of the 79 men and women who attended the first course, one may say that the School has proven to have a definite place in the handling of the problems of alcohol.

We received many letters, after the first session closed, from persons who had not participated. A few hundred urged that the School should declare itself for total abstinence. A few hundred urged that the School should declare itself for moderation. We have also received many letters from the alumni of our School, and none of them has asked us to espouse any cause except the cause of science.

I have used the words "science," "scientific study" and "scientific school" repeatedly. It may be in order to say, in a few words, what is meant by scientific study.

A philosopher said that the scientific attitude is, in some respects, unnatural to man. I believe that what he meant was that man's thought, by nature, is governed by sentiments and wishes, and that it takes a special effort to guard the thought processes against the intrusion of emotions and wishes. Scientific thinking is determined by such a special effort, which in practice never succeeds completely. But this aspect of scientific thinking is not the monopoly of the scientist. Much more characteristic of the scientific attitude is the recognition that casual observation does not necessarily reveal the truth. Uncontrolled and unaided observation in itself may be insufficient for grasping the true nature of the observed.

We are all familiar with the impressions of the child in a moving vehicle. The observation of the child is not that it is in motion, but rather that the trees and houses are moving. The child does not have sufficient experience to see the relation between the observation of motion and the observer.

For thousands of years man had seen the sun rising and setting, and reason told him that he was observing the sun rotating around the earth. But reason was not right. Reason was directed by insufficient knowledge. When astronomers and physicists had accumulated facts which threw light on the observation of the rising and setting sun, it was found that we had misobserved the sun rotating around the earth and were actually observing the earth rotating around its own axis as well as around the sun.

Now it is of particular interest to us, who are discussing the scientific attitude, that the discovery that the earth is not static should have aroused antagonistic emotions. Nobody could have a vested interest in the immobility of the earth. It could not form the object of anybody's wish. Nevertheless this discovery came into conflict with wishes. The discovery implied that if the authority of the ancient philosophers, on which our forefathers had relied for hundreds and hundreds of years, was shown to be faulty in this instance, it might be faulty in many or all instances. The discovery threatened to rob man of his security in forming judgments, to take this authority away from him, to deprive him of landmarks from which he could take his orientation. It was a threat to the security of the reasoning of those times. Men were threatened and they had to make an attempt to save their security. They were not able to see the future implications, and they were not able to look forward to a new security.

That wishes and anxieties may stand in the way of the discovery of the truth, and that observations are not given completely by the sense organs, are well illustrated in this example. The most outstanding characteristic of the scientific attitude is not merely to make observations, but to test and to retest them and to test their significance in the light of all the facts that might have a bearing on them. Nonscientific opinion is based on what we call reason, and therefore may or may not represent truth. In many aspects of human life scientific belief cannot be held, but only nonscientific belief, and in these cases nonscientific belief is by no means of a lower order. But where scientific evidence and scientific tests can be obtained, judgment should not be left to easily deceiving and easily deceived reason. Reason can be plausible and convincing in the absence of all evidence.

May I illustrate this through an anecdote?

In the pre-refrigerator, or rather, pre-icebox days, it was the custom in certain parts of Europe to hang geese intended for the dinner table out of the window at night. The students in a certain university town used to run around with pruning shears and cut the geese down. It happened that the goose of the President of the University disappeared one night, and the rumor was spread that the perpetrator of this crime was the brother of one of the young professors. The young professor felt greatly embarrassed. He called on the President and in a long speech proved that it could not have been his brother. The President listened very attentively, then said, "My dear young colleague, your irrefutable logic has convinced me that it could not have been your brother—but I saw him cutting the goose down."

In our course you will find that we shall accept reasoning only when it follows from observations which have been tested and viewed in the light of many other relevant observations.

THE CURRICULUM

In devising the curriculum our first consideration was to show the complexities of the problem. We found it more important at this time to give a broad picture than to enlarge on any specific aspect. I know that the lecture program may disappoint many of you. The disappointment of the different members of this group may lie in different directions. Those who are interested primarily in the question of what to do with the alcoholic may find it a bore to have to listen to such lectures as, let us say, the philosophy of the temperance movement or the economic aspects of alcohol in modern society. On the other hand, those who are interested in alcoholism primarily as a national manifestation may be impatient with the lectures which are devoted to the individual problems of the alcoholic and to the treatment of the alcoholic. But I can assure you that unless those interested in the public care and therapy of the alcoholic learn about the economic and social involvements which have led their patients to the need for treatment, efforts at rehabilitation will be frustrated. And those who are interested in alcoholism as a national phenomenon will never be successful until they have realized the importance of those individual problems whose aggregate forms the national manifestation. It is with this in mind that we have devised the curriculum.

The course opens with a lecture on the alcohol problem in general. The object of this lecture is to show the many component parts of—and approaches to—the problem in their proper perspective. This is desirable, because in the subsequent lectures of a specific nature each specialty appears to be the crucial matter of the problem. In a lecture of an hour or so, the specialist cannot escape giving the impression that his special knowledge is the key to the problem. He has to crowd many facts into that hour and cannot digress to show the relation of his special data to other special data. This easily becomes a source of confusion in the minds of the students, and thus it is important to assign the proper weights to each specialty at the very beginning of the course.

EFFECTS OF ALCOHOL ON THE INDIVIDUAL

There is, next, a group of five lectures pertaining to the effects of ethyl alcohol on the individual. There are many other alcohols which are contained in alcoholic beverages in minute amounts but when alcohol is spoken of without further qualifications, ethyl alcohol is meant.

The physiological aspects come first, because it is only through the physiological properties of alcohol that alcoholism becomes a problem. If alcohol did not have those physiological properties which it does have, if it had the properties of milk or water, we would not be gathered here. So while the physiological investigations have not yielded the answer as to why some men crave alcohol to excess, the social and personal aspects of alcoholism can be discussed only after having acquired some knowledge of the properties and effects of alcohol as contained in beverages. The first physiological lecture will be given by Dr. Haggard. In that lecture you will hear what happens to alcohol in the body; how it is absorbed into the blood stream; how alcohol is gotten rid of by oxidation, and by elimination through the kidneys and lungs. A knowledge of how the body deals with alcohol is prerequisite to the understanding of what alcohol does to the body. Certain aspects of the psychological effects, too, can be understood only through a knowledge of what happens to alcohol in the body. Before we can talk relevantly about alcoholic intoxication, or about being "under the influence," we must know what "concentration of alcohol in the blood" means, and how concentration of alcohol in the blood is modified by many factors. This first lecture will not touch upon effects, but that need not disappoint you, for the effects will receive full consideration in other lectures.

The second physiological lecture is entitled, "The Concentration of Alcohol in the Blood and its Significance." The best opportunity for the discussion of this subject seems to be right after the metabolism of alcohol has been dealt with. The statistics of traffic accidents will be discussed later in the series, but Professor Greenberg will give you an idea of the extent to which chemical determinations of "drunkenness" are reliable and how such chemical tests may be interpreted. You will also have the opportunity to see an apparatus which Professor Greenberg has invented and which is practically a self-contained, fool-proof laboratory, making its own determination of alcohol concentration.

The third physiological lecture is on the effects and aftereffects of small and large amounts of alcohol on the body and is given by Dr. Haggard. Note that the first lecture dealt with what the body does to alcohol when it absorbs it, and that this third lecture will describe what happens or does not happen to certain body organs after small, medium, or large amounts have been taken in. Much of the lecture will refer to what does not happen, for many superstitions of the "Wets" and of the "Drys" alike must be debunked. Some of you may be shocked when you are told that 1 or 1½ ounces of absolute alcohol—the amount contained in 2 and 3 ounces of whisky, respectively—does not cause any physiological harm to this or that bodily organ. But the statement of this fact does not involve any kind of evaluation of the use of alcoholic beverages. It merely states that this is the physiological effect. The physiologist, as physiologist, is not concerned with the social involvements. He is not concerned with whether this small intake may later lead, in a specific case, to larger intake and even to addiction. In his lecture he is concerned only with what happens at and around the time the alcohol is taken by an individual. The physiologist cannot go beyond that factual statement for, otherwise, he would be leaving his own field. Generally, statements on the effects of alcohol do not involve either approval or disapproval of its use.

From Dr. Haggard's lectures it is seen that the oxidation of alcohol liberates a large number of calories. This indicates that excessive use of alcohol may have nutritional involvements. These nutritional aspects of the problem are explained by Dr. Norman Jolliffe of the New York University College of Medicine, a man who has had great experience with the alcoholic bodily diseases, and who will tell you about one of the most important aspects of alcohol physiology, namely, the role of large alcohol intake in the causation of certain nutritional deficiency diseases. These diseases are primarily responsible for some of the manifestations which are commonly referred to as the diseases of chronic alcoholism. Dr. Jolliffe will give you a clear picture of how these nutritional deficiencies come about through changed relations between vitamins, on the one hand, and intake of calories on the other hand. This should be of particular significance to those who are interested in teaching the effects of alcohol in the high schools. These nutritional aspects of alcohol can be fitted into the science curriculum or the biology curriculum in a way which the high school students understand. They are normally taught about biological oxidation and about calories, and in connection with biological oxidation this question of alcohol and nutrition can be cogently introduced. The fact that the stomach undergoes such and such changes in 20 years of heavy drinking and that a hobnail liver might develop in 15 or 20 years, has no immediate appeal. But nutrition takes place every day. Calories are taken in every day. Vitamins are taken in every day. And today we are so conscious of these matters that we go about selecting our food quite deliberately. Gracie Fields said about an alcoholic over the radio, "He tears down in the evening with gin what he builds up in the morning with vitamins." The building-up process in the morning was through a conscious selection while the destruction in the evening was perhaps not conscious.

The fifth lecture which comes under the heading of the effects of alcohol is entitled, "Effects of Small Amounts of Alcohol on Psychological Functions." This, too, belongs in the physiological field because it does not deal with psychological motivation but rather with psychological functions more or less on the physiological level. I shall discuss in that lecture the effect of alcohol on psychomotor coordination, reaction time, and related phenomena. From that material it will become evident that alcohol is not a stimulant but a depressant.

PERSONALITY AND ALCOHOLISM

Up to this point the course deals with the effects of alcohol, but then we shall proceed to analyze origins. We enter now on a group of lectures which relate to the personality aspects and the sociological factors in the use of beverage alcohol. But this group of lectures is preceded by a brief talk on the "Drinking Mores of Social Classes" and two lectures on heredity. Professor Dollard's lecture on social mores will have little to do with alcoholism, but it will serve as a background for later lectures. Some of you have formal training in sociology; many of you, however, do not have this training but have specialized in entirely different fields. So those who have had sociological training will be patient with us when we talk in somewhat simple terms about social theories.

It would be a waste of time to talk about personality aspects and the sociological factors if alcoholism were entirely a matter of heredity. If that were true, there would not be much more to say. I shall endeavor to give, in a brief lecture, some factual data which show the importance or unimportance of the factor of heredity in alcoholism. Next, Dr. Anne Roe will illustrate the heredity question by the results of an investigation which she carried out on children of alcoholic and normal parents reared in foster homes. The question of environment versus heredity will be the main subject of Dr. Roe's lecture.

Thus the ground will have been cleared for the discussion of the role of personality and of society. Last year I found quite a bit of confusion among our students about these matters. One student said, "Well, here is a lecturer who says that the whole thing is personality, and another lecturer says that everything is social factors. So what's true? If the experts disagree, what confidence can we have?" The answer is that the experts do not disagree. There is no conflict between the views of the sociologist and the physiologist. Personality can manifest itself only in society, and social factors have their effects on individuals. As a matter of fact, I would say that personality is the style in which the individual reacts to society.

The general discussions on social mores and on heredity will enable you to understand those lectures which deal with personality and with social factors specifically in connection with alcohol.

The question of personality and alcohol will be expounded by Dr. Carney Landis, who will describe the theories of alcoholic personality. While his review will be critical, he will not prejudice your choice of theories. The question of body build and personality type will receive due consideration in that lecture.

From the sociological and psychological lectures it will be seen that much aggression is suppressed because of social and personal requirements. But alcohol can release aggression and these aggressive tendencies can manifest themselves on the oral level as well as on the physical level, and, in the extreme, may result in crime. The aggression may even turn against the "self" in the form of suicide. Alcohol and aggression will be the subject of a lecture by Dr. Banay. You see, therefore, that although the lecture schedule does not mention crime and suicide, both questions are taken care of.

THE SOCIAL FACTORS OF INEBRIETY

We shall proceed next to a group of lectures on social factors in alcoholism and begin with a discussion of the functions of alcohol in primitive society. Professor Horton will show how anxieties are generated in primitive societies, how aggression becomes inhibited, and how these primitive societies from time to time feel that aggression must be released in some controlled form and that this may be brought about by alcoholic binges. It is of interest to review the anthropological material because, although our society differs greatly from primitive societies, particularly in its complexity, there are many elements involved which can be understood best through the primitive forms. Many manifestations of inebriety, many drinking customs that are current today, seem to be mysterious, un-understandable, but suddenly attain to meaning when we see them in the light of this anthropological material.

Next the function of alcohol in complex societies will be shown in a lecture by Professor Bacon. He will analyze those social factors which tend to perpetuate the use of alcohol as well as inebriety, and those social factors which tend to inhibit the use of alcohol or at least alcoholic excess. The difference between the rate of alcoholism among men and women, the practical absence of alcoholism among Jews, are evidence of those unwritten social laws which act sometimes with relentless rigor. The knowledge of such factors equips one better to think about possible solutions. One can then exploit such factors which tend to control the use and abuse of alcohol within a society. It is in this sense that we think of sociological research contributing toward the prevention of inebriety.

EFFECT OF INEBRIETY ON SOCIETY

Another group of lectures relates to the effects of alcohol on society. These discussions largely serve the purpose of characterizing the magnitude of the problem. There has been much abuse of statistics on both sides of the question and much of the indifference and ridicule of the problem may be attributed to the statistical contortions. It is important, therefore, to reconsider these matters in the light of scientifically oriented statistics.

Mr. Benson Landis will lecture on the economic aspects of alcoholism. In an hour he will not be able to show you all the economic involvements but at least he will be able to give you a picture of the expenditures involved in alcoholism, the expenditures arising out of the jailing of inebriates, out of alcoholic mental diseases, accidents, and absenteeism. These expenditures will be compared with revenues and with the costs of the rehabilitation of the alcoholic.

A lecture by Professor Bacon will be devoted to the effect of inebriety on the family—the disruption of society through inebriety is illustrated by the effects on the family. Nonsupport, neglect, maltreatment of children, and divorce are related to inebriety, but the statistical characterization of the magnitude of these effects is not on safe grounds. The analysis will show that the marital adjustment of the alcoholic is poor, even in his prealcoholic period.

"Alcohol and Pauperism" will be dealt with by Father Murphy, who is director of the Catholic Charities Bureau of the City of Cleveland, and who has first-hand experience with alcoholic involvements in that population which may be called the population of paupers.

The alcoholic traffic accident is the subject of a lecture by Mr. Berry, a director of the National Safety Council. This, too, is an aspect of the effects of alcohol on society. A definite determination of the contribution of alcohol to traffic accidents cannot be made but it is evident that it is a fairly large contribution. It is also evident that in a machine age such as ours inebriety poses an additional problem.

The Controls of Inebriety

A number of lectures are devoted to control factors in the alcohol problem—the church, the temperance movement, formal education, law, and community activities. Some of these possible controls have been noted already in the anthropological and sociological lectures.

It may astonish some of you to find that a panel on the philosophy of the temperance movement is part of the curriculum of a scientific school. But the scientist must recognize that total abstinence is as much a part of the alcohol problem as is any positive form of drinking. The temperance movement has been a controlling factor for well over 100 years. Even many temperance workers have not found out that there is a whole philosophy behind their movement. They have not recognized it because of their preoccupation with strategies. The panel discussion will be led by Mr. Harry S. Warner, and Rev. McPeek and I shall take part in it. This discussion will be followed by a lecture on the attitude of the churches toward the alcohol problem, which will be delivered by Professor Bainton. The attitude of the churches toward the whole problem is relevant in gauging the possibilities of the participation of the pastor in the rehabilitation of the alcoholic on the one side and, on the other, in his participation in community leadership in shaping opinion on the alcohol problem.

The present legislative controls will be described by Professor Baird. He will give an analysis of the content and intent of present-day statutes. You will find that much that you thought to be ancient law never had the status of law but was in the category of exhortations. It also appears that purposes which we believe we see in the statutes are often not inherent in them.

Then the question of the legal aspects of prohibition will be taken up by Mr. Dunford who is the legal counsel of the Anti-Saloon League and who gave the lecture on this subject last year, although under a different title and with different aspects. And I can assure you that he will give a most objective presentation.

Prohibition has many aspects other than temperance philosophy and law. There are many political issues and many propagandistic issues. Mr. Anderson, the director of public relations of the New York State Medical Society, will give us an analysis of "Wet" and "Dry" propaganda. Quite frankly, I have encouraged Mr. Anderson to "lay them both out flat." Propaganda is an accepted weapon. It is practically a necessary evil. In a scientific discussion it is necessary to determine what is propaganda and what is the net residue of the problem.

The Treatment of Inebriety

Next we go into a series of lectures on the care and treatment of alcoholics and, in a certain way, care and treatment is also a control measure. It is, in a way, a step toward prevention—one of the many steps. Dr. Fleming of Harvard University Medical School will give a talk on the treatment of the individual alcoholic. He has developed some new ideas on this subject with which some therapists may not agree, but he and his followers can claim success, and that is the crucial test where therapy is concerned. However, Dr. Fleming will not limit his lecture to his own ideas but will describe several methods, including the much talked of conditioned-reflex or aversion treatment.

Practically everybody who talks about the rehabilitation of the alcoholic mentions the role of religion. The Rev. McPeek will give you a historical sketch of the role of religion in the treatment of inebriety.

The various forms of treatment, no matter what their nature may be, require the cooperation of the social case worker. There are very few social workers who have had a large experience with alcoholism. Miss Sybil Baker, general secretary of the Family Department of the Brookline Friendly Society, is one of the few who have had great experience in this field and her work has been devoted largely to alcoholics. She will give us a talk on the specific requirements of social case work in connection with inebriety.

Directly related to therapy will be a lecture by the Rev. Otis Rice on the pastoral counseling of inebriates. Mr. Rice has had first-hand experience in treating alcoholics. And he has the psychological and psychiatric training which he can add to his pastoral qualifications in dealing with this subject. In this lecture we shall hear about the assets, but also about the liabilities, of the minister in dealing with inebriates.

The last lecture in the series is a highly significant one. The speakers you are going to hear up to that time have given a view of alcoholism from the outside. In the final lecture we shall hear the inside story, as told by one of the cofounders of the famous fellowship of Alcoholics Anonymous, whose anonymity I respect here. I may truly say that as far as the rehabilitation of the alcoholic is concerned, there is no therapeutic activity which comes near to the success that this extraordinary group of Alcoholics Anonymous has achieved.

This brings our course to an end. Last year the students left with a feeling that they knew less about alcohol and alcoholism than at the beginning of the course. I shall not be disappointed if you develop the same feeling, for it is the beginning of a true understanding of the problem.

Lecture 2

The Problems of Alcohol

E. M. Jellinek

THE lectures you will hear in the next 4 weeks will present to you many aspects of the problem of alcohol and there may be a tendency to view those aspects as subjects of independent existence. Such a tendency comes from the preconceived idea that the problem of alcohol arises from the mere existence of the chemical substance alcohol. If that were the entire source of the problem then, according to one's predilections, all that must be done is to apply the principles of education, of legislation, of broad social measures or of rehabilitation toward the disuse or moderate use of that substance. Such a view would imply that only the principles of the various measures seem to be relevant and that the various measures can be applied irrespective of the nature of the problem. Furthermore, as far as the substance in question is concerned, it would appear sufficient to list facts illustrating its possible harm, thus justifying the measures. But such a view does not take into account the obstacles that must be overcome.

Merely being aroused by the obstacles may generate zeal but at the same time the passion may stand in the way of recognizing the nature of the obstacles and thus in the way of dealing with them effectively. Passion distorts the outlines of the objects which form the obstacles; it often magnifies the unimportant and may screen the truly significant. When emotion says that an object is dangerous, one is inclined to attempt to counteract its effects without knowing how it originated, how firmly it is founded, and what makes it survive.

In this lecture I shall endeavor to put the many elements of the alcohol problem together and to show these various elements as well as the various control measures in their proper perspective. This may aid you further in integrating the many subjects of our course.

I have indicated before that the source of our problem might not be the mere existence of the substance called ethyl alcohol, and that the source might be less obvious but more potent. There are many substances on this earth, solid and liquid, which man could eat and drink without any harm, or very little harm, and which he nevertheless does not utilize as foods or beverages. It would seem that man swallows only those substances from which he expects certain benefits. I use the word benefit in the sense of giving satisfaction irrespective of whether that satisfaction is ethical or not. There are substances which are shortlived in their use as foods and beverages; they are subject to fashion. Fashion can make up for essential properties but only for a short while. The substances which are independent of fashion, which survive in their use through the ages, have properties which fulfill some definite purpose.

Ethyl alcohol, as contained in various alcoholic beverages, is one of those substances that has remained in wide use through thousands of years. It has been subject to fashion only in the sense that at times certain beverages containing alcohol were preferred and at other times other such beverages. That the use of alcohol has persisted through ages in which great cultural changes have taken place, that it was and is used in greatly divergent cultures, although not without exception, and that it has persevered in spite of the observed dangers of excess, suggest that alcohol fulfills some function which man, rightly or wrongly, values. Let us see whether we can deduce this function from the properties of ethyl alcohol.

You will learn from Dr. Haggard the physical and chemical properties of ethyl alcohol which make it possible to use it, especially in preference to other alcohols. But that it can be used does not explain its use. You will find that in small amounts alcohol may cause, among other symptoms, dilatation of the peripheral blood vessels and a flow of gastric juice, and that in large amounts it interferes with motor coordination, with speech, with respiration. Evidently the wide use of alcohol is not explained by these effects. As you proceed in your studies you will find that the most outstanding characteristic of alcohol is that it is a depressant, but not a stimulant, and that it acts primarily on the central nervous system. Alcohol is a depressant not in the sense that it causes a depression of mood but in the sense that it depresses, decreases, cortical activity. With small amounts the decrease of cortical functions is slight but with larger amounts it becomes progressively greater. This depression, as I said, is the outstanding physiological property of alcohol. Can this property account for its persistent use? It does not seem plausible that man should want to depress his cortical activity. But perhaps the decrease of this activity does fulfill a function which is sought by man. In seeking an answer we shall try to see the behavior of the individual in his environment and the behavior of the environment around the individual, and thus we may find the basic need which man attempts to satisfy through alcohol, the function of this substance in the scheme of human life.

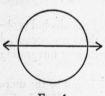

FIG. 1

Let us represent the central nervous system, on which alcohol primarily acts, by a small circle divided by a cord which is kept exceedingly taut [Figure 1]. Let us say that above that cord are the overt elements of behavior and below it the covert elements. The function of that taut cord is to keep the covert elements from penetrating into the sphere of overt action, inhibiting them from becoming overt factors of behavior, and so the cord may be called the inhibitions. To a certain extent the covert elements somehow seep into the upper sphere and exert a disguised influence. We may now consider how this inhibiting cord is brought about and what it inhibits.

The human organism possessing this central nervous system is placed into an environment consisting of objects of nature such as the atmosphere, mountains and streams, and fellow human organisms. The life of nature as well as the life of society, that is, what is going on in this environment, imposes certain restrictions on the movements of this organism. I shall represent the environment, natural and social, by a large circle, and the single human organism by a smaller circle; and, in order to avoid misunderstandings, I shall draw an even smaller circle within the small circle to represent the central nervous system of that organism; but for the time being I shall omit the taut cord [Figure 2].

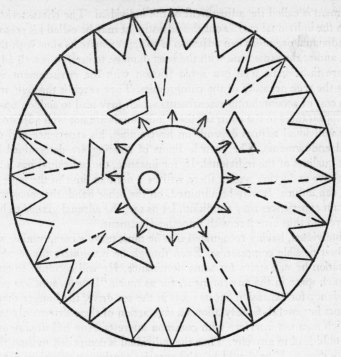

Fig. 2

The arrows on the periphery of the small circle denote that the organism tends to expand, just as on our war maps the arrows denote the drives for expansion of our armies. From those maps I have also borrowed the little blocks used to denote tank traps but which in our diagram will signify the barriers nature presents to the expansive tendencies of the organism.

The large circle, the environment, is lined with spikes and those symbolize the restrictions, the forces, with which society opposes the expansion of the individual organism. These spikes have a disturbing property: They can elongate themselves. This property is suggested by the broken-line spikes superimposed over the solid ones.

The individual organism wants to seize upon everything that will secure its well being. It will want the sunniest and the shadiest place for occupancy, the place where the best water and the best food are found, where the maintenance of comfortable existence requires the least effort. Before this organism experiences the restrictions of its environment it takes all these matters for granted, it is not aware of its subordinate position. When it first finds out the true lay of the land it is bewildered, disappointed and hurt.

The individual organism originally tends to get everything and when it is opposed it attempts to subordinate its environment. On the other hand the environment will concede only as much as the individual appears to have a claim to. In time the individual organism finds out that it cannot have its way and tries to make the best of it, tries to compromise. This compromising with the environment is called the adjustment of the individual. The characteristic way in which the individual carries out this adjustment may be called his personality. If the individual organism can adjust so as to approximate its aims with the least friction, and at the same time with the least damage to itself, it is well adjusted. There are individuals who can avoid friction with the environment without grasping the true necessity of the compromise. They reach it through artifices, and at a cost of accumulating resentments which may lead to sudden upsets. In spite of appearances to the contrary these individuals are not well adjusted. The way the individual adjusts depends on his training, his experience and certain inherited endowments. The possible limits of training are determined by the inherent qualities of the individual. If, for instance, the individual has inherited an overactive endocrine system there will be a definite limit to the poise which training can induce. It may be admitted, on the other hand, that poor training and certain experiences may condition, let us say, the adrenal glands to become overactive and thus interfere with smooth adjustment.

The individual, having recognized that he must make a compromise, will try for the best possible compromise. Even though he recognizes the necessity of subordination he will strive for some dominance. He will continue to struggle for as much space in the environment, for as much "Lebensraum" as possible. The tendency for expansion has its roots in the sex drive, the hunger drive, the life instinct in general. Society allows a satisfaction of these drives only to a degree which does not interfere with common interests. Any full display of these drives would lead to anarchy. Thus the individual is compelled to limit the display of his desires. If he should have to exercise continuous conscious control of his instinctual desires he would be continuously aware of frustration. In order to avoid that situation the individual tends to banish wishes which are in conflict with the prohibitions, the taboos of society, into the region below the cord of that small circle [Figure 1] by which we symbolically represent the central nervous system. The individual more or less consciously suppresses these wishes so that they will not interfere, at least overtly, with his functioning in the environment. This process of suppression is fostered by society through the medium of training, which also makes for the tautness of the cord. This training begins in infancy. The culture is transmitted by the parents, later by the school, the church, the occupational group to which the individual belongs, and so on. The nature and the content of this training depend largely upon cultural patterns. The pattern of culture is largely national. Within the national pattern there may be the cultural pattern of class and of occupational groups, and within class and group there may be differences in cultural patterns according to age, and there is also a cultural pattern differentiation by sex. But, nevertheless, all these patterns have much in common through the national cultural pattern.

The elements of these cultural patterns in their various combinations determine what kind of elements are to be suppressed. In one culture a display of affection may be practically required as assurance of the absence of hostility, while in another culture demonstrativeness must be suppressed because it interferes with the hard requirements of maintenance of life in that particular society. In one culture only close relatives are objects of sex taboos and in other societies any person of the age class of the parents or any member of fairly large groups may be banned as a sex object. Society is anxious that the cord should be kept taut. It is to the interest of society that these elements should not escape to the surface, should not become dominant. They would disrupt society, they would vitiate the ideals of the culture. If anything interferes with the degree of tautness of the inhibiting cord, if it relaxes a bit, then a few of the suppressed elements are able to escape. The more this cord relaxes, the more of these elements will emerge; and when the cord collapses entirely, all of these elements have free access to the surface. The relaxation of the cord signifies the release of inhibitions. Small shocks may cause a slight temporary relaxation of the inhibiting cord. An unexpected situation may throw the individual off balance and ordinarily suppressed behaviors may become manifest. This is what is meant when it is said that a person was caught "off guard." "Losing one's head" in a situation of stress also has this meaning.

The individual pushes below the inhibiting cord not only tendencies which conflict with the taboos of society but he also tends to eliminate from the overt elements any painful associations relating to his frustrations and memories of having transgressed taboos or even of having violated them in his imagination. While the conflicting wishes are *suppressed* more or less consciously, the painful associations are *repressed* unconsciously.

The suppressed and repressed materials cause tensions, they batter against the inhibiting cord and often they emerge clad in a symbolism which is not evident to the individual; and even though the symbolism is not understood it may produce feelings of guilt and anxiety and increase the discontent. Anxieties arise from the anticipation of punishment as well as from the anticipation of not being able to achieve desired goals, and from feelings of insecurity. Tension is painful and it interferes with smooth functioning. The individual looks, therefore, for certain ways by which this tension from repressions, from guilt and from anxieties may be relieved, at least temporarily. Such ways are many and some of them are useful, or at least acceptable, to society while others may be harmful and socially unacceptable. We shall return to this point later.

Society recognizes the necessity for some relief from tension and is ready to "close one eye" on occasions and even to foster some means which offer such release and relief. Dancing is a slight concession to the sex taboos; sports give an opportunity for the release of suppressed aggression within wholesome limits; stage plays—even if they are realistic—permit one to live for a while in an unreal world; hobbies, such as collecting, satisfy the urge for acquisition in a legitimate way. All these activities provide a temporary, slight relaxation of the inhibiting cord; some of the suppressed material is allowed to emerge for a while.

Nothing facilitates the release of suppressed material more than a slackening of judgment. It is largely judgment resulting from training and experience that keeps the inhibiting cord taut. Anything that decreases cortical function decreases judgment and this loosens the inhibitions. If this can be achieved by a means that requires no effort, man will avail himself of it. Through the use of alcohol this desired relaxation of tension is achieved, and it is achieved without any intellectual contribution. It becomes understandable now that a substance which decreases cortical function will be sought and used. I do not wish to imply that the use of alcoholic beverages originated in the desire for a sedative. The origin of the custom may be seen, rather, in symbolic uses in the course of which the sedative action is discovered and exploited.

BACKGROUND OF USE OF ALCOHOLIC BEVERAGES

Small quantities of alcoholic beverages reduce cortical functions to a small degree only and thus release inhibitions only slightly. Under the mild influence of alcohol, suppressed behavior is released to no greater degree than in games, sports and other forms of entertainment. Because of this, most societies have accepted the moderate use of alcohol, at least at certain times and in certain places. Even where moderate drinking is fully accepted it would run counter to the tolerance of society if one were to have a drink in the middle of one's work—or if one were to play games at this time. The use is approved when there is no task before the person, when it is permissible to relax, preferably in the evening. But even in the evening there would be no approval for a man taking a small drink on a crowded bus. That is, society gives its approval, even for moderate drinking, only when and where the relaxation attendant upon such drinking apparently does not interfere with the functioning of the drinker or the interests of his fellow men.

Let us follow on and see how this function of alcohol is utilized and how it develops into a problem or problems.

When society is not complex, when it is primitive, that is, when the interests of the individuals composing that society are not very divergent, then there can be a certain degree of solidarity and the restrictions of society will not be too great. Also, in such a society the sources of anxiety, the sources of insecurity, are not greatly individualized but are rather common to the whole tribe. Under such conditions an occasional relaxation of restrictions and relief from anxieties suffices to release the tension. In this primitive society which has a great deal of solidarity, the release of tension can be brought about practically ceremonially. It can be brought about at communal festivals. These communal festivals need not be alcoholic binges but they frequently are. In these communal drinking bouts there is, through the use of intoxicating beverages, a collective allaying of anxieties and a collective release of the suppressed aggression. Such a communal collective release suffices for a while, it will keep the members quiet and satisfied.

Individual drinking in this stage of society is hardly known. There is practically only communal and ceremonial drinking, and these collective releases of aggression and reliefs from anxiety are not frequent. They may be more frequent in one primitive society than in another. That will depend largely on how far the society has advanced in complexity and how far it is hemmed in by its environment—let us say by hostile tribes, or by the insecurity of food supply, and so forth.

Through their symbolism and mystic effects, fermented beverages attained to high prestige early in history. Their properties gave them a prominent place in early religious cults. In the course of ritual practice the anesthetic effects of alcoholic beverages became associated—although not consciously—with that feeling of well-being which release of inhibitions and relief from tension affords. This association induced man to seek occasions on which the valued objects, the fermented beverages, should be used. The fermented beverages, instead of being accessories to a ceremony, became the central part of it. Thus originated the periodic drinking bouts of primitive societies. Undeveloped techniques and limitation of supply, as well as limited demand for relief, restricted the bouts to few occasions.

When society becomes more complex through specialization, competition, class segregation, and consequent individualization of interests, social—economic restrictions and frustrations grow by leaps and bounds, anxieties increase and more aggression must be suppressed and repressed. In other words, tension increases in intensity and frequency. Since the sources of tension in the more complex society are individual, communal means of release no longer suffice. Individual releases are sought. Since there is a substance which can give the desired relief, harassed man will want to take recourse to it. And since this substance is one which is honored and valued through the role which it has played in ritual, its somewhat more frequent use is not initially conspicuous, there is no social barrier to it, particularly since the profanation of the cultic object takes place only gradually. From tribal, communal use it enters first into the solemn gathering of the clan, later of the narrower family. It appears on all solemn occasions, such as deliberations on important questions, the sealing of pacts, the celebration of important events. The use is still on a quasi ceremonial level, but the occasions become greatly multiplied, the *titulus bibendi,* the alibi for a drink, is found more frequently and thus the unconsciously sought relief is satisfied more frequently. The guest who enters the home is honored with a drink; the use of the beverage is thus transferred from public to private ceremonial. The urn with the precious wine appears in the home to celebrate privately a public event, and later to mark domestic events, such as the birth of a child, the birthday of a family member or friend, marriage, any individual success, any occasion for rejoicing and any occasion of solemn sorrow. This type of use is current also in present-day society and even in families which do not use alcoholic beverages on any other occasions. The ritual use is thus transformed into a folkway. The highly increased frequency of use also becomes possible through the development of techniques of preservation and easier supply and through organization of supply.

The increased frequency of quasi ceremonial use requires a constant stock of supply in the home and the proximity leads quite naturally to occasional use without any special motivation. Thus takes place the last step of profanation of the originally sacred object: It becomes a beverage of daily use, a "refreshment." At that stage a *titulus bibendi* is no longer required for the use of the beverage; it may be taken at any time. It must be understood that while the frequency of the occasions for use affords more frequent satisfaction of relief from tension, not every occasion on which the beverage is used serves the purpose of relief even unconsciously. Our emphasis in this course on relief from anxiety, release of aggression and other tension releases, may give you the impression that we wish to imply that every use of alcoholic beverages is induced by tensions. It would be sheer nonsense to hold such an opinion. I would say that in modern society the beverages are used more frequently as condiments, as refreshments, as a compliance with custom and for prestige purposes than for conscious or unconscious sedation and relief. The latter function still plays an important role but among average users only occasionally, and most of the time only among a certain type of users. The emphasis on relief from tension is only to show the particular function of alcohol through which it attained such social value as is attributed to it. While all drinking is far from being only a seeking of relief from tension, addiction—compulsive drinking—does definitely serve that purpose.

The tribe utilized the drinking bout and many other forms of communal releases, probably unconsciously, for the purpose of avoiding "explosions." But as society became more complex and organized, higher authorities of society developed, the danger of tensions became manifest, and authority deliberately began to utilize the pleasure drives of man to deflect the potential dangers of tensions. It was discovered rather early that compliance with restrictions requires rewards. Authority, whether the family head, the teacher, the employer, or formal government, has always fostered the gratification of pleasure drives up to a certain limit, but those limits have not been easy to guard at times. Government has not only utilized pleasure drives for deflecting malcontent but it has also been tempted to exploit the drives as a source of income through taxation. But where there is income, there is usually a tendency to develop the source of income. Thus authority, willing to allow a pleasure drive up to a certain limit only, might come into conflict with itself by developing the source of income to a level which is not compatible with the limits set for the pleasure drive. Whatever concerns pleasure drives tends to be ambiguous.

First, society utilizes pleasure drives; and when these grow into excess, it attempts to control them. The control is difficult when the organized authority of society, namely government, has conflicting interests in the matter, and even more difficult when the medium of the pleasure drive is an object which, through ceremonial uses, has attained to prestige and the use of which has developed not merely into a habit but into a custom, into a folkway.

I have spoken advisedly in general terms of pleasure drives rather than in terms of alcohol, for the latter is only a specific form of the general case and is related, as are all the other forms, to the basic problem of tension.

I shall now give you a schematic presentation of that social problem of which the use of alcohol is only a part.

The Subordination of the Individual to Society Generates

TENSION

Tension is painful and demands

RELIEF

This demand creates

TWO PROBLEMS

PROBLEM	PROBLEM
of elimination or reduction of conditions which create tension	of finding a mode for relief of tension

Obviously the problem of eliminating, or even reducing, the sources of tension is difficult. The range of possibilities is small. In modern societies some sources of anxiety, such as threats from floods and fires, have been greatly reduced through control measures. But the anxieties arising from social sources are less amenable to control. There has been, of course, legislation designed to reduce friction between classes and to reduce the hardships of competition. Some of these measures have had some success and others have created even more tension.

There are more possibilities in finding modes of release or relief of tension. Any of the modes may become exaggerated and consequently dangerous. We arrive thus at the problem of management of releases which, with its sequences, may be seen as follows:

PROBLEM OF MANAGEMENT OF RELEASES

this may be divided into two problems

Selection of Type of Release	*Control of Degree of Release*
This may be brought about through	This may be brought about through
The Ethical Standards of Religion	*Religion*
Mental Hygiene	*Mental Hygiene*
Substitution of desirable forms of release for the less desirable	*Social Disapproval*
Educational measures for creating appreciation of the desirable forms	*Legal Control*
Differential approval of society relating to different forms	

Society selects forms of release through facilitating certain forms. Thus the taxpayer does not object to having tax money spent on the development of sports within reason, for sports are recognized as a wholesome release. But sports, too, can be exaggerated, and the exaggeration may lead to diseases. Education steps in and shows the useful and harmful ways of sports. Law must step in and regulate certain sports when they tend to become brutal. Thus in most states there is a Boxing Commissioner who enforces the acceptable standards.

Social disapproval of exaggerated degrees of releases from tension are effective when society is unequivocal about the disapproval. The young man who oversteps the socially accepted limits of freedom in dancing, who abuses the privilege of that form of release, will soon find that he is barred from dances, that he is deprived of that release. The contempt for his behavior may be so strong that it may even interfere with his progress in his vocational life and he may be compelled to change his environment, to look for some place where his reputation is not known.

Religion is a relief from tensions—not a release. Religion compensates for the frustrations of life and offers a purpose when frustrated man sees no more purpose in life. Religion can equip man to utilize only the best of releases and to a wholesome degree only. Religion can equip man for tolerating frustrations without bitterness, without accumulating tensions. I am speaking of the true religious outlook and not of morbid religious compulsions which are as destructive as any distortion of noble ideas or any exaggeration of releases.

There are many ways to keep the various manifestations of the pleasure drives of man within bounds, to eliminate the undesirable ones, to foster the socially acceptable ones. The success of those ways depends upon the understanding of what those manifestations represent, how they arise and what they fulfill in man's life.

All this applies to the use of alcohol as to any other manifestation of the tendency to avoid the pain arising from tensions.

Social disapproval of inebriety, where it is strong, has worked much more powerfully than formal law. Inebriety among Jews is practically unknown, although they are not abstainers. The ceremonial use of wine in the Jewish culture is still alive and more prominent than in any other present-day culture.

The social disapproval of drunkenness in women is much greater than of drunkenness in men. Where this differential disapproval is strongly rooted, it reduces inebriety among women to a negligible occurrence. In England there are 2 male inebriates to 1 woman inebriate; in the United States the ratio is 6 to 1; and in Norway, 23 to 1. You see that social standards can have a strong influence on inebriety. And social standards can be changed if they are tackled with deep understanding and long patience.

Education, too, has been utilized in relation to alcohol. That it has not been all too successful does not indicate that the idea of education is hopeless but that perhaps the means of education have not been altogether felicitous. Education concerning the use of alcohol is one of the problems among the problems of alcohol, because the question of what should be "taught," and in what way and whom the education should reach, has not yet been answered. The deficiency is due mainly to the assumption that it is sufficient to realize that alcohol is bad and to educate against what is bad. The orientation of education must come from deeper insights.

Education can aim at the public acceptance of legal restrictions of consumption and toward the realization of individual responsibility in upholding the restrictions. It can aim at giving the individual the proper means to compensate for the pain of inevitable frustrations, the means not to develop unnecessary anxieties and to tolerate consciously the tensions of everyday life. These two types of education are cogent as they take into account the factors which generate inebriety. Education may aim at the dissemination of knowledge concerning the potential dangers of alcohol and thus diminish the demand for it. This has been the prevalent form of alcohol education. But this type of education is based on the principle of fear; it falls into the same category as the advertising of toothpastes and deodorants.

I do not mean to imply that there should be no instruction on the properties of alcohol. Alcohol is one of the world commodities and it is fully as justified to discuss in the school the properties of this substance as it is justified to discuss the properties of iron or leather. But in its scope the instruction on alcohol should not differ from the instruction on iron. Instruction is basic to education but *per se* it does not constitute education.

Legal restrictions have been applied to most pleasure drives. To some degree, and in some form, censure is applied to stage and screen plays, and there have been and are, in some places, restrictions on the attendance of minors. The sports, as already mentioned, are subject to some legal regulations and in every society—apart from the unwritten laws—formal, legal restrictions have been placed on the sex drive. In all these matters there has been at least some consideration of function, social role and folkways. The use of alcoholic beverages, too, has been subject to legal measures. There have been restrictive as well as totally prohibitive measures. As in the case of education the legal measures have generally not taken into account the origins of the use of alcohol, the function which society attributes to it, the social factors which reinforce it, and those which tend to keep it within bounds.

It is neither my object to discuss the various problems of alcohol in detail nor even to touch lightly upon all problems. The object of this lecture is rather to show how the problems of alcohol grow out of a basic problem of society and that the various problems around alcohol are not adventitious but are genetically connected with the main problem. I shall, therefore, not continue with the enumeration and brief sketching of the many problems of alcohol but shall broach the question of the magnitude of the problem and then go into a brief discussion of the individual problems of inebriates.

The Magnitude of the Problem

The magnitude of the problem can be expressed in terms of the number of individuals involved in it as well as in terms of the effects of inebriety on the individual and on society. Since alcoholic diseases, death from alcoholism, alcoholic mental disorders, divorce, crime and other effects will be dealt with in several lectures, I shall touch now only upon the question of the population involved in this problem.

There are approximately 100 million men and women of drinking age, that is, of age 15 years and over, in the United States. Of the

100 million persons of drinking age

50 million use alcoholic beverages; of these,

3 million become excessive drinkers; and of these,

750,000 become chronic alcoholics.

By excessive drinkers we shall mean those persons who drink to an extent which exposes them to the risk of becoming compulsive drinkers and developing chronic alcoholism. By compulsive drinkers—commonly called alcohol addicts —we shall mean drinkers who, although they wish to stop drinking, are irresistibly driven to it through an unconquerable fear that without alcohol they will not be able to exist. By chronic alcoholics we shall mean persons who, in consequence of prolonged excessive drinking, have developed a bodily disease or a mental disorder, irrespective of whether they arrived at this stage through compulsive drinking or not. By inebriates we shall mean the aggregate of un-complicated excessive drinkers, compulsive drinkers, and chronic alcoholics.

Let us express the problem now in relation to the users of alcoholic beverages only, instead of to the entire population of drinking age. Of

1,000 users of alcoholic beverages,

60 become excessive drinkers and compulsive drinkers without chronic alco-holism; and of these,

15 become chronic alcoholics with or without compulsive drinking.

Thus the phenomenon of inebriety arises only in a fraction, 6 per cent, of the population of users; but since this latter population is large in number—50 mil-lion—even this fraction of it is numerically large: 3 million. Of the 3 million inebriates, about 2,600,000 are men; and of these, about 2,100,000 are be-tween the ages of 30 and 60 years.

These are the persons who figure in absenteeism, who neglect their families, who cause hazards to traffic and industry, who, in brief, cause the social and economic burdens of inebriety.

In relation to the number of users of alcoholic beverages, the number of in-ebriates is small, but it is a number which plays a role in the health and in the social and economic life of the nation. I may add that the problem is enhanced by the fact that as yet science is not able to point out the individual who is liable to become an excessive drinker, and not even the individual who is liable to become either a compulsive drinker or a chronic alcoholic. It is not impossible that science will succeed in finding the criteria of selection, but to date there has been no indication of it.

The Individual Problems

The problem of inebriety, although it has its deep-lying social origins, is nevertheless the aggregate of many individual problems. You may well ask what kind of persons the inebriates are. I shall go only into the question of personality organization, not personality types, and shall ignore whether they are rich or poor, their occupations, their education and their social status. But it may be said that all strata of society are represented.

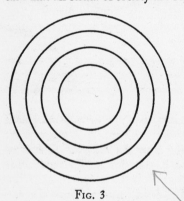

Fig. 3

In conversation one sometimes refers to a person as being well-balanced or well-inte-grated. Let us represent the well-integrated personality by concentric circles [Figure 3]. In this well-organized personality any shock coming from outside is equally distributed and does not cause any undue stress on any component element of the personality, but is carried by all its parts as an equal burden, that is, as a minimum burden. Under severe conditions the normal personality may some-times become slightly disturbed and the cir-cles may not be quite concentric, but not to a degree of crossing each other. Further-more, the tendency will be to return quickly to the concentric pattern.

There may be then various degrees of less well-integrated but by no means abnormal personalities, and these may be denoted by a smaller or greater departure from the concentric pattern [Figure 4]. If some stress from outside dis-

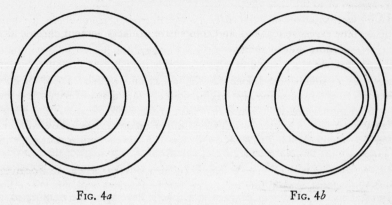

FIG. 4a   FIG. 4b

turbs these patterns there may be a tendency of the circles to intersect, at least temporarily, and in the case of the pattern in Figure 4b there may be some difficulty in untangling the intersecting circles, in returning to the original status.

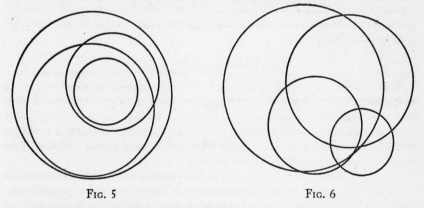

FIG. 5   FIG. 6

Then there are the personalities which are so poorly organized that some or all of the circles intersect. The neurotic personality may be represented by a pair of intersecting circles [Figure 5], and the psychotic personality by a fully intersecting system of circles [Figure 6].

When a temporary intersection of circles occurs, as in the less well-integrated normal personalities, or when permanent intersections exist, as in the neurotic and psychotic personalities, the stresses coming from the external or internal environment place the whole burden on such an intersection and the functioning of the personality breaks down conspicuously.

The well-integrated personality is subject to fewer anxieties than the personality which is less efficiently integrated, but is by no means free of anxieties. The well-organized personality, however, is able to manage anxieties easily and to make up, that is, to compensate, for frustrations in a useful and socially accept-able way. It should not be thought that this well-organized personality does not use alcohol. The well-integrated person is strongly represented among the mod-erate drinkers.

The less well-integrated but nevertheless normal person whom we have symbolized by slightly excentric circles will be more sensitive to disillusionment and frustrations, will develop more anxieties and will be liable to develop more guilt feelings than the personality represented by the concentric circles. Never-theless, under ordinary conditions, the slightly excentric circles permit of good management of tensions. It is only in situations of more than ordinary stress that the tension management fails and that pain arises which demands more than ordinary relief. In such situations this kind of personality organization will tend not only to compensate but to overcompensate for pain and will resort to artifi-cial means of adjustment.

The personality with some or much disorganization, that is, with few or many intersecting circles, has a low tolerance for frustrations and anxieties. The greater the degree of disorganization, the less tolerance. Here the need for com-pensation is not the exception but the rule; props are continuously in evidence.

The restrictions of the environment on all these various personalities are the same but they are felt with differing intensity and thus the responses differ too. The possible ways of adjustment, the possible means of compensation, of relief, are manifold. The greater the urgency and the more frequent the occasion for relief the more likely is recourse to gross relief and to easily obtained relief. The more or less disorganized personality may thus be inclined to seek that gross re-lief in easily obtainable intoxication. Yet not all these personalities choose this way of "adjustment," by far not all. Their degree of disorganization does not make inebriety an inevitable way out. If the disorganized personality is in an environment in which there is little discouragement of drunkenness, it will probably accept it as the means of escape. The same personality may reject this means in an environment which places a heavy penalty on drunken behavior or in which, let us say, "queer behavior" is less conspicuous than inebriety. The continuous need for relief that these personalities feel compels them to seek intoxication. On the whole, these disorganized personalities supply a large num-ber, perhaps 40 per cent, of the compulsive drinkers. Since disorganization is a personality disorder, it may be said that these persons come to inebriety through an illness. And since relief from their conflicts is the object of their drinking practically from the very beginning, they may be referred to as primary com-pulsive drinkers, or primary addicts.

But there are many, perhaps more, persons who do not start their drinking career with a personality handicap. By no means does the personality with the somewhat excentric circles have a weak or abnormal constitution. Probably the majority of humans have neither the organization of concentric nor of intersect-ing circles, but rather of slightly excentric circles. If a person with the latter per-sonality organization is placed in a group where the standard is frequent and copious alcohol consumption, he might or might not become a compulsive drinker, according to whether or not a stress situation of more than ordinary degree will arise in the course of his drinking experience.

Originally this person manages his anxieties and frustrations without artificial props. But in the course of his drinking experience he finds that the effect of alcohol can achieve much that otherwise has to be carried out by a more or less conscious effort. If a strong stress situation should arise, this person might apply his experience and let alcohol do the job. But he then finds that the ordinary amounts which he used to take do not suffice for the desired result. He actually has to come to frank intoxication. It may be that following this occurrence he will have the tendency to overcome every minor shock by intoxication. I like to say that he has become pampered by the effects of alcohol. This pampering may make the man as dependent upon alcohol as the disintegrated personality has been from the very beginning. Once he becomes dependent the intoxicating experiences may disintegrate the personality, and when he comes to the notice of the psychiatrist he makes the same impression as the man who came to his compulsive drinking through a diseased personality.

Thus this type of drinker, to whom I refer as the secondary compulsive drinker, ultimately becomes a diseased person. It is justifiable to speak of all compulsive drinking as a disease, but it is not justifiable to say that all compulsive drinking originates in disease. The origin may be relevant from many viewpoints, but the fact that ultimately all compulsive drinkers are diseased persons brings them into the realm of medical and public health problems.

The rehabilitation of inebriates becomes a large problem in modern society because of the economic involvements and because of the significance of rehabilitation as one of the many preventive measures, ranking equally with legislative and educational measures.

RECAPITULATION

You have seen the use of alcoholic beverages becoming secured in society through the value which attaches to them as symbolic and ritual substances. You have seen the use spreading beyond ritual because of the relief from tension which alcohol affords through its depressing effect on the activity of the central nervous system. Through gradual profanation, the once sacred object becomes a substance of everyday use, a condiment, a refreshment, and its original ritual use is transformed into folk customs. This process, in turn, facilitates excessive use for relief from tension.

Alcohol thus appears not as an original source of a problem but rather as a means for solving it and as a means out of which more and more problems arise. And as complex society generates increasingly greater tension the alcoholic means of solving it becomes more prominent. The problem becomes enhanced through organization of the supply and the vested interests behind it. The relief obtained from alcohol, originally utilized by society, becomes an object of control. The problem of control becomes complicated through the clash of vested interests with emotionally oriented reform forces. And the various control measures, such as legislation, education, and broad social measures, grow as the use of intoxication for relief from tension grows, and in the same way as control measures relating to other forms of relief from tension. To these general control measures is added the specific problem of the rehabilitation of the alcoholic.

But all these control measures will work only if they are applied with a full understanding of the problem which they are intended to control and only when all control measures are brought into proper relation to each other, when they are brought into proper balance.

DISCUSSION*

Couch: Is external restraint the only solution for an alcoholic who has not come to the point where he himself wants to stop?

Lecturer: Decidedly not. Let us take the incipient alcoholic. He is arrested for drunkenness. He gets 30 days. He comes out, and the first thing he does is get drunk. Or take the alcoholic who committed a crime and is imprisoned for 3, 6, or 9 years. While in prison he had no access to liquor. He has lived years without alcohol, and yet after he leaves prison, in spite of the best intentions, he gets drunk at the first opportunity. That happens all too often. It requires a psychological process of entire readjustment to stop the compulsive drinker. Inaccessibility of liquor, enforced abstinence itself, do not do the trick.

Question: What can society do with the incipient alcoholic who is not desirous of reforming his habits?

Lecturer: Ordinarily one cannot convince the incipient alcoholic that he is one. He believes that he has perfect control over his drinking. He will resent any suggestion. But it might be possible to intercept alcoholism by giving this person a chance to find out by himself—not by pointing at him, not by trying to convince him, but by bringing about a situation in which he will begin to free-associate and suddenly awaken to the realization that he is on his way to becoming an alcoholic. The realization must come from inside; only reinforcement can come from outside. There may be ways and means to facilitate, to precipitate, the process of insight, but no general rule can be given for bringing these processes about. The means will vary from one individual to another.

Berger: If frustration leads an organism to seek depression of function, why does the organism seek a depressant that releases the impulses that only increase frustration?

Lecturer: Actually, the alcoholic wants to stop when he finds that the punishment, the physical as well as the social punishment, the frustration which follows the binge, is much worse than the frustration which he tries to relieve through intoxication. Nevertheless he has been so accustomed to relieve immediate tension, immediate pain, that the future pain becomes unimportant. Also, the alcoholic always believes that "this time it will be different."

Question: Does alcohol make possible a *real* adjustment to tension?

Lecturer: There might be a slight degree of sedation which could be helpful in allowing time for readjustment, to collect oneself for the necessary readjustment. That is possible, but only in the case of mild sedation. Intoxication, however, could not serve as what you call *real* adjustment.

Question: Is it not true that in many of us the aggregate of our inhibitions constitutes a very serious impoverishment of personality and if so, could a reasonable alcohol intake serve to enrich us?

*These proceedings were recorded by mechanical means. It occurred frequently, especially during earlier lectures, that students failed to identify themselves by announcing their names before speaking; and occasionally the name could not be heard distinctly on the record. In these instances the remark or query of the student is preceded by the word "Question."

Lecturer: I don't think that alcohol can create anything. It might facilitate the emergence of something that is there, of something that has been held back, but it cannot create.

Shattuck: Isn't the use of alcohol for relief a dangerous use under any circumstances?

Lecturer: Only in the terms of statistical probability; in the sense, for example, that there is a probability of getting knocked down by a car when crossing a street. On some streets that probability is not negligible. Everybody who crosses the street is exposed to that probability, yet only a few really get knocked down.

Chairman (Rev. McPeek): Some questions have been directed to me regarding a statement in the book, *Alcohol Explored.* In connection with Dr. Wittman's investigation at Elgin State Hospital there is a statement on page 155 which reads as follows: "The most striking finding was that the need for religious security and standards rated so highly among the chronic alcoholics that they indicated an interference rather than a contribution to good adjustment." The question is, can religion interfere with good adjustment?

Lecturer: According to my primitive theology, true religion is a source of strength, but some persons might make out of it a source of weakness. A person may put his trust in God for guidance, fully realizing his own responsibilities and his own part in following that guidance. But he might also have a twisted view of religion, he might see in it something that exonerates him of all responsibility. This is not so much a religious feeling as something akin to magic. The believer expects the higher power to "side with him," right or wrong, remove all obstacles, fulfill all wishes. The inebriate who has lost the respect and support of his family and friends is seeking something that will make him free of all responsibility, that will keep him out of the gutter, that will give him his daily bread without any contribution on his part. It is in this sense that the need for religious security may indicate an interference with good adjustment. The person who expects his will to happen all the time does not have the proper adjustment.

Chairman: The second question is a companion to this and also relates to *Alcohol Explored.* The following sentence occurs on page 7: "However, when we understand the part played by the behavior of the intoxicated person in giving the alcohol problem its rank of capital importance among social issues, it becomes clear that a moral issue is also involved." The phrase, "it becomes clear that a moral issue is also involved" is the one to which it is desired to direct your attention. What is the moral issue or what are the moral issues as you see them in the alcohol problem?

Lecturer: No doubt some manifestations of intoxication are of an immoral nature. There may be an overstepping of sex taboos, there is a tendency toward blasphemous speech, and there may be a general lowering of accepted ethical standards, especially as the severity of intoxication progresses. It is a rather common assumption that the person who exposes himself to a condition in which he will produce this immoral behavior must be immoral before he incorporates that substance which brings the behavior about. Sometimes we may be right, and sometimes we may be wrong. Some of the ideas of the Middle Ages about disease now seem ridiculous. It was assumed that diseases with disgusting manifestations would occur only in an unworthy person. When we are dealing with a seeking of intoxication as a symptom of a personality disorder, we have no grounds to assume immortality in that person. There is no more justification for such an assumption than in the case of the person with a disgusting disease. But when intoxication results not from a morbid compulsion, when the drinker gets drunk voluntarily and with full knowledge of the consequences, he gives evidence of intentions which are contrary to moral standards.

Lecture 3

Metabolism of Alcohol

Howard W. Haggard

MANY of the facts with which I shall deal under the topic "metabolism of alcohol" are familiar to some of you. But for the sake of a consistent presentation, I am making the assumption that none of you is familiar with the preparation, properties and chemical composition of alcoholic beverages; with the way in which alcohol is absorbed into the body, distributed within it, and eliminated from it; and with the process by which alcohol is oxidized in the body. The term "metabolism," as I shall interpret it here, means everything that happens to the alcohol from the time a man drinks it until it disappears from his body. In a subsequent lecture I shall deal with what alcohol does to the body; in this lecture I deal with what the body does to alcohol.

As a preamble, let us go a little way into chemistry; first, to define the nature of alcohol, and second, to lay a foundation for the discussion, which will come later, of the chemical changes which alcohol undergoes during oxidation in the body.

In our discussions here we use the term alcohol, unless otherwise qualified, to designate one of many alcohols: ethyl alcohol, or ethanol; it is the alcohol intentionally present in alcoholic beverages. I use the word "intentionally" because, in the manufacture of some beverages, other alcohols may unavoidably occur in small amounts. All of the alcohols are intoxicating if taken in sufficiently large amounts, but each is characterized by certain peculiarities of its physiological action which tend to distinguish it. The alcohols, with a few exceptions, and these exceptions do not concern the alcoholic beverages, are composed of the same elements as are sugar and starch and fat: the elements carbon, hydrogen and oxygen. The difference between sugar or starch and alcohol lies in the number and particularly the structural arrangement of these elements. Chemically an alcohol may be thought of as water in which one of the hydrogens has been substituted by an organic radical. You will recall that water is H_2O— two hydrogens and one oxygen. If, now, we remove one of the hydrogens and replace it by what is known as the methyl radical CH_3—one carbon and three hydrogens—we have CH_3OH which is methyl alcohol. If we had made the substitution with the ethyl radical, C_2H_5, we should have C_2H_5OH, ethyl alcohol—the alcohol about which all our discussion centers. Similarly, substitution with the propyl radical, C_3H_7, yields C_3H_7OH, propyl alcohol; and with the amyl radical, C_3H_{11}, yields $C_5H_{11}OH$, amyl alcohol. Amyl alcohol, which in an impure state may occur in distilled spirits, is called fusel oil.

As I said earlier, all of these alcohols will, in sufficient amounts, produce intoxication, but each is characterized by certain peculiarities in physiological action. Thus, on the basis of amounts taken at one time, methyl alcohol is no more intoxicating than is ethyl alcohol; but methyl alcohol is oxidized—destroyed—in the body extremely slowly while ethyl alcohol is oxidized rapidly. Both alcohols leave the body slowly by elimination in the breath and urine; their respective rates of disappearance are determined by speed of oxidation. Thus a man who drinks, say, a pint of whisky in 1 day, has no ethyl alcohol left in his body the next day, but a man who drinks this amount of methyl alcohol does not get rid of it completely for perhaps a week. He not only has a long period of intoxication, but if he drinks within the week he is in great danger of accumulating methyl alcohol—that is, taking it in at a faster rate than that of its disappearance. A similar danger of accumulation does not exist for ethyl alcohol. The persistence and accumulation of methyl alcohol render its use dangerous. In addition, as I shall show presently, the small amount of methyl alcohol which is oxidized is converted into a far more poisonous and persistent substance than that formed from ethyl alcohol. It is peculiarities of physiological action such as these which make methyl alcohol unsuitable as a beverage alcohol and ethyl alcohol particularly suitable.

Oxidation

I have repeatedly mentioned the oxidation of alcohol in the body. Oxidation is the process by which all food substances, such as sugars and fats, liberate their chemical energy in the form of heat and work. Oxidation means that there is a chemical combination with oxygen; the oxygen is brought in the blood from the air of the lungs. All oxidation, whether of sugar, fat, or alcohol, is a controlled process. The rate is determined not by the mere presence of the substance and of oxygen, as in a fire outside of the body, but by a physiological regulation which, for sugars and fats, is determined by the body's over-all needs for energy, and, for alcohol, by an enzyme system functioning primarily in the liver.

Ethyl alcohol, again like sugar and fat, is oxidized in the body to carbon dioxide and water but the process takes place in several steps. The first step is the conversion of the alcohol, mainly in the liver, to a compound known as acetaldehyde. The reaction may be expressed thus: Ethyl alcohol, C_2H_5OH, reacts with oxygen, O; the oxygen exercises its oxidative powers by combining with two of the hydrogen atoms in the alcohol to form a molecule of water, H_2O. Of the alcohol there thus remains C_2H_4O, which is ethyl alcohol with H_2O removed from it; C_2H_4O is a compound called acetaldehyde. Acetaldehyde is far more toxic than ethyl alcohol but it is also oxidized with great rapidity, so that only minute and appreciably innocuous amounts can accumulate. The oxidation of acetaldehyde occurs not only in the liver but in any part of the body. In this oxidation, water is not removed, but oxygen is added. Thus C_2H_4O becomes, with the addition of oxygen, $C_2H_4O_2$ which is usually expressed as CH_3COOH and which is acetic acid, the acid of vinegar. Acetic acid is a rather innocuous substance which itself is oxidized with the final formation of water and carbon dioxide.

The reactions that I have described for the oxidation of ethyl alcohol apply, in general, to the oxidation of all alcohols. Thus the small amount of methyl alcohol which is burned is apparently first converted to formaldehyde, a particularly irritating and unpleasant substance to which may be due the characteristic toxic action of methyl alcohol leading to blindness. The higher alcohols, propyl, butyl and amyl, may each exist in two or more different forms called isomers in which the same elements are present in the same amounts but in different arrangements. Some of the isomers are oxidized to aldehydes, as is ethyl alcohol, but of a different composition and action, and some to ketones which are oxidized only very slowly in the body. The aldehydes of some of the amyl alcohols are oxidized to acids which, unlike the acetic from ethyl alcohol, may exert a marked physiological action.

Of all the alcohols, ethyl alcohol, from its general properties and by the nature of its chemical reactions, is the best suited and also the safest for human consumption and indeed of all substances having a sedative and intoxicating action. In its unoxidized state, ethyl alcohol has a toxicity nearly as low as any alcohol; it is oxidized rapidly; and the primary product of oxidation is oxidized even more rapidly and cannot accumulate; and, finally, the final products of oxidation are nontoxic. There are substances other than ethyl alcohol which might be used as safely as sedatives and intoxicants, but ethyl alcohol, in addition to this feature, has other properties which give it preference. Its boiling point is above the temperature of the body and therefore it does not develop a high vapor pressure in the stomach after it is swallowed; and it mixes readily with water, while many other substances with similar physiological action do not. Add to these properties the fact that ethyl alcohol can be prepared with the greatest of ease by fermentation, and I believe you have the major reasons why it is, and always has been, the sedative and intoxicant of choice.

The primary steps in the oxidation of alcohol, as I have said, occur mainly in the liver through an enzyme system present in that organ. If the liver of an animal is removed and alcohol is given, it is oxidized no more rapidly than methyl alcohol and is lost only slowly from the body by elimination in breath and urine. The process in the liver establishes the rate at which alcohol is oxidized. The rate varies somewhat with the amount of alcohol present in the blood and it can be influenced by certain drugs, but for an average figure we might say that in a man weighing 150 to 160 pounds the liver would carry out the primary oxidation on about 7 to 10 grams of alcohol per hour, that is, roughly, 0.25 to 0.33 ounces by weight, corresponding to 0.6 to 0.8 ounces, by volume, of whisky. From this amount of alcohol there is produced, during the hour, nearly the same weight of acetaldehyde which is oxidized with the liberation of heat. To the extent of this heat liberation, that continuously derived from the oxidation of carbohydrates and fats is curtailed; so that the total rate of energy expenditure of the body, a carefully regulated process, is not altered. The calories derived from alcohol replace those of the other foods and take precedence over them to the extent to which the alcohol is burned. Alcohol and acetaldehyde, unlike sugars and fats, cannot be stored in the body; they are oxidized continuously as long as they are present.

CLASSIFICATION OF ALCOHOL

Since energy is liberated in the body from alcohol, and since this energy can replace the heat which would be liberated from sugars and fats, alcohol must be classed as a food. Classing it as a food, of course, may be objectionable to those who have strong convictions against the use of alcohol and whose concept of food is the rather idealistic one that a food is "good" for the body. The physiologist is not concerned with quality in his definition. Alcohol is a food. It may be a "bad" food in that, unlike most other foods, it may, when taken in large amounts, exert an intoxicating effect before it is utilized in the body. There are other reasons than that of nicety of definition in calling alcohol a food. If it were not a food, many of the well-known diseases of chronic alcoholism would not occur. Dr. Jolliffe will discuss alcohol and nutrition, but let me say here that alcohol provides calories, although it does not provide any minerals, vitamins or proteins. It is as inadequate a food as is refined cane sugar. The excessive use of either over a long period of time may lead to the diseases of dietary deficiency. We formerly believed that many of the physical disturbances of chronic alcoholism were due to the direct toxic action of alcohol; we now know that many result from a deficient diet.

So far in my discussion I have continually spoken of alcohol, ethyl alcohol, as if we were dealing with a chemically pure substance—a colorless, limpid fluid, with a specific gravity of about 0.8, with little odor but a powerful burning taste. It has in this pure state a great affinity for water, which has sometimes given rise to the erroneous belief that in the low concentrations in which it appears in the body it has a similar affinity for water. Alcohol in the body does not act as a dehydrating agent. The characteristics which I have enumerated are those of pure alcohol, but practically no one drinks pure alcohol; they drink alcoholic beverages. Therefore, I shall digress for a few moments here on the nature and composition of these beverages, for they have a bearing on the physiological effects of alcohol.

PRODUCTION OF VARIOUS BEVERAGES

For all practical purposes the beverages can be divided into three categories: wines, brewed beverages, and distilled spirits. The wines are made by the direct fermentation of part or all of the sugar in fruit juice, usually grape; the brewed beverages are made by the conversion of the starch of cereals into sugar by the action of enzymes and the subsequent fermentation of the sugar; and the distilled spirits are produced by fractional distillation of wine or brewed beverages to concentrate the alcohol in the distillate.

The active agent in fermentation is yeast; this microscopically small plant, widely distributed in nature, produces an enzyme, an agent which expedites chemical changes, which is capable of breaking down compound sugars such as sucrose into simple sugars, and another enzyme which converts the simple sugars into alcohol and carbon dioxide. To prepare wine of a sort it is only necessary to leave fruit juice, palm juice, coconut milk, or any other sugar-containing vegetable fluid, exposed to the air in a warm place. The yeast necessary for the formation of alcohol may be present on the fruit and so be carried to the juice; if not, it will settle on the exposed surface of the juice as dust from the air. In the commercial manufacture of alcoholic beverages, the chance presence of any variety of yeast is not depended upon, and carefully cultured yeast is added. Fermentation continues, unless artificially stopped, until all of the sugar has been converted to alcohol or the concentration of alcohol has risen to between 10 and 14 per cent, at which strength further action of the yeast is inhibited. The resulting beverage is fruit juice, part or all of the sugar of which has been changed to alcohol; the water, minerals, solids, and even some of the vitamins of the juice, may be present. In the natural wines the concentration of alcohol ranges between 4 and 12 per cent. Fortified wines—for which the term "arrest of fermentation" is sometimes used—are made by the addition of distilled spirits, usually brandy, to natural wines to increase the content of alcohol. Thus sherry, which is a fortified wine, contains some 20 to 22 per cent of alcohol.

In making brewed beverages a step in addition to that of fermentation by yeast is essential because the enzymes of yeast do not act upon the starch of cereals. The conversion of the starch is effected by malt, which is sprouted grain, usually barley. When grain sprouts, an enzyme is formed which normally converts the starch to sugar for the use of the young plant. In preparing a brewed beverage, the ground-up cereal is mixed with water, and malt is added; the enzymes of the malt convert part of the starch of the grain to sugar. Yeast is then added and some of the sugar fermented to alcohol. The result is a cereal broth containing some 3 to 6 per cent of alcohol and many of the solids and minerals of the grains and some of the vitamins. Usually the beverage is flavored with hops to give it a bitter taste. And incidentally, although hops are supposed to cause sleep, they actually have no more physiological action than any other flavoring substance, such as chocolate or vanilla. The bitter taste, like that from any other source, tends to arouse hunger.

The natural wines and brewed beverages were the only alcoholic beverages until fairly recent times, that is, recent in the light of the great antiquity of such beverages. Distilled spirits appeared only when the process of distillation was developed and applied. Alcohol has a boiling point lower than that of water. When wine or beer is heated in a vessel, the steam that rises at first contains a higher concentration of alcohol than is in the beverage. When the steam is condensed, the fluid—the distilled spirits—has a correspondingly high concentration of alcohol. No solids pass over in distillation, therefore distilled spirits consist of water and alcohol—usually about 50 per cent by volume—and other volatile flavoring materials present in the wine or beer. It contains no minerals or vitamins. Distillation was first applied to wine to make brandy and, later, to beer to make whisky.

In the modern brewery, every sanitary precaution is taken to produce a pure and clean product. If it were not clean it would be offensive to taste and quickly spoil. In the early days of the distillery, however—and even in some fairly modern distilleries—there appeared no reason for this sanitation since the high concentration of alcohol in the distillate destroyed any bacteria that might be present. The lack of sanitation in the preparation of beer for distillation in the distilleries of the past resulted in a crude product which was not fit for consumption. It was therefore passed through the hands of a rectifier. He purified the crude distillate with charcoal, perhaps redistilled it, flavored it with fruit and colored it with caramel to imitate brandy. The whisky of a hundred years ago did not taste like modern whisky; it was more like vodka.

About the middle of the last century the modern flavor was developed, and by accident. Much of the whisky of this country was produced in what is now the Middle West; the farmers made whisky out of their surplus corn, for it was cheaper to ship whisky than the bulk grain. But barrels were needed. From the east, salt fish was shipped west in excellent oak barrels, but they smelled of fish. This odor could be removed by burning, charring, the inside of the barrel. When whisky was put in such barrels some of the ingredients of the charred wood were dissolved, the whisky was colored brown and acquired a taste of charred wood—and the flavor of modern whisky.

In the crude and inefficient early stills the concentration of alcohol reached in the distillate was only about 50 per cent, and this percentage became 100 proof. There were no hydrometers, such as are used today, to determine the concentration of alcohol; instead, gunpowder was moistened with the distillate and if it could be made to burn that fact was "proof" of at least 50 per cent alcohol. The old term has persisted in modern usage. To find percentage, proof is divided by 2; thus 100° proof is 50 per cent alcohol, and 80° proof, 40 per cent.

There are other distilled spirits besides brandy and whisky, as, for instance, gin. This beverage was designed as a medicament and was made by steeping juniper berries and other herbs in alcohol diluted to 50 per cent—a sort of medicinal tincture. It was supposed to be helpful in the treatment of kidney disease but, as has been true of other so-called medicaments—notably the soft drink sarsaparilla, which was long used for the treatment of disease—gin became a popular beverage. Rum is distilled from fermented molasses. Cordials are made in much the same way as gin, with various fruits and spices, but with the addition of a large amount of sugar to form a sirup. The essential feature of distilled spirits, in whatever form, is the high concentration of alcohol and the absence of any of the solids which were present in the original vegetable material from which they were made.

During fermentation, ethyl alcohol and carbon dioxide are not the only volatile substances produced. In very small amounts, many higher alcohols, many ketones and aldehydes, some acids and, in even smaller amounts, a large variety of other substances, are formed. These are sometimes called congeners. Thus whisky contains, in addition to water and alcohol, coloring material, and possibly 100 or even 200 different ingredients. I doubt whether any of these ingredients contribute appreciably to the toxicity of the beverage. Some of the substances, particularly the amyl alcohols—fusel oil—have a bad name among connoisseurs of fine whiskies, but in the amounts present I do not think the name is fully justified. In fact, I am always suspicious of any physiological information advanced by such connoisseurs, and of most "popular" physiology on the subject of alcohol. The "finest" long-aged bottled-in-bond whisky which would delight the palate of the fastidious drinker may contain much more fusel oil than the much lighter spirit blends, and, indeed, than the raw distillate from which the "fine" whisky was made by aging in oak. Aging does not, contrary to popular belief, decrease the content of fusel oil; it increases it slightly because water and ethyl alcohol evaporate to a greater extent from the barrel. Aging undoubtedly changes the taste of the raw distillate, not by removing the offensive fusel oil but by the development of aromatic substances which disguise the taste.

The only physiological effect of the so-called congeners of whisky, on which I can speak with any certainty, is an influence on the rate of oxidation of alcohol. The alcohol of some distilled spirits is oxidized more rapidly in the body than is that of others. The difference, as we have shown experimentally, is due to the action of some congeners which we have been unable to identify. Through their action on the liver, the oxidation of alcohol is slowed and the alcohol therefore remains in the body a longer time and, for the same amount consumed, gives a higher toxicity and greater aftereffects. Various distilled spirits may show marked differences in these respects.

DILUTION, ABSORPTION AND DISTRIBUTION

As I have pointed out, alcoholic beverages may contain from 3 to 50 per cent of alcohol. In concentrations below 15 or 20 per cent, alcohol causes little irritation in the tissues, the mouth, throat, esophagus and stomach, with which it is brought in contact; and below 5 or 6 per cent, no irritation. The distilled spirits, unless diluted before they are swallowed, are definitely irritating—the consequences of this irritation, both immediate and subsequent, I shall discuss in a later talk. At present I am not concerned with the high concentration of alcohol which may exert an influence on the surface of the digestive tract, but with those extremely low concentrations which exert their functional influence after absorption. The surface tissues will tolerate a concentration as high, perhaps, as 20 per cent without any appreciable effect; a concentration of $\frac{1}{100}$ as much, 0.2 per cent, in the blood would result in deep intoxication. So long as the alcohol, no matter how much or how high the concentration, remains in the digestive tract, that is, unabsorbed, no intoxication will develop. In dealing now with absorption and its corollary, distribution, we are concerned with the processes by which alcohol, taken into the digestive tract, reaches the blood and is diluted to the low concentrations which may occur within the body.

If the beverage contains more than 4 or 5 per cent of alcohol, this dilution commences in the stomach. Fluid is secreted by the stomach and is added to the contents to bring about dilution to these percentages. Part of the alcohol, some 30 or 40 per cent, is absorbed directly and rapidly through the walls of the stomach; most other foods are not absorbed from the stomach but only from the intestines, and therefore far more slowly than alcohol, because there may be considerable delay in the passage of material from the stomach to the intestine. The absorption of alcohol from the stomach is not simply a filtration through the walls into the blood circulating about the stomach but a vital and controlled process. The absorption is rapid at first and then becomes slow; if the stomach contents are retained and not passed to the intestine, absorption finally virtually ceases. Full absorption occurs only when the stomach contents pass into the intestine. Absorption of the alcohol from the intestine shows no slowing off, as in the stomach, but is extremely rapid and to the full amount. Alcohol is absorbed from the intestine as rapidly as it passes from the stomach. Thus nearly all factors influencing the rate of absorption are exercised by and in the stomach. It is important to bear in mind that any influence which affects rate of absorption correspondingly affects the extent of physiological action from the alcohol, for, as I have pointed out, it is only the alcohol which is absorbed which is "in the body."

The presence of food in the stomach at the time the alcohol is drunk slows absorption from the stomach and delays passage into the intestine. A drink taken on an empty stomach has a much greater "kick" than one taken after a meal. Some beverages, notably beer, contain, in addition to alcohol, considerable food substances which in themselves slow absorption and thus lessen the effects of the alcohol. There are certain individuals who, if they drink immoderate amounts of strong alcoholic beverages, develop what is known as pylorospasm, that is, a spasm of the muscular valve which separates the stomach from the intestine. Closure of this valve prevents the passage of the contents of the stomach into the intestine. Some alcohol will be absorbed directly from the stomach but the remainder, usually more than half, remains in the stomach, possibly for many hours. Pylorospasm frequently terminates in vomiting. This protective reflex against the absorption of alcohol may be entirely physiological, that is, due to some peculiarity of the stomach, or it may possibly be psychological and be exercised unconsciously in response to some personality trait or emotional state of the individual. Needless to say, those who regularly develop pylorospasm and vomiting after drinking more than moderate amounts of alcohol do not become excessive drinkers.

Alcohol that is absorbed from the stomach or intestine enters the blood circulating in the capillary vessels surrounding these organs. You will recall that the blood is forced from the left side of the heart into the great arteries of the body; that these arteries divide into successively smaller but more numerous branches; that the fine terminal branches open into a vast number of microscopically small vessels called capillaries; and that the capillaries empty into veins which carry the blood back to the heart. There is no passage of alcohol into or out of the blood of the arteries and veins; the passage is only through the walls of the capillaries. These capillaries are extremely numerous in all the tissues of the body; thus a piece of muscle with an area equal to that of the cross section of a common pin may be permeated by as many as several thousand capillaries. Across the wall of the capillaries, alcohol can pass freely to and from the tissues.

After a drink, the alcohol in the digestive tract passes, as I have described, into blood in the capillaries about the stomach and intestines. From there it is gathered into veins and flows toward the heart; in the heart the blood carrying the absorbed alcohol is mixed with blood from all parts of the body and pumped out in the arteries for distribution. There is, however, one important addition to this scheme of circulation that I have described. The blood passing about the stomach and intestines flows through not one set of capillaries, as elsewhere in the body, but through two sets. The veins leaving the organs of digestion do not go directly to the heart but to the liver. In the liver the blood passes through the second set of capillaries and only then to the veins going directly to the heart.

By the peculiarity of circulation the liver is allowed to act upon all blood from the organs of digestion before it is circulated throughout the body. In a later talk, Dr. Jolliffe will discuss the disturbances caused in this circulation by the development of cirrhosis of the liver. My reason for mentioning it here has to do with the fact that the initial oxidation of alcohol occurs in the liver. As the alcohol is absorbed it is oxidized in the liver at the rate at which this organ is capable of oxidizing it, and only the residue enters the general circulation of the body. Usually the rate of absorption greatly exceeds the rate of oxidation so that a considerable portion remains in the blood. It is possible, however, to drink an alcoholic beverage sufficiently slowly so that virtually none appears in the blood leaving the liver. The rate and amount would be of the order of ½ to ¾ of a glass of beer sipped slowly over an hour.

The alcohol carried in the blood leaving the liver is distributed through the capillaries to all tissues of the body. The amount taken out, and held temporarily by the various tissues, will depend upon the concentration in the blood and the amount of water in the particular tissues. The alcohol is gradually distributed evenly in the water of the body. The body is about 72 per cent water; the blood is more fluid than other tissues and contains about 90 per cent. Therefore, when all of the alcohol is distributed, the blood contains about 1.25 times as much per unit as the rest of the body. Consequently it is possible to predict from the concentration in the blood how much alcohol has been absorbed and, conversely, from the amount absorbed, the concentration in the blood. Thus if a man had, at completion of distribution, 0.05 per cent alcohol in his blood, he would have about 0.04 per cent $\left(\frac{0.05}{1.25}\right)$ in his body as a whole. For a man weighing 150 pounds, 0.04 per cent would be 0.06 pounds or 0.96 ounces by weight and 1.2 ounces by volume of alcohol. From this calculation it does not follow that a man *drinking* 1.2 ounces of alcohol would reach this concentration in his blood. Rate of absorption would be an important modifying factor. Thus if it took him 2 hours to absorb the alcohol, he would have lost by oxidation and elimination, during this time, about a quarter of the alcohol, so that the maximum amount in his body at any time would be perhaps 0.8 of an ounce by volume and the concentration in the blood between 0.035 and 0.04 per cent.

During the time that absorption is taking place rapidly, these simple relations that I have described here for concentration of alcohol in the blood and the amount in the body do not hold precisely. Absorption into the blood may be more rapid than distribution from the blood to the tissues, so that the concentration in the blood rises out of proportion to the amount absorbed. There is a practical corollary to this occurrence. The circulation of blood to the brain is more rapid than to most other tissues of the body, therefore the distribution is more rapid in the brain; and the concentration in that tissue follows closely that in the arterial blood. The effects from alcohol are exercised upon the brain and vary in intensity with the concentration. Consequently if a strong alcoholic beverage is taken on an empty stomach the sudden rise in the concentration in the blood due to slow general distribution may result in what is called overshooting of the concentration. The effects of a small amount are experienced as disproportionately great, but only for a very short time, since, with slowing of absorption, the progressing distribution of the alcohol lowers the concentration in the blood—and in the brain. This overshooting is the explanation for the brief "kick" from the cocktail before dinner. The same drink taken after a meal would have lost its "kick" because, with the slower absorption from the full stomach, overshooting would not occur.

ELIMINATION

Alcohol, as I have pointed out, enters the blood by absorption and leaves it by oxidation and elimination. Oxidation, I have dealt with; elimination is a far less important feature. The urine, as secreted, has a somewhat higher concentration of alcohol than the blood; the relation is about 1.3 to 1.0. The amount eliminated in the urine varies from a fraction of 1 per cent of the alcohol drunk to as much as 5 or 6 per cent. Alcohol is ventilated out of the blood in the lungs by the air breathed, but the evaporation is slow since each liter of air takes away only $\frac{1}{1250}$ as much alcohol as in each liter of blood passing through the lungs. The total amount lost may vary from 1 or 2 per cent to as much as 10 or 15 per cent, depending largely upon the amount of alcohol that is taken. The alcohol not lost by elimination, that is, from 80 to 98 per cent of the amount drunk, is lost by oxidation.

With the essential facts of absorption, distribution, oxidation and elimination before us, we are now in a position to deal with what is known as the "blood alcohol curve." Such a curve, one of which is shown in the accompanying illus-

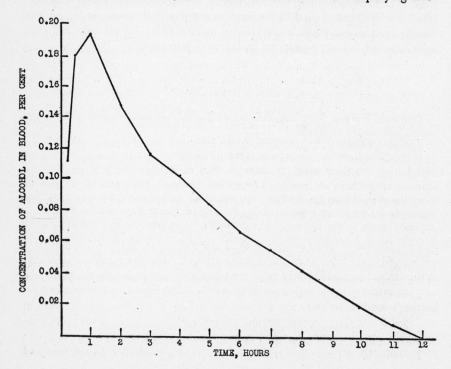

tration, shows the concentration of alcohol in the blood at intervals after it is drunk. This concentration is the resultant of the interplay of amount, body weight, and rates of oxidation and elimination.

Concentration and Blood Alcohol Curve

The curve shown is from a man weighing 165 pounds (75 kg.) who drank, on an empty stomach and at one time, 8 ounces of whisky containing 4 ounces (3.2 ounces by weight or about 100 grams) of alcohol. The concentration of alcohol in the blood was determined at frequent intervals. During the first half hour, absorption was rapid and greatly exceeded the rates of oxidation and elimination and also of distribution. Therefore, the concentration rose sharply to 0.18 per cent. During the next half hour absorption had slowed and the rise was only to 0.19 per cent. Frequently, in such experiments, rate of absorption may, for a time, nearly balance rates of oxidation and elimination, and a plateau lasting for an hour or more may occur at this point in the curve. After 1 hour the rate of absorption had decreased below that of oxidation and elimination and the concentration in the blood fell to 0.145 per cent. Since no more alcohol was taken, the fall continued and at 12 hours all of the alcohol had disappeared from the blood. This curve, which is a fairly typical one, applies only to this particular man for the amount he drank and the conditions under which he drank it. If the amount had been less or he had been heavier, the concentration would have been lower and the alcohol would have stayed in his blood a shorter length of time. If he had eaten a meal before drinking, the concentration would have been lower but the alcohol would have persisted for nearly the same length of time. Generalizations cannot be made in these matters except on the basis of "averages" and for definite conditions, and definite beverages.

DISCUSSION

Question: Do you think that dilution of the alcohol concentration of beverages would lead toward moderation?

Lecturer: I think so. I probably have sentimental reasons for that as well as sound physiological ones. The idea was vigorously advocated by my late teacher, Dr. Yandell Henderson, in a book called, *Dilution: A Plea for Moderation.* It is true that the dilute beverages have less irritating effects upon the throat, esophagus and the stomach. Also, the more dilute the beverage, the less actual alcohol is consumed, other things being equal. One of the great stumbling blocks, unfortunately, to making more dilute distilled spirits is the Government's definition of whisky; if the concentration is brought below a certain point, the product can no longer be labeled whisky. This regulation was intended to protect the economic aspect of purchase but it has been a barrier to greater moderation. In those countries where dilute beverages are used, there is less intoxication and less alcoholism. I think that the wider use of brewed beverages and reduction in the concentration of alcohol in distilled spirits and wines would be a move toward moderation.

Bancroft: I understand that grain alcohol is more pleasant to drink. Then why is it that when a man starts to drink wood alcohol, he seldom goes back to grain alcohol?

Lecturer: Many people find grain alcohol unpleasant but drink it because they want intoxication. In most social circles, wood alcohol is not viewed with favor. But in that stratum of society which has discovered and approved wood alcohol as a beverage, the primary purpose is probably prolonged intoxication. And wood alcohol certainly gives prolonged intoxication, and also probably, in some respects, gives a different feeling of intoxication.

Question: Why is alcohol not a dehydrating agent within the body?

Lecturer: That question bears upon the old idea that alcohol exercises a part of its action on the body by withdrawing water, just as alcohol in high concentrations does outside of the body. The concentration of alcohol in the body for mildest intoxication may be of the order of 0.1 per cent, and for rather deep intoxication 0.2 to 0.3 per cent. Alcohol in these low concentrations is not a dehydrating agent. Simple organisms, like the paramecium, which are quite sensitive to dehydration, will live in apparent comfort in that and much higher concentrations of alcohol. Let me put it this way: Glacial acetic acid is a powerful corrosive agent which will destroy the skin and flesh with which it is brought in contact; diluted acetic acid, called vinegar, is not corrosive, and if diluted even more, is not even irritating.

Question: On the basis of absorption and elimination, why does one who has been intoxicated by drinking wine, after apparently becoming sober, appear again to be intoxicated on drinking water?

Lecturer: The only answers that I could give would be, first, that the water woke him up the next morning so that he realized he was drunk; and second, any actual effect would be psychological, like the fainting that is supposed to occur—and does in those who believe, but only in those—after drinking Coca Cola in which an aspirin tablet has been dissolved.

Mrs. Lewis: We heard during Prohibition that some men became sick or died after drinking some bootleg beverage which was not aged in charred barrels and for this reason had fusel oil left in it. Is this correct, or was that theory incorrect?

Lecturer: That is not correct. Some people died after drinking the beverages of the Prohibition era because some of these beverages contained wood alcohol. Dr. Hunt of Harvard has shown that bootleg liquor not containing wood alcohol was no more toxic than aged whiskies. The charred barrel does not take out fusel oil.

Mrs. Colvin: If a small amount of gasoline were added to water and swallowed, would it be partially oxidized in the body and give out a small quantity of heat as alcohol does?

Lecturer: Gasoline is not burned in the body. Alcohol does not give out a small amount of heat, but a large amount, for its weight. Gasoline is not a food.

Question: Do mixed drinks increase intoxication?

Lecturer: No. To mix drinks, you have to have at least two drinks, and two drinks are always more intoxicating than one. If mixing were to cause intoxication, some cocktails, with their complex composition, would be exquisitely intoxicating. The idea that mixed drinks are more intoxicating is an outgrowth of social customs which have been promulgated by the gourmets who think that anyone who mixes his liquor can't be a gentleman. Of course, if one believes that mixing causes greater intoxication, psychological factors will be brought into play.

Question: Was not alcohol formerly used in the treatment of diabetes?

Lecturer: Yes, it was. That was before the introduction of insulin. The diabetic who could not burn sugar could burn alcohol and derive energy from it. In 1910 the physicians of the United States were asked to list the 10 most useful drugs; enough of them voted for alcohol so that it appears as Number 9 in the list. If a similar questionnaire were circulated today, alcohol would not be included, but, of course, a number of drugs would be which were not known in 1910.

Question: Will you say something about tolerance to alcohol?

Lecturer: Very little is known about tolerance. There is no true toxicological tolerance developed for alcohol as there is for some alkaloids, such as nicotine and morphine. The greatest individual differences in the intoxicating effects from alcohol are seen at the moderate concentrations in the blood. Thus one man may show little or no sign of intoxication when this concentration is as high as 0.15 per cent; another may be definitely under the influence when the concentration is 0.10 per cent. These are the levels at which psychological differences are particularly marked, for the signs of intoxication are shown in general behavior and not in such deep-seated disturbances of the nervous system as those which cause unconsciousness and death. The important feature is this: At such high concentrations, the habitual drinker and the novice show little difference. When the concentration in the blood reaches, say, 0.4 per cent, both are unconscious; when it reaches 0.7 to 0.9 per cent, both are dead. For an alkaloid like morphine, on the contrary, the novice, if suffering no severe pain to counteract the depressing effects of the drug, would probably die if he swallowed 1 grain; the addict may take as much as 10 grains a day.

Alcohol is burned no more rapidly in the habitual drinker and it is absorbed no more slowly. It is true, of course, that the larger the individual the lower the concentration in the blood for a given amount of alcohol, so that, all other factors being equal, the large man has a greater natural tolerance than the small one. Aside from such differences I think that tolerance is mainly psychological. As I have said, there is an inherent and natural difference in the response of different men to the same moderate concentration of alcohol, but above and beyond that, they learn, on repeated drinking, to anticipate the effects of alcohol and to compensate for them. The novice has an unfamiliar feeling; he has not developed "sea legs" and he does not know how to behave, and he behaves badly; the habitual drinker does know the feeling and he has learned to control his behavior to a certain extent.

Question: If large quantities of alcohol can cause death, why do we not have more instances of acute alcoholic death?

Lecturer: Largely because of the habit of drinking distilled spirits fairly slowly. Acute alcoholic death could not be caused by beer or light wine because of the enormous bulk of the fluid. Thus, for illustration, we shall say that the presence in the body of some 16 to 20 ounces of alcohol—that is, fully absorbed—would kill a man of average size. That would correspond to 1 to 1¼ quarts of whisky—absorbed, remember. Few people, indeed, drink this amount of distilled spirits out of the bottle in a few minutes, and none could absorb it within several hours, but the attempt, with somewhat larger amounts, might be fatal. Usually, spirits are drunk more slowly—one drink after another—and eventually enough is drunk to cause deep intoxication well below the fatal level; the man ceases drinking before there is danger of his dying. As I said, acute alcoholic death from drinking beverages of low concentration of alcohol is out of the question; to get 20 ounces of alcohol in his body, a man would have to drink, and absorb within a short time, 5 or 6 gallons of beer. He might drown.

Question: You said that alcohol is burned in the body as a food with the liberation of energy. Are the alcoholic beverages fattening?

Lecturer: Alcohol is rich in energy; a gram of sugar or starch will yield some four calories, a gram of fat, nine calories, and a gram of alcohol, seven calories. Thus the calorific content of pure alcohol is, weight for weight, greater than that of pure sugar and only a little less than that of pure fat. Dr. Jolliffe will expand on this feature in his discussion of nutrition; I bring it in here only as a preamble to the reply to your question.

Alcohol apparently cannot be altered to fat in the body. But if a man eats all the carbohydrates and fats necessary to fulfill his calorific requirements and then, in addition, drinks an alcoholic beverage, there will be some sparing of carbohydrate and fat with the deposition of fat as would occur if he ate either carbohydrate or fat gluttonously. As a matter of fact, the use of the alcoholic beverages would, in most instances, curtail the subsequent intake of other foods to the extent of the calories they supplied, so there would be no deposit of fat. Dr. Jolliffe will also elaborate this point.

Now to get specifically to your question: What is understood by the popular—vernacular—expression "fattening food," is a rich food. A lady concerned about her figure speaks of butter, cream, gravies and pastries as fattening foods, and of lettuce, apples and oranges as nonfattening foods. Richness is a matter of calorific content; a rich food furnishes per pound or pint a large number of calories—a nonfattening food, a small number of calories. There is a wide difference in the calorific content of different alcoholic beverages, determined largely by the per cent of alcohol present. One might say that whisky, which provides some 1,600 calories per pint, is a rich—fattening—food. It has about the same calorific content as cakes, cookies and honey, and about half that of butter. At the other extreme is modern American beer with about 200 calories per pound or pint. I should not call it a "fattening food" since it is in the same calorific category as oranges, apples, raw carrots and onions. These are near the bottom of the list as "nonfattening foods" and are only exceeded by such articles as watermelon, 125 calories per pound, cucumber—without dressing—75 calories per pound, and celery and lettuce—again without dressing—about 80 calories per pound.

The Concentration of Alcohol in the Blood and Its Significance

with a Demonstration of the Alcoholometer

Leon A. Greenberg

WHEN alcohol is swallowed it passes to the stomach and is there diluted by the gastric secretions. A portion of the alcohol is absorbed, at a diminishing rate, through the stomach wall into the blood stream. Alcohol is one of the few substances taken in the human diet which may be absorbed in large amounts directly from the stomach. Even in the case of alcohol, however, the major portion passes from the stomach into the small intestine, where absorption is rapid and complete. The rate of absorption from the stomach and the rate of the passage into the intestine are influenced by many factors such as the dilution of the alcohol, the nature of the alcoholic beverage, and the presence or absence of food in the stomach. The rate at which alcohol enters the blood—hence the amount actually "in the body"—may thus be widely variable, depending upon the factors which influence absorption.

Alcohol which has been absorbed, that is, entered the body in the sense in which I use the expression here, follows a course which is much less variable than is absorption. The alcohol absorbed from the stomach and intestine enters the blood. This blood is carried by a large vessel, called the portal vein, directly to the liver. During the period of absorption, the alcohol concentration in the portal vein is higher than in any other part of the body. At the liver, the blood carrying the alcohol absorbed from the digestive tract is mixed with blood coming from the lower part of the body. The mixed blood is carried in a still larger vein, the vena cava, to the right side of the heart where it is further mixed with the blood returning from all other parts of the body. Thus the alcohol absorbed is diluted by the total blood of the body. The blood carrying the alcohol is pumped by the heart to all tissues of the body and the alcohol it contains is then shared by the tissues.

DISTRIBUTION OF ALCOHOL

After absorption of alcohol has ceased, that is, when there is no more alcohol left in the gastrointestinal tract, and the blood has shared its alcohol with all the tissues of the body, a condition of equilibrium is said to have been reached. The concentration of alcohol—the amount per unit of weight or volume—attained in the various tissues after this equilibrium has been reached is not equal throughout the body. Some tissues and fluids, such as blood and cerebrospinal fluid, have a relatively high concentration of alcohol; other tissues, such as muscle, have a moderate concentration of alcohol; and still others, as bone and fat, a low concentration. These variations depend primarily upon the amount of water that is present in the tissues. The amount of alcohol per unit of water in these various tissues is essentially the same. In other words, alcohol dissolves in the water of the body. It distributes itself in the various tissues and the fluids of the body in proportion to the amount of water in each of these tissues. Blood has a high content of water, therefore it has a relatively high concentration of alcohol. Bone and fat have a low content of water, therefore they have a relatively low concentration of alcohol.

Because of this peculiar, unequal distribution of alcohol throughout the tissues, it follows that the concentration of alcohol in the blood, for any amount of alcohol absorbed, will be greater than that which would develop if the alcohol were dissolved in a mass of water equal to the weight of the body. The concentration in the blood established by any unit of alcohol absorbed will depend both upon the relative masses of different tissues in the body and upon their total mass—that is, the weight of the man. The former relation is reasonably constant and the latter relation—body weight—is the primary determining factor. Knowing the weight of a man it is possible to estimate closely, from the concentration in the blood, the amount absorbed; and conversely, the concentration can be estimated if the amount absorbed is known. Except for very large amounts of alcohol, the rate of disappearance of alcohol from the body, and hence from the blood, by oxidation and elimination after drinking is fairly constant for some hours; therefore, from the concentration in the blood it is possible to predict with reasonable accuracy the amount of alcohol a man has drunk at some time before the concentration was determined.

There is no doubt that it is the alcohol present in the brain itself that is responsible for the intoxicating effect of the alcohol. But the brain is not available for analysis, except post mortem. The concentration in the brain can, however, be determined indirectly. There is a constant relationship between the concentration of alcohol in the brain and that in other tissues and fluids of the body. Analysis of any one of the available tissues or fluids of the body can therefore provide valuable evidence toward the diagnosis of intoxication.

Choice of Material for Analysis

The first consideration in such diagnosis is the choice of material for the actual analysis in determining the concentration of alcohol. This choice has been a subject of lengthy discussions and differences of opinion among scientific investigators. Some have based the selection on the reliability or simplicity of methods of analysis which can be applied to a particular material; others, on the ease of obtaining the specimen for analysis. This lack of unanimity of opinion, which concerns no basic principle but only practical details, has been given an unfortunate publicity; this publicity has often left the layman with the impression that there is disagreement among experts regarding the validity of the tests for intoxication made from the concentration of alcohol in blood or urine or expired air. The fact of the matter is that all the scientific workers are in thorough agreement as to the principles as well as on the significance of the chemical tests in the diagnosis of intoxication.

I should like now to deal with the choice of body materials available for analysis and the advantages and the disadvantages of each of them. These materials are: the spinal fluid, blood, urine, saliva and the breath. Breath, of course, is not truly a body fluid, but it does reflect very accurately the concentration of alcohol in the blood passing through the lungs.

The spinal fluid, because of its intimate topographical relationship to the brain, has been advocated by a few investigators as the ideal fluid for indicating the concentration of alcohol in the brain. The intimacy of this relationship, however, is more apparent than actual. It is, in reality, small compared with the contact, both in volume and intimacy, that exists between the blood in the cerebral blood vessels and the brain. The spinal fluid is not as good an index of intoxication as the blood. Furthermore, it is practically an impossibility to secure a specimen of spinal fluid outside of a hospital. The choice of this fluid for the diagnosis of intoxication is a poor one.

Blood reflects the concentration of alcohol in the brain more directly than does any other obtainable fluid. It has been a standard of reference in all scientific studies dealing with the amounts of alcohol in the body and the physiological effects from the alcohol. No particular difficulty is experienced in obtaining it and there is no difficulty in the analytical determination of the alcohol. It is easily stored and easily transported. However, for blood, a physician is required to draw the sample and a trained technician to do the analysis. Over and above these requirements there are certain legal obstacles to the procurement of a blood sample. If it were not for these practical difficulties there is little doubt that all authorities would be in thorough accord on the use of blood as the material of choice in the determination of intoxication.

Urine has the advantage of being available without too much cooperation on the part of the subject and without the need of a specially trained individual in collecting the sample. It may even be obtained without the subject's knowledge of what it is to be used for. A great deal of investigation has been carried out to show that the concentration of alcohol in urine, as it is secreted in the kidneys, bears a constant relationship to the concentration of alcohol in the blood at the time that the urine is secreted. It must be borne in mind, however, that the urinary bladder is a storage chamber which collects the urine secreted continuously by the kidneys over an extended period of time. The urine found in the bladder at any time represents not that being secreted at the time of the test but that which was secreted over the period of time since the bladder was last emptied. In a series of laboratory experiments, Dr. Haggard and I have shown that alcohol, once it has found its way into the urine in the bladder, is not, in the range of physiological concentrations, reabsorbed into the body. The concentration of alcohol in the bladder urine represents the average concentration of alcohol in the blood for the past several hours, that is, since the last time the individual voided, rather than the concentration which is prevailing at the time that the sample is secured. This average, moreover, is influenced both by the concentration of alcohol in the blood and the rate of secretion of urine at different times during the period.

Good illustrations of the possibility of making an error in the use of the concentration of alcohol in the urine were shown in some of our experiments. Subjects consumed about a half pint of whisky before going to bed. After 10 to 12 hours of sleep, without voiding, the blood contained little alcohol, and in some cases none whatsoever, while the urine from the bladder showed a considerable concentration of alcohol. It is true that these are extreme examples. A valid concentration of alcohol in the urine can be obtained when the bladder is first emptied and then urine collected for a short period, say 1 hour, and this sample used for analysis. The concentration in this second sample reflects accurately the concentration within the blood during the hour.

Saliva may be used to indicate the concentration of alcohol in the blood, but in practice this use has been extremely limited. The collection of saliva requires considerable cooperation on the part of the subject, as anyone who has tried to produce an adequate sample of saliva for experimental work can easily testify.

Finally, the breath has been widely used for the determination of alcohol in blood. During its passage into and then out of the airways and the lungs, the respired air comes in contact with a tremendously large area of blood vessels. Alcohol passes from the blood into the air so rapidly that even in the short time of a single breath an equilibrium is established. In this equilibrium there is a constant relationship between the concentration of alcohol in the blood on the one hand and in the air on the other. Thus one can be accurately predicted from the other.

The use of breath has obviated a number of practical difficulties encountered in the use of the blood or urine. A sample of breath can be collected with a minimum of cooperation on the part of the subject; it can be obtained without the legal difficulties encountered in drawing blood; and its collection does not require the services of a physician. The breath gives the exact concentration of alcohol in the blood at the time the sample is taken. And, finally, the alcohol in the breath is easily analyzed. For this purpose we use an apparatus which was developed in our laboratory about 3 years ago in a joint project with the Connecticut State Police. In the apparatus we have incorporated features which remove the responsibility of analysis from the police, or from whoever uses it. The concentration of alcohol in the blood is shown directly on a dial on the front within 8 minutes after the subject breathes into the apparatus. I shall demonstrate the operation of this apparatus in a few minutes.

I have discussed so far the concentration of alcohol in the various tissues and fluids of the body and the availability and the usefulness of these fluids for the determination of the concentration of alcohol in the blood and, therefore, the concentration acting on the brain. This brings us to the second general topic of this discussion.

SIGNIFICANCE OF CONCENTRATION OF ALCOHOL

What is the significance of the concentration of alcohol in the blood in the diagnosis of alcoholic intoxication? During the last decade a large amount of research has been inspired by the increasing importance of answering this question, particularly in relation to automobile driving and traffic hazards. Before the wide use of the automobile the hazards of intoxication were confined largely to the inebriate and possibly his immediate family. He did not present an important threat to public safety; whatever efforts were made to curb his course were most often made in the direction of saving his soul. Now, however, when there is a fair possibility that at some time during his excessive drinking he may find himself in operation of a motor vehicle with all its potentialities as a lethal weapon, the situation takes on quite a different aspect. We may have little concern with what he does with his own life but we have a very genuine concern for public safety when he is at the wheel. He presents a menace on the highway which no amount of traffic planning, no amount of superior equipment, no skill on the part of the sober drivers on the road can obviate. When he comes to grief, the public may suffer with him.

As a pedestrian, he is likewise a problem, and one of public safety. The motorists, in seeking to avoid striking him, may, because of his unpredictable course, become involved in accidents affecting many others. The man I speak of here is one who is deeply and unmistakably intoxicated. His condition would be recognized whether he is in or out of an automobile. But an automobile requires more accurate and speedier coordination for safe operation than is needed for the ordinary activities of life. A man might be slightly intoxicated and yet be able to walk and talk convincingly straight and to appear to the observer as sober, but still his mild degree of intoxication can become a dangerous degree when he sits behind the wheel of an automobile. It shows up in traffic accidents. The pedestrian may be deeply and unmistakably drunk, he may be staggering on the road, but it is rare that a man so deeply drunk is able to drive a car. The so-called drunken driver is usually in some lesser but still highly dangerous degree of intoxication. To express these important differences the words "drunkenness," "intoxication," and "under the influence" are employed. The terms "drunk" and "intoxicated" express conditions which ordinarily require no determination of the concentration of alcohol in the blood for their identification; the concentration only shows what is already known, but it does express it in quantitative terms. It is in the diagnosis of "under the influence" that the concentration in the blood is most useful. But it does not solve the problem entirely, for even when the concentration has been accurately determined, the question still remains to what extent, if any, the ability of each particular driver has been impaired by the concentration found. The concentration of alcohol in the blood which may render one man unable to drive safely may be without appreciable effect upon another.

Here, then, is a medicolegal, scientific problem of challenging importance. How, in view of individual variations in tolerance, are science, law, and common sense to be combined so as to diminish accidents in which alcohol is a factor? The problem, as I see it, may be resolved into two main questions: (1) Can there be established definite relationships between the concentration of alcohol in the blood and the effect, even when this concentration is moderate? And (2) can there be established, by law, a figure or value for concentration of alcohol in the blood which it shall be mandatory upon the courts to accept as proof of the defendant being under the influence of alcohol?

For the answer to the first question, we can look only to the scientific investigations of the last 15 years. Numerous studies have been made during this period to show the relationship between the concentration of alcohol in the blood and its effect upon the performance of the individual. In most of this work the criteria used for judging intoxication were such obvious symptoms as staggering, unsteady gait and thickness of speech. Using these admittedly gross criteria of intoxication, the finding was virtually unanimous among investigators that anyone having 0.15 per cent or more of alcohol in his blood cannot escape impairment of his faculties. Although those who have a greater tolerance may not appear to be very drunk, their performance has been shown to be definitely impaired when the concentration of alcohol in the blood is at or above this level. Equally unanimous has been the finding that any person with an alcohol content in the blood below 0.05 per cent is sober and shows virtually no effect from the alcohol.

This does not mean that at concentrations of alcohol between these two values intoxication may not occur. It means merely that the criteria used for intoxication were such as to preclude slight intoxication which did not interfere with ordinary activities but which might nevertheless render an individual unfit to drive an automobile safely in an emergency. Failure to use less strict criteria of intoxication has been due to the admitted uncertainty of the clinical diagnosis of mild or slight intoxication. And the interpretation of the chemical tests standardized against such uncertain diagnoses can certainly be no more exact than the criteria from which they are derived. The chemical test has thus proved weak just where it is most needed. It is between the concentrations of 0.05 and 0.15 per cent that individual variations are most marked. Investigators who have used the blood test extensively admit the diagnostic uncertainty of the method for concentrations in this range. Thus at present the usefulness of the blood test for intoxication may be summarized in such general terms as these:

(1) Demonstration that the blood contains no alcohol is absolute proof of nonintoxication. This sounds rather obvious but the importance of this should not be underestimated. I say this advisedly because I have seen, in the last 3 years during which the Connecticut State Police have been using the Alcoholometer, many instances in which men and women have appeared intoxicated without being intoxicated. They had sustained a psychological shock in an automobile accident and, as a result, they were dazed and confused; they even staggered and their speech was incoherent. In the opinion of the police officer at the scene they presented the clinical symptoms of intoxication, yet when they were tested, no alcohol was found in the breath. Police officers have told me that before they began to use the chemical test there must have been many instances in which individuals who were accused and found guilty of driving under the influence of alcohol had probably had no alcohol or, at most, very little. It is just as important—even more important—to exonerate the innocent as to find and convict the guilty.

(2) The presence of alcohol in the blood demonstrates that alcohol has been consumed.

(3) The fact that the concentration is at or below 0.05 per cent indicates that the amount of alcohol taken has not been sufficient to impair driving.

(4) The fact that the concentration is 0.15 per cent or more indicates definite intoxication.

From our present knowledge we are also justified in saying that an occasional individual with an amount of alcohol in his blood only slightly greater than 0.05 per cent may be so affected that his normal performance is impaired.

An Arbitrary Standard

There seems to me to be one way in which this problem could be solved definitely and efficiently. It would be in the arbitrary establishment of 0.05 per cent as the dividing line between sobriety and "under the influence." The burden for sobriety could then be put where it belongs. Hairline diagnoses and decisions, clinical, chemical and judicial, would be obviated. On such a basis many individuals tolerant to alcohol would be unnecessarily controlled, out of consideration for the susceptibility of a few. But such control is accepted elsewhere, as for example in our speed laws. In view, however, of the extreme danger from a drunken driver, a drunken operator of various machines, or even a drunken pedestrian, it seems only reasonable to provide a margin of safety to the public by demanding unquestionable sobriety from even the least susceptible.

In making a diagnosis of intoxication, one is dealing with the individual and not with statistical generalizations. If no standard value of blood alcohol is established by the law to differentiate the sober and the intoxicated, then any attempt to use the blood test for precise diagnoses in court will lead to much legal quibbling with expert testimony and also to the eventual discrediting of a useful diagnostic aid.

If there is to be established by law a value for concentration of alcohol in the blood which it shall be mandatory upon the courts to accept as meaning intoxicated, or under the influence, it will be necessary to recognize these facts and to meet them. This can be done only by adopting as a criterion not the value at which the majority are just on the verge of serious intoxication, but rather the value below which all men are reasonably sober. In other words, we must discard all consideration of physiological variations in the response to alcohol and establish an arbitrary legal criterion. From present knowledge we are justified in holding that anyone with a concentration of alcohol at or below 0.05 per cent is sober.

The Alcoholometer

Before demonstrating the Alcoholometer, let me define, as I understand them, the main desiderata for medicolegal procedure for determining the concentration of alcohol in the blood. They are these:

1. Accuracy.
2. Result obtainable within a few minutes.
3. Minimum cooperation from the individual upon whom the test is made.
4. Full automatic determination and recording of the concentration of alcohol under all conditions.
5. A tangible record presentable in court.

The purpose of the Alcoholometer, to be described hereafter [see Figure 1], is to fulfill all these conditions through replacing the skilled technician by a portable robot which collects a sample of expired air, analyzes its alcohol content under optimum conditions, and registers the result in terms of alcohol con-

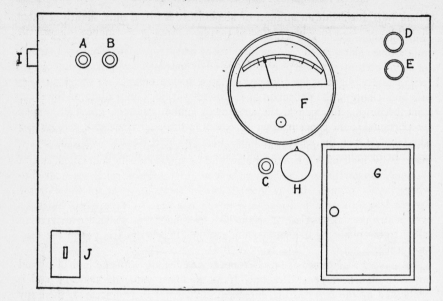

FIGURE 1

centration in the blood. With this Alcoholometer, an operator with no more skill than that required to follow simple directions, that is, press a button and read a scale, can obtain an accurate value for the concentration of alcohol in the blood in less than 10 minutes.

The principle on which the Alcoholometer operates is as follows: (a) the collection of a sample of expired air without loss of alcohol through condensation of water; (b) the reaction of the alcohol with iodine pentoxide, yielding a quantitative production of free iodine; and (c) photoelectric measurement of the intensity of color produced by the liberated iodine in a fixed volume of starch and potassium iodide solution. The subject breathes into the Alcoholometer, which automatically samples 100 cc. of the expired air. Two solenoid valves hold the air sample in a tube which is kept at a constant temperature of 45° C. in order to avoid condensation of moisture. In view of the high solubility of alcohol in water this is an important feature.

The entire apparatus has been built into a metal case. An automatic timing mechanism in the Alcoholometer accurately controls the proper duration of each of the essential operations as well as the proper sequence of their occurrence.

The iodine pentoxide tube [see Figure 2] is contained in a small reaction chamber built into the Alcoholometer which is maintained at a temperature of 140° C. by an electric heater. A small vane pump blows air at a constant rate of 2 liters per minute through the first iodine pentoxide tube and sodium thiosulfate tube for the absorption of iodine. This process removes all traces of organic vapors which may be present. The air is then blown through the sample tube and carries with it the sample of expired air into the second iodine pentoxide tube. All of the iodine liberated here by alcohol is then bubbled through the solution of starch and potassium iodide contained in the colorimeter tube.

The latter is a glass tube containing 30 cc. of 0.1-per-cent solution of starch and potassium iodide and is placed in a fixed position in the colorimeter. In this tube a blue color is produced, the intensity of which is proportional to the amount of iodine present. The intensity is measured by means of a chemical photoelectric cell, a filtered light of fixed intensity, and a microammeter. As the intensity of the blue changes, the deflection of the meter varies. The reading of the meter then becomes a function of the amount of iodine produced which is, in turn, proportional to the concentration of alcohol in the expired air and, indirectly, in the blood. Once the iodine pentoxide tube has been standardized, that is, the amount of iodine yielded per milligram of alcohol has been determined, the

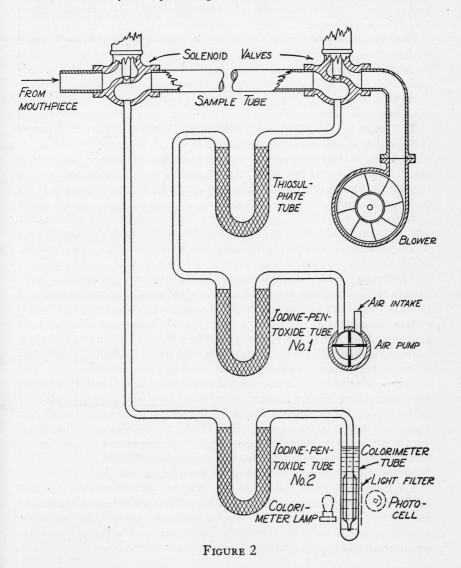

FIGURE 2

microammeter can be calibrated directly in terms of milligrams of alcohol per cubic centimeter of blood.

On the front panel of the metal case [see Figure 1] are located all of the controls essential for the operation of the machine, as well as the meter for reading the concentration of alcohol.

The machine operates entirely on 110 volts alternating current. When the switch J is turned on, the heaters start to function. When the temperature in the reaction chamber reaches the proper level the red signal light D goes on, and remains on as long as the temperature is maintained. Starting at room temperature it takes 8 to 10 minutes for this temperature to be reached. The starting button A will initiate the operation of the machine only if the heaters have produced the proper temperature for a correct analysis.

Once the action of the timing mechanism is initiated by the starting button it continues to operate by itself and in 15 seconds it turns on the pump. The first phase of the analysis is a 3-minute purging period to clean out the iodine pentoxide tubes. Since any iodine produced in this phase would invalidate the subsequent determination of alcohol, the button A will not operate so long as a colorimeter tube is in position.

The sample of expired air may now be taken. Slight pressure on valve button B opens the solenoid valves of the sample tube; release of the pressure closes them. With the valves opened the subject blows into the sample tube using a mouthpiece inserted at opening I. At the end of the expiration, button B is released and the valves close. A colorimeter tube must now be inserted in the colorimeter before the sample of expired air is passed through the iodine pentoxide tube. This is done by opening the colorimeter door G and inserting the tube in a cylindrical slot made to receive it. If a tube is not inserted, button A will not initiate the second phase of the analysis. Thus no error can be made in this direction.

The timing mechanism is again started by slight pressure on button A. In 15 seconds the pump starts and the sample of expired air is blown through the iodine pentoxide tube and then through the solution in the colorimeter tube. The pump continues for $3\frac{1}{2}$ minutes. Twenty seconds later, the colorimeter light goes on and remains on for 1 minute, during which time the meter F may be read. During this time the blower is also in operation, aerating the sample tube so that it will be ready for the next analysis. The entire analysis is now completed and the timing mechanism stops in position for the next test. If, after the test is completed, another reading of the meter is desired, it may be obtained simply by pressing colorimeter button C. This turns on the colorimeter light and a reading may be made on the meter. The button C is also used for adjusting the meter to zero setting occasionally. To do this an unused colorimeter tube is inserted. The button is pressed and the needle adjusted to zero reading by means of the calibrating potentiometer knob H.

For the purpose of calibrating the microammeter in terms of concentration of alcohol in blood a simple procedure is followed. Various known amounts of alcohol are passed through the iodine pentoxide tube and the liberated iodine is collected in the colorimeter tube in the usual way. The readings of the microammeter are plotted against the amounts of alcohol used. Since the coefficient of distribution of alcohol between blood and air is known, and the exact volume of expired air used in all analyses is constant, calculated values for concentrations of alcohol in blood may be substituted for any point on the curve.

The accuracy of the readings on the Alcoholometer is approximated here in terms of the degree of agreement with simultaneous determinations made on blood specimens. In Figure 3, 91 simultaneous observations of actual determinations on blood, and estimates from air analyses of the Alcoholometer, are plotted against each other. A glance at this graph suffices to show that such differences as are observed between the results of the 2 methods are entirely negligible in clinical investigations. The correlation between the results obtained by the 2 methods is obviously so high that any further statistical analysis would be supererogation.

[At this point the Alcoholometer was demonstrated on 3 subjects, A, B and C, weighing respectively 213, 130 and 180 pounds. Subjects A and B each drank 2 highballs, and subject C drank 1 quart of beer, 2 hours after a meal. One hour after drinking, the concentrations of alcohol in the blood shown by the Alcoholometer were, respectively, 0.02, 0.04 and 0.03 per cent.]

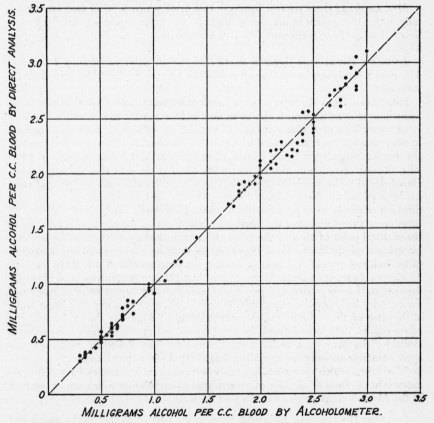

FIGURE 3

DISCUSSION

Question: Are alcohol and its visible manifestations ever produced within the body by something other than liquor?

Lecturer: There are, I think, two questions there: First, is alcohol or any other intoxicating substance produced in the body; and second, can intoxication be produced by drinking substances other than alcohol? Alcohol may possibly be present in the body in minute traces even when none is taken, but the amount is too small to be shown by the ordinary chemical tests. The only intoxicating substance produced in the body is acetone, which may develop in uncontrolled diabetes. Some of the methods used for the chemical determination of alcohol will not differentiate between alcohol and acetone. Acetone has about the same intoxicating powers as alcohol. There are chemical tests which will differentiate acetone. To the second part of the question, the answer is yes, there are a great many substances which, when swallowed, will produce intoxication like that of alcohol. Wood alcohol is one such substance. I cannot see any legal difference as to what sort of alcohol has caused intoxication. That is, I do not think a man could successfully plead "not guilty" to alcoholic intoxication on the grounds that he had consumed no alcohol—grain alcohol—but only methylated spirits, or plead "not guilty" to intoxication because he had drunk gasoline.

Mrs. Lewis: If there are two jiggers in that drink which is being used experimentally, is that the amount in the average highball which you would get outside? I wondered if what the experimenter is taking would represent one highball, or say, two highballs.

Lecturer: The average jigger as served over the bar today varies from 1 ounce to 1½ ounces. It might even be 2 ounces and still be a jigger. In the drinks here, 2 ounces were used.

Potts: How about the time element here? How much time leeway do you have? Sometimes after an accident it may be an hour before they get to it.

Lecturer: This particular piece of apparatus, or any other test except those used on urine, tells what the concentration of alcohol in the blood is at the time that you take the sample. Naturally, if a man is involved in an accident, it is most desirable to know what the concentration of alcohol was in the blood at the time that the accident occurred. Usually, the man is brought to the barracks and tested about a half hour after he has been picked up. Now these gentlemen who are used in the experiment here are drinking relatively small quantities of alcohol. They won't exhibit any symptoms of intoxication; they are below the threshold of the chemical test for intoxication. From the practical point of view of the people who are picked up on the road in accidents involving alcoholic intoxication, 95 per cent of them have taken much larger amounts of alcohol, and even after 1 hour or 2 hours, the concentration is still above the level which would exonerate them. Men are often brought into the police station obviously drunk, but, if no objective evidence is obtained, they may appear before a magistrate the next day looking quite respectable. When the officer charges that they were drunk at the time of the accident and the magistrate asks "What was the evidence?" the officer replies, "He looked drunk, he acted drunk, and that is all the evidence that is available." In many cases, as far as our Connecticut State Police are concerned, this apparatus serves not only for immediate diagnosis but also to provide objective, permanent evidence, which they are able to show a week later, or a month later. This evidence is in the form of the tube of blue-colored starch solution which can be put back in the Alcoholometer to give a reading on the scale.

Question: How can one distinguish between the odor of alcohol in the mouth and the alcohol in the blood stream by this method?

Lecturer: If I were to rinse my mouth with whisky, and to blow into the machine immediately, it would show a high concentration of alcohol; but absorption from the mucous membrane tissues is so rapid that at the end of 10, or at most 15, minutes, you would not find a trace of alcohol from my mouth. Now, actually, even if it were possible to bring a suspect, picked up on the road, to the machine and test him immediately, it wouldn't be advisable to do it because the objection could then be raised that that man may have just had a drink and that his mouth was still full of alcohol. The police always wait at least 15 minutes before making a test. This delay guarantees that they are not getting any local odors of alcohol from the mouth.

Davies: Just a further question to that. The tartar on the edges of the teeth, especially of false teeth, always produces a hiding place for alcohol or other strong or stringent drinks or tastes, and after a period of time the oxidation goes on in the mouth as well as in the stomach. There's a chemical change that occurs in the mouth that will produce that odor over a period of time after it has been taken into the mouth. Now what would you do with that?

Lecturer: There is no alcohol retained in the mouth beyond a few minutes, and no oxidation of alcohol in the mouth.

Davies: Does it remain on the teeth?

Lecturer: No.

Stout: I've heard several chiefs of police say that the dangerous person in an automobile was not the person who was intoxicated so that the physical manifestations could be easily observed. They felt that the person who had had just enough so that he felt real good was dangerous. The person who was "under the table" was scared or unable to get into a car. And yet you used the figure of 95 per cent of the cases that could be easily observed, and the machine was used only for evidence.

Lecturer: Actually that is so, and it has been so here in Connecticut. I've seen many of them.

Stout: So you would feel that the man who has just had a few drinks perhaps isn't a dangerous driver, judging from accidents that have happened in Connecticut?

Lecturer: No, I wouldn't say that, I don't think that I implied that at all. I merely said that it so happens in Connecticut that of those who are arrested, a large percentage are obviously drunk. But I think that the man who isn't obviously drunk may be a very dangerous man in an automobile.

Question: What about the use of the Alcoholometer or other tests on pedestrians involved in accidents?

Chairman (F. W. McPeek): Very seldom is there an arrest for drunkenness, is there? Generally, the arrest of a pedestrian is for being a public nuisance.

Lecturer: That's right.

Womer: We have a very efficient division of our motor vehicles department in Connecticut and they discovered that there were a great many more cases than the actual records show. So they tried going to the various police courts and getting copies of the blotters, and they discovered that many people who were arrested on a charge of drunken driving, by the time their case came before the court, the charge had been changed to something else. And, after they had investigated a few courts, none of the other courts in the State would even give our own State department the privilege of looking at the records.

Chieco: Are there any safeguards for the protection of the rights of the accused at the time when he takes this examination? Is counsel present to see that the examination isn't tampered with?

Lecturer: I have known of no demand for such protection ever having been made.

I hold no special brief for any group of police but I can say with certainty of the Connecticut State Police that they can be trusted implicitly to make an absolutely fair test with the Alcoholometer.

Davies: The test just shown would be a very good argument for moderate drinking. I wonder if that would be correct if the personal factor of the individual were taken into account. The police have no way of judging a personal factor. The personality of the individual may not even be known to the police.

Chairman: Are you bringing up the problem of tolerance?

Davies: No. I'm wondering if it isn't just a mechanical thing and if there isn't always a certain number of discrepancies in mechanical things?

Lecturer: You are questioning a possible discrepancy in a mechanical thing? That is, may it not be wrong to a certain extent? I pointed out that we built a number of safety devices into it so that the wrong thing could not be done by the police officer or the man who is running the machine. Certainly it's a machine, and a machine can get out of order, but it is so made that if it does, the answer will be low. That is, if it failed because the current went off, a contact broke, or for any other reason, the concentration would either not record or would record low, that is, in favor of the subject, not against him.

Mrs. Colvin: I'd like to ask if the dilution of the alcohol has any appreciable effect?

Lecturer: Yes, it does. We have carried out a great deal of research here in regard to the effect of dilution on the rate of absorption of alcohol and, consequently, its effects upon the concentration of alcohol in the blood. We find in general that there is an optimum concentration, that is, optimum from the point of view of speed of absorption. In other words, up to a certain point, the diluted whiskies are absorbed more rapidly than the concentrated alcohol. Again, the composition of the beverage may affect absorption. Thus the cereal ingredients in brewed beverages greatly slow the rate of absorption so that for equal amounts of alcohol as diluted whisky, on the one hand, and beer on the other, that from the whisky will be absorbed much more rapidly than that from the beer, with a correspondingly higher concentration in the blood.

Matthew: I'm wondering, Doctor, if there's any way with this machine that you can detect whether a man has been drinking beer, so-called legal 3.2, or whether he has been drinking hard liquor? It makes no difference how drunk he is. We're interested in whether this machine will detect the difference.

Lecturer: I like that question because it's a problem that we've had. I think it's a general problem. It is known as the "two-beer alibi." It has been a very common experience to have a man who is obviously drunk insist that he has only had "a couple of beers," which, of course, would not make him drunk. I saw one interesting instance of that in which the Alcoholometer was used. The man tested showed a concentration of alcohol in his blood of 0.22 per cent—that would correspond for the average-sized man to some 12 ounces of alcohol actually present in his body and, of course, to a larger consumption, since some may not have been absorbed and some certainly was oxidized and eliminated. Two glasses of 3.2-per-cent beer would contain about ½ ounce. If we were to believe that this man actually had taken nothing but beer, we would have to believe that he had absorbed all of the alcohol from considerably more (to allow for oxidation) than say 6 or 7 quarts of beer, taken—and absorbed—within a matter of minutes. He could not hold that much beer; he could not absorb the alcohol from it at a rate so much faster than he oxidized the alcohol that this concentration would develop in his blood. Actually this man had been drinking hard liquor, but even in his intoxication he remembered that unsophisticated people—and even courts— sometimes accepted the "two-beer alibi." His intoxication led him to try to use that alibi with the State Police. They are not unsophisticated.

Lecture 5

The Physiological Effects of Large and Small Amounts of Alcohol

Howard W. Haggard

IN my previous lecture I spoke about the action of the body on alcohol; today I shall talk about the action of alcohol on the body. I shall not, however, deal with "behavior" as influenced by alcohol; this will be covered separately in a discussion of psychological effects.

My previous talk was prefaced with some elementary chemistry; today I preface similarly with some elementary biology and physiology. Fundamental to both is life; but no one, of course, knows what life is. We do, however, know its manifestations. One of the most basic of these is seen in the inseparable association between life and the expenditure of energy—the transformation of the chemical energy derived from food into energy as heat and movement. When the body ceases to move and is no longer warm, it is dead. That is the first point I wish to make.

The second concerns structure. About a hundred years ago, with the development of the modern microscope, it was found that the body is not homogeneous but is composed of a vast number of microscopically small and discrete units which are called cells. Each cell is living; each is capable of transforming energy —liberating energy. The total transformation of energy by the body is the sum of that of the individual cells.

You are familiar with the fact that certain elementary organisms, such as the amoebae of ditch water, consist in their entirety of a single cell. That single cell possesses the fundamental attributes of the human body; it is capable of taking in food and liberating the energy of the food as heat and movement.

If we were to take a mass of such elementary organisms and put them together we would have—like man's body—an aggregation of cells. But this aggregation would not act like a man. The difference would not result from any difference in fundamental properties; it would result from the presence on the one hand, and absence on the other, of cooperation and division of labor among the cells. In the aggregation of one-celled organisms, each cell acts only for itself with no cooperation with other cells. There can be, therefore, no coordinated or total activity. In man, on the contrary, the cells cooperate, each acts in relation to all other cells to give a coordinated and total activity.

This cooperation is furthered by a division of labor in which certain cells take over an entire function for all other cells. This division of labor results in specialization and anatomical differentiation which gives us the various tissues of the body. Thus one group of cells in the body is highly specialized to carry out movement. These are the muscle cells, and the groups of these cells form the muscles. In their specialization they have lost some of the functions possessed by the single-celled organisms. Thus they cannot digest foods; digestion is carried out for them, and for the body as a whole, by another group of specialized cells. Similarly, the functions of elimination, of stimulation, and all others, are carried out by still other specialized cells to give, as long as the cooperation is maintained, freedom for specialization with corresponding efficiency. A man can carry out a vastly greater scope of activities than the one-celled organism, not because the cells of his flesh have different fundamental attributes but because they work together and are specialized for their tasks.

A group of cells specialized to some function is called a tissue, as nervous tissue, connective tissue, glandular tissue, and so on. The tissues make up the various organs of the body: the heart, which is mainly muscular tissue, the liver, which consists of glandular cells held in a matrix of connective tissue, and so on.

A group of organs working together to carry out some function for the body is known as a system. Thus all the organs of the alimentary tract, with their various tissues of specialized cells, function together to reduce the food from the form in which we eat it to a form which can be used by the cells of the body. This system consists of the mouth and teeth, gullet, stomach, small and large intestines, salivary glands, pancreas, and liver. There are many other systems: the circulatory, the nervous, the urinary, and so on. The point of importance for our consideration here is that specialization and organization, such as I have described, have given man an enormous scope of activity; but this scope—and indeed the very existence of every cell of the body—is dependent upon the normal functioning of each separate system. Thus a special vulnerability is introduced; the muscles may be capable of doing excellent work but they are dependent upon the digestive system for food, upon the heart and blood to bring the food and oxygen, and upon the nervous system to initiate action. If digestion fails, if the heart stops, or if the nervous system is deranged, the muscles can no longer carry out their normal activity. The cells may even die of starvation or asphyxiation although no disturbance originated in them.

INTOXICATION

The resistance of various tissues of the body to disturbing influences varies enormously. The functions of the body as a whole are affected correspondingly with the effect on any one system. Thus if a man goes up in a plane, his respiratory system in the rarefied air brings less oxygen to his blood; his blood, in turn, brings less oxygen to all the organs of his body. Shortage of oxygen must be very severe before it affects directly the cells of the tissues which make up the digestive system, the muscles, the urinary system, indeed, all the systems except one, the nervous system. It is extremely sensitive to shortage of oxygen. As the plane rises, the man's judgment is impaired and, next, the coordination of movements, because, even though the muscles are capable of working, their activity depends upon stimulation and integration from the nervous system. Their functional impairment is to the extent of the impairment of the nervous system. The man staggers, he even falls. At still higher altitudes, he loses consciousness; the most highly developed part of his brain has ceased to function.

At still higher altitudes, the less sensitive nervous center of his brain, which controls breathing, also ceases to function. He then stops breathing, not because the muscles of his chest are incapable of working, but because they no longer receive from the nervous system the stimulation which brings them into activity. With failure of breathing, extreme oxygen deprivation develops; the heart continues to beat for some minutes and then its cells fail and the organ stops. If, short of respiratory failure, the man had been brought to the ground and hence to a normal pressure of oxygen, he would have recovered his consciousness and his muscular coordination. He might have a headache for some hours and feel uncomfortable, but there would be no persisting damage; the derangement would be functional, that is, the organic structure of the cells of his tissues would not have been injured.

Few of you have had the experience I have described from low oxygen, but all of you have had functional derangements of your nervous systems, for I am sure you have all bumped your heads, jarred your brains, and had dizziness or even unconsciousness; many of you at one time or another have fainted; some of you have received inhalational anesthesia for a surgical operation.

When I was describing the progression of *symptoms* from oxygen deprivation, I was describing also those of alcoholic intoxication. Now I do not mean that alcohol deprives one of oxygen; it acts directly on the nervous system to disturb its functions. The concentration of alcohol in the blood which would abolish such functions is far lower than that which would have any appreciable direct effect upon any other tissue, such as muscle or heart. What I am saying is that the intoxicating effects of alcohol are exercised upon the brain; that the disturbance there is functional; that all effects on behavior, as slurred speech and staggering, are caused indirectly by the disturbance of the nervous system. I am saying also that alcohol does not, in the concentrations present in the blood, cause organic damage in the brain—it does not destroy the cells. Alcohol does not corrode them, dissolve them, or withdraw water from them. In sufficiently high concentrations, it does provide a medium in and about the cells of the brain which disturbs their activity. The disturbance in the activity is exhibited not in the brain but in the organs controlled by the brain. The man appears drunk.

LOCAL EFFECTS

In a moment I shall return to the manifestation of the various functional disturbances and deal with the pharmacological classification of alcohol. For the present, while we are still discussing fundamental reactions, I want to digress on another action of alcohol—one on the surface of the body. I include as "surface" the lining of the digestive tract—the inner surface from which there are no openings into the flesh of the body. Alcohol may, under special conditions, have a direct irritant action on this surface. If diluted alcohol—say under 10 per cent—were put into the eye it would cause no injury and no irritation. But if the concentration were 50 per cent, burning, smarting and redness would result. Similarly, if strong alcoholic beverages are swallowed the surface of the digestive tract is irritated. The *immediate* indication of this irritation is, again, through the nervous system. The nerve endings in the throat and esophagus are affected precisely as they would be from the inhalation of the vapors of smelling salts.

In response, there is a reflex action, again as from smelling salts. A deep breath is taken and the heart beats faster. These two stimulating effects—and the only stimulating effects from alcohol—are from no action of the absorbed alcohol; they occur before there is time for absorption, and are very brief. This stimulation is the basis for the old-time use of strong alcoholic beverages as a stimulant in threatened fainting; it was as effective—no more so—as smelling salts.

Irritation, if frequently repeated, may lead to inflammation. Inflammation, contrary to the functional action I have described for the nervous system, is organic. That is, there are demonstrable anatomical changes in the inflamed tissues. If, over a long period, one were to inhale the vapors from smelling salts, a red and painful inflammation of the throat would develop. Similarly, when strong alcoholic beverages—spirits—are drunk without dilution, the throat and stomach are irritated. The irritation, if frequent, may lead to inflammation. The inebriate who drinks his whisky "neat" may have a "whisky" tenor voice and chronic gastritis. These are the only direct irritant actions of alcohol on the body. The brain of one who drinks 50-per-cent alcohol fails to *function* entirely when the concentration of alcohol about its cells is well below 1 per cent; the drinker would become unconscious and die long before he could drink enough to develop a concentration in the blood sufficient actually to irritate and inflame the nerve cells.

We come back again now to the fact that the sedative and intoxicating actions of alcohol are due to an alteration in the activity of the brain induced by the presence of alcohol in and about the cells of the brain. I am not here touching upon any nonspecific indirect effects of a more persistent nature such as those which, in the very heavy drinker, may, after many years, result from dietary deficiency. I am concerned with the immediate action of alcohol as a sedative and as an intoxicant. There is nothing unique about this action; it can be induced indistinguishably in every detail by a great many other substances. These substances are classed—pharmacologically—as volatile anesthetics. Alcohol is a volatile anesthetic.

CLASSIFICATION OF ALCOHOL AS AN ANESTHETIC

If you look for the classification of alcohol in a text book of pharmacology, you will probably find that it is referred to as having sedative, narcotic, hypnotic and analgesic action as well as anesthetic. This fact signifies only that all of the many useful drugs which depress the central nervous system have not only a primary, predominant action according to which they are classified therapeutically but exhibit, in some degree, the effects common to depressants in general. A convenient classification of all depressants is that of: (*1*) sedative-hypnotic drugs; (*2*) narcotics; (*3*) analgesics; and (*4*) general anesthetics. A sedative drug is one of which the predominant action is quieting; it induces calmness and relieves nervous tension. A hypnotic drug is one which promotes sleep without first inducing intoxication. To this sedative-hypnotic group belong such drugs as the bromides and the barbiturates. A narcotic may be defined as a drug which induces analgesia, that is, relief of pain accompanied by deep sleep or stupor. In small doses, the pain may be relieved without the sleep. A narcotic may also relieve tension. To this group belong morphine and the related alkaloids. An analgesic relieves pain without producing sleep. It has little effect in relieving tension except that resulting from pain. To this group belong such drugs as aspirin. An anesthetic induces a progressive descending depression of the central nervous system. This progressive feature is peculiar and definite and serves unmistakably to classify anesthetics. As evidence of the depression in general there may be sedation, analgesia, narcosis and hypnosis preceding the special therapeutic feature of anesthesia—loss of all sensation to pain. To this group belong ether, chloroform, and alcohol.

You may correctly call alcohol a sedative if you refer only to its calming effects—relief of tension—in small amounts. You may even class it as a hypnotic if you limit your attention to its sleep-promoting effects. You may, if you wish, say that it has a narcotic effect in that, in somewhat larger amounts, it relieves pain and causes deep sleep. No one will argue with you if you refer to the analgesic effects of alcohol. It has, in some degree, all the therapeutic actions shown by the drugs which characterize these various groups, sedative, hypnotic, narcotic and analgesic. In fact, any one of the drugs which is specifically defined under the general classification I have given will have overlapping action, for all are depressants of the nervous system. Any of the sedative-hypnotic drugs, if given in large enough amounts, will produce unconsciousness. Thus bromide, in overwhelming amounts, will cause coma, but that is not its predominant and characteristic pharmacological action. Because of the overlapping action there is considerable lack of precision in definition for therapeutic use: Thus the physician may order a sedative or analgesic dose of morphine for his patient but this would not result in the classification of morphine with bromides on the one hand or with aspirin on the other.

Similarly, a man might use alcohol to obtain analgesia, to relieve an aching tooth, but that would not classify alcohol as an analgesic. Another might drink it to obtain sedation, but while it exercised, in the amounts used, a quieting action, this would not alter its general classification as an anesthetic. And still another man might drink it, again in appropriate amounts, to induce narcosis, but the fact that he obtained narcosis would not justify the classification of alcohol as a narcotic.

I emphasize this matter of definition because, unless we make a correct pharmacological definition of alcohol, we cannot discuss its fundamental action and take advantage of the wide knowledge obtained of the action of other anesthetics. It may pain some who have been engaged in temperance teaching that I decline to classify alcohol as a narcotic. This classification has a particularly unpleasant connotation—a fact of which these teachers are fully aware—because of the widely known ease of addiction to morphine and similar drugs, and the serious consequences. The connotation vicariously extended to alcohol by classifying it as a narcotic may have weight in temperance exhortations, but it is bad pharmacology. Of all educators the temperance advocate needs to be most temperate in his statements. And why should he strain for effect when there are enough bad things to say about the excessive use of alcohol without exaggerating? The fundamental distinction between a narcotic, such as morphine, and an anesthetic, such as alcohol, is that one has a selective depressant action on the central nervous system and the other a progressive. Thus morphine will cause depression of breathing before it causes unconsciousness. The nervous center controlling breathing is located at the very base of the brain. The action of an anesthetic starts at the top of the brain and, with increasing doses, it progresses deeper and deeper, with correspondingly more powerful effects on those parts affected earlier by smaller doses—a progressive descending action. Thus if a man takes a small amount of alcohol, any effect experienced will be from the mild depression of the cortex of the cerebrum, the highest part of the brain, which is concerned with judgments, inhibitions, and tensions. In large doses, the effect on the region will become greater and muscular coordination, which is mediated at a lower level of the brain, will suffer. With still more alcohol, the centers controlling sleep will be affected. And there will be correspondingly greater effects on higher structures, so that with large enough amounts unconsciousness in the sense of true surgical anesthesia will develop, but breathing will continue with little depression. If the amount of alcohol taken were extremely large, the respiratory center would, as a final stage, be depressed. Breathing would cease; the heart would continue to beat for a few minutes and then stop, not from the direct action of alcohol but from the asphyxiation caused by respiratory failure.

And finally, to labor for one last minute this classification of alcohol as an anesthetic, let me again call your attention to its chemical composition. There are some relations between pharmacological action and chemical structure. The chemical formula for ether, admittedly an anesthetic and one which will produce drunkenness indistinguishable from that of alcohol, is $C_2H_5 \ O \ C_2H_5$, and of alcohol C_2H_5OH. Ether may be thought of as two molecules of alcohol, $C_2H_5O \ H \ HO \ C_2H_5$, from which a molecule of water has been removed. Ether and alcohol are more nearly related chemically and pharmacologically than first cousins.

Possibly a dozen theories have been advanced for the action of anesthetics upon the brain cells. Many years ago attention centered particularly about the possible effects of anesthetics on the fat-like lipoid material which is present in the membrane about cells and fibers. The potency of anesthetics was found to vary directly with their relative solubility in fat and water. The theory developed was that, because of the high lipoid content of the nerve cell, the anesthetic was concentrated—and therefore had its greatest effect—on this cell. This attractive hypothesis has been rather badly abused by exaggerations which imply that the anesthetic actually dissolves the lipoid from the nerve cells. Such an action does not occur. Indeed, it is generally believed today that the Meyer-Overton theory of anesthesia, with which I am dealing here, is little more than an analogy and affords no true insight into the action of anesthetics.

Other theories have centered about the reduction of surface tension on the nerve cells by anesthetics; the alteration of the permeability of the cell membrane; and the alteration of the colloids in the nerve cell. All of these actions, as postulated, are reversible and leave no permanent injury to the cell. In recent years, the theories of anesthesia have centered less about the cell membrane and its lipoids and colloids and more about the most fundamental process of the cell—its energy-transforming functions. These theories suggest an inhibition of the oxidation in the cell with corresponding depression of functions. This inhibition is presumed to be affected by the action of the anesthetic upon the enzyme system by which cellular oxidation is carried out. The inhibition is reversible in that it disappears when the anesthetic is removed, and its intensity is proportional to the concentration of the anesthetic present. These theories suggest that alcohol—and other anesthetics—cause a functional derangement of the oxidative processes of the brain cells in some ways similar, but produced in an entirely different way, to that caused by shortage of oxygen, as at high altitude. The feature of progressive descending action would be compatible with such a theory since the resistance of the brain to any change in oxidative function or nutrition is least in the higher centers and greatest in the lower.

While I am still in the realm of definitions and theories, I want to deal with a hypothesis which does not concern the ultimate anesthetic action of alcohol but which recently has been advanced to explain the peculiar reaction of certain individuals to alcohol. It is the theory of an allergy to alcohol. The postulated allergic reaction is not in the nature of that of ordinary allergies, as hives, hay fever and gastric upset. It is uncontrollable drinking after a single drink. This peculiar behavior is the basis for the universal injunction that the "cured" problem drinker must remain entirely abstinent and cannot use alcoholic beverages in moderation. If he attempts to do so, he will find that he has started upon a spree. It is probably gratifying to him to have his peculiarity explained on the basis of an abnormal body chemistry—an allergy—rather than a psychic peculiarity. Moreover, allergy is well known to everyone and the statement "I am allergic to alcohol and cannot drink" gives an excuse which is sympathetically received by the insistent hostess who is urging drinks upon her guests. The fact is, however, that there is no true allergy to alcohol in the sense that there is to pollen and many foods and drugs. The term has been used metaphorically by the psychiatrist to explain to his patient that he has a peculiar reaction to alcohol; and the term used by the psychiatrist was "psychic allergy." A psychic allergy may perhaps be defined as a peculiar mental response which, in this application, consists in uncontrollable drinking following the use of any alcoholic beverage. Certainly the man who gives this response may say he is allergic, provided the metaphorical use of the word is understood by him and no implication is made that a true physical allergy is offered as an explanation for the physiological effects of alcohol. Men who show this peculiar response to alcohol do not show, as might otherwise be anticipated, a lower tolerance to the intoxicating effects of alcohol. They simply cannot stop drinking once they have taken a drink.

EFFECTS ON FUNCTIONS OF VARIOUS ORGANS

I have emphasized the fact that, barring the inflammation of the digestive tract from the direct action of alcohol in high concentrations, all actions causing sedation and intoxication result from a functional disturbance of the nervous system. There are other physiological effects of alcohol seen in the functions of the kidneys, of the liver and stomach, and possibly of the adrenal glands. To what extent these effects are due to nervous control and to indirect functional alteration of the activity of glands and other structures, we do not know with certainty. They are not the cause of sedation or intoxication, but they are a part of the physiological effects of alcohol. Let us consider some of them in the light of such knowledge as we now have concerning them.

First, the influence of alcohol on the secretion of urine. You will notice that I employ the words "on the secretion of urine" rather than "on the kidneys." There is a difference. So far as can be discovered, alcohol has no direct or detrimental action on the kidneys. The flow of urine is usually increased after alcohol is taken and during the time the concentration in the blood is rising but not while it is descending. Recent studies have suggested that this diuresis results from no direct stimulation of the kidneys but indirectly from the effect of alcohol on the pituitary gland. This gland is a small extension of the lower part of the brain. It produces secretions which, carried in the blood, affect the activity of many other glands of internal secretion throughout the body. One of the secretions of the pituitary gland, called the antidiuretic element, acts upon the kidneys to impose restraint on the rate of formation of urine. Alcohol appears to act upon the pituitary gland to diminish the secretion and hence the restraint upon the kidneys. Alcohol, therefore, usually increases the flow of urine and this in considerable excess of the amount of fluid which may be taken with or as the beverage.

The fact that alcohol affects this one secretion of the pituitary might lead us to suppose that it affects others. It may or may not—we do not know. The supposition might lead us to wide speculations—intriguing—but only speculations. The pituitary gland influences growth; it influences the sexual development and sexual cycles; it influences the thyroid gland and the adrenal glands. The adrenal glands influence the storage of sugar in the liver, the distribution of mineral salts in the body, and the transformation of fats in the liver. All of these functions may be altered in severe intoxication. Is the pituitary gland implicated as it is with the diuresis from alcohol? We do not know. I cannot give you any sound general theory to coordinate these physiological effects of alcohol; I can only describe them.

The liver has, as one of its functions, the storage of sugar as glycogen. Following the ingestion of large amounts of alcohol, the glycogen is reconverted to sugar and passed into the circulating blood. The concentration of sugar in the blood may thus rise and the liver be depleted of glycogen. A similar reaction, but more intense, may occur from emotional excitement. There is, so far as is known, no particularly detrimental result. I am not drawing inferences; I am simply describing what may occur. Still without drawing any inferences, it has been observed that when the concentration of sugar in the blood is high, the intoxicating effects of alcohol are diminished.

There is a strong suggestion that in very severe intoxication—and please remember I am not dealing with moderate amounts of alcohol but with those which cause deep intoxication—fat in the liver may be inadequately handled by that organ and therefore tend to accumulate. It is possible that the substance choline may be implicated here. Sometimes after very severe intoxication the liver may be swollen and even yellow, but this fact should not lead us to any premature conclusions, however great the temptation, as to the genesis of fatty liver and cirrhosis of the liver in chronic alcoholism.

Alcohol in moderate amounts leads to an increase in the flow of gastric juice and to contraction of the stomach. The sensation of hunger may develop. These changes occur when alcohol is administered intravenously as well as by mouth and are therefore not due solely to a local action on the stomach. The medical prohibition of alcohol for those who have gastric ulcers is because of the increased flow of acid gastric juice. There is no evidence that alcohol ever causes ulcers. Moderate amounts of alcohol do not interfere with digestion—they may even promote it; large amounts, causing deep intoxication, stop it completely.

Alcohol, again in large amounts, may affect the so-called water balance of the body. It was once believed—and still is, I suspect, by some people—that alcohol exercises a direct dehydrating action in the body as does full strength alcohol outside of the body. Under this concept the alcohol was supposed to dry out the body and give rise to the intense thirst of the hang-over. Ether, the anesthetic used in surgical operations, gives the same hang-over as does alcohol, but ether certainly has no avidity for water in or out of the body. What happens from severe intoxication is that the water of the body is shifted in its distribution. Normally, the body is about 60 to 70 per cent water; about two-thirds of this water is within the cells of the body and one-third outside of the cells. The amount outside, the so-called extracellular fluid, which includes that of the blood, is ordinarily maintained with considerable constancy. That in the cells fluctuates; it increases after drinking water and decreases from the secretion of urine and sweat. When it has decreased to a certain amount the sensations of thirst develop. After large amounts of alcohol there is, except for the brief diuresis, no excessive loss of water from the body. There is, however, a flow of water from the cells to the spaces about the cells; the intracellular water decreases and the extracellular increases. What significance, other than causing some thirst, this alteration of distribution has, I do not know.

An increase in the loss of potassium in the urine has been observed after large amounts of alcohol, and again the significance is not entirely clear. Likewise, the vitamin C in the liver and the combined vitamin B in the brain are decreased in severe drunkenness, but how these changes come about and how they tie into the sum total of the physiological effects of deep intoxication, I do not know. In spite of the very large amount of study that has been devoted to the physiology of alcoholic intoxication, there is, as I have indicated, a great deal that is not known or of which the significance is not yet appreciated. Do not make the mistake of oversimplifying the physiology and drawing the conclusion that any and all changes are bad or good. Under present knowledge they are just changes. The physiology is enormously complex and appears especially so in the present stage when the knowledge for demonstrating a basic physiology has not been gained—or at least no adequate theory has been advanced based on the knowledge we have.

In concluding, I wish to anticipate a question. It is on the possible medicinal use of alcoholic beverages. Alcohol in moderate amounts is used primarily for its mild sedative effects. It is, for people past middle age, one of the safest sedatives. Alcohol increases the size of the blood vessels on the surface of the body; makes the skin appear red and feel warm. Many elderly people, with the cold decay of age, get much comfort from a small amount of alcohol; it relieves the aches, pains and chilliness of age, lessens the tensions and irritabilities, and increases the appetite. Alcohol does not greatly affect normal blood pressure but it does prevent the pressure from rising in worry, anxiety, and mental concentration. Alcohol would certainly not be taken to stimulate thought, but it might to relieve the rise of pressure from worry.

DISCUSSION

Question: Please describe the progressive deterioration of the brain cells in alcoholism leading to insanity.

Lecturer: You mean alcoholic mental disease?

Question: The kind of insanity that results from excessive drinking.

Lecturer: The mental diseases which may be associated with chronic alcoholism will be dealt with in a later lecture so that here I shall say only a little, and that little directed at what I presume called forth your question. I emphasized the fact that the action of alcohol on the nervous tissue is primarily functional; that no organic—that is anatomical—change can be found in the cells. Possibly behind your question is the belief, widely held at one time, that alcohol injures, corrodes, destroys the nerve cells and thus leads directly to diseases of the nervous system, such as paralysis, and to mental disease. Actual anatomical injury has been strongly—and I think wrongly—emphasized in some temperance teaching. The most terrifying of the threats of eventual bodily derangement has been that of insanity due to direct injury of the nervous system explained by simple analogy of egg white coagulated in strong alcohol. Such simple analogies are often misleading. It would seem to me that the most important feature of the excessive use of alcohol is not so much the danger to the individual of bodily diseases, but the broader social implications of drunkenness: the drunken husband, the drunken wife, the drunken son or daughter, the drunken motorist. In schools, I think the problem of alcohol can, perhaps, best be presented to the students not in its biological but in its broad sociological aspects.

I have digressed from your question. Only a small number of all of the very heavy drinkers develop insanity. The mere fact that a man drinks heavily and becomes insane is not, of course, proof that he became insane from drinking. To assume so is *post hoc* reasoning. Might we not as logically say that the insanity caused his excessive drinking —that is, that he was not insane from drinking but drank because he was insane? In many instances, as you will find from later lectures, the latter is the actual occurrence. Such individuals are classed as symptomatic drinkers in that their heavy drinking, either wild or periodic, is a symptom of an existing or a developing psychosis.

There are still other complications to a direct answer to your question. Some of the mental diseases associated with prolonged excessive drinking arise not from the direct action of the alcohol but secondarily from nutritional deficiencies induced by the inadequate diet of the alcoholic. Again, in many of the well-classified mental diseases, such as manic-depressive psychosis and schizophrenia, there may not, in spite of the exhibition of extreme symptoms, be any demonstrable anatomical change in the brain cells—I believe "progressive deterioration of the brain cells" was the term you used. No such organic alteration as you seem to have in mind has been demonstrated as a result of the direct action of alcohol on the brain.

Question: Does excessive use of alcohol lead to hardening of the arteries?

Lecturer: No. There was once a belief that the arteriosclerotic accident called "coronary occlusion," which affects many men in their fifties and sixties, was actually less common in very heavy drinkers than in nondrinkers. If this is true, it might be open to several interpretations, one of which might be that very heavy drinkers may not live long enough to have the disease.

Question: Is alcohol in any way a cause of cancer?

Lecturer: No. The use of alcohol in any amounts, small or large, has nothing whatever to do with cancer. It might, of course, if my slightly facetious comment on the last question were sound—that is, very heavy drinkers might not live long enough to have cancer and therefore the incidence of cancer among them would be less.

Question: Is there any truth in the notion that whisky aids in the treatment of influenza?

Lecturer: No. Whisky has no specific medicinal property in the control of any infection. It would, however, relieve some of the symptoms of influenza, such as the ache in the back; and it might lessen the temperature. Alcohol acts as an analgesic. Aspirin, which is also an analgesic, does not shorten the course of influenza but it relieves the aches and pains. This is called symptomatic treatment—the treatment of symptoms. It makes the patient more comfortable but has no effect on the disease. Before the days of aspirin, and even after, a stiff drink of whisky, a hot toddy, or an eggnog was often used to make the ill man feel comfortable, but they have no beneficial effect on the actual course of the disease unless the disease is influenced by sedation.

Question: If alcohol is a sedative, why has it been used to revive persons who have fainted?

Lecturer: I covered that question, but perhaps inadequately, in my talk. Strong alcoholic beverages stimulate, by direct contact, the nerve endings in the throat and gullet. As the result of a brief nervous reflex occurring before the alcohol is absorbed, the heart beats more rapidly and the blood pressure probably rises. The stimulation, as I said, is the same as that of smelling salts. It would not occur with a beverage of low alcohol content, which causes no surface irritation. One does not revive a fainting man by giving him a bottle of beer. After alcohol is absorbed, it may exercise its sedative action to lessen the nervous tension which has resulted from the shock which caused the fainting.

Question: Is there anything, physiologically speaking, to the idea that a person who has been on a severe alcoholic binge, should taper off?

Lecturer: It will do him no physiological harm to stop completely. He may be nervous, jittery and shaky; his head may ache and his hand tremble. Alcohol used as a sedative will give symptomatic relief just as would any other substance with a sedative action, as, say, paraldehyde. The man knows from experience that a drink will make him feel better—and he probably craves that drink not only for the relief from the hang-over but for the same underlying causes from which he has been in the habit of drinking excessively. You, perhaps, have in mind the devastating effects and suffering that occur in the man addicted to morphine or other narcotics on abrupt withdrawal. Symptoms of such severity do not develop in the alcoholic. He may be miserable but he has not developed the altered physical state in which the cells of his body fail to function normally except in the presence of the drug.

Question: Will a man engaged in hard labor burn alcohol which he has consumed more rapidly than one engaged in a sedentary occupation?

Lecturer: All experimental evidence indicates that alcohol is not used to any great extent for the energy of physical work and is not, therefore, oxidized more rapidly during work. The energy of alcohol is liberated mainly as heat.

Question: If it can't be used for work, how can it be classed as a food?

Lecturer: For the same reason that fat can be classed as a food. The muscles in performing work burn carbohydrate in preference to fat. Most of the energy of fat is liberated as heat. By far the greater part of energy liberated in the body from all foods appears as heat. When alcohol is present and being oxidized, its energy is contributed to the total necessary heat production and to this extent fats and carbohydrates are not used to produce heat—they are spared. Fat is admittedly a food, but if a man were to try to subsist on a diet of pure fat he would get into serious trouble. He could not burn the fat completely; he would develop an acidosis; he would, in time, be short of vitamins, minerals and proteins. He would develop nutritional deficiencies just as he would if he tried to live exclusively on alcohol. Certainly alcohol is a food. This is a feature that Dr. Jolliffe will amplify in his lecture on alcohol and nutrition.

Question: Does excessive drinking during pregnancy have any physiological effect on the unborn child?

Lecturer: I think you have, perhaps, a number of things in mind which are not explicit in the question. First, you use the word excessive; excess is essentially harmful by definition. And I think that it is harmful rather than physiological effect that you are thinking of. If a pregnant woman drinks an alcoholic beverage, the alcohol reaches the child in about the same concentration as that appearing in the blood of the mother. If the mother gets drunk, the baby will be drunk. If the mother is anesthetized, say with ether, the baby will be anesthetized. The volatile anesthetics can penetrate the placental barrier and hence reach the child. You may recall reading that one of the oppositions brought, many years ago, against the use of anesthetics in childbirth was that it was unseemly to have a child brought into the world in the midst of the drunken debauch of the anesthetized mother. The nervous system of the unborn baby is immature. This immaturity, contrary to your possible expectations, does not give an increased sensitivity to insults, as from asphyxiation or intoxication, but an increased resistance. My guess is that the baby would, after a drunken debauch on the part of the mother, have less of a hang-over than she. If the use of alcohol did not harm the mother's health, there is no reason to believe that it would harm the baby's health or development. If, however, the mother's excessive drinking interfered with her normal nutrition, that might affect the baby. If the mother got drunk and fell down, that also might injure the baby. Many of the early physiological studies showing harm to the offspring of, say, rats, from mothers given large amounts of alcohol, were made before we had knowledge of vitamin, mineral and protein requirements. The nutrition of the animals was seriously affected by the excessive amount of alcohol, and that of the offspring correspondingly.

And finally, I may wrong you, but I have a feeling that behind your question there is possibly something of the idea of a particularly telling warning against drinking in general, addressed to expectant mothers and based on a threat of danger to the unborn child, something on the order of: "Fifty per cent of the children of mothers who use alcoholic beverages die in the first year after birth," or "If you drink, your baby may be an alcoholic." Those are unfair threats. They are a form of "black magic." Suppose a mother does have a drink and her baby does die during the first year—many do from many causes. Think of her unjustified mental state of guilt and self-recrimination. No amount of good intention can compensate for such mental anguish. Suppose the baby lives, as it probably will, and the mother remembers the threat, as she may, and worries for years over the possibility that she may be guilty of causing her child to become an alcoholic. It is wrong! There is such a thing as mental hygiene as well as physical hygiene. In our efforts to promote physical well-being we must not destroy mental well-being.

Question: Does drinking by the mother cause jaundice in the baby?

Lecturer: That question is, I think, based upon liver injury from alcohol. Many babies have jaundice for a time after birth and from many causes. So far as is known, alcohol used by the mother is not one of them.

Question: If a mother drinks while nursing, will alcohol appear in the milk and affect the baby, and will it develop a taste for alcohol?

Lecturer: The concentration of alcohol in the milk will approximate that in the blood of the mother. If the mother is quite drunk, but still able to nurse, the milk might contain some 0.2 per cent of alcohol. For an alcoholic beverage, that is quite dilute! If the baby drank, say, 8 ounces, it would get a total of 0.016 ounce of alcohol, or about 6 drops. It would get considerably more in many other articles of food which are not ordinarily considered as containing alcohol. Thus, 12 drops of vanilla extract in a glass of milk would provide a beverage of about the same concentration of alcohol. The answer to both parts of your question is no.

Question: Are the diuretic properties of alcoholic beverages due to the alcohol or to other ingredients?

Lecturer: They are due to the alcohol. Gin has long had a reputation as a diuretic; it has been used to treat kidney disease. The supposition was that the juniper berry oil, which is characteristic of gin, was the diuretic element. In reality, pure alcohol mixed with water to the same proof as gin exercises quite as great a diuretic action as does the gin.

Question: Did you not state that alcohol always has some effect on the behavior and performance of the individual?

Lecturer: As I recall, my only remark on behavior was to the effect that I should not deal with it as influenced by alcohol, and that this subject would be dealt with in another lecture. But I shall exceed my own limiting statement for a moment because I think I know what you have in mind. You mean this: If I were to take even a small amount of alcohol, it would have some effect on my behavior. I suppose it would. I think if I drank a glass of water it would also have some effect. What the effect might be, I do not know, but I suspect that it would be strongly influenced by the effect I might expect. I might even be influenced in reaction by the situation that caused me to take the very small amount of alcohol, or the glass of water, or whether I knew it was alcohol I drank. In these matters, we are dealing not with demonstrable physiological functions, as covered by the topic of my lecture, but with psychological functions. Moreover, in dealing with psychological functions concerning alcohol, some people are prone to make the assumption that any alteration that follows is in the direction of a detriment. Alcohol in rather moderate amounts may decrease ability to perform certain complicated acts, but the only justifiable conclusion is that alcohol interferes with the performance of the particular act. The same amount of alcohol taken when relaxation and rest are desired may increase the abilities and performance in these directions, but that fact would not justify a sweeping statement that alcohol increases efficiency and performance in general. There have been psychological tests carried out with delicate measuring apparatus which show that changes do occur after comparatively small amounts of alcohol but, as I said before, they might occur from a great many other things, as eating a good meal, for instance, or even drinking a cup of coffee. And I repeat again that change cannot be interpreted as having any significance in respect to general efficiency. I am not, of course, a psychologist, but in viewing some of the psychological studies carried out on alcohol I have come to the conclusion that the greatest variable in interpretation of experiments on the effects of alcohol is the preconceived belief of the experimenter.

Question: Would it be your contention that alcohol does not lead to any particular disease?

Lecturer: I realize that some of my statements—if accepted—would cause some disillusionment to those who have commented strongly on the medical threat of disease from alcohol as a deterrent to the use of alcohol. I have not been defending alcohol in my denials of alcohol as the cause of certain diseases. I have been defending medicine. I also, admittedly, have my own biases; one of them is against the medical threat. Its basic defect is often that inherent in the story of the man who called "wolf, wolf" and lost both his integrity and his merit as a publicist. This comparison does not mean that no wolf exists: it does. But the continued long-range threat of a wolf in the form of eventual medical complications of alcoholism that actually materialize only for a very few out of the many who drink, leads, in turn, to indifference and disregard. Exaggeration is found out and followed by revulsion. The physical infirmities of chronic alcoholism are dramatic; it is only natural that, in a desire to make a quick and vivid impression, the early "temperance workers" dramatized the horrible example of disease. But the fact is that threat of eventual physical disease from excessive use of alcohol is especially ineffective because it is the least important of all dangers. The real danger—real disease if you will—is drunkenness. The importance of drunkenness is not so much physical as it is sociological.

Question: If one were to use alcohol for its sedative properties—that is, in small amounts—at the close of the day when there were no immediate responsibilities, and continue this use over a period of years, would the quantity needed to produce the relaxation increase?

Lecturer: That question has, I suspect, a background of tolerance to narcotics. What you have in mind, perhaps, is this: If a man used morphine for sedation under the conditions you describe, that is, daily use, he would find, in time, that he had developed a tolerance to the drug and would need more and more for sedation. A time would come when he would need daily an amount which would, if taken in the beginning, have killed him. He has developed a true physiological tolerance to the sedative, hypnotic, and lethal effects of the drug. A similar true drug tolerance is not developed for alcohol. The amount which would kill the man on the first day would also kill him after years of use. The so-called tolerance developed for alcohol is toward drunkenness and is not so much in what the man feels as in what he shows. He learns by experience to control, to some extent, the manifestations of drunkenness.

The man you have described as obtaining relaxation from a sedative amount of alcohol will get this effect from the same moderate amount even after years of use, provided the need for sedation does not increase. This man gets a comfortable relaxation; he has no desire and no intention of getting drunk. But suppose he has business or family troubles; to obtain the same degree of relaxation that he had in normal times, he would have to take more alcohol. He would have to get drunk, perhaps. But it does not follow that he would. What he will do, will depend upon the particular man. If he has come home every evening with the feeling, "now I will take a dose of some sedative and get relaxation,"—if he feels he must do it, I should think he might be in danger of taking an extra dose under exceptional strain. I should not say that this man was a moderate drinker, no matter how small the amounts he actually drank. Moderation is in intention as much as in amount. For the moderate man, alcohol is not used as a crutch against life so much as for the enjoyment of life, as is eating, or sleeping, or resting. The moderate drinker—in the true sense of the word—probably does not enjoy getting drunk or even want to get drunk. He does not regard alcohol as a "medicine," to be gulped down, in spite of an unpleasant taste, for the "kick" and relief. When used in that way the man is not a moderate drinker. I suspect that the rather heavy emphasis I have put on the pharmacological action of alcohol—and necessarily so in my discussion—may have created in your mind a therapeutic bias. Moderate drinkers do not drink for medicinal purposes; they drink because they enjoy the beverage and it increases their enjoyment.

Alcohol and Nutrition: The Diseases of Chronic Alcoholism

Norman Jolliffe

IN any study of the physical effects of chronic alcoholism, primary consideration must be given to the nutritional deficiencies which may be caused by
alcohol. I am speaking here not of occasional intoxication and not of the
behavior of the intoxicated man, but of the bodily injury that may be caused by
the excessive use of alcohol over many years. During these years the drinker has
obtained much of his "food" from alcohol. It has been an important item of his
diet, for alcohol is rich in energy. Alcohol as a food, a source of energy, provides
some 7 calories per gram or 200 calories per ounce. A gram of carbohydrate
furnishes 4 calories, and an ounce, 114 calories; a gram of fat furnishes 9
calories, and an ounce, 270 calories. Thus, as a source of calories alcohol ranks
between carbohydrates on the one hand and fat on the other.

There are distinctions between the utilization of calories from alcohol and
from carbohydrate or fat, but these distinctions are mainly in the rate of use and
in storage. A man could eat carbohydrate or fat to the extent of say 5,000
calories in a single day; of these calories, his body would use what was needed to
replace the energy expended during that day and the remainder would be stored
in the form of fat to be used another day or to remain indefinitely. Thus if his
expenditure of energy for this particular day was 3,000 calories, he could store
2,000 calories in fat—a little less than 7½ ounces of fat. There is, to the contrary, an upper limit to the extent to which the calories from alcohol can be
used in any 24-hour period, and apparently none of the alcohol is stored as fat.
A certain amount of alcohol is eliminated in the breath and urine—perhaps as
much as 10 or 15 per cent if the amount drunk is large—but the rest is burned
in the body. If a man drinks more alcohol than he can utilize in one day, some
remains to be used the next day. Now for a man of average size—154 pounds—
the maximum amount of alcohol ordinarily oxidized in a 24-hour period corresponds to about 1,600 calories. If he is larger, it will be more, but we shall deal
here throughout with a man of average size. Sixteen hundred calories is just
about the number obtained from a pint of whisky.

The average rate of energy expenditure for a man of average size is some
2,500 calories. Consequently, the drinking of a pint of whisky a day would
supply about two-thirds of his daily energy requirements, his daily need for
calories. Alcohol would thus make up something like two-thirds of his daily diet,
his daily nutrition. You can thus see why, for the continual excessive drinker,
alcohol becomes a primary nutritional factor.

Now how does alcohol in these amounts affect nutrition and cause diseases of
nutritional deficiency? First, strong alcoholic beverages, such as the distilled

spirits, especially when drunk undiluted, affect the mucosa or lining of the stomach. As a result there may be vomiting with loss of food, and there is most certainly loss of appetite. The loss of appetite limits the desire for and the intake of food.

Second, after a long period of excessive drinking, certain changes, distinct from those caused in the stomach by the direct action of alcohol, develop in the mucosa of both the stomach and the intestine. As a result of these changes there may be impairment of digestion and particularly impairment of the absorption of nutrients such as the vitamins.

A third nutritional effect from the prolonged excessive use of alcohol may be an increase in the actual need for certain food elements so that the chronic alcoholic may require even more of them than does the normal individual.

These three possible nutritional impairments are aside from the matter of calories, which I shall discuss in a moment. They may result in (1) diminished hunger and diminished intake of food; (2) diminished utilization of the food that is eaten; and (3) increased need for certain food elements.

ROLE OF ALCOHOL CALORIES

The fourth impairment of nutrition is that of the substitution of calories from alcohol for calories from foods that supply other dietary needs than the need for energy. Hunger is a very precise index of the dietary requirement for calories. Hunger does not give any clear indication of a need for vitamins, minerals or proteins; it specifies only calories—enough calories to replace those expended by the body. Hunger, as I say, is an excellent judge of the requirement for calories; year in and year out most people judge, to a fraction of 1 per cent, their output and input of energy—that is calories—by their hunger. Few of us vary in weight by more than 3 or 4 or 5 pounds in a year; this constancy of weight means that hunger indicates the exact amounts of food, in calories, needed over an extended period. This does not mean that if, as the result of a banquet, you eat on one day 1,000 calories more than you need, you will put on some 3 or 4 ounces of fat and keep this gain of weight indefinitely. What you will do is eat less at the next meal, or during the next day or two, until the 1,000 extra calories are expended. Over a year, hunger will judge the intake of food on a calory basis so accurately that the calories expended will be balanced by the calories eaten to within an error of less than 1 per cent.

Hunger makes no distinction as to source of calories. It accepts those from alcohol as readily as from any other food. Thus if a man drinks, say, a pint of whisky a day, 1,600 calories of his consumption of other foods will, over a period of months and years, be reduced by an average of 1,600 calories a day or else the man will gain weight rapidly. Whisky, as you have been told, contains no vitamins, minerals or proteins; a pint of whisky is nutritionally just 1,600 pure calories. In taking such calories a man omits from his diet—to a corresponding number of calories—the meat, bread, potatoes, vegetables and fruits which supply vitamins, minerals and proteins.

Now you might say it would be a simple matter for the man who was daily using 1,600 calories from whisky to compensate for his nutritional deficiency by overriding his appetite and eating a supply of food which would give him his normal amount of nutrients. Even if he did, it would not correct the deficiency. This fact was once a medical mystery. An alcoholic would be brought to the hospital with, say, beriberi or polyneuropathy, a disease known to be due to nutritional deficiency. An examination of his diet might show that he was obtaining the nutritive elements that would keep a normal man from having this disease—and yet he had it. It was therefore thought that the direct action of alcohol produced the condition. We now know that this is not true. He had a dietary deficiency, but we did not then recognize it because we did not know about the so-called vitamin-calory ratio. I want to explain this ratio:

The average American diet contains about 2,500 calories. As judged on a certain scale for measuring vitamin B_1, called "milligrams equivalent," this average American diet provides about 6,800 milligrams equivalent of vitamin B_1. The vitamin-calory ratio, the number of milligrams equivalent of the vitamin divided by the number of calories, thus equals approximately 2.7, as shown in the following equation:

$$\frac{\text{Vitamins } 6,800}{\text{Calories } 2,500} = (\text{ratio}) \ 2.7$$

If this ratio falls below 1.7 for the average diet of a population group, as it will if the foods eaten contain too little vitamin B_1, there will be a high incidence of beriberi. If the ratio is above 2.3, then there will be a very low incidence of beriberi. Between these values there is some beriberi.

Now, for illustration, a certain man eating the average American diet, and therefore obtaining enough nutrients to remain free from beriberi, adds to this diet—and remember it supplies all the nutrients he needs—a pint of whisky a day. There will then be added to the denominator of the fraction in the equation above, 1,600 calories; but there will be added to the numerator no more vitamins. The equation now becomes:

$$\frac{\text{Vitamins } 6,800}{\text{Calories } 4,100} = (\text{ratio}) \ 1.66$$

Thus without cutting down on what has been his normal intake of vitamins, but only by increasing his calories, he has reduced the ratio to the point where he will develop some signs of vitamin B_1 deficiency. This ratio is based on the work of Dr. George Cowgill of the Yale Department of Physiological Chemistry. What it means is that the need for certain vitamins, especially the so-called B vitamins, increases with the calories in the diet.

The concept set forth in this ratio gave to the physician an explanation of why some men, even though they were eating well, nevertheless developed beriberi when, for a long period, they increased their calories by those from a pint of whisky a day. Whether or not a man drinking this amount of whisky will develop beriberi depends on the nature of the diet he is eating. If he eats heartily of meat and whole wheat bread and other good sources of the B vitamins, he may be able to maintain his vitamin-calory ratio and prevent the development of the deficiency disease. If he is eating the average American diet he will, in time, probably show signs of deficiencies even though he may eat an extra amount of food. But remember that he does not usually eat that extra amount of food, or even the usual amount. The calories from alcohol ordinarily reduce his food intake, his squeamish stomach reduces it further, the disturbances in his intestines diminish the absorption of those vitamins he does obtain, and the changes in his body increase the amount of vitamins he needs. It is not surprising, therefore, that in time many excessive drinkers show signs of nutritional deficiencies.

Now what are these diseases of nutritional deficiency which the chronic alcoholic may develop? The most common and best defined are polyneuropathy, pellagra, encephalopathy, and Wernicke's syndrome. I shall discuss each one.

POLYNEUROPATHY

Polyneuropathy (formerly called polyneuritis) is identical with so-called Oriental beriberi and is caused by deficiency of thiamin or vitamin B_1. There are many manifestations of this disease, varying in nature and severity. The earliest and mildest is sometimes called the neurasthenic syndrome. A syndrome is a combination of symptoms; in this syndrome the symptoms are anorexia, that is, loss of appetite; increased fatigue, and disturbed sleep. Now, of course, there are many other causes for that syndrome of anorexia, fatigue and disturbed sleep. A husband who is in trouble with his wife; a broker in trouble on Wall Street; or a student in trouble with his studies may have anorexia, fatigue and disturbed sleep. But one of the causes is vitamin B_1 deficiency, and one of the ways of getting this deficiency is to drink excessive amounts of alcohol daily without due regard to the rest of the diet.

After having anorexia, fatigue and disturbance of sleep for a period of time, certain susceptible individuals develop a more severe form of the syndrome. They acquire, in addition to the other symptoms, such disturbances as "heart consciousness," that is, the feeling of the heart beating; or they may develop queer sensations in the fingers and toes. They are prone to develop pains in the joints and muscles, and also disturbances in the motility of the intestines which lead to constipation or diarrhea. These are early symptoms of beriberi. After a time, walking may become difficult, eventually the legs may become paralyzed and, in extreme cases, even the arms and eye muscles.

PELLAGRA

Another disease found in chronic alcoholics is pellagra or pseudopellagra. Remember that these diseases of chronic alcoholism, even when they are called alcoholic diseases, do not require alcohol to produce them. But they are frequently found among alcoholics for the dietary reasons which I have explained. Twelve or fourteen years ago, when we first started studying this subject, there were quite a number of patients on the wards at Bellevue who were diagnosed as having pseudopellagra. The condition was identical with the pellagra seen in the South. Pellagra at that time, and before, was thought to be due to some toxic action of Indian corn. Since the patients in Bellevue were not taking corn— unless it was corn whisky, and very few of them in New York City were drinking corn whisky—it was hard to believe that it was pellagra. But since it looked like pellagra, it was called pseudopellagra, and sometimes alcoholic pseudopellagra. After a time we began trying to sign some of these people out, that is, make the final diagnosis, pellagra rather than pseudopellagra. Then members of the Board of Health came to the hospital and they took 2 or 3 or 4 hours of our time for every patient we had signed out as having pellagra. "No," they would say, "that isn't pellagra, that's pseudopellagra." So we just stopped arguing with them and to this day there has been no official death from pellagra in New York City for years and years, although there have been many, many hundreds. It keeps the record clean.

What is this disease of pellagra? It is a deficiency of niacin or nicotinic acid. Alcohol is involved in the production of pellagra in exactly the same way as in the deficiency of thiamin which causes polyneuropathy. Alcohol in excessive amounts cuts down the intake of foods containing nicotinic acid, it probably increases the requirement for nicotinic acid, and it upsets the vitamin-calory ratio.

Pellagra occurs most commonly among people who use Indian corn as their chief source of energy. Corn, in contrast to wheat, rice, oats and barley, contains a very small amount of nicotinic acid. In pellagra the mouth becomes sore and the tongue coated and red. There is inflammation of the skin, especially where it is exposed to the sun. Diarrhea may develop. In severe cases the mind is dull and there may be actual mental illness.

The bread-enrichment program began in about 1941, and since 1942 or early in 1943 all pan-baked bread is, by war order, enriched with thiamin, riboflavin, niacin and iron. Before that date a plain, good, ordinary bread did not carry enough niacin or enough thiamin in it to meet its own needs, that is, to balance its own calories according to the vitamin-calory ratio. Thus it did not have any vitamins to spare for balancing the calories from alcohol. Enriched bread contains approximately four times the amount of thiamin and niacin that it needs to take care of its own energy requirement, that is, its own vitamin-calory ratio. It formerly had a vitamin-calory ratio below 1.7; now it is about 4 or 5; bread thus furnishes, to those individuals who are drinking excessively, amounts of vitamins above those needed to take care of the bread calories, and in that way it helps take care of the lack of thiamin and niacin in the whisky they drink. This is evidenced by the fact that since the bread-enrichment program started the incidence of polyneuropathy and of pellagra in our wards has been reduced to one-fourth of what it was before enrichment. There are, of course, other factors than bread-enrichment involved in the decrease. First, our alcoholic admissions have fallen from around 12,000 to 8,000 a year. Second, the economic situation of the people is improved and they are eating better, as shown by our consumption of food.

Encephalopathies

Another alcoholic disease is nicotinic-acid-deficiency encephalopathy. This disease was formerly known as encephalopathia alcoholica, in the belief that it was caused by the direct action of alcohol. The patient with this disease passes into a stupor, but this stupor is not the result of the anesthetic action of alcohol, for it remains after all the alcohol is out of the body. Patients in this condition show what we call the "sucking" and "grasping" reflexes. If you touch the patient's lips with a tongue depressor, he will purse them up as though sucking; at the same time, if you put your fingers in his hands, he will squeeze, and the harder you try to get away, the tighter he will squeeze. This condition represents an acute complete deficiency of nicotinic acid, while pellagra largely represents a chronic and less complete deficiency. The acute complete deficiency may be suddenly superimposed on the chronic state.

As a copartner of this disease, we have another one called Wernicke's syndrome. I might have mentioned this immediately after polyneuropathy, because the Wernicke syndrome represents an acute complete deficiency of vitamin B_1 in contradistinction to a milder chronic deficiency which would be manifested as polyneuropathy or beriberi. Thus Wernicke's syndrome has the same relationship to beriberi as nicotinic-acid-deficiency encephalopathy has to pellagra. The symptoms of Wernicke's syndrome are similar to those of nicotinic-acid-deficiency encephalopathy. There is stupor and clouding of consciousness, but instead of sucking and grasping reflexes, these patients are unable to move their eyes in any direction.

CIRRHOSIS OF THE LIVER

There is one particular disease, which may be associated with alcoholism, in which many of you may have an especial interest because this association has been so frequently and strongly emphasized. It is cirrhosis of the liver. There are several varieties of cirrhosis of the liver. Some are due to infections such as malaria, but the one associated with alcoholism is called Läennec's cirrhosis or sometimes "hobnail" cirrhosis. Now this disease may develop in individuals who use no alcohol. Thus it is found among the inhabitants of countries where alcohol is little used, as Arabia and Syria; and it is found in men and women in our country who have never used alcohol or have used it only in moderation. But the fact remains that it does occur more frequently in very heavy drinkers than in nondrinkers or moderate drinkers. Here, then, is a situation analogous to, say, beriberi which is not caused by alcohol, which may occur in those who never use alcohol but which does occur—for nutritional reasons—more commonly in those who drink excessively. There are reasons to believe that nutritional deficiencies of some sort are a factor in causing cirrhosis. It is certain that cirrhosis is not caused by the direct action of alcohol any more than is beriberi, but the particular nutritional deficiency which underlies its development has not yet been conclusively demonstrated.

In cirrhosis, the liver usually first enlarges from the abnormal accumulation of fat and then, later, fibrosis, that is, scarring, develops. Scarring causes shrinking and deformity of the liver such as might occur in the scar of a deep burn on the skin. Because of this shrinking or contraction, the blood vessels in the liver are pressed upon and constricted and the passage of blood through the liver is impeded. The serious results of cirrhosis come mainly from the impediment to the flow of blood, and the reason lies in the fact that all the blood circulated to the stomach and intestines must pass through the liver before it can be returned to the heart. The flow of blood from the whole gastrointestinal region is thus dammed back by the cirrhosis of the liver.

In the early stages of the disease there may be very few symptoms and none at all which points to the liver. On physical examination the liver may be found greatly enlarged, but the only symptoms may be some indigestion and some tiredness, as in the neurasthenic syndrome which I mentioned earlier. Then, as time goes on and the circulation of the blood is increasingly impeded, there are developed what are known as channels of collateral circulation. That is, detours of a sort are formed by blood vessels so that blood can be carried around the obstruction in the liver and returned to the heart. These collateral channels are shown as enlarged veins over the abdomen, and in the esophagus, or gullet. The veins of the esophagus may become greatly dilated and undergo the same structural change as occurs in the varicose veins of the rectum which are called hemorrhoids. The dilated veins in the esophagus are thin and not supported by any strong surrounding tissue; they tend to rupture and bleed, just as a hemorrhoid may. Hemorrhage from these vessels of the esophagus is one of the common causes of death in cirrhosis of the liver.

Another disturbance that occurs in well-advanced cirrhosis of the liver is ascites, that is, a dropsical condition with fluid in the abdomen. The ascites may be due to two factors. One is the back pressure of the blood in the impeded vessels of the abdomen. The other is a disturbance in the protein content of the blood. The damaged liver is, in turn, unable to form protein for the blood in adequate amounts. As a result of the low content of protein, the blood is unable to withdraw water from the tissues and carry it to the kidneys as it normally would. The fluid therefore accumulates in the abdomen.

Repeatedly I have called attention to the fact that the disturbances of chronic alcoholism, with which I have dealt here, are not caused directly by alcohol. They are secondary to nutritional deficiencies that might develop without the use of alcohol. They do develop, however, more frequently during the excessive use of alcohol because this excess interferes with the normal diet. All sweetened carbonated beverages, such as the cola drinks, and also cane sugar and sugar candy, can be just as serious nutritional offenders as alcohol if they are used in equal excess. Refined sugar is a pure carbohydrate. It contains no vitamins, minerals, or proteins, nothing except calories. It requires thiamin, niacin and riboflavin to oxidize it. Anyone who drinks, say, 20 Coca Colas a day, is nutritionally in about the same situation as one who drinks a pint of whisky. Of course, the sugar does not cause gastric disturbances, or impaired absorption and utilization of vitamins, but it does increase the requirements for vitamins because of its vitamin-free calories. The sugar-loaded dietary supplements are, in this respect, as bad as alcohol.

DISCUSSION

Mrs. Lewis: Is Korsakoff's syndrome the same as Wernicke's disease, and if so, is it also due to nutritional deficiency?

Lecturer: It is not the same as Wernicke's syndrome; no one knows the cause of Korsakoff's syndrome or psychosis. It occurs in a great number of alcoholics, but it may also occur from a blow on the head—a brain injury. One of the conditions that may precipitate a Korsakoff psychosis is pregnancy. In Korsakoff's psychosis the individual forgets what he has been doing, but won't admit it, so he fills in the gap in his memory with what he would like to have been doing. For instance, we have a man on the ward with Korsakoff's psychosis and we ask him, "What have you been doing this morning?" He has been in the hospital for weeks, but he says, "Well, I just flew in from Havana." "Well, what did you do yesterday?" "I had six or eight drinks down at Sloppy Joe's." Korsakoff's psychosis occurs in many conditions other than chronic alcoholism, but it has a very high association with polyneuropathy, and therefore many investigators have thought it is a thiamin deficiency. But the syndrome occurs so frequently in patients who do not have a thiamin deficiency that I question this etiological theory.

Heimburger: Is hunger physiological or psychological?

Lecturer: Hunger is primarily physiological but it can, as is true of most functions, be influenced psychologically. Thus hunger can be made more acute by the odor of some appetizing food. If one were not hungry, and had in fact eaten too much, not hunger but distaste might be aroused by the same odor.

Mrs. Mann: I would like to know where the so-called alcoholic convulsion comes into this picture—whether that has anything to do with nutritional deficiencies or with amounts of alcohol drunk.

Lecturer: Alcoholic convulsion is a serious complication of excessive drinking and is associated with an edema—a watery swelling—of the brain. I cannot tell you the cause of the edema of the brain. It probably results from some chemical imbalance in the osmotic system in the circulation of the spinal fluid, but I don't think anyone can say just how it is brought about. It certainly is not the result of any of the nutritional diseases we know at the present time.

Mrs. Mann: I asked this because I am frequently questioned as to what relation, if any, alcoholism has to epileptic fits.

Lecturer: Alcohol does not produce epilepsy but if a man is an epileptic, alcohol will make the disease worse. In other words, alcohol apparently lowers the threshold or increases the sensitivity of the trigger mechanism for convulsion. There are people who have an epileptic type of convulsion only after they have been drinking.

Mrs. Mann: They are, then, not necessarily epileptics? Or are they?

Lecturer: A man may be an epileptic and never have a convulsion because he hasn't had the exciting stimulus to bring it out.

Mrs. Mann: That is what I did not understand.

Lecturer: There are epileptics who may never have had convulsions but we can detect their disease now by means of the electroencephalogram without their having convulsions. A great many of those people will have convulsions if they drink heavily, but only at that time.

Mrs. Mann: I have seen a number of these alcoholic convulsions and also a great many epileptic convulsions, and I can see no difference whatsoever between them, but as far as I know the people I have seen with alcoholic convulsions have never had convulsions when they were sober.

Lecturer: I have seen that, too. They may be individuals with brain injuries. If an individual gets a fractured skull, he may later have an epileptic type of convulsion.

Mrs. Mann: But it does not necessarily mean that they are epileptics?

Lecturer: That depends on your definition of epileptic.

Mrs. Mann: Well, maybe I don't know enough about that. I am asking merely because I am asked so frequently.

Lecturer: Well, I think your answer is that if there is any tendency at all toward convulsion, alcohol greatly increases that tendency.

Mrs. Mann: But the tendency must be there first?

Lecturer: I would think so, because we have so many thousands of people who drink very large amounts and never develop convulsions. I would think that they would almost certainly have to have either a brain injury or an epileptic tendency.

Mrs. Mann: Possibly they had a brain injury while they were drinking at some time, because there are people I have known who did not begin to have convulsions until, let us say, the very late stages of their drinking. Possibly they had fallen and injured their brain and did not even know it.

Chairman (E. M. Jellinek): When an alcoholic, late in life, develops true epileptic convulsions, it will frequently be found that a history of epilepsy exists in the family. I should also like to point out that the incidence of excessive drinking among epileptics is much greater than in the general population.

Mrs. Coles: Isn't it possible for epileptic-type convulsions to follow accidents when there is no previous tendency or inherited weakness in that direction?

Lecturer: Many people have convulsions as a result of accidents.

Burtner: I would like to ask what you mean by neurasthenic syndrome? I don't know what the word syndrome means.

Lecturer: A syndrome is a collection of symptoms that occur in a fairly definite pattern.

Miss Yorke: You have said, as I understand it, that excessive use of alcohol might cause a vitamin B_1 deficiency. Now what effect, if any, does it have upon vitamin A?

Lecturer: As far as we know there is no special effect on vitamin A. Loss of appetite may decrease the intake below the desired level. Irritation of the gastric mucosa and damage to the intestinal mucosa might hinder absorption of any of the vitamins. But as far as we know, there is no relation between calory intake and vitamin A, as there is for the B vitamins.

Miss Cox: Have there been any experiments made, that you know of, on trying to introduce vitamin content into alcoholic beverages?

Lecturer: Yes, some of the earliest papers on the subject, back about 12 years ago, reported on this. Among the first were Blankenhorn and Spies, of Cleveland. They took a group of people with alcoholic polyneuropathy, put them in the hospital, gave them a quart of whisky a day, and then cured the polyneuropathy by nutritional means, while the patients were still drinking. Strauss, in Boston, did approximately the same thing. It would make no difference, as far as the theory is concerned, whether a man drinks the whisky and takes his vitamin in a separate pill, or puts the vitamin into the whisky. I do not know of anyone who has actually put it into the whisky and run that sort of test, but there would be no difference.

Chairman: Two chemists of the Seagram Laboratories have reported in the QUARTERLY JOURNAL OF STUDIES ON ALCOHOL on the keeping qualities of vitamins in whisky. Thiamin and niacin kept very well, but riboflavin was destroyed by light unless the whisky was kept in the dark. The tests did not go beyond the question of keeping quality and commercial production was not undertaken. In order to avoid misapprehension, I should like to add that whatever amount of vitamins may be put into whisky it would not prevent drunkenness or addiction. The utmost result would be the prevention of polyneuropathy and the other deficiency diseases.

Mrs. Lewis: Is cirrhosis of the liver or polyneuropathy more easily cured by nutritional treatment?

Lecturer: The polyneuropathy can usually be cured. The cirrhosis usually cannot.

Question: We have been discussing vitamin deficiencies through the use of alcohol in whisky. Are there any reasons why we should limit it to whisky only? What about the use of beer or wine to a similar amount of alcohol?

Lecturer: Beer and wine, of course, contain less alcohol than whisky. Beer contains a good many nutrients. Formerly, it used to be a much better food. Now we pasteurize and filter it, and remove a large part of the B vitamins that were in it, but by no means all. So you cannot put beer in the same category, nutritionally, as alcohol or whisky. Beer does carry some other nutrients. As for wine, I think the light wines carry some other elements of nutrition, the same as grape juice. The sugar is changed to alcohol, but a lot of the other nutrients remain as before. The fortified wines, of course, are midway between the light wines and the distilled spirits. The vitamins in these nutrients are not distillable, they are not volatile, so they do not distill over, they remain behind in the still and hence are absent from whisky.

Davies: In Europe some few years ago it was customary for doctors, when a nursing woman had a deficiency of milk, to order a pint of stout malt beer. That was supposed to increase the milk supply of the mother. The question is, would that have any ill effects upon the baby?

Lecturer: I wouldn't think so. I think it would be neither particularly efficacious nor deleterious.

Davies: Then it wouldn't follow that that child would become an alcoholic?

Lecturer: Oh, ridiculous, ridiculous!

Davies: It wouldn't follow?

Lecturer: No. If that would follow, everyone would be an alcoholic. Just think of all the elixirs we have taken, when we were children, as medicine. We'd all be alcoholics.

Heimburger: Would you care to discuss the value of brewers yeast in the diet where there is a deficiency of vitamin B_1?

Lecturer: One could talk for hours and hours on that subject. There is no doubt that if you will take an adequate amount of brewers yeast along with a diet that is deficient in vitamin B_1 you will never develop any of the vitamin B deficiency diseases. Neither, if you take thiamin, would you develop a B_1 deficiency. The advantage of brewers yeast is that in addition to B_1 it contains many other vitamins—niacin, riboflavin and other members of the vitamin B complex. Brewers yeast is rich in protein of high biological value. The disadvantages of getting your B_1 from brewers yeast are that it takes a relatively large amount and many people do not like the taste, and in many it causes eructations of gas, which they also do not like. It makes no difference whether you get your B_1 in brewers yeast, as a synthetic, in enriched bread, in food, or how you get it.

Lecture 7

Effects of Small Amounts of Alcohol on Psychological Functions

E. M. Jellinek

THE rather obtrusive changes of behavior brought about by alcoholic intoxication gave rise to psychological speculations long before a science of psychology had come into existence. Poets, writers, theologians, physicians and philosophers—that is, observers of human behavior in general—have been amused, puzzled, or seriously worried by these behavior changes and they have speculated on the reasons for drinking and on the causes of inebriety. They also ventured estimates of the nature, extent and possible consequences of the effects of alcohol. These speculations ranged from witty sayings to scattered paragraphs and whole dissertations. A collection and systematic presentation of this material would be of far more than curiosity value, for many of these speculations show surprising insight and point toward fields of research which sometimes do not appear too clearly on the academic horizon.

The Bible, the sacred writings of India and Persia, Greek and Roman writers, thirteenth-century German poems, Rabelais' Gargantua of the sixteenth century, and particularly the plays of Shakespeare, contain telling observations on drunken behavior and on the milder effects of alcoholic beverages.

The striking individual differences in the manifestations of drunkenness were a matter of early observation. Hebrew, Hindu and Arab legends of apparently great antiquity described the impish, the garrulous, the tearful, the belligerent and stupid types of drunkenness. The popular explanation of these differences was that at the planting of the first vine the devil sprinkled the soil with the blood of monkeys, lions, pigs and other animals and the characteristics of these animals went over into the juice of the grape. In the sixteenth century Hans Sachs, the Meistersinger of Nürnberg, related these individual differences to the underlying characters of the drinkers.

The impairment of vision, motor behavior and judgment in intoxication are repeatedly commented upon in the Bible, but also the relief that wine affords to pain and anxiety is mentioned there: "Let him drink, and forget his poverty, and remember his misery no more." And Isaiah saw the relation of addiction to national crises: "There is a crying for wine in the streets; all joy is darkened, the mirth of the land is gone."

The modern psychiatric view that, strictly speaking, ordinary acute intoxication is a temporary psychosis was recognized in ancient India where mental disorder and drunkenness were designated by the same word. This view was most appropriately expressed by Seneca who said that ". . . drunkenness is nothing but an insanity purposely assumed." The present-day psychological formulation that the inhibitions are removed in intoxication was also expressed nearly 2,000 years ago by this Roman lawyer: "Drunkenness . . . removes the shame that veils our evil undertakings."

That the sharpening of wits under the influence of alcohol was only pseudo-intellectualism also did not require trained psychologists for its recognition. In a Russian sermon of the eleventh or twelfth century it was said that after the fourth cup "they cast the fishline of the word into the depth of divine wisdom."

Another often-mentioned effect of intoxication was described as a pseudo-effect by Shakespeare. Alcohol is commonly referred to as an aphrodisiac, but the porter in Macbeth says: "Lechery, sir, it provokes, and unprovokes; it provokes the desire, but it takes away the performance; therefore, much drink may be said to be an equivocator with lechery."

We could spend many hours in reciting examples of the wisdom of the past. My purpose, however, is not to illustrate that wisdom but rather to furnish you some material with which you can compare the achievements of experimental psychology which, in the second half of the nineteenth century, took a hand in research on alcohol. You will be able to see whether scientific psychology has contributed much, or little, to our knowledge of alcoholism.

You may already sense that an analysis of psychological experiments will not yield too favorable an evaluation of the contributions of that science to our problem. In justice, however, one great merit of psychology should be mentioned before talking about its deficiencies.

FIELDS FOR PSYCHOLOGICAL EXPERIMENTATION

Although the observers who antedated scientific psychology made many acute observations and gave many excellent explanations, they regarded alcoholic beverages as stimulants. It was left to scientific psychology to show that alcohol is not a stimulant but a depressant. This discovery alone would warrant the labor that has gone into psychological experimentation. But since novels, plays, essays and proverbs are read and heard much more, and have a greater influence on public knowledge than scientific discourses, the idea that alcohol is a stimulant is rather common. Out of that mistaken idea have arisen many misuses of alcoholic beverages.

With the advent of experimental psychology one could have expected attempts at answering many of the puzzling questions posed by the excessive as well as by the moderate use of alcohol. I deliberately say *attempts*, rather than *solutions*, because it would be unjustified to expect full solutions from science, particularly from such a relatively young science as psychology.

One could expect psychology first, to contribute to the knowledge of the kind of psychological functions that are affected; in what way and to what degree, by small, medium, and large quantities of alcohol contained in various beverages. Also, whether or not different kinds of beverages, such as beer, wine and distilled spirits, affect such functions in different ways.

Second, physiological psychology could study not only the nature and degree of the effects of alcohol on psychological functions but also in what way these effects are brought about.

Third, psychology could explore the factors which determine whether a given individual will become a compulsive drinker or remain able to control his drinking. Also, it could explore the processes which lead to becoming more accustomed, in time, to the effects of alcohol; and the processes which lead to forming an irresistible habit of drinking to intoxication.

Fourth, psychology could investigate the mystery of alcohol tolerance, which means in plain words, "Why does one man seem to be affected by one cocktail to the same degree as another man by four cocktails?" I do not mean by this the differences brought about by accommodation to the effect, but the differences which seem to exist among individuals even prior to any long experience with alcoholic beverages.

Investigations of the second, third and fourth questions have not even been attempted by experimental psychology, although some incidental observations, made in connection with experiments answering the question of kinds and degrees of effects, throw some light on the other questions.

How the effects of alcohol on the nervous system come about is almost entirely a matter of speculation. The trouble is that many hypotheses have been submitted as if they were facts; but the factual evidence is lacking. There has been an explanation current, and it is still believed by many, that the brain cells become dehydrated by alcohol. I think Dr. Haggard has explained to you that in the concentration in which alcohol circulates in the body, no dehydrating effect occurs. Likewise, there is no evidence or likelihood that the highly diluted alcohol will dissolve the fat sheath of the nerves. Various hypotheses on the interference of alcohol with electric nerve processes also lack experimental verification. There are other hypotheses but all suffer from lack of evidence although some of them are at least not impossible.

You may ask how, if we have no evidence whatever of any change in the tissues, the chemistry or the physics of the brain, we can assert that the central nervous system is affected by alcohol. The answer is that changes in overt psychological behavior which can easily be observed after alcohol intake, such as changes in reaction time, perception and various reflexes, are all controlled by the central nervous system. There is evidence that alcohol has an effect on the central nervous system; what is lacking in evidence is the mechanism of these changes. As a matter of fact, the only acute effects of alcohol on the human organism seem to be the effects on the central nervous system.

The question of motivation in drinking and drunkenness had not been dealt with experimentally by psychology until a few months ago. Dr. Masserman's experiments have been too recent to permit of an evaluation as yet. In general, the question of motivation has been left to psychiatry and naturalistic psychology.

The way one becomes accustomed to the effects of alcohol is preeminently a psychological question but so far only physiologists have tackled it and they have not found any satisfactory answer as yet.

I shall speak about alcohol tolerance in connection with the degree of the effects of alcohol on psychological functions. The entire effort of experimental psychology has gone into explaining the kinds of psychological behaviors which alcohol affects, the degree to which it affects them, and the order in which the effects occur. One might be inclined to say that such investigations are directed at the obvious, that everybody knows that coordination is impaired, memory, perception, and all useful behaviors are adversely influenced in intoxication. Psychologists, however, have not been greatly interested in frank intoxication but rather in the effect of small and medium amounts, let us say the alcohol contained in three highballs. It was a meritorious task to investigate this question, for in spite of general agreement on the gross effect of intoxication, there was little agreement on the effects of the moderate and middling use of alcoholic beverages. Some maintained that small and medium amounts of alcohol were practically necessary for men engaged in heavy work; that alcohol helped to overcome fatigue; that it restored muscular strength; and that generally it stimulated psychological activities. Others, not convinced of this, thought that any small amount of alcohol affected behavior in the same direction as intoxicating amounts, but to a smaller degree. This question became of great interest to industrial management and they encouraged the psychological investigation of it. Psychologists never got away from that course.

Some Quantitative Findings

Nearly 200 psychological investigations have been carried out on the effects of alcohol on psychological functions. I could use many blackboards for the tabulation of the numerical results of these experiments, but I cannot see much utility in such detailed enumeration of the data. In nearly one-quarter of the experiments only 1 subject was used, and that subject was frequently the investigator himself. In most of the experiments only 2 or 3 subjects were used. Only 16 per cent of all the investigations had 20 subjects or more. To discuss the differences among experiments dealing with such small numbers would be futile. But in spite of the defects of the individual experiments there is, in the aggregate, an undeniable evidence of a trend. Of all the psychological functions measured none showed a stimulating effect of either small or medium amounts of alcohol. As a matter of fact, all functions took place on a lower level, even though after ½ ounce of alcohol the lowering of the level was so slight that it was negligible for all practical purposes.

I know that you will want quantitative results and I shall not withhold them, but I must caution against jumping at conclusions.

All the averages which I shall enumerate here refer to the effects of 1 to 3 ounces of alcohol, or 2 to 6 ounces of whisky, between 30 to 60 minutes after ingestion. In these amounts the given times represent the point of maximum effect.

As to fatigue and muscular strength, it can be said that physical fatigue is not overcome by alcohol but that a feeling of general well-being gives the impression of relief from fatigue. As a matter of fact, muscular output, as measured by an apparatus called the ergograph, showed a decrease of about 10 per cent.

The ability to distinguish slight differences between intensities of light and sound was decreased by 50 and 30 per cent, respectively. But the differences in the stimuli tested were of such fine degree that they have little practical significance. They were not of the order which are encountered in everyday pursuits.

The reaction time, that is, the time it takes a person to give the proper response to any signal such as a word, a sound, a light, or a touch, has been the subject of many experiments. This is a simple behavior, yet not only in the psychological laboratory but in everyday life we are accustomed to observe and make judgments from the speed or response to a stimulus.

Under ordinary conditions a normal person takes, on the average, ⅕ second to respond to a signal, let us say the flashing of a light, by pressing a button. Under various conditions the differences in reaction time are so small that they must be measured in thousandths of seconds, called milliseconds. Yet, since the normal average time is ⅕ second, that is, 200 milliseconds, a change of only 10 milliseconds represents a change of 5 per cent. Scientists have devised apparatus suitable for the measurement of such brief time intervals.

Pressing a button in response to the flashing of a light has been used by many psychologists for observing changes in reaction time after drinking various amounts of alcohol. Some of the results are shown in the accompanying table.

The Effect of Alcohol on Visual Reaction Time

Alcohol Equivalent to Glasses of Whisky	Per Cent Slowing of Reaction Time 1 Hour after Drinking*
1½	6
2½	12
3½	34

*The per cent change is based on the reaction time measured before alcohol was given; this averages approximately 200 milliseconds.

Perception, measured by the short exposure of letters, syllables and words, was decreased on the average by 10 per cent; and perception as measured by the cancellation of a given letter in a standard text within standard time decreased on the average by 7 per cent.

Tasks of continuous adding were lowered in adults on the average by 13 per cent, but in school children of 10 to 14 years of age the average impairment was only around 6 per cent. School children have more practice in adding than adults and this factor of practice or familiarity is of great importance in evaluating the experimental results, as we shall see later.

You will want to have some data on the effect of alcohol on learning—I should rather say here, memorizing. In an experiment on memorizing lines of poetry, the memorizing of 25 lines took more than twice as long when a glass and a half of whisky was taken on "an empty stomach" than when no alcohol was taken. When, however, 2 glasses of whisky were taken with food, the time required for memorizing 25 lines increased by only 16 per cent.

The effect of small amounts of alcohol on reasoning is not known; only experiments with alcohol equal to ½ pint of whisky have been performed. In these experiments, reasoning showed an increase of 67 per cent of errors. The fairly large amount of alcohol was taken in a few minutes, and the experiment showed little more than one could have guessed.

Some of the functions mentioned here are elements of what is commonly called judgment, and one can therefore expect judgment to be impaired too.

Various investigations show in different terms that judgment may be impaired, after 2 ounces of alcohol, by 20 per cent.

The speed of the eye in following an object, moved rapidly back and forth, was slowed by 3 per cent after taking the alcohol. The somewhat less-simple finger movements required in tapping were slowed by 9 per cent. This finger tapping requires little skill. Far greater dexterity of the fingers is required when a board with rows of small holes must be filled rapidly with pins placed into the holes; after alcohol, the performance on the pinboard was decreased by 19 per cent. Much more complicated is the act of tracing with a pencil an involved pathway, and the tracing showed 60 per cent more errors after alcohol than before.

I know that these averages will make a greater impression on many of you than the cautions which I should like to offer in relation to their interpretation. I have mentioned the factor of familiarity with the task, and I should like to elaborate somewhat on this factor.

IMPORTANCE OF FAMILIARITY OF THE TASK

The performances discussed thus far were what may be called laboratory tasks. They are not the kind of tasks one carries out in everyday life, although they resemble some of them. A task such as sewing is more complex, that is, many more elements enter into it than into these laboratory tasks. One would expect, therefore, that the ability to sew would be impaired to a greater degree than tracing pathways. Yet when women well versed in sewing were given alcohol, their production decreased by only 10 per cent. The explanation of this unexpected result may be that alcohol affects familiar tasks much less than unfamiliar ones. Although the laboratory tasks are simpler, they are, nevertheless, unfamiliar. Tracing of pathways, for instance, is a task people do not perform in their ordinary occupations; they learn how to do it while the experiment is carried on. Students who were accustomed to typing but were not professional typists increased their typing errors by 40 per cent on taking alcohol, but lost only 3 per cent of their speed. While the impairment was greater here than on sewing, it was again smaller than on the simpler but unfamiliar task of tracing pathways. The students on whom these experiments were performed were not accustomed to drinking, and that may have increased the effect of alcohol on their work. This assumption seems to be borne out by an experiment in which typesetters, accustomed to alcoholic beverages, took part. Typesetting requires even more skill than typewriting, but the typesetters did not increase their errors at all after alcohol. On the other hand, their speed was reduced.

It would seem that on the whole the effect of small amounts of alcohol on skilled performances increases as the tasks become more complex, but that the effect on a complex but familiar task may be less than on a simpler but unfamiliar one, and that the effect may be less on persons accustomed than on persons not accustomed to drinking. Furthermore, the so-called simple laboratory tasks do not seem quite appropriate for drawing conclusions concerning the effect of alcohol on skill.

All the experimental results discussed here have been used as arguments against driving an automobile after drinking even small amounts of alcoholic beverages. On the other hand, some people have countered with the argument that, although even small amounts of alcohol can be shown to have some effect, the effect is too small to have any practical consequences. But both sides seem to have missed the point. It is useless to quarrel over the question whether two highballs slow the reaction time by 10 per cent or by 30 per cent. It is useless to argue whether these two highballs narrow the field of vision to a large or only to a small extent. Even if there were no slowing of reaction time, no narrowing of the field of vision, and no loss of skill at all following the drinking of two highballs, there would remain a fact which everybody can observe without laboratory gadgets and which is the final reason for the warning against driving after drinking. This fact is that alcohol creates a sense of well-being which in the anxious man may restore confidence but in the normal man may lead to overconfidence. Over-confidence means willingness to take chances, and taking chances may bring disaster on the road.

The various findings of experimental psychology are widely used in illustrating to young people the dangers of alcohol. They are told that all psychological functions become impaired by drinking alcohol, no matter how small the amount. Rather frequently the teachers get into an embarrassing situation, for they are confronted with such comments as "John does much better after one or two highballs." The zealous teacher may not have the right answer because of his or her continuous seeking of "impairment by alcohol" and carefully avoiding anything that might suggest that there are also other effects.

Two Aspects of Efficiency

It would appear rather obvious that alcohol could not, through any fundamental action, give at one and the same time increased alertness and decreased alertness, increased efficiency for performance of tasks and decreased efficiency. The preponderance of evidence from psychological experiments is that alcohol decreases alertness and decreases efficiency for performing tasks, yet for some men it does seem to work in the opposite way and thus to have this double and opposing action. But again, before drawing any conclusion as to this action of alcohol from such observations, it is well to study the men in whom alcohol seems to increase efficiency for the performance of tasks. On such an examination it will be found that these men have little confidence in themselves, are so shy, so greatly subject to anxieties, that they are hindered, or, as the psychologists like to say, they are inhibited in doing what they truly are capable of doing. Alcohol may lessen these inhibitions, increase their confidence, and make it possible for them to perform better than they usually can, even though the performance is less than they would be capable of if their inhibitions were removed in some other way. This sounds complicated and paradoxical, but an illustration may make it clearer:

John Smith is fond of shooting at a target; when he is alone and on those rare instances when he has full confidence in himself—forgets himself—he can hit the bull's-eye 9 times out of 10 shots. But when he enters a competition he becomes inhibited, he has a feeling of being tied, and he can hit it only 4 times out of 10. Two highballs remove his anxieties and his shyness in competition; he can then hit the bull's-eye 7 times out of 10. The effects of alcohol make it possible for John to perform a task which, as a rule, he feels that he cannot perform, but nevertheless it does not let him perform it to the best of his real ability. It is thus not a simple matter to say what has happened to John's efficiency. It is obvious, however, that John would do better by training the strength of his self-confidence than by giving it a crutch with alcohol. This is particularly true since men whose production is facilitated by alcohol are especially liable to rely more and more on the crutch and thus finally become dependent upon it.

There are many other features which complicate the question of alcohol and efficiency. Thus, when the subject of automobile accidents and "driving under the influence" is discussed, nearly always someone maintains that either he or somebody he knows drives more efficiently after one or two highballs. If one pursues the discussion long enough, it develops that the driver in question "drives more carefully" because he knows that the drinks may have interfered with his driving ability. Thus alcohol does not make these persons better drivers, but fear of the possible consequences puts them on their mettle and makes them especially cautious and careful. Unfortunately, in most drivers the alcohol destroys fear of consequences and, with it, even their usual caution. Thus the argument of "driving more efficiently after one or two cocktails" has no weight in the question of alcohol and traffic accidents.

Generally, as you have seen, psychologists have given all of their attention to the effects of alcohol on those functions which we may call actions, and have neglected to investigate the effects on the emotions, sentiments and moods. But behind the actions are emotions. The actions cannot be arbitrarily isolated from them. In the search for impairment of functions the psychologist neglected to investigate what the drinker gets from alcohol and thus he has failed to help us understand alcoholism. The help has come entirely from clinical psychiatry. But the clinical observations of the psychiatrist could be tested for their significance by experimental means.

There is one more point on which I should like to enlarge. The question of tolerance has been touched upon by psychologists from one aspect only. They have not investigated the factors which are responsible for greater or lesser sensitivity to the effects of alcohol in one man than in another. But the data of psychological experiments have been used to show how extraordinarily great is the variation from individual to individual. I contend that the variation has been greatly increased through the methods of experimentation. You have learned that not the amount of alcohol consumed but its concentration in the blood determines the effect. Consequently, in experiments, alcohol should be administered per kilogram of body weight. This was done in very few psychological experiments. In most experiments a given quantity, let us say 2 ounces of alcohol, was given to each individual irrespective of body weight. Thus one subject might have had only 3/4 of the alcohol concentration that another, lighter subject, had, and if the former showed a slighter effect that should not be attributed to a greater tolerance but merely to his greater weight.

I have data from two experiments on reaction time. The effect is measured in terms of the difference between the pre-alcohol and the post-alcohol performances. One experimenter gave 1 ounce of alcohol to each of his subjects; the other gave ⅟₆₀ ounce for each kilogram of body weight. In the first experiment, individuals differed from the grand average twice as much as in the second experiment. From this it would appear that the crudeness of experimental method is responsible for the impression that individual differences are very great. No doubt there are differences in tolerance, but they are probably 50 per cent smaller than is generally accepted.

Psychological experiments have yielded some valuable knowledge concerning the effects of alcohol but they have left much territory unexplored. The greatest drawback of these experiments is that they tell us little about the effect of alcohol on the total behavior. They refer to parts of the total behavior, and one is at a loss to say whether such parts can be reasonably considered separately from other parts with which they ordinarily act together. It is somewhat in the nature of describing a brick house in terms of bricks only, without considering that in a house the bricks are related to mortar, to windows and doors, to design and to the whole landscape in which the house is placed. These experiments contribute little to the knowledge of why people drink, except that the psychological effects themselves are somewhere and to some extent among these reasons.

The most important conclusion that may be drawn from psychological experiments with alcohol—and these include many experiments which have not been described here—is that the various effects studied show that alcohol is a depressant, not a stimulant. It affects first the higher brain centers which control the voluntary behaviors and emotions, while the lower centers which control such vital functions as breathing are affected only in severe intoxication. Briefly, alcohol acts in the same way as the well-known anesthetics. Since it is an anesthetic, one can correspondingly predict its effect in small and large quantities on efficiency on the one side, and on sedation and relaxation on the other side.

DISCUSSION

Berger: Would the psychological effects differ according to the speed of drinking?

Lecturer: Yes. If, on one occasion, a man should gulp down half a pint of whisky, but on another occasion spread it over an hour, the maximum alcohol concentration, and, consequently, the psychological effect, would be much greater in the former than in the latter case. Dr. Haggard has explained to you the phenomenon of overshooting. This overshooting would be very pronounced in the case of gulping.

Generally, if you wish to compare the results of different experiments, or would like to combine several of them, you must be sure of the comparability of a number of conditions connected with these experiments. You must know whether alcohol was given per pound of body weight or whether the same amount was given to everybody irrespective of weight; and whether it was given on an empty stomach, or soon, or fairly soon, after a meal; and what particular alcoholic beverage was used. You would have to know exactly the dilution, the rate of drinking, whether the subjects were habituated to alcohol or not, and many other factors. Unfortunately, in reviews of the literature, these criteria of comparability are very often neglected, and sometimes the results of two experiments which were carried out under different conditions are shown to conflict with each other. Such a conflict is then used to demonstrate that we "just do not know anything about alcohol." On the other hand, some people combine the results of experiments done under different conditions and thus arrive at meaningless averages.

Allen: The point has been made that small amounts of alcohol may impair motor functions. Does it follow that years of moderate drinking, that is, for the purpose of relaxation, cause permanent impairment?

Lecturer: In the small amounts that we have spoken of here, the effects are entirely transitory. They last only as long as the alcohol is in the blood, or at least as long as there is a sufficient amount in the blood, and then the functions return to normal. There is neither permanent nor cumulative effect from such small amounts.

Suemper: It is a theory that the drinking of alcoholic beverages brings about a relaxation of moral restraint. Are there any trustworthy experiments which deal with this theory?

Lecturer: Neither trustworthy nor untrustworthy experiments exist on this point. On the other hand, common observation shows us that in advanced intoxication, morals may relax. In moderate drinking, no loosening of morals is observed.

Mrs. Coles: Would you clarify the statement that moderation is not limited entirely to small amounts? Did you refer to secret drinking—closet drinking?

Lecturer: I did not have secret drinking in mind. Small amounts in themselves do not justify the statement that John Doe drinks moderately. Motivation is one of the points that must be considered. Why does John Doe drink? Does he drink in order to get a "lift," or does he use alcohol as a condiment? Does he drink when he has a task before him, or does he drink only when it is the right time for relaxation—say in the evening when, for the next 12 or 14 hours, he will not be called upon to perform a task? Does he drink beverages of low or high alcohol content? I would add that anybody who would spend money on alcoholic beverages in disproportion to his budget would not be a moderate drinker in my eyes, even if he were consuming very little.

Question: Do you mean that the question of frequency comes into it?

Lecturer: If you mean how frequently on any given day, I would say that frequency must be considered. But if you mean on how many days of the week or year, I would not consider frequency.

Berger: Is there any amount of alcohol small enough that it can be taken without danger in driving?

Lecturer: In connection with quantity, you must also consider time. If you take 2 ounces of whisky, I'd say wait about 1 hour before you drive. If you take 4 ounces, wait 2 hours, and for each additional ounce, add 1 hour. You can see that after 8 ounces you'd have to wait 6 hours, and so you'd better let somebody else drive. If you are scared of whisky, it might even be unsafe for you to drive after just wetting your lips with it. But in that case not the alcohol but the fear of consequences interferes with your driving.

Question: Dr. Haggard pointed out yesterday that bread and milk and other foods retard the absorption of alcohol into the bloodstream. Would this have any effect on the motor responses?

Lecturer: Yes. Since the presence of food in the stomach slows the absorption of alcohol, it follows that after a meal the same amount of alcohol will result in a lower blood-alcohol concentration than it would on an empty stomach. The physiological as well as the psychological effect depends on this concentration, and, therefore, the effect of a given amount of alcohol will be less after a meal than when drunk on an empty stomach.

Question: This may exhibit my lack of knowledge of chemistry and particularly of biochemistry, but milk is a food which also goes through the walls of the stomach, I understand, so that it takes but a very short time for it to be absorbed into the bloodstream as well. Now, will milk slow down the absorption of the alcohol into the bloodstream?

Lecturer: Milk is not absorbed into the bloodstream as milk and it does not pass through the walls of the stomach. There are fats, proteins, sugar, and other substances in milk. These substances must be digested and this digestion occurs mainly in the intestine. The presence of milk in the stomach retards the absorption of alcohol.

Mrs. Colvin: It has been mentioned that motivation has some influence on the effect of alcohol on the individual. What part does motivation play?

Lecturer: If a man says that he will drink in order to feel gay, he indicates a readiness to accept the effect. I suppose those who go to a party with the set purpose of enjoying themselves will feel the effect more easily than if they come to it without any preconceived ideas. I think the readiness or unreadiness to respond has some effect. I know people who go to a party where drinking is done, and although they themselves do not drink—perhaps because they do not like the taste—they become quite "high" just because they are willing and ready to accept even the second-hand effect.

Mrs. Colvin: If a person were to take alcohol without knowing it, would there still be any effect from it?

Lecturer: Yes, there would be an effect. But if the amount were rather small and well diluted, and the drinker did not know the taste of alcohol, it could happen that because of the unawareness of the nature of the substance no such behavior manifestations would occur as at another time when the same small amount of alcohol was taken with knowledge of its nature.

Harrel: Is there any difference in these tests on the lessening of efficiency with the use of alcohol between the habitual drinker and the total abstainer?

Lecturer: Yes, very definitely. The first glass of whisky might cause a small shock in the total abstainer. He would not know what to anticipate; he knows that there is some effect, but does not know the nature of it. If he anticipates a very great effect he may respond very strongly. He may respond strongly because he is afraid that he will respond very strongly. The habitual drinker knows what is going to follow and can compensate for this effect up to certain limits.

Hunter: In an experiment, the subjects received a flavored beverage which disguised its alcohol content and, on another occasion, a beverage of the same flavor and appearance but without alcohol. Did the fact that the subjects did not know whether they were receiving alcohol or not have any effect on the results?

Lecturer: This experiment has been much discussed in the literature, but no acceptable interpretation has come forth. It has been found that in order to disguise the taste of alcohol effectively, a flavoring substance would have to be used which, itself, would have potent physiological action. Therefore no conclusion could be drawn from such an experiment.

Robinson: There are certain experiments conducted by aviation companies having to do with the effect of altitude on conduct and behavior after drinking the same amounts of alcohol, and these indicate that altitude does produce some pronounced changes.

Lecturer: Quite a few of these investigations have been published. As a rule, the experiments have not been carried out in airplanes but on mountains of various altitudes. McFarland of Harvard University has carried out such experiments at several levels of altitude in the Andes. He found that memory, perception, and reaction time were more affected by alcohol at high altitudes, than at sea level.

Reen: Would you place a user of small or moderate amounts of alcohol in the same general classification as the user of small or moderate amounts of morphine or cocaine? Would you refer to the moderate user of alcohol as an addict?

Lecturer: I would not classify him as an addict. The use of even small amounts of such narcotics as morphine and cocaine is not socially accepted. Even the moderate use of these drugs implies that that person is disregarding social standards and is on his way to becoming a transgressor. While in view of the fact that in our present culture moderate drinking is fully accepted by the majority I would not see in the moderate use of alcohol any tendency to transgress.

Lecture 8

Drinking Mores of the Social Classes

John Dollard

IN the next few days psychologists, anthropologists and sociologists will talk to you about individual and social motivations in the use and abuse of alcoholic beverages. These specialists, in the brief time allotted to them, will have to make many assumptions. Particularly they will have to assume that all of you are conversant with the basic concepts and theorems of society. From the roster of students I see that there are among you some specialists in this field, but most of you have been trained in other fields. Thus in subsequent lectures it may appear to you that the use of alcoholic beverages and the social behavior relating to drinking is quite specific, perhaps artificial behaviors, which may be regarded as an entirely different category from all other behavior. Such is not the case. Behaviors may differ greatly in form, in goal, in usefulness, but they all have in common that they are largely products of learning and that the trend of learning is determined by the specific pattern of the culture in which the learning takes place. The behavior around drinking follows the same basic laws as behaviors relating to housing, clothing, games and all other human activities.

The social controls exercised by various social classes on drinking and the effects of permissiveness in certain social classes toward drinking have not been studied explicitly. But we have abundant and conscientiously gathered materials on four or five American cities in which the attempt has been made to distinguish the social groupings in the local community. Incidentally, in connection with these studies, some data on drinking behavior have appeared. Social scientists concerned with the problems of drinking would find it very useful to follow some of the techniques of anthropologists who, having come back from primitive people, look at our society with the novelty of perception of one who has compared his own intuitive observations of our everyday attitudes with those of markedly differing cultures. The data presented in community studies by social anthropologists are suggestive of a point of view, but are not absolutely definitive even of the hypothesis of social class that is being presented.

Perhaps if the recognition of social classes rested on research alone it would be difficult to convince anybody of this stratification, but we experience class distinctions in daily life. We are all products of our social system. In the various levels in American society we see somewhat different training, somewhat different excellences and weaknesses of habits and ideals of life.

If the control of the drinking of alcoholic beverages or any similar drug, or the control of any dangerous impulse, were dependent upon police and formal means of coercion, our society would be an anarchy. About this we feel fairly sure. If we are going to study the problems of alcohol we must examine the *informal* ways by which drinking behavior is defined and controlled in our society. There are two major controls:

The first is conscience. Conscience has various names, scientific and otherwise, but we all know what it is. It is that force in each individual which stands against unrestrained pleasure-seeking and controls his behavior toward socially disapproved pleasure. Each of us learns from early childhood to feel it is "wrong" to indulge in certain forms of impulse gratification. In simple drinking situations we can see a marked difference in the degree of strength of the personal conscience as a restraining mechanism. Some people are able to drink mildly. They might be called "one-drink people," or "two-drink people." Then conscience interferes and they stop. Most of us probably feel the danger of assault upon our personalities by alcohol. That danger is also expressed in the voice of conscience.

Conscience is apparently rooted in biological life and developed with the aid of childhood training, the precepts of family and religion, and our cultures. Conscience stands, then, as the first barrier against excessive indulgence of impulses and sometimes against any indulgence in alcohol. The functioning of conscience is not the subject of this discussion, but it should be pointed out that if an individual is not supported by the mechanism of conscience, he loses his most valuable ally in the control of drinking.

The second system of control of behavior is our social system. One of the myths of American society is that we are socially and ideologically a democratic people. It is a myth that mobility—movement from one social group to another —is completely free in the United States, that the status of a man is measured by the difference between his own natural talents and those of other men, with social environment discounted.

While it is true that the democratic system or principle probably works better here than it has ever worked anywhere else, and is more characteristic of our society than of any other, classless democracy is still far from a fact. Research shows that we have a system of ranked social groups. We do not have a chaos of struggling individuals. This social system controls our most intimate behavior and thoughts. Our thoughts and behavior patterns differ, depending upon where we stand in the system.

Position in our social system is indicated by our friends and associates, the group of people with whom we feel comfortable, natural and at ease. At the borders of this group there are people with whom we do not feel comfortable, natural and easy, sometimes because their behavior seems crude and uncouth or because they seem to have some kind of prestigeful aura from the past which we do not share. We find, on intimate association, that the habits and attitudes of such people are not compatible with our own. Davis, Gardner and Gardner described the social class hypothesis thus. "People have a range of social characteristics within which their friends and associates must fall; it is possible to describe this range, and for people in similar social positions it tends to be identical." Personal recognition of an individual as one with similar standards of behavior is the clearest form of recognition of social class. We are members of that social class with which most of our intimate social participation takes place. A social class, therefore, is composed of families and groups of associates who could participate together in intimate social hours. Our social class is determined not only by the kind of people we know, but by those who could sit down to dinner with us. Certain associates may undoubtedly be valuable in a personal sense, have good personal characteristics, and be in our environment, and yet not seem suitable to invite to our homes. But people in the same social class share motives and social connections; their children are marriageable. It is expected that one's children will marry one's friends' children or people like them.

This type of social class group apparently determines many things—one's clothes, for instance, and one's standards of behavior. There are perhaps 20 per cent of the people in this country who do not have formal meal hours. They eat "off the stove" or "out of cans." They do not have a fixed meal, a family gathering. Eating together is not just a matter of ingesting calories in certain other groups; it is a social ritual. Try not coming home for dinner or saying you will wait until 9 o'clock, and see what your wife does!

Social class differences are reflected not only in domestic routines but even in habits of speech. In certain social groups, people do not say "This is him," and "haint." Those who say "haint" are not morally or psychologically inferior to those who use better English, but disparities in speech patterns characterize groups in most social systems.

We have learned a little about drinking behavior within the different social groups in this country. But before discussing such differences we must differentiate the various social classes in their social attitudes and in the customs which they enforce and, in a rough sense, compel their members to accept. Class analysis is a mode of thought, a best guess, which is now approaching the stage of probability of a scientific hypothesis.

CLASSES IN AMERICAN SOCIETY

Social anthropologists have distinguished three social classes in American society. We call them Upper, Middle, and Lower. Somewhat artificially, we divide each class into two subclasses: Upper-Upper, Lower-Upper, Upper-Middle, Lower-Middle, Upper-Lower, and Lower-Lower. The existence of these class groups is not a fiction of scholars. People who get $10 to $25 a week, $25 to $50 a week, and so on, do not classify themselves. But social class groups exist in the minds of people who rank certain social groups as "above" or "below" their own. Social classes, therefore, are discovered in our society rather than invented by scientists. Our social class system may be roughly outlined as follows:

Class	Per Cent	Description
Upper-Upper	2	Old families, "society"
Lower-Upper	2	New families, "nouveaux riches"
Upper-Middle	10	Nice, morally respectable people with some wealth
Lower-Middle	28	Respectable people, but not much money
Upper-Lower	33	Poor but honest folk; the working element
Lower-Lower	25	The "no 'count poor"; the ignorant, shiftless

About 2 people out of 100 belong to the Upper-Upper class. It may be symbolized by the words "old family" or "society." There are local names for this class, like the "Boston Brahmans," the "Philadelphia Main Line," the "St. Cecelia Club in Charleston." Membership in Upper-Upper class means a heritage of wealth and power, a long lineage which has had distinction over a number of generations. Direct entry into this class is impossible in any one lifetime because you cannot invent yourself a lineage—you have to inherit it. You do not get in, but your children may if you marry someone with Upper-Upper lineage.

The Lower-Upper group contains about 2 people out of 100. These compose the group which, if you are looking up the social ladder, you cannot distinguish from the Upper-Upper class. But the Upper-Upper people regard them as new families that have only been in the community for a comparatively brief period. What can you do with people who have been here only 150 years, if you are of pre-Revolutionary stock? The Lower-Uppers are sometimes called the "nouveaux riches." There are certain psychological strains and stresses attendant on this position, but these people are frequently very wealthy and talented. Their trouble is that they never really belong to the highest social stratum with which they associate; they are *in* but not *of*. Lower-Upper children can associate with Upper-Upper children but Lower-Upper adults cannot associate on terms of equality with Upper-Upper adults. Therefore, the ties between Lower-Upper parents and their children are weakened. The children cannot lean on their parents for social support and cannot respect them as children ought to be able to do.

Now, a bigger and stronger group is that of the Upper-Middle class, which includes about 10 people out of 100 in this country. They are spoken about as "nice, respectable people." There is sometimes a barb in this, but it means a stable, moral class that tends to emphasize wealth. Its representatives are the great controlling factors in business and industry. This class does not emphasize lineage or wealth acquired long ago. Upper-Middles do not have that. In the Upper-Middle class the family is a rather isolated unit. Parents show great concern about children who have talent and skill. The great breeding ground for talent and strength in a society like ours is the Middle class—that is, the Upper- and Lower-Middle classes.

A much more numerous group is the Lower-Middle class—28 in 100—although I would not be sure it is not 35 or 22. Members of this class tend to think of themselves this way: "We haven't very much money, but we are respectable people." Like the Upper-Middle class, the Lower-Middles are concerned with ethics, morals, talent and social serviceability. They have, as an ideal, primarily to gain an income, to become financially better off. Psychologically, they are a very secure group. They are comfortably aware of not being Lower class and they have little contact with the Upper class. Education, neat homes and personal cleanliness are matters of great importance in the Lower-Middle class.

The Upper-Lower is a big group; the largest, we think—33 per cent. They are sometimes called the "people on the other side of the tracks," the working element, "the masses" (in contrast to "the classes"). Our popular speech is full of such terms. We do not realize we are ticketing people when we put these labels on them. The Upper-Lowers, too, value money, but they are not so responsive to social controls as are the Middle class and are not so conservative. They do not place the same emphasis on high ethical thought and self-discipline as do Middle-class people.

At the bottom of the group, 25 per cent of the population, are what we call the Lower-Lowers. We often refer to them as ignorant people, shiftless, "riffraff," or dirty, which is not always true. They do not value education, do not drive their children to school and do not, or cannot, save. Their income level is very low, and they are not used to saving in order to get later the reward for self-denial.

CLASS DIFFERENCES IN DRINKING BEHAVIOR

What is most evident about drinking behavior in these various class groups is that it differs a good bit. This is very important to notice. If we want to focus an educational program, we have to know where to focus it. Most Lower-Middle people are firmly opposed to indulgence in drinking, but this is not the case with Lower-Uppers.

In the Upper classes, drinking is not a moral issue. People at the top of our social structure drink a good deal; both sexes drink. Men and women drink in the same groups, in party style. There are, however, certain stiff controls here which do not exist in some of the lower classes. One is condemned in the Upper classes, not for drinking, nor for drunkenness, but for antisocial behavior while drunk. Fighting is taboo; aggressive behavior is heavily penalized even when expressed only in verbal assaults.

It is crucial to recognize the attitude of the Upper classes toward drinking because behavior patterns tend to sift downward in our society. Middle groups are likely to become tolerant and, perhaps, ultimately imitative of the customs of the topmost groups into which they, as individuals, would like to move. It might be said that the failure of Prohibition legislation lay in our social class system, for the highest people socially did not taboo drinking and their social customs were stronger than legislative controls.

In the Lower-Upper class we have the "cocktail set" who drink a good bit more recklessly than the people in the old families in the Upper-Upper class. The new families of wealth are in a rather insecure, frustrating position. They are constantly comparing themselves with the families who socially "own" the territory in which they live. The wealthy newcomers want to have an old homestead of their own; they want to have the prestige of lineage. Realizing that their great-grandfather was "just a butcher," rather than a powerful landowner, they suffer from a helpless feeling of inadequacy. Parental controls are weak and the scars from social competition painful, so Lower-Upper young people may try to escape from their social discomforts by drunkenness. There are case studies in several towns which lead us to suppose that there is some excessive, destructive drinking in this particular class group.

In the Upper-Middle class we have a strong evaluation of wealth and talent, and, ordinarily, moral values have restraint. However, the apparent nearness to the Upper classes and partial identification with this group have some effect on the drinking habits in the Upper-Middle class. In general, the men drink on social occasions, at their poker games and at casual gatherings in friends' houses, but Upper-Middle class women rarely drink. Drinking is not customary in mixed groups. Evidently, Upper-Middles have a neutral attitude toward drinking.

In the Lower-Middle class we would expect to find, with both sexes, a very strong taboo on drinking. Lower-Middle people value highly the traits of respectability which differentiate them from the Lower group. They emphasize this by rejecting the customs found in Lower classes. (Negroes in the Middle classes, for instance, will reject the spirituals and songs characteristic of Lower-class churches. In this way they emphasize their difference in the social scale from the Lower-class individuals of their own race.) Lower-Middle men and women are the most stringent in exerting social control over drinking.

In the Upper-Lower class, which is the chief labor group, there is much more drinking. The Upper-Lowers do not have the same taboos as the Lower-Middles, but they do have some occupational restraints. A railway workman, for example, will tend to have an occupational taboo on drinking in some situations. In general, the Upper-Lowers drink at home and in the taverns, which provide a kind of club for Lower-class people. But if they are to be mobile into Lower-Middle class they have to change such habits.

Lower-class persons usually become openly aggressive when drinking because they have not been trained to exercise the control of aggression that is demanded of those at the top. In the Lower class, it is not a disgrace to get drunk and fight even if this behavior has dangerous consequences. A Lower-class man may be aggressive in the family toward wife and children. This group does not have the "drink like a gentleman" taboo. Differences in ethnic backgrounds are also conspicuous in the drinking customs of the Upper-Lower class—Irish, Jewish and Italian immigrants, for instance, retain customs that still have a "home color" when they settle in this country. There are differences as to beverages and controls of behavior. In the City of New Haven there are about 40,000 Italians; they drink wine with their meals. Some other ethnic groups, including the Jewish, have apparently a rather strong internal taboo on excessive drinking.

In the Lower-Lower class, drinking is socially unrestrained. There is the Saturday-night-to-Monday-morning binge, without much social control. Both men and women drink, although usually not in mixed groups. In the Lower-Lower class there is overt aggression; people are arrested for drunkenness, breaking the peace. There is much chronic drunkenness in this class.

None of these class controls is rigid. Of course, there are cross-class factors which tend to make some people drinkers in spite of their Lower-Middle taboos. Then they begin to move out of the Lower-Middle class, and the most tragic case is that in which the movement is downward.

The delineation of class lines in this discussion may seem too sharply marked. We are immediately reminded of the American dream of change of place through economic success, social usefulness and individual talent. Such mobility is not fiction; it is a fact, more so here than anywhere else. But we must remember that social mobility does not mean moving from $35 to $45 a week, or even to $200 a week. We can have Al Capone moving up in wealth but remaining a Lower-class Italian man. We cannot change our social skins very fast. Nevertheless, a man may change his social habits and ideals. These include standards of morality, propriety, clothes, recreation, liking for salads or for liquor, or the number of baths to be taken—all these are critical details of behavior.

If you are going to change your social level you will have to change your social habits, and this may mean your drinking habits. If you move from Middle to Upper, you will have to learn to drink. You may think this would be very simple, but social anthropologists have watched carefully nurtured Upper-Middle-class people moving into the Lower-Upper class who found it extremely difficult to learn the expected drinking habits. A lady who has been an eminently respectable person for 45 years and whose husband, for business considerations, moves in the Upper-class group, is expected to drink freely but finds it next to impossible. The Upper-class associates consider her a "dud," she spoils the party, and she gets pushed out. If she wishes to have her children know these people she will have to make a pretense, at least, of social drinking. You should not underestimate the difficulty in learning to drink if you are not used to it.

No doubt you are much more clear about and more impressed with the difficulty in learning *not* to drink; this familiar problem has been given a good deal of study. But if the Upper-Middle person moves up to the Lower-Upper group he has to change his habits in the direction of more alcoholic indulgence. If the custom of such indulgence is to be decreased, effort will have to be made to move more people into the Middle-class group and get more and more people to understand and accept the relative stringency of attitude of this group.

The task of changing social habits is no small undertaking. Such change cannot be accomplished by force alone, or law alone, because the sanctions which make people feel comfortable in their habits exist in their own social groups, and they do not care what outside groups think about them. Their habits have been built up and rewarded in the course of a long personal development, so changing some of these habits would be fairly difficult and slow. No one should feel badly who has tried to accomplish social changes swiftly and has failed.

DISCUSSION

Chairman (*E. M. Jellinek*): I should like to take advantage of my position as chairman and start the discussion myself. Dr. Dollard said that the Upper-Upper class includes 2 per cent of the population; the Lower-Upper 2 per cent; and the Upper-Middle 10 per cent. The two Lower classes were 33 and 25 per cent, respectively. Now, Dr. Dollard said that the drinking habits are most pronounced in the Upper classes and in the Lower-Lower class. This bears out some of the impressions which I received from certain statistical studies.

I found that during each of the past 10 years or so approximately 4,000 to 5,000 people, men and women, were admitted for the first time for an alcoholic mental disorder. Of those, 20 per cent were hospitalized in private hospitals. Private hospitals are extremely expensive. It would take a family income of at least $4,000 a year to put a relative into such an institution. The percentage of the population who can afford to put their relatives into such hospitals is very far below 20 per cent. That is, the income stratum which more or less coincides with the upper social stratum contributes more than its share toward alcoholic mental disorder. One may conclude that this will be true not alone of inebriates who have mental disorders but of inebriates in general.

Of the remaining 80 per cent, who go into the state hospitals, detailed statistical studies have been made. No such studies are available concerning patients in the private hospitals. It has been found that patients with alcoholic mental disorders in state hospitals are in the lowest economic and lowest educational strata of all mental-hospital inmates. This has led to the conclusion that alcoholism is a "poverty disease." That 20 per cent are in expensive private hospitals is being overlooked. Naturally there will be some representation from the Lower-Middle and Upper-Lower classes, but I do not think that they affect the percentage from the Upper-Middle and the two Upper classes appreciably.

Question: Is there any difference in the drinking mores of the urban and rural groups?

Lecturer: We do not have adequate studies of rural structure. The admission rate from urban areas, however, is higher than from rural areas.

Question: The Upper-Middle class description can be applied to the Lower-Middle class group, where there is an attempt to imitate the higher class group. The women drink very heavily. The women drink equally in mixed groups, especially in country clubs and parties in the homes and summer camps. There is general mixed drinking and heavy drinking.

Lecturer: Our knowledge of this is very spotty. It probably differs in communities that we have not studied. The "imitators" are conspicuous because they are so different from the thing we look for. They may consist of only a few cliques, and if the whole community were studied we might find this set relatively small in comparison with the whole Upper-Middle class. We are rather puzzled as to what to do with the small town which does not have a traditional Upper class—say a new town. The one thing we seem to find is that the Upper class is a sort of absentee class. They do not spend much time there. They maintain a residence, but spend a lot of time in other places. They really live for social contacts outside of the town. We know that this absentee Upper class group is nevertheless quite influential.

Womer: So far as Connecticut is concerned, I would say that the art of drinking has flourished in the past 5 years, and the increase was greatest in the class that you say was the backbone and had a strong taboo. I have felt strongly that much ground has been lost in that Lower-Middle class. There have been great inroads made upon it.

Question: In South Carolina there is a tremendous factor in the shifting pattern in the Middle classes. The churches are exerting a great influence in putting the taboo on drinking, even though the whole state has legal sale of liquor. There is a strong educational and religious influence going on.

Lecturer: We have to consider also the fact that the people create the churches. It is not only that the churches lead the people, but the people shape their churches so that they can represent them and lead them. The Lower-class people do not appear in leadership roles in the church. These patterns may be changing. It takes time, however, to make a society like this. Changes may be due to war conditions, to some trends in the classes, the slow effects of education, more mobility. Nobody knows all about this process.

Question: Have you thought of the possible solution of the alcohol problem for these various classes? What shall we do about it? It has been said here that we cannot change customs. You have mentioned bathing as a custom. There are still many millions of people who do not bathe. Yet some of us have learned the status of bathing and the custom is gradually changing. I would expect that the problem of excessive drinking could be attacked in the same way if we can get it into the schools as widely and precisely as the hygienic effects of bathing are taught. What is the approach to the Lower classes? Shall we let them go and be a poison to society, or is there some approach to them?

Lecturer: I think all I can do is put the facts before you, but I do not want to dodge your question. I do not think that the result of what I presented is that this problem is impossible to attack. Drinking habits are informally propagated, they are informally supported in the various groups where they now exist, but as with any other basic habits, solution is not impossible. The government is now going about changing our food habits. Food habits are strongly entrenched but we have to change them.

As to changing habits—if we want to learn something new we have to be driven to it. We must be motivated to it. We try the new habit in the face of certain signals and cues. Once we try it, we have to be rewarded for it. We have got to motivate people not to drink to excess. The educational program in the schools has the aim of getting children to try not drinking and keep on trying it for the rest of their lives, but the social system is going to keep on pushing in and say, "Be grown up." We know how to get a habit, but we do not know how to create motivation.

Question: Considering the fact that so many of our men of lower social groups are receiving commissions in the Army, what effect does that have on the social class system you have outlined today? Will they come back after the war belonging to a different class than they were in previously?

Lecturer: I am working with one of the Army branches that is doing research on the troops. I think very little class change is going on. They have an elaborate system of culling out people who have certain qualifications for leadership, and with this goes superior class position. I doubt that this is a selection among people from the Lower-Middle class and the Upper-Middle and Upper classes as officers. We get very few officers out of the Lower classes. Change in arbitrary rank system, like the Army, carries over only a little into civil life. People who worked in a garage will go back to a garage. The Army is not giving any fundamental education, just a trade education.

Davies: We have a great many new people in Florida. Some leave the Ten Commandments north of the Ohio River. Their social practices have had a profound influence, especially on the tourist section. Most of the rich outsiders entertain with cocktail parties and our ladies think it is smart to do that.

Lecturer: It shows imitation is working. I suppose our American Upper class, though not in racial stock, is fundamentally derived from the British Upper class. I suppose if we want to get one quick, simple answer, it is that they drink because the British do. They are in a relatively subordinate system to the British and French, and take some of their character and their clothes from across the water. They have a long history in the world and in America also. The American Upper class have a great deal of power and freedom. There is nobody from above to criticize them. Their moral standards in other regards are also somewhat liberal, more liberal about divorce, for example, than other groups. They feel, "Who is there to punish us? We are tops, and we can do as we please."

This does not mean they are a group of idlers. They represent family tradition and, among many other trends, *noblesse oblige.* A great part of their income goes into charity and taxes.

Question: Our observation was that the families in Virginia with the greatest social prestige, based on lineage, are a remarkably abstemious group in the upper-age limit, but the young people are changing their attitude considerably.

Question: In what group would you place moving-picture actors?

Lecturer: A man's social class is determined by the group of people with which he actually participates. It is not what he thinks it is, it is what other people accept him as, and the way they behave toward him. Movie people are mobile. They are generally in the Middle class, although they have a very eccentric environment in Hollywood. One of the big movie houses in New York gave a reception for Clark Gable and sent announcements to the social register. Nobody came. Will Rogers came to New York after a tour around the world. Some Upper-class friends invited him to a party. Will talked. The next day he sent the chairman of the committee a bill for $2,500. They were surprised, but he said, "You did not invite my wife."

DeMille: What is the chance for a child born in the Lower or Middle class to change his status to a higher?

Lecturer: There are no statistical studies on this question but there are fairly good observations. The chances of Lower-Middles are good because the parents have already made a great step into that class, across probably the severest class line we have—that between Lower and Lower-Middle, and the movement from Lower-Middle to Upper-Middle is relatively easy. It is very rare for an individual to cross two class lines and move from Lower into Upper-Middle or from Lower-Middle into Upper. The Lower-Middle class has the habit of industry; its members rigorously control their children; they worship education, which is one of the primary tools of changing position, so that their chance is relatively good. The Lower class has a much poorer chance. The early social training in the Lower-class family is not so conducive to later social mobility as it is in the Lower-Middle.

Robinson: What would you say would be the effect on children's permanent behavior patterns where members of the home practice drinking, or where liquor is made available to youth by parental approval or presence in the refrigerator?

Lecturer: You can say, in general, that one of the things children learn to do is to watch their parents for what they are not told about; and especially if they love their parents they tend to identify and copy parental behavior. I would have no doubt that children who saw their parents drinking would have a weaker sanction against it, perhaps no sanction at all, than those who did not. However, depending on how much the parents drink, and how they drink, the children might assimilate the idea that, "yes, one drinks, but one drinks like a lady, or like a gentleman," which is a kind of sanction that they might also learn. One can learn from one's parents not only intemperance but also the taboos surrounding drinking.

Couch: If our society is founded on selfishness, on parental systems of rewards which are perhaps missed in certain ways and misinterpreted in others, what hope is there for a better world?

Lecturer: I would say the hope is that if we learn how to manage our society and set up the reward system properly we can have any kind of people we want. But first you would have to define "better," that is, the desired and practical end. We can have the kind of world and the kind of people we want, but we have to create the kind of conditions that produce them. This is a hopeful view because it centers attention on the necessary conditions and does not take a detached and metaphysical notion like "selfishness" and start attacking it as an abstraction.

Bruehl: I wonder whether the statement that the mores and taboos are more free and more liberal among the Lower classes isn't somewhat dependent upon whether or not there is involved the question of concealment—cover-up. I wonder whether it might not be that the people in the Lower class are a bit more open and free in what they do, that their offenses are more likely to be made public, that they are people who don't know how to get around the courts and how to keep their records out of the public view.

Lecturer: I distinguish three class groups, and I have already agreed that the top and bottom groups have somewhat more liberal standards. I was contrasting the Lower class with the Lower-Middle class, which is a big group, apparently about a quarter of the population. There is a real difference there, not merely an appearance. It is not merely that the Lower-class people are caught and the Lower-Middle ones are not. There is a very real difference in what is done, because the conscience structure in the Lower-Middle class is very strong.

If you take the Upper class, what you say is probably true. Their standards are more liberal because, as I have said, they do not fear criticism. When the Lower-class man gets drunk he probably ends up in jail, while when the Upper-class man gets drunk a policeman brings him home, punches the doorbell, and says very respectfully, "We saw Bill down on the corner and we thought we'd bring him home."

Lecture 9

Heredity of the Alcoholic

E. M. Jellinek

THE science of heredity has a brief history but a long past. Even primitive peoples assume that characteristics of the parents are transmitted to the offspring. The primitive explanation is that spirits place tiny models of the parental traits into the embryo. The ancient Hebrews, Greeks and Romans attributed a great role to heredity and even assumed that certain diseases were hereditary. Laws of heredity have been known, however, only since Mendel's experiments in 1866, or, to be more correct, since the rediscovery of his investigations in 1900. Knowledge of the carriers of heredity, of the mechanism of biological transmission, is of even more recent date, although some hypotheses on chromosomes and genes were current nearly 100 years ago.

The clarification of what kind of traits are biologically transmissible is a slow process. Although it has been known by qualified students of heredity since the 1870's that acquired traits are not transmissible biologically, this finding has not become part of public knowledge. Particularly slow was the development of distinctions between biological transmission and influences of the environment.

Beginning largely with the scientific observations of Darwin, naturalists found that individuals and whole groups may take on certain characteristics, particularly characteristics of behavior under specific environmental conditions, and they also found that even biologically inherited traits can undergo modifications through environmental influence. When the individuals were placed in a different environment, the modifications brought about by the previous environment disappeared; they were not perpetuated in the offspring. This was proof that the modification had not left an impress on the germ cells of the individual; one may say that these modifications had not entered into the genes.

Only after these investigations did it become evident that similarities between parents and offspring may be of two kinds:

(1) Those which can be accounted for only by direct biological transmission.

(2) Those which can be accounted for by imitation, by exposure to example, or by the same kind of environmental influence acting on parent and child.

Admittedly, the distinction is often extremely difficult and cannot be left to theorizing. On the other hand, when the trait under consideration is an acquired one, environmental influence may be assumed, but a possibility of a hereditary disposition for responding to the environmental influence may be conceded.

One more matter requires clarification. A sharp distinction must be made between inherited constitution and congenital constitution. Not all the characteristics with which the child enters this world are inherited. Direct biological transmission can be brought about only through the genes. Only what is present in the egg and what is added to it by the sperm plasm at the time of fertilization constitute hereditary transmission. Once the fertilized egg has started on its development, it cannot receive any more traits from the parents, but it can be influenced by its environment; and environment is to be understood in a very wide sense. There is an intrauterine environment and that is the environment to which the individual, in its earliest stages, is subjected. If this intrauterine environment is defective, then the developing embryo will be subjected to modifications. Such modifications will not be inherited traits. They do not come from the genes of the father or of the mother, but they are brought about by the stresses of the intrauterine environment.

Studies on heredity in alcoholism embrace a wide variety of questions which may be broadly classified in the following three groups of problems:

(1) Does parental alcoholism, chronic or even acute, cause such damage to the germ cells as may manifest itself in defects of the soma or psyche of the first-generation offspring?

(2) Does parental chronic alcoholism bring about a true mutation in the offspring?

(3) Is there a hereditary liability factor involved in alcoholism?

(a) Is alcohol addiction directly transmissible?

(b) Is a constitution inherited which is more liable to resort to escape through intoxication?

The first two problems relate to the effects of alcoholism; the third, to the genesis of alcohol addiction. From the standpoint of practical research, the third question is of greatest interest and this lecture will be restricted to an analysis of this one problem. I shall leave the other aspects to the question period.

The problem of germ damage, and therefore damage to the offspring, through parental alcoholism has attracted many investigators and has given rise to hundreds of papers. Investigations of the parentage of alcoholics, however, are less numerous. This is surprising in view of the many definite statements made in psychiatric papers relative to the hereditary factor in alcohol addiction and alcoholic psychoses.

The distinction between biological and social transmission and the discovery of modifications of biological characters through the environment have had great influence in reorienting investigations on the role of heredity in alcoholism. Other findings of the science of heredity which have influenced the trend of studies are that acquired traits are not transmissible and that in many instances not a disease or a certain attribute is transmitted, but rather a disposition, a readiness to acquire such a disease or such an attribute.

Initially the question asked was: Is a craving for alcohol or a craving for intoxication transmitted biologically? There may be one or two stragglers who still pose this question, but generally this has become an obsolete standpoint. There are some surmises relative to hereditary transmission of tolerance to alcohol. No evidence exists on this point, and it is difficult to express even an opinion on this matter, because "tolerance to alcohol" itself is ill-defined. There is some experimental evidence on the heredity of alcohol taste-thresholds, but it is not clear whether this is of relevance to our subject.

The question, as it is now asked, relates to a hereditary disposition to alcoholism, or, I should rather say, to a greater risk of alcoholism among persons who come from families with pathological personality deviations. This is a question which carries wide implications. What it really means is this: Is it only a highly selected group of the population which is liable to develop alcoholism, or can this disease appear in the general population? In other words, are there internal "musts" about alcoholism, or are other factors, such as social factors, among the determining influences?

The interest in this question among students of inebriety is extraordinarily great. The literature on alcoholism abounds with hypotheses and beliefs on this question, and there is a fair number of quantitative investigations of the question. Why should this interest be so great? The etiology of inebriety is baffling. It would, therefore, be most convenient to have heredity as a ready explanation.

This easy explanation has led many a writer on alcoholism simply to disregard the evidence—if he has ever looked at it at all—and to declare that hereditary disposition is the key to the question.

Looking at the literature on inebriety one gets the impression that all excessive drinking is due to an inherited constitution. The majority of discussions on alcoholism state, without examination of the evidence, that alcoholism is a product of "nonspecific heredity." The records, however, indicate no more than that members of families in which mental deviations are present have generally a greater probability of succumbing to alcoholism than those coming from mentally sound stock. Many psychiatric papers, in discussing constitutional factors, do not specify whether they mean hereditary or congenital constitution, but from the context it appears that hereditary constitution is usually meant. In other instances there is no doubt as to the author's stand. Kolle says, "Of importance is only the realization that hereditary constitution is the decisive factor." Stephan says, "One does not become an addict. One is an addict." Juliusburger stated that "Alcoholism is innate, not produced by environment." None of these three writers carried out any investigation of his own.

Oddly enough, many authors, after discussing the environmental influence and finding that the large proportion of those who became inebriates did so through environmental factors, end up with the sweeping statement that "inebriety grows on the ground of hereditary constitution."

What is the actual evidence?

First, may I touch briefly on the question of the occurrence of inebriety among the parents of inebriates? This question has been investigated frequently, and the reports of the different investigators are rather consistent. I have combined such investigations embracing 4,372 alcoholics, and of these, 2,799 had either an inebriate father or mother—that is, 52 per cent of all the alcoholics investigated were born of inebriate parents. Since a biological transmission of "craving for intoxication" cannot be assumed, this gives evidence of the great risks to which the offspring of alcoholics are exposed through example and neglect.

We may now turn to an analysis of the best available statistical material on the occurrence of psychopathological deviations among the parents of alcoholics.

Estimates of the incidence of hereditary liability in inebriates, based on 15 studies by 13 investigators, are presented in the accompanying table. Studies on small samples are not included, since the chance variation of estimates from small samples is of a disturbing degree. Owing to this restriction some otherwise

Hereditary Liability of Inebriate Patients
(Excluding Inebriety of Parent)

Investigator	Nature of Sample	Number of Patients	Patients with Tainted Heredity	
			NUMBER	PER CENT
Binswanger	Pathological intoxication	174	130	75
Croon	Criminal inebriates	655	553	82
Koller	Psychotic inebriates	215	151	70
Rybakow	Psychotic inebriates	600	372	62
Boss	General run of inebriate patients	909	336	37
Boss	" " "	166	70	42
Gabriel	" " "	728	240	33
Kant	" " "	180	86	48
Koller	" " "	191	78	41
Künzler	" " "	303	114	38
Ostmann	" " "	420	147	35
Schabel	" " "	207	87	42
Wegener	" " "	300	96	32
Maleika	General run of inebriate patients	146	33	23
Preisig and Amadian	"Reformed" inebriate patients	100	26	26

rather fine studies are not included. It has also been necessary to exclude investigations in which only selected factors were considered, or in which the net total could not be determined because of overlapping of the subgroups. For reasons mentioned before, the numerous investigations which inquire exclusively into the occurrence of alcoholism among the parents of inebriate patients are not considered here. Also, the incidence of parental alcoholism unconnected with other abnormalities has been excluded. This seemed to me advisable in an investigation of heredity in alcoholics since, if the question at issue is whether or not alcoholism is a pathological manifestation in which hereditary constitutional predisposition plays a role, one cannot prejudge the question by including alcoholism itself as a specific factor. Furthermore, in the case of familial alcoholism it would be impossible to separate biological from social inheritance. This does not imply that the investigation of the incidence of parental alcoholism in alcoholics is of no relevance.

The first four entries in the table show an incidence of 62 to 82 per cent of hereditary taint. All four of these studies are based either on psychotic patients or on criminals. If the conclusions are restricted to the type of population from which the samples have been drawn, namely to the alcoholic psychoses and other psychoses with incidental inebriety, no exception can be taken. However, these investigations have frequently been used to show that there is an extremely high incidence of hereditary tainting among inebriates. Patients with alcoholic psychosis do not form more than approximately 10 per cent of the entire alcoholic population. In psychotics, one generally does expect considerable hereditary liability, and since most of the psychoses which are classified as alcoholic psychoses are, with the exception of delirium tremens and the Korsakoff syndrome, closely related to the schizophrenias, a high incidence of hereditary taint is inevitable without any implication of the alcoholism itself. The highest incidence is found in Croon's sample of criminal alcoholics. Whether the author knew it or not, he was investigating hereditary tainting of criminals in whom alcoholism was incidental, but they were not a sample of alcoholics. Dr. Abraham Myerson warned against conclusions drawn from determinations of hereditary factors of any given abnormality in vagrants, since hereditary liability and psychopathy were prevalent in such groups independently of the factors under investigation. Others, too, have voiced the necessity for this precaution, but apparently without much avail.

In contrast to this, the next nine studies in the table, which are based on a "general run" of inebriate patients, show consistently a hereditary liability factor of 32 to 48 per cent. The lower estimate of Maleika of 23 per cent is merely due to the fact that he considered only the occurrence of definite psychosis among the parents of alcoholics, while the other investigators included other psychopathies of the parents. Thus Maleika's estimate is not inconsistent with the other investigations. The estimate of 26 per cent obtained by Preisig and Amadian must be restricted exclusively to the type of patients on which their study was made. They selected "reformed" alcoholic patients. It has been frequently pointed out that psychopathic alcohol addicts do not lend themselves readily to therapy. Thus, a sample of reformed alcoholic patients is not likely to include much psychopathy or hereditary tainting.

In speaking of hereditary disposition in inebriety in general, therefore, one must use the estimates obtained on the "general run" of alcoholic patients. These show that the incidence of hereditary taint in the total group of alcoholics probably does not exceed 35 per cent. This leaves us with a large alcoholic population in which inebriety has developed independently of any hereditary liability. As far as the 35 per cent with hereditary taint are concerned, the heredity assumes all types of psychosis and psychopathies and no evidence has ever been adduced to show that this heredity, by necessity, had to express itself in inebriety. The only permissible conclusion is that not a disposition toward alcoholism is inherited but rather a constitution involving such instability as does not offer sufficient resistance to the social risks of inebriety. The inherited constitution is merely a suitable breeding ground for inebriety. The incidence of 35 per cent hereditary liability in inebriates is above the incidence in the general population. Nevertheless, the limited incidence of this inherited constitution does not justify the assumption, frequently made, that inebriety is largely dependent upon "nonspecific heredity." It must also be said that the fact that 35 per cent of the alcoholics came from mentally abnormal families is not absolute evidence that "heredity" was operative in them. Furthermore, there are numerous indications, such as cultural and sex differences in the incidence of inebriety, which tend to show that even when the hereditary constitutional factor is present it does not become operative without intercurrent social factors. To the mental hygienist the realization of these facts is of the utmost importance, since their implication is that he is not faced by implacable fate.

DISCUSSION

Graham: I have a question relating to a statement which I heard a professor of psychology make a number of years ago. If it is significant, it is very significant—otherwise it is ridiculous. Speaking of the fact that acquired characteristics are not transmitted, he said this relative to apparent inherited alcoholism: If a newborn babe is kissed by a parent who has just indulged in an alcoholic drink, the parent might possibly transmit to the child an influence that would affect its desire. I wonder if there is anything in that?

Lecturer: I don't know anything about the transmission of traits, except "bugs," through the medium of osculation. Inheritance is only what is transmitted through the genes. Hereditary traits cannot be acquired after the fertilization of the ovum. Traits acquired after conception do not belong to the hereditary mass. The child that comes to the world with so-called hereditary syphilis has, in reality, not hereditary but congenital syphilis. The disease was transmitted after germination. If an alcoholic mother should be in a poor nutritional state, if she should suffer from vitamin deficiencies, she would constitute a very poor intrauterine environment, and her child would come into the world with possible constitutional handicaps. Here, again, we would not be dealing with heredity, but with a congenital phenomenon.

Gross: Are there statistics pertaining to the normal population in the United States with which these figures can be compared? In Switzerland they used the wives and husbands of paretic patients as a normal sample for comparison with alcoholics.

Lecturer: There is no actual census of the incidence of psychopathies in the general population. Even knowledge on the incidence of psychosis is incomplete. Only the figures on hospitalized persons are available. Those psychotics who are at large are not known, but there are estimates of what that proportion may be. In Maryland, a survey was made of noninstitutionalized psychotics. If one adds those to the hospitalized, there would be an increase of about 20 per cent. We have some idea of the incidence of epilepsy and a very good idea of the incidence of moronism. Moronism occurs in about 1 per cent of the general population. Epilepsy occurs in a fractional percentage of the population, perhaps in 0.3 to 0.4 per cent. As far as psychosis goes, up to 10 per cent of the population either had, have, or will have a psychosis. The incidence of psychoneurosis is least well known. Cobb estimated that there are about 2,500,000 persons in this country who have a neurosis severe enough to require medical assistance. This would be about 2 per cent of the general population. Some psychiatrists estimate the occurrence of neurosis as high as 25 per cent, but that would include rather mild degrees of maladjustment. Cobb's estimate of neurosis may have to be doubled. Moronism is not classed as a psychopathy, but if the interest is in "mental abnormality" the morons may be added. Adding them, as well as the so-called psychopathic personalities, to the psychotics, neurotics and epileptics, the total deviations from normal mental standards may be estimated as affecting 20 per cent of the total population.

Shepherd: The phrase "psychopathic stock" was used. Is psychopathy always inheritable?

Lecturer: I think I said that the fact that some alcoholics come from psychopathic parents does not necessarily mean that they inherited some psychopathy. The psychopathic constitution need not be inherited. We do not know the laws of heredity in mental disorders. We cannot speak of these matters in terms of Mendelian laws. Actually we know such laws of transmission only for simple traits, such as eye color, and for a few diseases.

Question: May I ask for a definition of psychopathy as contrasted with psychopathic personality?

Lecturer: Psychopathy is really a collective term. You can use the word psychopathy to cover neurosis, hysteria, or psychosis. Some people use the term a little too broadly, and include under it even quite common mood swings. Psychopathic personality is difficult to define. If experienced psychiatrists sit together at a diagnostic staff meeting and a patient with a psychopathic personality is presented, there will be good agreement among the psychiatrists that the patient is a psychopathic personality without psychosis. But when you ask these psychiatrists to tell you what the psychopathic personality is, they'll hem and haw; but, nevertheless, they have a good idea of it. Somewhere in his *Confessions* Saint Augustine suddenly exclaims, "What is time? If I am not asked, I know it, but if I should answer the question, I don't know it." There are many phenomena in life which we know and don't know, and psychopathic personality is one of them. But to be somewhat less vague: In neurosis, as a rule, only a certain part of the personality is affected and the trouble is emotional. In the psychopathic personality the entire personality, all of its behavior, is affected and the most characteristic aspect is emotional emptiness. In the neurotic the neurosis itself is a kind of adjustment; the psychopathic personality does not even attempt to adjust.

Mrs. Colvin: Is a moron a psychopathic personality?

Lecturer: No. Mental deficiency is not classed within the psychopathies. Often there is mental deficiency with psychosis, but generally they are not classed together.

Potts: Since only 35 per cent of the inebriates come from psychopathic stock, and since the psychotic population is nowhere near 35 per cent, does it not show that alcoholism is at least partly a problem of eugenics as well as a problem of environment?

Lecturer: The incidence of 35 per cent psychopathic parents among inebriates is not much in excess of the probable 20 per cent incidence in the general population. One cannot reduce alcoholism to a problem in eugenics. Even those drinkers who show some hereditary liability do not necessarily become alcoholics. Many other factors must contribute to create the alcoholic. Harping on eugenics would sidetrack the more important factors.

Law: If hemophilia is a hereditary characteristic, why is it that it only appears in men?

Lecturer: It is a sex-linked characteristic transmitted through the women in the family but the women themselves are not subject to the disease. There are other sex-linked characteristics, for instance, color blindness. An eye disease, retinitis pigmentosa, also runs in certain families as a sex-linked characteristic. In connection with that I should like to give you an example of the difficulties which one encounters in making investigations of heredity in humans. A friend of mine had collected some material on retinitis pigmentosa and brought the data to me for statistical analysis. Age and sex of patients were nicely recorded and there was a column showing the occurrence of the disease in parents, grandparents, aunts and uncles of the patients. As I ran over the data I had an odd impression that in the case of the younger patients there was a good deal of "heredity," but that the older patients showed much less. I arranged all the data according to the ages of the patients and found that in the age group 10–19 years there was a great deal of that disease in aunts, uncles, grandparents, and so forth. In the age group 20–29 years there was less mention of the disease in these relatives, but still a goodly proportion; then in the age group 40–49 years there were very, very few such mentions. The explanation is simple: Younger people, children, youngsters, come in with the mother, or with an older sister, or with the father, but usually with the mother who knows a great deal about the parents, grandparents, and other relatives, and can give ample information. The patient who comes in at the age between 40 and 50 comes in alone or with a friend. His mother and father are probably dead, and the patient knows little about diseases in his grandparents. In those cases one simply does not know whether there was any relative with that disease or not. The older the patient, the less reliable the information. I tried that out on some other investigations of heredity and found the same phenomenon. I have brought this up in order to give you an inkling of the pitfalls in such investigations, and how reliable, or unreliable, statements in this field may be.

Question: Is there any evidence to show that excessive use of alcohol affects the life of the sperm and ovum cells, the ability to procreate, the likelihood of offspring being moronic or stunted?

Lecturer: Much has been written on this question. There have been many experimental investigations on animals and there have been many statistical investigations on humans. As far as the animal investigation is concerned, those who have reviewed the material critically say either that it is inconclusive or that there is no proof of germ damage by alcohol. Certain animal experiments tend to show that there is germ damage. Others show just as definitely that there is none. Dr. Haven Emerson said, in summary, that the evidence, as it exists, is inconclusive, that one cannot make any positive statement at this time.

One thing is sure, that alcohol reaches the sperm. There is no doubt about that. Alcohol goes into all the body fluids and into all the tissues. There have been investigations on whether or not alcohol reaches the seminal fluid. It was not necessary to make these investigations, since by physical and chemical laws it had to reach it. On the other hand, there is no evidence that the sperm is influenced in any way other than by slowing its motion. No effect other than this slowing has been shown.

Now as to the effect of alcohol on the procreative ability: It is difficult to come to any definite conclusion from statistical data. It must be considered that full-fledged chronic alcoholism occurs largely between the ages of 45 and 55 years, and at those ages, according to our vital statistics, only a small number of men become fathers anyway. True, the effect of alcohol on procreative capacity may manifest itself before the development of frank chronic alcoholism, but the fertility statistics of alcoholic families do not bear out such an assumption. It is a fact that has been observed in America as well as abroad that the average number of children in alcoholic families is greater than in nonalcoholic families of the same social, economic and educational level. While this does not allow the conclusion that alcohol increases fertility, it surely does not indicate a lessening of procreative capacity.

As to the other part of your question, if you investigate whether there is a greater incidence of moronism in the offspring of alcoholics than in the general population, you will find that there is. As I said, in the general population you will find about 1 per cent morons. But you will find morons among 8 to 10 per cent of alcoholic families. Thus you would be inclined to say that moronism is a characteristic, perhaps a product, of alcoholism. But now let's go the other way around and investigate the ascendants of alcoholics. Let's take the alcoholics and investigate their parents and grandparents for moronism and you will find that some 10 or 15 per cent of your alcoholic patients come from moronic families. Thus the moronism in the offspring of alcoholics is not due to the alcoholism of the parents, but to the moronic heredity of the drinking parent.

I shall touch upon another statistical aspect of the question of germ damage. One of the much-used arguments is that infant mortality (mortality between the ages 0 to 1 year) is much higher in alcoholic families than in nonalcoholic families of the same occupational, social and economic level. Is this an effect of germ damage? If the germ were damaged, one could expect greater mortality. But I want to show you how infant mortality is influenced by external factors. I should like to show this on the basis of infant mortality among illegitimate children. For many years it has been observed that the mortality rate of illegitimate infants is much higher than among those of legitimate birth. It was assumed that the illegitimate children came from poor biological stock. The figures which I will give you are fairly exact, but they will not be entirely exact as I am quoting from memory. In Germany, around 1898, the mortality rate among infants of legitimate birth was about 18 per cent and among infants of illegitimate birth, 40 per cent. At that time a few physicians advocated doing something about this and societies were formed for the care of illegitimate infants. Somewhere around 1912, the mortality rate had dropped to 12 per cent in the legitimate group and to 18 per cent in the illegitimate group. The care given to the illegitimate infants reduced the difference in the mortality rate to an extraordinary degree. After the first World War the societies that had been formed for the care of illegitimate children were short of funds; they did not have enough to keep up their social work—not even enough money to provide half of the milk required. Around 1920 the mortality rate for legitimate infants was still 12 per cent, but for illegitimate children it had risen to 33 per cent. In 1923, national legislation for the care of illegitimate children was introduced, and by 1926 the infant mortality rate for both legitimate and illegitimate children was between 9 and 10 per cent. So you see what an error was made when it was assumed that the infant mortality rate of the illegitimate children was due to poor biological stock. The fact that we find a great excess of infant mortality among the families of alcoholics is in no way evidence of germ damage. It falls into the same category as illegitimate birth. It is a matter of neglect. The number of children in the alcoholic family is greater than in the nonalcoholic family from the same social economic stratum. The budget of the alcoholic family is burdened with the expense of alcohol, and therefore a smaller budget must be distributed over a larger number of heads. Consequently there is less money available for nutrition, for medical care, for hygienic conditions in general; and, in addition, there is actual neglect on the part of mothers and fathers. The increased mortality rate, as well as the increased morbidity rate, are explained by the conditions governing those households. It is fortunate that the cause is neglect rather than germ damage because one can do something about the neglect while nothing could be done if it were germ damage. Nevertheless the statistics gathered on alcoholic families are overwhelming evidence of the great dangers to which the children of alcoholic parents are exposed. I must repeat that it is very fortunate that it is not germ damage, and I must also point out that germ tissue is the toughest of all human tissues. Even the germ tissue could be damaged by very high concentrations of alcohol, but it is so wonderfully protected that before such concentrations of alcohol would occur, the alcoholic father or mother would be dead. It takes much less alcohol to kill the father or the mother than to injure the germ cell.

Hall: You referred to a sample of over 4,300 inebriates of whom 52 per cent came from alcoholic parents. What was the extent and character of the alcoholism of the parents and is not this figure important on the question of heredity as a cause of inebriety?

Lecturer: The alcoholism in those parents was real honest-to-goodness inebriety, not just a matter of moderate drinking. This matter is of great importance as far as causation of alcoholism is concerned, but has no relation to heredity. The data do not mean that alcoholism was transmitted biologically. It was transmitted socially. That is the reason why we maintain here that the rehabilitation of the alcoholic is a step in prevention. When he is rehabilitated, he rehabilitates his home, and no longer exposes his children to the increased risk of alcoholism.

Miss Moon: Some eminent writers on alcohol claim that in the offspring of alcoholics, childbirth is more difficult.

Lecturer: Investigations of this question have been unsatisfactory. Some of them have been carried out by the bearers of great names but that does not vest them with authority. Devising surveys is a rather special art. There may be an outstanding bacteriologist, but his expertness as bacteriologist does not make him an expert in surveys. We are very often misled by the authority of the name. We have, in America, a worship of names. We go and ask Professor Einstein what he thinks about nutrition. I have enormous faith in Professor Einstein's mathematical deductions, but what he thinks about oatmeal is irrelevant to me.

Brown: It has been stated that children of parents who drink, even moderately, do not make as high grades in school as those children whose parents do not drink. Can this statement be scientifically verified?

Lecturer: No. It cannot. I have gone carefully over that kind of material. It has nothing to do with the drinking of the parents but with the kind of population that was sampled.

Lecture 10

Children of Alcoholic Parents Raised in Foster Homes

Anne Roe

T HERE have been hundreds of studies pointing out that among the off-spring of alcoholics infant mortality is high, and epilepsy, idiocy, psychosis and alcoholism are rife. Many of these studies have been interpreted as proving physical or chemical germ damage. The present consensus is that this does not occur from alcohol. Another interpretation has been in terms of a nonspecific hereditary factor, which is manifested in different individuals in such diverse ways as feeble-mindedness, epilepsy, inebriety, etc. But of this hypothesis, the Committee of the American Neurological Association for the Investigation of Eugenical Sterilization has stated that it is not warranted to "postulate any widespreading unitary trait back of all psychoses, feeblemindedness, epilepsy, and the like." Although they have not specifically mentioned alcoholism in this connection, it is clear that they do not accept any postulate of a general sort.

There is no question but that alcoholism is associated with these other disorders mentioned, either in individuals or in families. Thus it is fairly well established that approximately 35 per cent of alcoholics come from families with epileptic, psychotic or feeble-minded members, and it is not surprising that the alcoholics themselves or their relatives should show a high incidence of these disorders, some of which are known to be hereditary. Alcoholism can hardly be expected to prevent their transmission. Furthermore it has been shown that these defects do not appear more frequently in the children of unstigmatized alcoholics than they do in the general population.

But what about the incidence of alcoholism in the children of alcoholics? It has been shown to occur in 30 to 40 per cent of the offspring of alcoholics in general, and if one considers only "healthy adults" who are offspring of alcoholics, an incidence of alcoholism of 20 to 30 per cent is a fair expectation. Similarly, an incidence of mental and nervous disorders of about 20 per cent would be expected.

All of these data refer to children who have been raised by their own parents so that, as in many studies of heredity, it is impossible to be certain that environment has not been a factor. It has been sufficiently well established that the higher infant mortality among the offspring of alcoholics is adequately explained by the neglect and poorer care given them and there is no necessity to assume poor germ plasm as an explanation. It may be that recourse to alcohol by the offspring of alcoholics is also explicable as a result of environmental influences.

A study of the adult adjustment of children of alcoholics, who were separated from their own parents and brought up by foster parents who were not related to them, offers an important method of investigating this problem, particularly when a control group of children of normal parents, who were also raised in foster homes, is available for comparison. I am presenting some of the results of such a study to you today. The full report, including all the methodological details, is given in a monograph to be published shortly, which also reports the outcome of foster children originally from psychotic parents.

METHODS AND SUBJECTS

The records of the child-placing department of the State Charities Aid Association of New York City were made available to us, and from their thousands of cases we were able to secure the ones to be reported in this study. Children referred to the State Charities Aid came to them from all over the State and from private as well as public agencies.

We took as our subjects only white, non-Jewish children who were, at the time of the study, 21 years of age or older, who had been placed originally before they were 10 years old, and about whose own parents adequate data were available. There were some who met these criteria but whom we could not locate or who were so far away that interviews with them or their foster parents were impossible, but in the end we had 61 subjects in the groups to be reported on here.

Of these 61 subjects, 25 were offspring of normal parents, that is, neither parent was alcoholic, psychotic, epileptic, criminal, feeble-minded, a sex deviant, inadequate, or guilty of mistreatment or neglect of the children; and for each parent there was some evidence of adequate adjustment in at least one major social area (family, job, or community), and no indication of grossly inadequate behavior in the immediate situation resulting in the child's becoming a public charge. A number of these children were illegitimate; most of the others became public charges because of the death of one or both parents, and the inability of, or lack of, relatives to care for them. This sample is probably representative of all children of normal parents who become public charges.

The 36 remaining children each had a father who was an inebriate and, with one exception, the fathers were all classified as "heavy drinker with syndrome." By a syndrome is meant a picture of overaggressive, disorganized or escape behavior such as repeated loss of jobs, disorderly conduct, neglect or mistreatment of spouse or children. In addition, other types of deviant behavior are recorded of many of these fathers: 25 per cent were criminal or possibly criminal; 81 per cent were guilty of mistreatment or neglect of their children; and 3 were classed as sex deviants. Of the mothers, only 4 were considered normal; 5 drank heavily; over half were sex deviants; and 44 per cent mistreated or neglected the children. Psychotic, epileptic and feeble-minded parents were excluded from this group. This group of parents is not a random sample of drinkers, or even of heavy drinkers. It was so selected as to include those who possessed this characteristic in extreme degree, hence if alcoholism is hereditary in any sense there can be no question but that these persons could have transmitted this heredity.

Once these groups were selected and contact with the foster parents was established, carefully trained fieldworkers interviewed either the child or the foster parent and, wherever possible, both. The interviews were long, and the fieldworkers followed a carefully prepared schedule which was designed to elicit the important elements of the subject's life in the foster home and his present adjustment. Immediately after the interview the data were recorded in great detail, and by means of an elaborate coding system were rated in terms of a number of characteristics which will be discussed later. I will not here discuss the development and validation of this coding system—any who are interested will find it in the complete report.

Ideally, of course, the children should all have been removed from their parents at the same and at a very early age, and brought up in equally good foster homes under similar conditions. Practically, it was not possible to find such groups, even though the number of children brought up in foster homes is extremely large. I have gathered the essential comparisons in a table and I will discuss the entries individually.

Comparison of Two Groups of Foster Children

A. Background	Alcoholic Parentage	Normal Parentage
Total in each group:	36	25
Males	21	11
Females	15	14
Mean age when placed	5.56 years	2.60 years*
Placed in rural or small towns	67 per cent	28 per cent*
Mean age of foster father at placement	42.44 years	37.79 years
Mean age of foster mother at placement	40.74 years	33.84 years
Education of foster father	9.6 years	9.8 years
Education of foster mother	10.9 years	10.9 years
Personality problems in foster home	31 per cent	26 per cent
Incompatible foster parents	32 per cent	10 per cent
B. Foster Home Experience		
Adopted legally	56 per cent	92 per cent*
Education received	10.03 years	13.17 years*
Affectionate foster fathers	31 per cent	75 per cent*
Affectionate foster mothers	41 per cent	73 per cent
Given lenient discipline	33 per cent	52 per cent
Encouraged to entertain at home	45 per cent	76 per cent
Extra educational stimulation (rating)	6.3	8.0
Active in organizations during childhood	36 per cent	78 per cent
Foster homes rated as giving a satisfactory emotional background	24 per cent	54 per cent
Got into serious difficulties with others than foster parents	28 per cent	8 per cent
C. Present Adjustment		
Mean present age	32 years	28 years
Vocations:		
Professional, business, skilled	53 per cent	57 per cent

	Alcoholic Parentage	Normal Parentage
Farmers	6 per cent	0 per cent
Semiskilled, unskilled	41 per cent	43 per cent
Present health robust or better	71 per cent	78 per cent
Breadth of interests (rating)	6.08	8.50*
Belonging to organizations	32 per cent	73 per cent*
Mean number of close friends	4.41	6.38
Married	83 per cent	64 per cent
Unhappily married	35 per cent	20 per cent
Married who have children	67 per cent	50 per cent
Use of alcohol:		
Regular (not necessarily heavy)	7 per cent	9 per cent
Occasional	63 per cent	55 per cent
None	30 per cent	36 per cent
General adjustment ratings:		
Reasonably secure	54 per cent	53 per cent
Adequate	64 per cent	78 per cent
Normal personal relations	56 per cent	68 per cent
Responsible attitude	44 per cent	55 per cent
Over-all personality adjustment:		
Well adjusted	40 per cent	52 per cent
Fairly well adjusted	23 per cent	19 per cent
Maladjusted	37 per cent	29 per cent

*The entries marked with an asterisk are those which show a statistically significant difference between the groups. This means that the difference shown is one which may be expected to appear between any sample groups similarly chosen.

As you see, of the 36 in the alcoholic-parentage group, 21 were boys and 15 girls; in the normal-parentage group, there were more girls than boys. Most adoption agencies report more requests for girls than for boys.

THE FOSTER HOMES

The children in the alcoholic-parentage group were, on the average, twice as old as those in the normal-parentage group when they were first placed in foster homes. That this should be so is probably a result of the different reasons for which these children became dependent. Many of the alcoholic-parentage group became dependent as a result of court action; it is clear that children are not removed from their parents until the situation has become obviously impossible for them, and not until after other ways have been tried to rectify it. This means that the first few years of the lives of these children were spent in a home situation which undoubtedly left much to be desired. It is possible that in some instances the child nevertheless received a full measure of affection, or that the support and affection of one parent were sufficient materially to overcome the unfortunate effects of the deviant parent, but this could not often have been the case in this group, where the incidence of sex deviancy in and mistreatment by the mothers is quite high. Hence, in addition to any hereditary factors that may have been operating in the production of these asocial parents and transmitted to the children, we must also remember that they were probably subjected to traumatic experiences during the early years of their lives.

There was a considerable difference in the localities of the foster homes in which these children were placed. Many more of the alcoholic-parentage group were placed in farm homes or in small towns. This is partly a result of the more advanced age of the children in the alcoholic-parentage group, and of the greater number of boys. Both these factors operated to increase the number of farm placements because, particularly in the early days of foster-home care, many children were placed in homes where they were wanted primarily for assistance with chores. This difference in location needs to be considered in assessing differences in educational and social opportunities, as well as the more subtle differences arising in the homes themselves and in the attitudes of the foster parents.

There are differences in the average age of the foster parents, at the time of taking the children, which need also to be kept in mind as possibly influencing factors, since we found that older parents were more likely to exercise rigid and severe discipline. But it is interesting that there are no differences in the education of the foster parents so far as this is recorded. These data were available for comparatively few of the foster parents, however, and for more of those in the alcoholic- than in the normal-parentage group. It is obvious that those with little education would be more likely to evade a statement on the subject, so that it is possible that a difference does exist.

A striking finding in both groups is the extent of the presence of personality problems in these foster homes. These were found in over a fourth of the homes in both groups. Some of them were not serious, but not a few of them were, and all of them unquestionably affected the way in which the children were handled, since there is a significant relation between this factor and severity of discipline in the homes. There is also some relation between this factor and the child's adult attitude toward reality as well as ability to develop satisfactory personal relationships. These problems most often appeared in the foster fathers, two of whom were heavy drinkers, one extremely jealous and assaultive toward his foster son, and several severely ill tempered. It often happened that in the early days of placement work the foster fathers were not seen, or were seen only casually, before the children were placed; fewer such instances occur now, although it is difficult to see how children could have been left in some of these homes at any time.

Marital incompatibility of the foster parents is more frequent among those who took children of the alcoholic-parentage group, and this also undoubtedly affected the life in the foster home.

These differences in the homes, before the children were placed in them, may be summarized as follows: A disproportionate number of the alcoholic-parentage group were placed in farm homes where much assistance was often required of them, and with older and more difficult foster parents. Let us go on now to the next section of the table and discuss what happened to the children in these homes.

EXPERIENCES IN THE FOSTER HOMES

All but two of the children of normal parentage were adopted, but only 56 per cent of the other group. Adoption is usually carried through as soon as the agency permits it and is less predicated upon acceptable qualities in the children who are adopted than it is upon the attitude of the parents. It would seem that those who adopt their foster children have, from the start, more of the attitude of own parents and are more likely to have taken children because they wanted children as such, than for any of the other possible reasons that can be involved.

The normal-parentage group received significantly more schooling and reached higher levels of achievement. The question is whether these children received more education because their foster parents valued education more highly, or were more able and willing to give it to them, or because the children themselves were more able to take additional training. After consideration of various lines of evidence, I believe it probable that the latter possibility is somewhat more likely, that is, that the children of the alcoholic-parentage group are on the whole less gifted in intelligence. This is *not* to be assumed as having been caused by the alcoholism of a parent; it is, however, probable that children of alcoholic parents are less likely to become public dependents if that parent or the spouse is of superior intelligence, or from families of superior intelligence. In general, however, it should be noted that these children were all relatively well educated. In New York State in 1940 the median years of education for all native whites then 30 to 34 years of age was 9.7; the mean for our alcoholic-parentage group is above this, and no child had fewer than 6 years of schooling.

Differences between the groups in the affection of the foster parents for the children are striking and important, since this appears to be one of the potent factors in the development of a well-adjusted personality. The children whose foster parents were not affectionate did not, as a rule, become maladjusted as adults, but it was clear that those who had affectionate and lenient parents had a better chance of becoming well-adjusted and contented adults. Leniency of discipline is naturally associated with affection of the parents. Among the fathers, those who administered strict discipline were considerably better educated than those who were lenient, but this was not true of the mothers. Severe discipline was also associated with the presence of personality problems in the home. The relationships between these factors are not surprising. In short, older parents, and parents who themselves had personality problems, were more strict, and even harsh, with the children in their care, and less affectionate. In all of these respects the children in the normal-parentage group were better off than those in the alcoholic-parentage group. It was interesting that presence or lack of religious interests in the mother had no significant relation to the type of discipline.

There was also more shared family activity in the normal-parentage group, and these foster parents gave the children considerably more encouragement in entertaining their friends in the home. Both of these activities seem to aid materially in the development of satisfactory social relations in later life. In addition, we had a measure of extra educational stimulation in the home, such as special lessons in music or dancing, attendance at plays, home library, travel, and so on, and by this measure, the normal-parentage group were also better off, and many more of them belonged to childhood organizations. This last is in part a reflection of the location of the foster homes, as we found that relatively more of the children in suburban and city homes belonged to children's organizations.

We found it necessary to have a general summary rating of the level of excellence of the emotional background of the foster-home care, and it is not surprising, in view of the above analysis, that on this summary measure a larger percentage of the normal-parentage group were considered to have had satisfactory foster homes.

Many difficulties arise when children are first placed in foster homes, however good the home, and however nice the child. Enuresis, temper tantrums, stealing from the foster parents, and similar problems are extremely common, as has been reported in other studies. These can be largely disregarded; they are usually temporary, although very distressing to foster parents who have not been prepared for them. However, a number of these children did get into serious difficulties in late adolescence which involved others than the foster parents, and which were of a nature indicating severe maladjustment. Of the children in the alcoholic-parentage group, 10 had such difficulties—5 boys and 5 girls. The girls were all sex delinquents; of the boys, 2 got into trouble because of drinking too much, 2 for stealing, and 1 for forgery. Two of the boys in the normal-parentage group also got into serious difficulties, 1 for drinking and 1 for truancy. In addition, several of this group, who did not get into overt difficulties, were referred back to the placing agency for psychiatric treatment. The relative incidence is higher in the alcoholic-parentage group, but in view of their poorer homes in general and more disturbed early histories, and in view of the fact that the difference is not statistically significant in this small group, it cannot be concluded that any resort to a hereditary factor to explain it is justified. We were unable to find any significant relationships which would give us a clue as to why some of these children got into difficulties and the others did not. Although there was no statistically significant relation between getting into such difficulties and our summary measure of foster home care, it is worthy of notice that no child with a home-background rating of "satisfactory" became delinquent, but, on the other hand, many children with "unsatisfactory" home backgrounds did not become delinquent.

The Foster Children as Adults

After this analysis of the background of these children, let us consider the question of how they turned out. They are all adults now, from 22 to 40 years of age, and it does not seem too soon to make some assessment of the adequacy of their adult adjustment.

The basic comparisons are given in the last section of the table. We note that those in the alcoholic-parentage group now average 32 years of age, and the others 28. The vocational distribution is very similar, as you see, and most of them are in very good health.

A measure of the breadth of their interests, apart from vocational activities, is significantly higher for the normal-parentage group. Significantly more of them belong to organizations now, and they have, on the average, more close friends. These measures, crude as they are, do indicate that the normal-parent-age group lead somewhat richer lives than the others, by the standards of our culture. Their greater facility in personal relationships and their broader interests probably reflect the emotionally and intellectually richer lives they led as children.

Considerably more of the alcoholic-parentage than of the normal-parentage group are now married. This difference is probably largely a reflection of the age difference, and in part of difference in localities of foster homes, since rural residents are likely to marry at an earlier age than urban ones. It is noteworthy, however, that at every age more of these people are married than is the case in the New York State population on the whole, the difference being greatest in the case of the girls of alcoholic parentage. This has particular significance, as will be shown later, in estimating the possibility of later development of alcoholism.

How successful these marriages are, is another problem. We do not have adequate data on it from all those who are married, but that some of the marriages are unhappy is clear, and the percentages for those in the two groups concerning whom we had this information are shown. On the other hand, we have scores on the *Burgess Marriage Schedule* for a number of people, and the average of all of them is almost one standard deviation above the mean of the group from the general population reported by Burgess and Cottrell; that is, by that test, these persons are more happily married than the population at large. That this is actually the case is, in my opinion, doubtful.

Of those who are married, many have children—two-thirds of the alcoholic-parentage group and one-half of the normal-parentage group. This difference, again, is in part, at least, a result of the age difference between the groups.

The next set of comparisons is of particular interest to us—their present use of alcohol. These data were obtained for 27 in the alcoholic-parentage group and 22 in the normal-parentage group. Differences between these two groups in those who use alcohol and those who do not are negligible, and there are *no* excessive drinkers among them. (The 3 mentioned earlier who had gotten into trouble because of their drinking in late adolescence are either not drinking regularly now, as is certainly true of one of them, or the information was not obtained.) Contrast this with the expectancy of alcoholism in children of alcoholics, quoted earlier as between 20 and 30 per cent. It is true that alcoholism may still appear in these persons, since it is typically a disease of later life. There are a number of factors, however, which suggest that this is not to be expected in these groups. Very few of these people are drinking much now—any who were slated to become inebriates should be drinking pretty heavily at their present ages; and most of these people have established reasonably satisfactory lives, including adequate personal and community relationships, and most of them are married. A number of studies have shown that the marital status of inebriates varies greatly from that of the normal population, and that the most significant of these variations is the failure to get married. This is also true of psychotics. It is not argued that marriage prevents the development of inebriety or psychosis, but that those whose personality structure is such as to be likely to develop either are less likely to marry. Hence, we have no reason to expect any greater incidence of alcoholism in the children of the alcoholic parents in this group than in the population at large, and perhaps some reason to expect less.

We devised a number of ratings of general adjustment in its different phases, and an over-all rating, which are noted in the table. Except for the latter, I have indicated only the percentages receiving the highest rating. The first measure in this group refers to feelings of personal security. All of these ratings were made after consideration of the whole interview and all of the available data. It was not possible to make all of them on every subject, and sometimes we felt the data for one person were adequate for some of these ratings and not for others.

The first measure in this rating refers to feelings of personal security in the areas of personal, social and family life. We rated these persons as reasonably secure; or as feeling some insecurity in major areas, but this insecurity compensated for by security in other areas; or as seriously insecure to an extent which hampered happiness or ability to function. There is no difference between the groups in the percentage who feel reasonably secure, and I do not think the proportion is much lower, if any, than would be found in any unselected population.

In the next measure, feelings of personal achievement and adequacy, the ratings for which are analogous to those just reported, the normal-parentage group come out a little the better, but the difference is not great enough for these small groups to have much significance. A similar difference exists in the next rating, that of adequacy of personal relationships. This is in accord with our earlier findings of less richness in personal relationships in the lives of the alcoholic-parentage group. Attitude toward reality, which we have rated in terms of acceptance or evasion of responsibilities, shows somewhat more tendency among the alcoholic-parentage group to indulge in escape behavior, but again the differences are not great.

For the final rating of over-all personality adjustment, I have reported the percentages for each of the three major categories. Here, again, the normal-parentage group came out somewhat better than the alcoholic-parentage group, but again such differences as were found are not large, and certainly not more than is warranted by the history of these people; if anything, less. There are as many seriously maladjusted in the normal-parentage group as in the alcoholic-parentage group. This measure, which shows no significant relationship to parental background, is related to certain factors in the history of the child. Statistically significant association was found only with the presence of affection in the foster parents, when these were rated together. That is, there is an association between good present personality adjustment of the child and his having been brought up by affectionate foster parents. This is not a close association, but it is a definite one.

It is pertinent to inquire how the adjustment of these people compares with that of the adult population on the whole. Are about one-third of all adults somewhat maladjusted by the criteria we have used? It is probably not a great overestimate, at any rate. Since our concepts of adjustment are presumably based upon a general social norm, half of the group would fall below that norm, but it is doubtful if as many as a third would be noticeably deviant. Nevertheless, such comparisons as we were able to make—in terms of responses on the Minnesota Scale for the Survey of Opinions, which was administered to some of our subjects and which I have not reported in detail here—would indicate that this group is not less well adjusted than the population at large, but better adjusted.

DISCUSSION OF THE FINDINGS

Let me now attempt to summarize the outstanding findings of this study. These two groups of children, one of alcoholic and one of normal parentage, were brought up by foster parents who were not related to them. The fathers in the alcoholic group exhibited many forms of socially deviant behavior other than alcoholism, and a large proportion of the mothers were also deviant in similar ways. Many of these families are of the sort whose members for some generations are and have been well known to various social agencies and are constant community problems. Although none of the parents was frankly feeble-minded, the general level of intelligence of these families is probably below the average.

Studies of such families have indicated a high incidence of various types of disorders and we would expect a similar incidence of disorders, if they are primarily due to heredity, in these children of alcoholics. The low-grade feeble-minded, the epileptic and the crippled, would not have been considered suitable for placement, since these disorders are apparent early in life, but alcoholism and psychosis cannot be predicted in the early years of life. Had these children of alcoholic parentage been brought up at home, the expected incidence of alcoholism would be between 20 and 30 per cent, and of psychosis about 20 per cent. For our group of normal parentage, the expectation would be about the same as for the population at large, that is, less than 1 per cent chronic alcoholics, and about 10 per cent who would at some time be incapacitated by psychosis.

Examination of the early histories of these groups reveals that the normal-parentage group were placed in foster homes at an earlier age, that these homes were in general better in many respects than those in which the alcoholic-parentage group were placed. Relatively more of the children of the latter group got into serious difficulties in late adolescence, and it was only among these children that sex delinquents developed. Yet, as regards their present adjustment, there are no significant differences between the groups, and there are as many seriously maladjusted among the normal-parentage group as there are among the alcoholic-parentage group.

The children of normal own parentage are perhaps somewhat less well adjusted than the population at large but not markedly so, and in view of the fact that for some of them there were early disturbed periods, and for some of them poor foster homes, this does not require particular comment.

The children of alcoholic parentage, however, cannot be said to have turned out as expected on the basis of any hypothesis of hereditary taint. Of these children, none is an alcoholic and only three use alcoholic beverages regularly. Alcoholism is predominantly a disease of later life, but from the fact that so few of them are drinking now, and that most of them have established adequate personal lives, there is every reason to expect that few, if any, ever will become alcoholics. And although some are maladjusted, and two seriously so, there is no reason to expect any greater incidence of psychosis than in the general population.

Some of these children had criminal fathers and a number of them had mothers who were sex deviants. Yet none of the few boys in these groups who stole or forged had criminal fathers, and none of the girls who became sex delinquents had sex deviant own mothers.

We must conclude that the reported high incidence of alcoholism and psychosis in the offspring of alcoholics is not explicable on the basis of any hereditary factor. It is clear that these children of alcoholic parentage, even though they had on the whole more disturbed early years and less desirable foster homes than the children of normal parentage, nevertheless have succeeded as adults in making life adjustments which are not significantly inferior in general to the adjustments made by the children of normal parents. Alcoholic parentage, then, does not preclude good adjustment; nor, under reasonably adequate life circumstances, make it more difficult. We may assume that an individual cannot do better than his heredity permits; hence it follows that the child's parentage gives only a very rough indication of his genetic constitution, and the alcoholism of a father, therefore, affords no grounds in itself for assuming poor heredity in the child.

But we cannot leave this study without asking ourselves how it happened that these children did turn out so well. Some of them, it is true, did have affectionate and lenient foster parents and happy childhoods, but what of those who were subjected to early mistreatment by their own parents, and then brought up in foster homes with unloving and harsh foster parents? How did it happen that in spite of these things many of them have become not only useful citizens, but reasonably contented persons, working adequately, with pleasant family lives and sufficient friends?

I think we must consider further explanations in both of the general fields in which we have sought them, heredity and environment. No one who has read the record of some of these lives and pondered on them can escape a profound sense of awe at the biological toughness of the human species. To me it seems clear that the biological orientation of the human organism toward integration is an essential character, and functions in the higher spheres of emotional and social life in a way analogous to the integrative neural mechanisms found by Coghill in the development of movement in the salamander.

We must also consider the child's environment outside of the family, on which attention was focused in this as in other studies. Had these children remained with their own outcast families, they, too, would have been, in a sense, outcasts. The children of respectable families would, in all likelihood, not have been permitted to play with them. They would not have had the kind of clothes the other children had; they would not have been invited to their parties; and nasty remarks about their fathers and mothers would have been shouted after them on the street. They could react only by identifying with their families and rejecting the community and all its customs, or by rejecting their families and striving ceaselessly somehow to achieve membership in the group which had despised them. It may be that one or the other orientation was early taken by these children and that that contributed in part to determine which ones had the most disturbed periods, and which ones are still maladjusted. We do not know. But there are not many who have not come to working terms with life in the community.

It seems very probable that residence in a home which is a respected part of the community, and the acceptance of the child as a member of that community, make possible the formation of an organized ideal derived from the attitudes and forms of behavior of the community which can function as an integrating force, even in spite of unloving and harsh parents. It is conceivable that the basic assumption of our society, the assumption of the dignity and worth of the individual, is sufficiently pervasive that it may offer support even to the child whose dignity suffers attack from his parents. This, and such good elements as even the poorest heredity must include, is perhaps the answer.

DISCUSSION

Chairman (E. M. Jellinek): Was there any alcoholism among the foster parents?

Lecturer: Two of the personality problems in the foster homes in which alcoholic-parentage children were placed were due to the heavy drinking of the foster father. I don't think it occurred in any of the others.

Question: How comparable were the two groups in mental ability and how was this determined?

Lecturer: It was not determined in terms of mental test rating. We did do a few tests; it was not practical or possible to give them to all children, so I have not reported any of those. On the basis of the histories of the groups, I would say, as I believe I did, that, on the whole, I thought the children of alcoholic parentage were of a somewhat lower level of intelligence than the children of normal parentage, but it was a very slight difference only.

Chairman: From the educational histories of the children it is apparent that even those of alcoholic parentage must have been well within the normal intelligence range since they had a higher educational average than the general population of the State of New York. Thus even if they were in general on a slightly lower intelligence level than the children of normal parentage, they were by no means of low intelligence.

Perry: Would you state, or repeat, what constitutes normal parentage? Was the differentiating factor between normal and alcoholic parentage merely that normal parentage was nonalcoholic?

Lecturer: Oh, by no means. I may not have stated it clearly. The process by which we judged this is perhaps the easiest way to answer that. We had a rating schedule in which there were 10 categories according to which all parents were rated. In these categories, alcoholism was one; psychosis was another. This included not only frank psychosis, but suspicion of psychosis. That was ruled out in both of these groups. Epilepsy was another. That was considered and also ruled out in both groups. Feeble-mindedness was another. That was also ruled out in both groups. Criminality was another. We accepted the latter for the alcoholic-parentage group, but not for the normal group. Sex deviance was another characteristic which was excluded from the normal group but not from the alcoholic group. Then we had a category of general inadequacy; you know, the sort of person who does not quite get along, really is not psychotic, not feeble-minded, but does not manage very well. Those were not accepted among the normal-parentage group, but were accepted in the alcoholic-parentage group. It was only necessary in the alcoholic-parentage group that one parent be alcoholic; it was necessary in the normal-parentage group that both parents be normal. In addition, for the normal parents, we had some positive evidence of adequate adjustment in at least one major social area, that is, either job, or family, or community.

Squires: What was, or is, the religious background of the children and that of the foster parents?

Lecturer: According to the New York State law children can only be placed in foster families of the same general religious faith as the child's own parents. This, I presume, was done. There are both Protestants and Catholics in the group. I don't recall the numbers. I made some attempt to investigate whether there was any relationship between the Protestantism or Catholicism of the family and any of these results. Nothing showed up at all. There was not even any association between the extent of religious interest in the parents and Protestantism and Catholicism. So that that factor has not been discussed at length. Is that what you wanted to know, Mr. Squires?

Squires: That was not exactly the thought in my mind. What I am interested in is, whether there was any indication in the survey that the children had received religious training.

Lecturer: Yes, we took that into consideration. We have a rating on religious interest of the foster parents and also on present religious interest of the children. These did not differ from one group to the other. I may say that the foster parents had higher ratings on the presence of religious interest than the children. We also have a rating on religious training. Practically all of them got a rating of two, which means that they were sent to Sunday School. Very few of these children now have religious interests. Few of them occasionally go to church. There was no difference between the two groups in that respect.

Haralson: The figures in the table under the title of "use of alcohol," "regular, not necessarily heavy" show 7 per cent for the children of alcoholic parents and 9 per cent for those of normal parents, which is a little odd. Now it has always been my understanding that in rural areas there is much less drinking among the population than in the cities; and also perhaps that there is more temptation to drink in urban areas. Would not these facts explain the difference there and, if the situation were reversed, would it not probably reverse these percentage figures?

Lecturer: The difference between 7 and 9 per cent in groups of this size is no difference at all; it is completely negligible. The figures I gave you for locality refer to the locality of the foster home in which the child was brought up. I did not give you the figures for the present localities, which are somewhat different. There is now less difference in the present location of these persons than there was when they were children. As a matter of fact, a slightly larger percentage of the alcoholic-parentage group are occasional drinkers, which means that if they happen to go to a party where liquor is served, they may have a drink, or a glass of wine or beer now and then, or something of that sort. But the differences are very slight, so small that I would say there is no difference at all.

Haralson: Just as a matter of curiosity, are any of these children in either group outstanding successes in life?

Lecturer: There are no famous scientists, or famous artists, or anything of that sort, among them. There aren't very many professional men or women. There is none whose name anyone would know, in fact.

Theories of the Alcoholic Personality

Carney Landis

O NE of the central questions which must be considered in any formulation of the problem of alcoholism or of the alcoholic psychoses may be phrased in this way: Is there a personality type, a relatively constant combination of psychological traits, which, appearing in an individual, renders him especially susceptible to the intemperate use of alcohol; or is there no such special personality type, but only alcohol acting on any or all of the varieties of personality? The man on the street might phrase the same question as follows: Is a man a drunkard *because* he is peculiar, or is he peculiar *because* he is a drunkard; or is he just drunk *and* peculiar?

DEFINITION OF PERSONALITY

Before we can theorize about these possibilities, it is necessary to define what we shall understand here by the word "personality." This word has had many different meanings and usages and there is no essential agreement even among psychologists or any of the students of human behavior concerning them. Allport, in his brilliant and comprehensive treatment of the origin and use of the term, selects 50 different and distinct ways in which the term "personality" has been used during the past 2,000 years. It derives originally from *persona,* the name given to the theatrical mask first used by the actors in the Greek drama, and adopted about 100 B.C. by the Roman players. The use of the mask in the theater led to several meanings, so that in the writings of Cicero at least 4 distinct usages are found: (*1*) as one appears to others (but not as one really is); (*2*) the part someone plays in life; (*3*) an assemblage of personal qualities that fit a man for his work; and (*4*) distinction and dignity.

The word was taken over by the early fathers of the Christian Church to designate the distinction between outward appearance and the true inner nature or essence of self; the personality signified the variable appearance or pose, in contrast to the true inner nature of man as derived from the Deity. Through the centuries philosophers have assigned special meanings to the word. For example, Wolff emphasized, as the chief criteria of a person or personality, "self-consciousness and memory"; Leibnitz defined a person as "substance gifted with understanding"; Locke said that a person is "a thinking intelligent being that has reason and reflection and can consider self as itself"; Lotze used the word personality to characterize "the ideal of perfection"; while Goethe regarded personality as the "supreme value."

In the law the term has still a different history. The Code, as established by Justinian, held that a slave was not a person, from which it followed that a person or a personality was "any individual enjoying a legal status." From this, the idea was modified so that an individual's material possessions came to be known as his personality, which led to the further development of the notion that personality referred to the living human being in his entirety.

Among sociologists the term personality has had a wide and complicated set of meanings, including "no human being"; "the bodily self"; "an expression of contempt"; "revealing qualities of others in offense to good taste"; "the integration of all the traits which determine the role and status of a person in society"; or finally and briefly, "a person's social effectiveness."

Among psychologists the term has had a wide variety of meanings, many of which have started with the phrase, "Personality is the integration or sum total of . . ." Typical of these is the definition that personality is the integration of those systems of habits that represent an individual's characteristic adjustments to his environment. A still different usage is that of Woodworth, who said that personality is the way in which one does things.

From all of these different usages Allport formulated the following which, for our present purposes, seems adequate: "Personality is the dynamic organization within the individual of those psychophysical systems that determine his unique adjustments to his environment." That is the definition of the word *personality* as used here.

PERSONALITY OF THE ALCOHOLIC

We may now consider the problem of the personality of the alcoholic in the light of this definition. We will try to find whether or not there are any systematic organizations of psychological traits, habits or general attitudes which determine the unique adjustment through intemperate use of alcoholic beverages by certain individuals, which unique adjustment seems necessary in order to complete the general life adjustment which they can make or must make to their environment.

In everyday conversation we are likely to hear that this or that person is a typical drunkard, implying that there is a unitary system of traits which characterizes most, if not all, alcohol addicts. Probably most persons would say that the *typical* drunkard could be characterized about as follows: He is friendly, garrulous, quick-tempered, unpredictable, not too truthful, extroverted, weak-willed, flashy, changeable, impulsive, poorly adjusted to life, superficially sociable, and inadequate as a son, husband or father.

This description is recognizable by most Americans as a reasonable characterization of the fully developed alcoholics they know. In spite of its apparent recognizability, psychological studies have all indicated that, to the contrary, very few alcoholics can actually be so typified. In fact, all of the studies which have been made thus far lead to the conclusion that there is no unitary grouping of personality traits or attitudes which truly characterizes any considerable number of the individuals addicted to the use of alcohol. It may be possible eventually to find some fundamental similarities in the personality of the alcoholic group, but if these similarities do exist they have, to date, defied scientific recognition, delimitation and definition.

EXTROVERTS AND INTROVERTS

If there is no unitary personality organization which can be termed typically alcoholic, we can next turn to see whether or not it is possible to find certain traits, attitudes or other psychophysical systems which are characteristic of any considerable number of alcoholics.

One of the most widely used personality characterizations is the division of human beings into two groups: extroverts and introverts. Hoch made a study of 200 patients suffering from different varieties of the alcoholic psychoses. He reported that patients who suffer from delirium tremens and Korsakoff's psychosis are predominantly extroverted, whereas those who suffer from alcoholic hallucinosis or other types of alcoholic psychoses tend to be introverted. Of all these patients, 73 per cent were extroverted and 27 per cent introverted. Of the extroverts, 78 per cent recovered from their alcoholic diseases, while of the introverts, only 22 per cent recovered. In other words, about three-fourths of alcoholic psychotics could be characterized as extroverted; and of these, three-fourths recovered from the immediate attack. As Hoch points out, introversion is closely allied to schizophrenia and extroversion to the manic-depressive psychosis. Hence, it is probable that the extroverted individual of a manic-depressive temperament tends to become alcoholic more often than does the introverted individual of schizophrenic temperament. The schizophrene, if he becomes alcoholic, does not tend to have a favorable outcome from his alcoholism or from his psychosis.

Hoch's report is in line with an earlier study of Pohlisch who found that among 75 chronic alcoholics without psychosis, 64 per cent were cyclothymic personalities, 5 per cent epileptoid, and 3 per cent schizothymic, while 28 per cent were unclassifiable.

CHARACTERIZATION OF ALCOHOLICS

Phyllis Wittman made use of several of the so-called standardized objective personality tests to study the personality of a group of chronic alcoholics who were not psychotic, in contrast to a group of similar individuals who were nonalcoholic. She reports that the alcoholic can be characterized as follows:

He has a comparatively weak degree of restraint, mental poise and stability so that he has difficulty in controlling his moods and desires as well as their overt expression. He is somewhat more selfish, conceited and, hence, more anti-social than the average individual, but not significantly so. He has relatively strong cycloid tendencies and therefore shows pronounced swings in mood and activity, together with distractibility and lack of attention. He is not particularly shy, sensitive or given to daydreaming. He is suspicious, self-centered, stubborn, scornful of the ideas of others and steadfast in his adherence to his own ideas.

These findings only represent trends and do not represent statistically significant differences between the alcoholic and the nonalcoholic groups. On the basis of another test, she reported that the most differentiating characteristics of the chronic alcoholic were as follows: He had a domineering but idealized mother who insisted on things being done her way; and a stern, autocratic father whom the patient feared somewhat as a child, so that the childhood home life had been one of strict, unquestioning obedience. He showed a marked interest in the opposite sex with many love affairs but poor marital adjustment. Finally, he showed a lack of self-consciousness, together with a marked ability to get along with and be socially acceptable to others. These self-descriptive findings are of dubious value for differentiating alcoholics from nonalcoholics. They more probably represent the sort of self-description which will be obtained from a majority of maladjusted persons irrespective of drinking habits. ✓

PERSONALITY STUDIES

A subcommittee of the Research Council on Problems of Alcohol has permitted me to cite certain unpublished findings derived from an intensive personality study of 29 alcoholics, 25 former alcoholics who have been "dry" for at least 2 years, and 21 nonalcoholic individuals. This material was obtained from the special case histories drawn up by a psychiatrist, a psychologist and a social worker who had met with each individual in question and obtained material relevant to certain of his personality characteristics.

These case histories were then subjected to a form of statistical analysis—the evaluation scale method—which I developed in connection with other personality studies based on the use of case histories. In carrying out this analysis, a complete history is read and a numerical valuation is given to separate features. Thus, for example, childhood home background is evaluated in terms of: (1) very unfavorable home; (2) unfavorable home; (3) somewhat unfavorable home; or (4) favorable home conducive to security and stability. On this particular valuation we found that there was a tendency for those who had recovered from alcoholism to provide evidence of having come from a more unfavorable childhood home than either the continuing alcoholic or the nonalcoholic. This particular difference was unexpected, since we usually consider that the early home life is somehow responsible for much of later personality development.

In the evaluation of aggressiveness–submissiveness, it was found that there were no dependable differences between the three groups of individuals under study, although there was a tendency for the more submissive persons who were alcoholic to remain alcoholic; or, stated in the opposite way, the more aggressive of the alcoholics tended to recover. However, neither aggressive nor submissive action or feeling was an outstanding characteristic of either the alcoholic or nonalcoholic group.

With respect to the attitude toward authority over him, the nonalcoholic is least rebellious, the alcoholic somewhat more rebellious, and the recovered alcoholic has a tendency to be frequently rebellious. This is probably associated with the aggressiveness shown by the recovered group.

There were no significant differences between the religious attitudes of the three groups.

With respect to the work history, the alcoholic had the least interest in his vocation or job, the recovered had somewhat more interest and the nonalcoholic had the greatest interest as indicated by a successful career. This is as would be expected; inebriety certainly interferes with anyone's efficiency on any job.

Both the recovered and continuing alcoholics differed significantly from the nonalcoholics with respect to neurotic trends and neurotic episodes. The non-alcoholics gave evidence of being comparatively well adjusted, whereas both the continuing and recovered alcoholics gave many instances of maladjustment and of neurotic or psychotic episodes.

The alcoholics showed little evidence of any personal life goal or ambition, the recovered alcoholics had somewhat more ambition, while the nonalcoholics tended to set higher standards for themselves and to achieve these standards.

In the reports of Wittman, as well as of several other investigations, much has been made of the relationship between family ties, sex and marital adjust-ment, homoerotic trends, and alcoholism. We failed to find any significant dif-ferences between the frequency of homoerotic trends among our three groups. This is directly contrary to most present-day psychiatric opinion. There was, however, a significant difference between the personal sex adjustment of the alcoholics and of the nonalcoholics. The alcoholics tended to be poorly adjusted while the nonalcoholics represented themselves as well-adjusted. Among the married members of these groups, the nonalcoholics said that they were enjoy-ing a successful marriage while most of the continuing and recovered alcoholics were divorced or separated. No significant differences among the three groups were found with respect to the emotional ties to the parents.

In general, then, the evaluation of these three contrasted groups indicated only that the intemperate use of alcohol affected those life and social adjustments which depend upon sobriety. Personality differences did not seem to be related to any of the background factors which have been thought to be of a determin-ing nature.

CIMBAL's CLASSIFICATION

One of the most useful classifications of the types of personality of alcohol addicts is the one that was made by Cimbal. He carried out an intensive study of the biographical histories of several hundred alcoholics who were not psy-chotic.

He divided such alcoholics into four general groups. The first he called decadent drinkers. Such individuals occur in families in which there has been a gradual social, moral and physical deterioration extending over several genera-tions. These persons, he said, never really come to true adult emotional and in-tellectual maturation but use alcohol, drugs or a life of adventure to make up for their own essential degeneration.

The second group he called impassioned drinkers. These he regarded as diametrically opposed in temperament to the decadent drinkers. They are tense, emotionally unstable, and develop a craving for intoxication out of a need for temporary relief from the tension arising from their emotional conflicts.

The third group is made up of the stupid, spineless drinkers who succumb to practically any form of temptation. Here are the vagrants, criminals, those of low-grade intellect, and deteriorated persons from the lowest strata of society.

They become addicted to alcohol since all other forms of enjoyment involve at least some mental and cultural activity, whereas intoxication is an entirely passive form of enjoyment which they can cultivate without any exertion on their own part.

The last group he called self-aggrandizing drinkers. Such persons become addicted to alcohol in the process of building up their own weak will and weak personality. They crave power and authority but have not the energy or ability to really reach their ambitions and so resort to alcohol as a method of building up their own ego.

Cimbal's types are both theoretically and clinically useful. His descriptions are clear and the application of his classification to alcohol addicts has potentially much practical significance. It certainly lends itself to the formulation of research procedures directed at the more complete understanding of each of these particular varieties of personality.

PSYCHOANALYSIS OF ALCOHOLICS

Psychoanalysts have attempted to provide a deeper understanding of the true nature of the personality of the alcoholic. Unfortunately, their formulations suffer from two major defects: No analyst sees more than a very few true alcoholics, principally because most alcoholics decline to enter upon or to continue through a complete psychoanalysis. (Among 1,593 consultations over a period of 10 years, the Institute of Psychoanalysis in Chicago saw only 36 persons diagnosed as "Alcoholism" and "Drug Addiction"; and of these only 4 were analyzed.) Secondly, the few alcoholics who have been psychoanalyzed seem to have been of a very heterogeneous personality structure. Judging from the published reports, one can only say that if they had any one factor in common it was probably some form of neurosis which had been complicated by excessive drinking. The personality factors which the analysts have emphasized are the oral-sadistic tendencies, sexual frustration or impotence, repressed homosexuality, and self-destructive tendencies. Other than the factor of repressed homosexuality, all of these are only characterizations of more or less manifest and superficial traits. The fact that the individual uses his mouth in drinking, tends to be cruel or suicidal when drunk, and gets along poorly with members of the opposite sex, is obvious and manifest in many alcoholics. Usually, we may say that these personality symptoms are only a direct reflection of the influence of alcohol itself and of social or family disapproval.

The repressed homosexuality has been analytically described as follows: "The psychic reason for alcoholic addiction is the incomplete repressed homosexuality which the individual cannot sublimate." It will be remembered that the evaluations of the case histories of 54 alcoholics, which I discussed previously, indicated that homoerotism was not more evident than it was in the control group of 21 nonalcoholic persons. From other and completely independent evidence we now know that the occurrence of overt homosexuality is much more prevalent than was hitherto believed. These studies, as yet unpublished, indicate that from 20 to 35 per cent of all human beings have had overt homosexual experiences. If homoerotism is thus prevalent, then the fact that it has been found in certain of the alcohol addicts is not surprising. All other evidence indicates that homosexuality is an independent personality factor which is not necessarily associated with other forms of personality disorder, neurosis, psychosis or addiction.

PHYSIQUE AND PERSONALITY TRAITS

Recently, a comprehensive scheme of interrelation between physical constitution and personality has been presented by Sheldon. On the basis of anthropometric measurements he assigns numerical values to three components of the over-all body build of any human being. The first component he calls endomorphy. In extreme, this is an exaggeration of the portion of the body trunk occupied by the digestive viscera, with the remainder of the muscular and bony structure being relatively weak and undeveloped. Such persons are fat and soft. The second component, mesomorphy, shows a predominance of bone, muscle and connective tissue. Such individuals are of a hard, athletic body build. The third component, ectomorphy, is related to thinness, linearity, flatness of the chest and delicacy throughout the body. No one of the three components exists in isolation, but there are differing degrees of each component found in the body build of every individual.

Each of the three components has associated with it a personality or temperament constellation. The traits going with endomorphy, he called viscerotonic. The outstanding traits of the viscerotonic person are relaxation, love of comfort, pleasure in digestion, greed for affection, deep sleep, and need of people when troubled. Associated with mesomorphy is the somatotonic cluster of traits: assertive posture, energetic attitude, need of exercise, directness of manner, unrestrained voice and need of action when troubled. Associated with ectomorphy are the cerebrotonic traits: restrained posture, speedy reactions, inhibited social attitudes, resistance to routine or habits, restrained voice, youthful intentness and need of solitude when troubled.

The viscerotonic individual shows an accentuation of his usual personality traits when he takes a moderate quantity of alcohol. He becomes more relaxed, more social, shows more tolerance and good will, and is more expansive in his emotional warmth. For him, alcohol is a distinct source of pleasure in that it brings relaxation and accentuates those features of existence which he loves. Alcohol agrees with these individuals and they seldom become addicted to its use.

In the somatotonic personality a moderate quantity of alcohol also accentuates the principal personality traits. These persons become openly uninhibited, noisily aggressive, more expansive, and show a full sense of power. Their postures are more assertive; their energies seem unlimited. The weak crust of culturally imposed inhibition crumbles away and candor is complete. Above all, they love this condition. With the proper amount of the other personality components present, such persons become chronic alcoholics or alcohol addicts.

The cerebrotonic personality finds alcohol essentially unpleasant. It increases the sense of strain; brings on dizziness and increased fatigue. There is no euphoria, but nausea or sickness is likely to be produced. Whereas persons with a predominance of either the components of somatotonia or viscerotonia tend to show an exaggeration of their already present personality structure under alcohol, the cerebrotonic becomes fatigued and depressed, and hence dislikes and resists alcohol.

The predominantly viscerotonic individual seldom becomes drunk, and but rarely a drunkard. Only when there is a combination of cerebrotonic and viscerotonic elements, which leads to internal personality conflict, do these individuals show any evidence of deleterious alcohol effect. In the somatotonic personality the effect of alcohol usually selectively depresses both the cerebrotonic and the viscerotonic components, releasing all of the hidden springs of action and conflict so that these individuals may, and often do, become alcohol addicts of the unpleasant variety. The alcohol addict who struggles against and sometimes conquers his tendencies toward inebriety is said to be exhibiting evidence of a strong cerebrotonic element.

Sheldon's formulation is an interesting one, and one which merits further investigation. If it can be shown that through the anthropometric measurement of the body build and personality analysis in these terms one can predict, and to a certain extent diagnose and control, the course of alcoholism, then this particular system will be of practical value as well as of theoretical interest.

This discussion has, so far, dealt with the problem of the personality of the individual who is essentially an alcoholic—the true addict—one in which the picture is relatively uncomplicated by any other form of psychopathology. There is, of course, a really considerable number of alcoholics who are also neurotic or psychotic, that is, symptomatic alcoholics. Whether these symptomatic cases are truly neurotic or psychotic conditions which have been exaggerated by alcohol, or whether chronic alcoholism can, of itself, result in a psychotic state, is a debatable matter and one which is outside the province of this lecture.

HEREDITY AND ENVIRONMENT

I believe that it is more than theoretically possible to derive a better understanding of the real role of personality and of psychological factors in alcoholism. In order to do this we must reorient ourselves to a viewpoint which has hitherto not been assumed with respect to these particular problems. Let us consider this as a nature-and-nurture problem. Every human being comes into existence with a physical constitution determined by his heredity. This physical constitution develops and matures in a physical and social environment. The psychological manifestations of this constitution we term personality. Some features of the constitution and personality are relatively unaltered by environmental forces, while others are quite subject to change and modification. An intensive study of properly selected individuals would reveal which factors in constitution and personality are important in alcoholism, as well as those which are unimportant. We could determine the relative fixity or changeability of each factor, and so pass on to new and significant knowledge concerning the essential problems of alcoholism.

There are three ways in which one can study the role of nature as it is modified or resists modification during development and maturation: (1) We can study the pedigree—the family history—of any individual, if access can be had to information concerning as many as possible of his ancestors; (2) we can apply the contingency method of statistical prediction, in which we make measurements of both physical and mental traits in people who are related by blood and people who differ in degree of social or environmental association; and (3) we can make use of the twin-study method. For practical reasons which go too far afield for exposition at present, the twin-study method is most suitable for the solution of the problem thus formulated. The twin-study method is difficult, time-consuming and demanding, but, at the same time, it is the most precise of all the methods of investigating problems of this sort.

In the United States, identical twins occur in about three out of a thousand births, while nonidentical twins occur about nine times in a thousand births. Identical twins result from a division of a single fertilized ovum in a very early stage of development. Since all cells derived from the same fertilized ovum have identical genetic constitutions, the two individuals coming from this ovum have exactly the same heredity. Such twins are always of the same sex, are similar in appearance, have similar fingerprints, and many physical and mental similarities. Since they are of identical heredity, any difference which develops between them must be due to some difference in the effect of environment or in the differential rate of growth or maturation. Nonidentical twins are derived from two different ova fertilized at about the same time by two different spermatozoa. Genetically, they are no more alike than any other two siblings. The fact that they are conceived and born at the same time does not make their heredity similar, although their environment both before and after birth is, on the whole, much more alike than that of other brothers and sisters.

Identical twins with identical heredity, when reared apart, furnish crucial material for experimental purposes from which we can be certain to obtain clearcut, definite information. Under such circumstances we have two individuals with exactly the same heredity who are subjected to different environments, different nutrition, different training, different social attitudes, and the possibility of different habit formations. If, then, we compare the attitude toward alcohol or the addiction to alcohol as it may occur in such separated identical twins, we have practically certain answers to many of the questions which at present are open only to theoretical discussion.

Alcohol and Germ Plasm

Lest anyone may misunderstand me in this matter, let me state specifically that such a study does not concern itself with the possible effect of alcohol on the germ plasm. There is sufficient evidence at hand at present to indicate that the over-use of alcohol continued through many generations is of no genetic importance unless it is attended by other factors which are themselves deleterious but which are only chance associates of the alcoholism. For example, a drunkard may find that his only available marriage partner is a woman who is the carrier of some genetically determined psychopathological process, such as schizophrenia. The children of such a marriage are liable to develop a schizophrenic psychosis. This psychosis they derive from their mother, while the fact that their father was alcoholic has been shown to have nothing to do with their schizophrenia.

Now, let me summarize briefly certain points which I have been discussing. Psychologically speaking, alcoholics are of many kinds, the addict and the symptomatic drinker constituting the two major types. The addicts may be divided into those whose drinking is occupational, in that it depends on environmental circumstance and opportunity; and the essential addicts, those whose drinking is an obsession. It is these essential addicts whose personality structure I have been considering. The symptomatic drinker—the psychotic or neurotic—may become alcoholic because of either opportunity or craving. Most of the theories of the alcoholic personality are based on a minimum of factual evidence. Such evidence as does exist is seldom clear-cut or definitive. Hence, the theories are often contradictory. I have provided an experimental hypothesis which, although difficult and expensive to carry through, would provide a sound experimental and factual basis for the better understanding of the essential problems of alcoholism.

DISCUSSION

Chairman (*E. M. Jellinek*): To my knowledge, only one twin study has ever been made in connection with alcoholism, and that was in Germany. One of the twins was a chronic alcoholic; the other one was believed not to be an alcoholic. While nobody was ever found who said that the latter twin was a drinker, the investigator had great suspicions that he also was a drunkard. That's all that came out of that study. I do believe that the study of identical twins would be a great contribution. It is not easy to find identical twins who have been brought up in entirely different environmental conditions and of whom at least one is an alcoholic. But even a sample of 10 twins would be of great significance. In the absence of more twin studies, the foster-child study which Dr. Roe presented sheds some light on this question. She made a study of foster children coming originally from alcoholic parents or from psychotic parents and reared in foster homes. In the children who came from originally alcoholic parents and then were placed in foster homes, no alcoholism developed. As far as this sample goes, there is no evidence of the transmission of alcoholism as a genetic factor. This may be regarded as a first approximation to twin studies. If these identical-twin studies are difficult to carry out, it might be possible to deal with the question from the foster-child angle on a much larger scale than has been done in our present study.

Allen: Is not the common criticism of a domineering home revealing of a psychotic personality? Would not a maladjusted personality distort even a normal home environment?

Lecturer: The case studies which we have made on a great many different kinds of human beings indicate several points which are well brought out by this question. The maladjusted neurotic person tells you that he came from an unhappy childhood home. It may be that he says his mother neglected him, that he was an unwanted child, or that his father was domineering, and so forth. There is some evidence, not too much, but some, that he is telling the truth, as he sees it at any rate. But is it true that someone else would see it that way? That evidence is not complete or too convincing, especially for the neurotic, that is, the person who is normally having a hard time adjusting because of anxieties, guilt feelings, phobias, compulsions, and so on. It is not true with the psychotic. It is not true with the normal individual. The psychotic who faces the question of home background will ask: "Do you mean how I feel about it since I got sick or how I felt about it before I got sick?" The normal individual will say, "Sure I had a good home. Of course things were rough sometimes, but it didn't bother me. It's all right, I got along." Physicians dealing with neurotic patients who are also alcoholics come to the opinion that their patients come from bad home backgrounds. I am convinced that this is due to the fact that they are getting information from neurotic personalities and has little to do with alcoholism.

Watson: Please discuss the two types of alcoholics—introverts and extroverts—a little further.

Lecturer: In this game, for it is a game, of trying to typify human beings, every student of human nature has taken his little fling and set up his rules and tried to make classifications. Jung, the Swiss psychoanalyst, said that you could divide human beings into two kinds: those who essentially looked outward to the world, who were interested not in themselves but in the world about them, were the extroverts; and, in contrast, introverts were those who were interested in themselves and how the world acts on them. This particular idea of introversion and extroversion has had a good deal of attention and research during the past 25 years. It has been found that introversion, that is, interest in one's own self and how the world acts upon one as a dominating motive in life, goes with a type of mental disease which we call schizophrenia. The extrovert type goes with manic-depressive psychosis and other types of mental disease. Today we say that introversion and schizophrenia are associated, and extroversion and the cycloid or manic-depressive psychosis are associated. If you attempt to typify alcoholics, who are not psychotic, as to whether they are interested in the world about them or whether they are interested in how the world acts on them, you will find that the extroverts have a greater tendency both to become alcoholics and to get over their alcoholism. The introverts, on the other hand, do not tend to become alcoholics, but if they do, they are more likely to stay that way. This particular classification has a certain degree of usefulness in that it's easy to say, "he's an extrovert," or "he's an introvert." If he is an extrovert, then alcohol will act this way on him, and you can approach the problem in this way; or if he is an introvert, alcohol is going to have different effects and you approach the problem in a different way. It has that much practical value.

Gross: Are those types described by Sheldon used only for the study of alcoholics, or can they be used also for a broader study in diagnostics?

Lecturer: Sheldon's hypothesis is what you might call a "shot in the dark" based upon a good deal of clinical intuition. Sheldon, following Kretschmer, believed as Kretschmer did that there are three essential types of body build. The pyknic type— the soft, fat individual, the athletic type, and the asthenic; and that you can get any combination of these. Kretschmer had said much earlier that the pyknic type is associated with manic-depressive insanity, and in that group would be the occupational drinkers, and so on. The athletic type of build is associated with fixed, rigid ideas which may be right or may be wrong, but whatever they are, they are firmly held. The asthenic type of build (the cerebrotonic type of Sheldon) are those who, if they develop a psychosis, will be schizophrenics, and they are going to resist alcoholism as long as possible. I think that Sheldon's classification has a much broader application than the study of alcoholism, but if his concept is correct, it does offer a method of approach to certain very practical problems, including alcoholism. Sheldon points out that the Prohibition Amendment was put over by the cerebrotonics, and that the viscerotonics and the somatotonics tried to beat it. That's speculation, of course, but of interest. Actually, Sheldon's reference to alcoholics is wholly incidental; there is only a page or two in his whole book on alcoholism. He tried to make a more definite, more well-rounded and more tangible system than Kretschmer's.

Shattuck: Do we have clues that any type of personality, any given definite type of personality, can drink safely?

Lecturer: We have no proof either way. You can do this, of course: You can say that your teetotaler is one type of personality, and he's safe. And you can say that your chronic drunkard is another type of personality, and that he isn't safe. That is not the question as you posed it. There is no definite proof that any type of personality is either safe or particularly susceptible.

Haralson: Is there any scientific proof that Prohibition led more persons to try alcoholic beverages, or is such a statement merely a loose report?

Lecturer: The one bit of evidence is this: In New York State between 1910 and 1942 there are available the admission rates for alcoholic psychoses to both private and public mental hospitals. The rates for all patients coming in for alcoholic psychosis started falling from about 7 per 100,000 of general population in 1909, then rose back to about 6 in 1917, then dropped very sharply to about 2 per 100,000 in 1920, and by 1927 it was again up to about 7 and has remained in that range ever since. Prohibition came in, you remember, in 1918, and continued through 1932. If one further analyzes this curve to find out how it is made up, this is the result: So far as women are concerned, there are about 5 men to 1 woman admitted regularly for alcoholic psychosis to New York State hospitals. The curve is low, regardless of age. Prohibition did not make a particle of difference so far as women coming into the mental hospitals with alcoholic psychosis are concerned. So far as men between the ages of 20 and 40 are concerned, there was some decrease during Prohibition, but not much. Men between 40 and 60 are the people who contributed to this decrease. Prohibition had some effect on the group between 40 and 60. That's the only scientific evidence that I know.

Lang: It has been said that Prohibition caused a great increase in drinking among women. Would the statements in the graphs that you have just shown tend to deny that opinion?

Lecturer: What I have said is about individuals coming to public and private mental hospitals in the State of New York. Out of every 6 that come, 5 will be men and 1 will be a woman, and so far as the women are concerned, Prohibition made almost no difference in the number coming to private and public mental hospitals in the State of New York.

Lang: Also, it has been said that Prohibition led to a large increase of drinking among young people, and yet you say that those admitted between the ages of 20 and 40 remained practically the same. Is there any increase, or evidence of increase, of alcoholism among those under 20?

Lecturer: No. It takes some years to achieve an alcoholic psychosis. The patients do not come into the mental hospitals until they have been using alcohol to excess for some time.

Mrs. Colvin: Under certain circumstances, can a personality be changed from the introvert to the extrovert type, or the other way around?

Lecturer: Ordinarily, no, but in mental diseases, yes. You do find in certain mental diseases marked shifts, so that you would say, "I certainly don't recognize him as the same person, he's a different personality." You find that in a fair number of patients suffering from a mental disease. It is not supposed to be true among normal individuals. It might occur as a great exception.

Chairman: Would it occur without psychotherapy?

Lecturer: It's possible but I don't think it's very probable. I don't think that it would occur as a result of taking alcohol—it's possible, but not very probable.

Crawley: Lately there are many women who drink alcoholic beverages in varying degrees. Will Dr. Landis correlate and explain such types as apply to women?

Lecturer: They are no different in type than men, so far as I know. Everything I have said about men is also applicable to women, either in Sheldon's system or in Kretschmer's system, and supposedly there is no difference; they are just as hypothetical in one case as in the other.

Watson: Are introversion and extroversion hereditary qualities in the individual, or are they acquired during the process of developing? The question awhile ago gave me the impression that they are hereditary.

Lecturer: If I gave that impression, I shouldn't have done so. No one knows. These are hypothetical qualities, and whether a hypothetical quality can be inherited or not is a subject for a research program, but there is no evidence one way or the other. There is this that could be said: If you would identify introversion as a group of psychological traits with a tendency to schizophrenia, then you would have to say that there is a tendency for heredity of introversion. If you would identify extroversion similarly in relation to the manic-depressive psychosis, then you would say there is a tendency there.

Question: Would not the alcoholic type necessarily undergo a complete personality change after a protracted period of total abstinence?

Lecturer: Again, I don't want to generalize too far from the data. In the study which I reported, based on 75 individuals, of whom 29 were still alcoholics and 25 had been sober for a period of 2 years by their own volition (that is, they were not dry because they were in a jail or mental hospital), there was no evidence of personality change. One of the things we tried to get out of those histories was: "Why did they stay dry for those 2 years?" We had 25 different individuals and we had 25 different reasons. There was no change in the personality as evidenced by the case histories. It may be that the men and women who took the case histories did not ask the right questions, but there is just no evidence for it anyway.

Chairman: Let us distinguish between personality structure and personality management. Given the same personality structure, we can manage or mismanage. In psychotherapy or any type of rehabilitation there is a process of giving the person the tools for management of such assets as he has; the assets may not change at all. But he is given the possibility of managing instead of mismanaging his assets. This may create the impression of a personality change.

Lecturer: I like the distinction between personality structure and personality function. I interpreted this question essentially as personality structure. There is no evidence of a change in structure of personality; there is certainly evidence of a change in personality function, the way they handle themselves.

Bancroft: Doctor, I have a question which may not be interesting to everybody but it is to me. We have a couple of men in their late sixties—twins. We have arrested them somewhere between 50 and 100 times for intoxication and begging. They are not always together when they are arrested, but almost always they are arrested the same night, and usually for the same thing—different times, different places, but the same thing. Might their behavior be due to their having the same heredity?

Lecturer: You asked the question I was hoping someone would ask. I am very much interested in studies of twins. I am not carrying them out, but I am interested in the possible use of twin material to study those personality traits or human characteristics which are innate and those which are due to nutrition, those which are social factors, those which are due to the weather, and so forth. They may yield some extraordinary findings, things that ordinarily have been argued about and concerning which there is no evidence. It is possible in 5 years to get somewhere between 15 and 20 pairs of twins who have been reared apart, one of each pair being a drunkard. A study of such twins would give an answer to a lot of the problems you have been asking about, because then you could say, "Well, look, this fellow has been subjected to the following home influence, or he was starved at this time, or this happened, and then he became an alcoholic, whereas the other one did not; or they both did." You would get answers that are so clear-cut that you would quit arguing. You say the twins you mentioned get arrested on the same evening; you can match that sort of situation with a good deal of other material. But you cannot answer your question as to whether it is innate or whether it is because they have lived together. Because if they have lived together, they have been influenced by the same circumstances; if they have lived apart, then you would get a beautiful demonstration.

If these two individuals had been reared apart, let us say between the age of 1 and the age of 20, and later on in life they came together and both went "on a bender" every time on the same night, you would have to say, "Well, there is something innate in that, because during all of their formative years they were totally separated." If, on the other hand, you find that one was a solitary drinker and the other did not drink, then you would have to say, "Look, it was determined socially." You would get the answers.

Alcohol and Aggression

Ralph S. Banay

THE expression "Dutch courage" is a common colloquialism which denotes courage artificially achieved through intoxication. The use of this expression is evidence that it does not take the observation of a specialist to discover that alcoholic intoxication releases aggression. But while this observation is common, there does not go with it a realization of all its implications and involvements. To the layman, Dutch courage implies that a man may take a drink in order to become aggressive; but when the psychiatrist speaks of alcoholism as covering a need for the release of aggression the layman is inclined to regard this as absurdly technical.

To the layman it may appear that the psychiatrist, as well as the psychologist, is even inaccurate in his use of such words as love, hostility, anxiety, and aggression. What in everyday life may be designated as an expression of displeasure or disapproval may be referred to by the psychiatrist as manifestations of hostility or aggression. If in a debate among friends one raises his voice above the usual tone of conversation, the others present may say that he showed signs of annoyance. But look at it closely: He wants his opinion to prevail, and when logic does not accomplish his aim he tries to impose his will through the cowing effect that shouting may have. This imposition of the will is aggression; and the shouting, the means by which the will is to be imposed, is a means of aggression.

The Psychological Dictionary defines aggression as "That aspect of the will to power which involves treatment of other individuals as if they were simply objects to be used in the attainment of the superiority goal." And again, according to the Psychiatric Dictionary "Aggression signifies action carried out in a forceful way."

Thus it may not seem so strange if the psychiatrist speaks in terms of aggression of those unmistakably forceful ways of infants by which they compel us to do things for them. The reaction of the infant to its environment, the changes which these reactions undergo in form and meaning, are of relevance to the understanding of the reactions of alcoholics.

DEVELOPMENT OF PERSONALITY

It may be said that the first form of aggression is the birth cry. The infant begins life with an expression of aggression. Gradually the infant discovers a source of pleasure through the mouth, through nourishment and feeding. Gradually also he discovers himself as a different entity from his environment. He is trained to establish habits, and he responds to this training with love or hostility. During these experiences of personality organization the child develops action-reaction patterns which will be characteristic of him alone, and will be the result of his early experiences in the environment and of the reactions to these experiences. In order to maintain himself and preserve his entity he has to express himself forcefully. This so-called oral phase of conveying instinctive wishes and desires and displeasures occurs in a very early stage of existence. A simple experiment will show you that if the nursing bottle is withdrawn from the feeding infant he will react with aggression—a cry, muscular movements, facial expressions of displeasure—and with a forcefulness in accordance with the amount of gratification he has been denied. If the food is removed soon after the beginning of feeding the cries will be more immediate and more forceful. And in direct relation to the time elapsed and to the gratification, the cries will be delayed and less intense.

The principle of the relationship between frustration and aggression can be demonstrated even at such an early stage of childhood. Many students of behavior attribute all the manifestations of aggression to the extent and manner, grade and quality, of the frustrations that the individual experiences during a lifetime.

Soon the child is trained in habits and discovers the significance of elimination. In fact, in his primitive and restricted mind the first impression that he receives, from the coaxing of the members of the environment to please in this function, is that it is a very important one and that it is a gift to his environment. Through the functions of eating and elimination the infant may achieve power over the environment in both the oral phase and the anal phase; in the oral phase, by refusing food, by developing feeding reactions, feeding tantrums, feeding problems; and in the anal state, through retaining the food without elimination and thus holding power over the attention, the love, of his immediate environment. When these functions become greatly emphasized, they may develop into props of the infant.

The child is at a disadvantage in the earliest stage of his existence. In order to preserve himself, his unity, his identity, he has to express a forceful emotion. This forceful emotion, which is aggression, goes back to the fusion of two primary impulses, namely, the life instinct and the death instinct.

Death instinct may sound startling to many of you. The idea of a death instinct or impulse is hundreds of years older than psychoanalysis and has played a role in philosophical and religious systems. Thus the Nirvana of Buddhism involves recognition of the death impulse. But psychoanalysis has given this idea wider meaning and has developed from it further ideas. The Freudian assumption is that if life arose from inanimate matter there must have come about at the same time "an instinct to abolish life once more and to reestablish the inorganic state of things." According to Freud the organism tends toward restitution of its original state.

The aggression involved in self-destruction can be deflected toward the outside world, and this form of aggression is termed sadism. In the well-adjusted personality there is a fusion of the life and death instincts resulting in constructive behavior. And aggressive tendencies may be transformed into socially useful acts.

The child has to preserve himself against the hostile world, he has to respond with hostility. In fact, the first impression, the first recollection, of the child appears to be a distorted image of the parents themselves; a distorted fantasy-picture of the environment. This becomes an important feature of self-preservation. Due to fear or insecurity, the individual distorts and emhasizes the danger that he is facing and develops an inward reaction-pattern of defense. The anxieties remain on the semiconscious or unconscious level, but the reactions to anxiety, primary to safety and well-being, remain around the conscious level and become a sadistic form of self-expression.

Sadism is nothing but a deflected or transformed defense reaction against the destructive effects of the death instinct. This sadistic trend can be fixed to an object or to an individual, to the outside world or to oneself, and in accordance with the strength and the nature of the fixation, it may become purely aggressive sadism, or it may take the form of masochism and may become a wish for suicide.

IMMATURE ADULTS

How these trends can, in time, be affected by the toxic effect of alcohol will be seen if we follow a little further the development of the child from the oral–anal state to the genital state when, in the normal course of events, his primary pain-and-pleasure reactions will be centered around the genital zone. Through a changing quality of emotion, he will go through a short period of affixing his emotional interests to the members of the immediate environment, primarily to the parent who was most gratifying to him and, indirectly, to the other one, to whom he shows loyalty, admiration, hero worship and a general elevation of the physical being of the father or mother. This stage, if it is not dramatized by unduly severe experiences or exaggerated by a too-indulgent, too-solicitous parent, will pass into a state of adolescence, and, later, maturity.

When the full-grown genital emotion can be transferred from the first love object to another individual, one may speak of a satisfactory emotional adjustment to reality. Inasmuch as all manifestations of life are directed by three functions—the thought, the action, and the feeling tone—the intellectual development of the child can and does proceed without any great interference unless there is some organic handicap, disease or retardation.

The action is an impulsive force, a release of the inner tension and the co-ordination of all functions in the organism as a whole. But emotional tones will develop independently of the intellectual reactions. The emotional reactions might remain—one may say, get stuck—at any of the three phases, oral, anal or adolescent;—and when physical and intellectual maturity are concluded, these emotional reactions compel the individual to act in accordance with a pattern which he should have outgrown. Such emotional maladjustment might play an important part in the development of compulsive drinking or alcohol addiction. On the other hand, alcoholic intoxication may lead temporarily to such maladjustment. The individual may prefer the behavior pattern of childhood but cannot yield to it without endangering his status in the community. Under the influence of alcohol, however, it is possible for him to return to his early behavior pattern.

Mild alcoholic effect may manifest itself in vocal aggression. The drinker may raise his voice and become assertive—vocal assertiveness. If we walk in on an afternoon cocktail party, our first impression might be that everyone is speaking louder than the occasion demands.

A more marked phase of aggressiveness is the verbal phase. The aggressive trend is expressed not just in the tone quality of the voice but by the selection of words with the definite aim to hurt others, to superimpose and aggrandize oneself at the expense of others. In this state of intoxication the defense mechanism of the ego is inoperative and the individual will be seen as a child. This is a rather common form of behavior in alcoholics. They show a strong trend toward showing off and this trend may sometimes manifest itself in sexual exhibitionism such as the child shows at the age of 2 or 3 years when he takes pride in exhibiting his genitals. The other characteristic sexual aggression of the alcoholic is peeping—again the innate curiosity of the child. These two sexual acts rank high among sex offenses committed by inebriates.

In the psychopathology of aggression one can recognize two distinct elements: One is hostility, and the second is the lessened anticipation of punishment. This is not restricted to the alcoholic make-up alone. It is part of the total psychopathological armament of crime to have a lessened anticipation of punishment, unless the punishment itself is welcome. The sadistic trend of the individual might turn against himself and develop into a masochistic trend which seeks real or symbolic punishment. Such a person may try to get the love or pity of his early love object through committing acts for which he expects punishment or through inflicting punishment on himself. This masochistic state, quite well known in alcoholic neurosis, may be fatal to the individual in the long run. It disintegrates his personality, it destroys his status in the community, it endangers his physical health, and may eventually lead to his determination to die by his own hand or, symbolically, through his habit. But you will find that the masochistic alcoholic who turns his aggression against himself will show, in the interval of abstinence, a tremendous narcissistic trend, that is, a tremendous aggrandizement of his ego which corresponds exactly to the emotional age of the phase when the oral tendencies, or the oral sadistic tendencies, were developed. In fact, due to this inflated ego, the alcoholic is much more likely to be bruised, to become even more sensitive. He seeks these unfavorable impacts with reality because, in turn, his masochistic cravings are then justified. Of course, not all alcoholics belong to the masochistic type. Nothing is more dangerous than to attempt to reduce alcohol addiction to some specific cause; there are always many causes.

The counterpart of masochism, open and undeflected sadism, is just as hopeless, and in those cases the alcoholic becomes a menace, to the environment, to the family, to the community. The sadistic type of the alcoholic neurotic may become a criminal offender in certain circumstances. In the state of intoxication the anticipation of punishment is minimized or there seems to be less danger in taking a chance. Judgment is impaired, the ego is inflated and the intoxicated individual may yield to the urge of instinct which he was able to control when he was not under the influence of alcohol. He may commit violent acts, sexual offenses, or violent crimes.

INEBRIETY AND CRIME

But the role of alcohol in crime has been, nevertheless, overestimated. It has been frequently asserted on the basis of "statistics" that 60 per cent of all criminal offenses are due directly or indirectly to alcoholic intoxication. It is quite difficult to evaluate these statistics because they are usually based on the information given by the patient or the offender. There is no objective evidence of the truthfulness of such information. It is the everyday experience of those connected with law-enforcement agencies that the individual will either overemphasize or under-emphasize his alcoholic habits. Those who minimize their drinking are usually the men arrested for drunkenness but for no other crime. The criminal, however, will say that he was under the influence of alcohol, and exaggerate because he expects leniency on this ground; or he may have imbibed deliberately in order to have an excuse for a carefully contemplated crime. On occasions, drinking might heighten his courage by removing the inhibitions, by impairing his judgment, but in reality the genesis of the crime anteceded the alcoholic indulgence or the alcohol addiction. Most of the statistics which have been presented in the past were based on statements by those arrested for crime. Consequently, one cannot give full credit to these statistics, nor to the conclusion that alcoholism is responsible for the majority of crimes.

An investigation was undertaken of 3,135 offenders committed to Sing Sing Prison in the 2-year period 1938 to 1940. The prisoners were classified as inebriates and noninebriates. The classification "inebriate" was based on statements by impartial observers, or admissions to a general hospital for an alcoholic disease, or admission to a state hospital for an alcoholic mental disorder. Of 3,135 prisoners, 697, or 22 per cent, were found to be inebriates. In the first year of the period the proportion of inebriates was around 24 per cent, and in the second year around 21 per cent. Allowing for random variations, one may say roughly that in a prison population such as that of Sing Sing, the incidence of inebriety would be around 25 per cent. On the basis of proper standards one thus arrives at a much lower estimate of the contribution of inebriety to crime than the usual estimate of 60 per cent based on the indiscriminate use of data.

In the accompanying table the incidence of various types of crimes is shown for the inebriate group of prisoners and the control group, the latter being composed of prisoners who were abstainers and moderate drinkers.

A word of caution is called for here. In discussing this table I am speaking of inebriate *prisoners* specifically, but not of inebriates in general. If I say that 21 per cent of the inebriate prisoners committed burglary, that should not be interpreted as meaning that 21 per cent of inebriates commit burglary. I emphasize this because I know how easily these statements become—quite unintentionally—distorted.

The leading offense of the inebriate criminals was assault, while in the control group this crime took only fifth place. Nevertheless the difference between the two groups in relation to the percentage incidence of assault was not so great that one can speak of it as the characteristic alcoholic crime. All one can say is that among inebriate offenders there is a greater tendency toward such a juvenile reaction as assault than among noninebriate offenders.

Of the acquisitive crimes, burglary was more common among the inebriate prisoners and grand larceny was more common among the noninebriate ones. Again the difference is indicative of broad tendencies rather than of essential characteristics. But the difference is in agreement with traits on both sides. Grand larceny requires considerable perseverance in purpose and a fair degree of integration of observations and coordination of actions. Since intoxication impairs the process of integration and interferes with sustained effort, one would expect such a complex crime as grand larceny to occur less frequently among alcoholic criminals.

As to the burglaries committed by the inebriate offenders, it is significant that frequently there was no desire to acquire anything valuable, or even anything outside the offender's means to acquire normally; burglary seems rather to have been a means for demonstrating cleverness in outwitting the proprietor or the law-enforcement agency. I remember one alcoholic who had been arrested 14 or 15 times for drunkenness. After a night of heavy drinking he kicked in a store window and took away a can of spinach as a demonstration of his prowess. He was sentenced on a charge of burglary and received a high-crime rating. But psychologically one cannot classify this type of offender as an acquisitive offender. You will find that many of these alcoholic crimes are only technically represented in the Sing Sing study, 24 per cent were committed by inebriates and 76 per cent by noninebriates. There is here some indication of the possible contribution of alcoholism to homicide. I say, "some indication," because it cannot be assumed that all of the homicides committed by inebriates would not have been committed if they had not been inebriates.

In the public mind, sex crimes have always been associated with habitual inebriety and with acute intoxication. This type of crime has always been regarded as the most characteristic alcoholic offense. Of the 697 inebriate prisoners in our study 53, that is, 7.5 per cent, were committed because of sex crimes and of the 2,438 noninebriate prisoners 122, that is, 5 per cent. This difference would appear to be small, but it is statistically significant: it is not a chance difference. It is indicative of a greater tendency toward this type of offense among inebriate criminals rather than of an "alcoholic characteristic." In both prisoner groups the incidence of sex crimes was low; as a matter of fact, in both groups it was of the lowest rank order. Taking both groups together there were 175 sex crimes and of these 30 per cent were committed by inebriate prisoners and 70 per cent by noninebriate prisoners. No doubt the inebriates contribute relatively more to this crime category than to crime in general. But so many factors play a role in sex crimes that it cannot be called characteristic of alcoholism. At the Bellevue Hospital in New York City a study was made of 100 sex offenders and it was found that 52 showed no psychological deviation other than the sex crime, 15 had nonalcoholic mental disorders, 7 were mental defectives, 6 had an alcoholic psychosis, and 20 were alcohol addicts.

It is common experience that criminal inebriates are more often arrested for exhibitionism than for rape, while in noninebriate criminals the reverse is true. Exhibitionism is an infantile tendency and its occurrence among inebriates is in keeping with the general picture of the immature reaction pattern of the alcoholic.

Inebriety, through its release of aggression, is undoubtedly a contributing factor to crime, but if we take into consideration the nature of the "burglaries" committed by alcoholics, the fact that assault is the leading crime among inebriate prisoners and that these assaults are more of the nature of a brawl, and, furthermore, that exhibitionism is more prevalent than rape among the sex crimes of the inebriate prisoners, it would appear that the contribution of alcoholism is greater in the minor than in the major crimes.

ALCOHOL AND SUICIDE

I have dwelt at some length on the criminal aggression in alcoholism and I should like to conclude with a brief mention of alcoholic aggression turned toward the inebriate individual himself. The severest form of this is suicide. The statistics on reasons for suicide are generally poor. There are no means by which we can now ascertain whether or not suicide is more common among inebriates than among noninebriates, but there are some statistics which throw interesting side lights on the question.

It has often been said, most prominently by Dr. Karl A. Menninger, that alcoholism is a substitute for suicide. If it is a substitute we should not expect suicide to occur more frequently among inebriates. Even in the absence of definitive statistics, based on personality studies and life histories of alcoholics, it may be stated that the suicide candidate and the alcoholic have much in common, and that when alcoholic intoxication fails to give relief the drinker may turn to actual suicide.

One of the best statistical studies on reasons for suicide was made in 1903 on the basis of 29,000 newspaper items dealing with suicides. From this it would appear that inebriety figured in at least 5 per cent of all suicides. It cannot be ascertained, although it may be surmised, that inebriety may also have played a role when "domestic trouble," "despondency" and "insanity" were given as reasons for suicide.

Whether or not compulsive drinking is an unconscious attempt at self-destruction there is much clinical evidence that the aggression released in alcoholic intoxication often turns against the self, at least in the form of severe self-recrimination.

DISCUSSION

Chairman (E. M. Jellinek): Some of you have been impatiently waiting for a psychoanalytically oriented lecture. It was evident that the case workers were gratified by having their wish fulfilled by Dr. Banay. It was just as evident that others, I should say the majority, felt uneasy about this exposition of the subject.

If nothing else, the language of psychoanalysis is a stumbling stone for the uninitiated. The ideas of psychoanalysis could be expressed, no doubt, in quite familiar terms, because many of the ideas are not entirely unfamiliar to you if you begin analyzing psychoanalysis. The reaction of the uninitiated to the explanation of a psychoanalytic idea and its corresponding term always reminds me of the man who was asked this riddle: "What is this? It grows on a tree, it's small, round, red and sweet, and there's a stone in it and it sings like a canary bird." The man said, "If you hadn't said that it sings like a canary bird, I would have said that it is a cherry." "It is a cherry." "Well, then why did you say that it sings like a canary bird?" "Oh, I added that in order to make it harder to guess." There is something of this element in the whole psychoanalytic terminology which, however, has its justification quite apart from the economy of its shorthand.

Furthermore, many of the ideas which are now spoken of as psychoanalytic theories have been expressed naïvely long before the existence of psychoanalysis. Mothers have always maintained that habits acquired in infancy might play a role in the development of the personality, and they have made conclusions from feeding reactions and toilet habits as to the future characters of their children. They have even recognized the significance of oral gratification. According to an English folk saying children who, for a long time, maintain the habit of putting their hands in their mouths will become drunkards. This is quite in agreement with some psychoanalytic views, namely, that compulsive drinking represents a fixation at the oral level.

In everyday life we make many telling observations but we fail to see the implications, or consciously or unconsciously refuse to see them. The observations of psychoanalysis do not differ in content from the ordinary observations, but the analyst recognizes the implications and develops them into their ultimate consequences. He forms these observations in their full import into a self-contained, well-rounded system. In the course of this, he broadens the connotations of many familiar words. Because these widened connotations imply the consequences of the observations our antagonism is often aroused by psychoanalytic terminology.

I should like to add a comment on Dr. Banay's statistics. The Sing Sing study, in my opinion, is the first truly relevant investigation of the role of alcohol in crime causation. If, in this study, inebriates are mentioned, inebriates are meant. The classifications are based on good criteria. On the basis of such relevant statistics it appears that inebriates may form 25 per cent of the prison population. This is a great reduction from the old estimates of 60 per cent, but this need not disturb those who use crime statistics as an argument against inebriety. After all, 25 per cent is quite a disturbing percentage and a powerful argument in favor of sobriety. A well-established rate of 25 per cent seems to me a much more valuable datum than a 60-per-cent rate whose validity vanishes on serious questioning.

Stoneburner: The City Welfare Director of Dayton, Ohio, made the statement that 78 per cent of all the people who were committed to the city workhouse were there for alcoholic reasons. How can this be reconciled with Dr. Banay's figures?

Lecturer: There is no conflict between these two sets of figures. The institution where I made my studies was a prison for felons. That is different in nature from the jail which you mention. It is rather plausible that the population of a jail or workhouse might show 78 per cent of alcoholics, but they are not criminals. Many of them were arrested on minor charges of drunkenness or disturbing the peace.

Chaney: Would you conclude from your findings that our educational system shows a marked deficiency during the early childhood period?

Lecturer: The dream of any psychologist or psychoanalyst would be to extend the educational processes to the time when the individual is very young. One should go even farther; instruction should begin with the parents who, in turn, could apply the fundamental information.

Helmintoller: In your opinion, does alcohol have any serious effect on the aggressive characteristics of the moderate drinker?

Lecturer: In general, the moderate drinker with a well-balanced and healthy personality would not show a detrimental effect.

Chairman: There are many different forms of aggression. There is vocal aggression, verbal aggression, and physical aggression. Within each of these forms there are also many degrees of intensity. Physical aggression may vary from a slight tap on the shoulder to murder. Verbal aggression may vary from charmingly sarcastic remarks to vile name-calling. A person who has to suppress and repress a lot of aggression, who has to be polite to persons to whom he would rather like to give a piece of his mind, accumulates quite a bit of aggression. If he has a little alcohol, let us say a glass or two of sherry, he might make that charmingly sarcastic remark. This mild form of aggression may result from a small amount of alcohol and, incidentally, might give him quite a bit of relief.

Watson: In the child's early development, is he conscious of these aggressive traits, or are they essentially involuntary? If so, at what age would you say the child begins to assert himself consciously?

Lecturer: I hope you are not Watson, the behaviorist! The general concept is that for the first 6 months the infant does not distinguish himself from his environment. Slowly the baby discovers his hands and feet and plays with them. But the child becomes a bit more integrated intellectually at around 12 or 13 months. Then he is able to recognize the environment and responds to stimuli in a more integrated manner. Not until the end of the twelfth month is the cortical development completed. A fully human reaction to the environment is not possible before the development of the nervous system is completed.

Hunter: Are there any statistics on crimes committed by moderate drinkers while under the influence of alcohol?

Lecturer: There is no general statistical study that I know of.

Chairman: There are people who make statistics of the occasional use of small amounts of alcoholic beverages by criminals and conclude that even moderation leads to crime. We could just as well make statistics on the incidence of ingrown toenails in criminals. We would find that there is a fairly high incidence. Would we conclude that ingrown toenails cause crime?

Brown: Is sadism hereditary? Is a large percentage of sadists likely to become alcoholics?

Lecturer: Sadism is a reaction pattern; a developmental condition. It is not a physical state which can be handed down from one generation to the next.

The interpretation of the sadistic trend is that everyone goes through sadistic phases but the sadism is deflected to the outside world; it is sublimated in accordance with cultural patterns.

Hertzfeldt: Is it a fact that many alcoholics actually fear success, from an individual and social point of view, more than frustration? If so, why?

Lecturer: If an alcoholic belonged to the masochistic type and if he identified himself with one of his parents, particularly a very successful parent, success might evoke guilt feelings and, in that case, he might shun success.

The Functions of Alcohol in Primitive Societies

Donald Horton

SINCE the middle of the nineteenth century anthropologists have been collecting observations on the life and customs of the hundreds of primitive societies now existing in the world or known to have existed recently. A majority of these societies had native alcoholic beverages before their contact with Europeans. Those of the minority who, for one reason or another, had never invented for themselves, or had never borrowed from their neighbors, the techniques of winemaking or of brewing were very much in the market for alcoholic beverages when Europeans made them available. They became eager customers of the traders except where governments intervened and controlled or prohibited the liquor traffic.

Viewed historically, the use of alcoholic beverages is a very ancient custom. We know, judging from the present distribution of brewed beverages, that the brewing of beer was probably discovered almost simultaneously with the discovery of agriculture itself, and it seems to have spread wherever the art of agriculture spread subsequently in the world. We may presume that the use of natural fermentation to produce wine is even more primitive and ancient. Of course, the origin of this technique is lost in the prehistoric period, but the chances are that it could have been an independent invention, that it could have occurred simultaneously in different parts of the world because the process itself is so simple. It seems likely that all that would be required of a primitive people to discover this property of fruits would be suitable containers, pottery perhaps; or, even antedating pottery, the bark container which would have been sufficiently substantial to contain a fruit mash and, eventually, wine. We know, as a matter of fact, that at the time of their discovery by Europeans, a number of small primitive tribes in scattered parts of the world, who apparently had never been in contact with people who had the techniques of winemaking and brewing, did have primitive simple wines made from tree sap or berry juice. In any event, we may presume that fermentation came before brewing, and that brewing itself is a very ancient culture trait, probably going back to the very origins of agriculture. Distillation we know to be a relatively recent invention, probably not antedating the Christian era by very many years, and it is generally thought, on the basis of present evidence, that the art of distilling was developed somewhere in India and from there spread throughout the oriental world and thus to the West.

At the time of first European contact with primitive peoples there were a number of areas, however, in which alcoholic beverages were lacking. Among the very simplest hunting peoples and seed gatherers the use of alcoholic beverages had apparently not yet been discovered. The Australian bushmen had none; the peoples of Siberia, in fact, of the whole Polar region, Northern Siberia, and, of course, the Eskimos, had no alcohol. Throughout northern and western North America and the southernmost part of South America the hunting people had not yet obtained, invented or borrowed the techniques for producing alcoholic beverages. But these people were very eager to use alcohol when they had the opportunity; so that we can assume that their failure to utilize it was a matter of their not having made the invention or not having come in contact with people who had it. The American Indians, particularly, were very enthusiastic over the use of alcoholic beverages, thus creating a considerable problem during the frontier period. I should mention, however, that there is one other area where alcoholic beverages were not used, namely, the island area of the Pacific—specifically Polynesia and Melanesia. Polynesia is the area which includes Hawaii and Samoa, and Melanesia includes the Solomon Islands. In these areas alcoholic beverages were not used, presumably because, due to the isolation of their position, the inhabitants had neither invented the technique of brewing nor received it from the mainland of Asia.

If we review the kinds of beverages now used, or formerly used by the primitive people of the world, we find that the variety is amazing. Among the horticultural and agricultural folk, whether they did gardening or large-scale farming, whether they worked with a hoe or used draft animals and plows, alcoholic beverages were nearly universal. A very great number of natural materials were used in their fermentations and brews—berries, fruits, honey, plant saps of various kinds (especially the sap of the palm tree in its many varieties), juice of the sugarcane, cow's milk and, in central Asia, mare's milk. It has been reported, too, that cow's milk had been used in Europe. Practically every natural source of sugar has been used to produce some kind of a fermented beverage. There is a tremendous variety of sources of starch for the brewing of beer—a great variety of tubers and cereals. Among the tubers a noteworthy one is the manioc of South America. Manioc beer is almost a universal drink in the jungle region of South America.

Maize, or Indian corn, produced the main beer of the American Indians in North, South and Central America; rice, millet and barley were used especially in Asia and its outlying districts.

Of course, distilled spirits are available to a great many people, mainly in the Asiatic area. These are distilled from rice, beer, sugarcane juice and so forth.

In the face of this world-wide distribution of alcoholic beverages, and their great variety and antiquity, what can we learn from primitive peoples that will be useful to us? Let me say frankly that a new recital of strange and mysterious primitive customs is of no great interest to me, and my guess is that you, too, would be dissatisfied with a lecture which concentrated on such curiosities. We are looking for information and ideas which will be useful to us in the solution of our own problems. The existence of this summer school, and your attendance here, are due to a recognition of the fact that the use of alcohol in our own society presents us with some profound and serious problems.

SURVIVAL OF CUSTOMS

Even the brief review of the antiquity and distribution of alcoholic beverages which we have just made suggests at least one important generalization, namely, that the antiquity of the use of alcohol, and its nearly universal occurrence as an item of human behavior, tell us that this custom is a very strong one as measured by its power to survive in the face of competing customs. This surmise or generalization is based on the anthropological doctrine, which is, after all, very easily confirmed by common sense, that a custom, a traditional way of thinking and acting, does not survive and spread from its point of origin unless it gives men some satisfaction, unless it solves some human problem. Think back over the long history of the use of alcoholic beverages. Then compare the changes that have occurred during the same period in other aspects of culture, other aspects of primitive customs; the ease with which many forms of behavior which seemed to be an essential part of primitive life have changed and disappeared under the impacts of higher civilization. That should give you an idea of what I mean when I say that alcohol appears to be a strong and successful custom in the face of competition with other customs. Think of how men, faced with the problem of obtaining game, invented the bow and arrow and various kinds of traps. Give them an opportunity to trade the bow and arrow for a firearm, or their native log-trap for a steel trap, and the native inventions disappear.

The primitive man, at the time of the invention of alcoholic beverages, undoubtedly carried his burdens on his back or on a rough sledge dragged along the ground. Somewhere along the way these customs disappeared and were replaced by others that fitted his needs in a more successful way. The beast of burden, the wheelcart, took the place of the old modes of transportation. But the use of alcoholic beverages has continued and spread, and every year penetrates into areas where it did not exist before.

Not only has this custom been successful in terms of sheer survival, but it has been successful in the face of very severe opposition. We know, for instance, that a good many of the higher civilizations of the past have fought against alcoholic beverages and tried to control and prohibit them. We know that in China at various times, in India, in Mesopotamia, and among the Incas and the Aztecs—the high civilizations of the Americas—attempts were made either to prohibit alcoholic beverages entirely or to control their use, and these attempts invariably failed. In other words, the use of alcoholic beverages as a custom prevailed in the face of definite, organized, and consciously directed opposition. At one period the Hindus went probably further than any others in attempting to make the manufacture, transportation, sale, barter or use of alcoholic beverages a capital offense. But this severe law apparently had as little success in stopping the development or continuation of this custom as any of the others. We have to conclude from this, then, that some important human value is involved here that makes alcohol hard to abolish. This observation, in turn, leads to another generalization, namely, that despite this value, the use of alcoholic beverages is frequently regarded as a dangerous custom, and attempts are made to control or abolish it.

RESTRICTION OF CUSTOMS

Sometimes the controls or the restraints are of a relatively limited sort. For instance, in a great many primitive societies men are permitted to drink as much as they choose, but women are severely restricted as to the amount they may drink. In a few instances, women are prohibited entirely from drinking the alcoholic beverage even though they may be the ones who make it in the course of their preparation of food. In some societies, permission to drink is only obtained after one has reached the age of maturity, however maturity may be defined.

There are also many kinds of limitations with regard to the proper time or the proper circumstances under which one can drink. These limiting conditions do not go nearly so far as the attempt at prohibition in higher civilizations. But it seems quite clear, even from these examples, that there is definitely an ambivalent attitude, an attitude which is contradictory, an attitude which, on the one hand, approves drinking and permits it to exist and has given it a long life, as the life of a custom goes; and, on the other hand, an attitude of some anxiety, of fear, of suspicion which leads to attempts to restrict the use of alcohol in various ways.

Two Aspects of the Use of Alcohol

These two generalizations suggest that one way that might be useful to us in approaching primitive drinking customs would be to try to get further information on these two aspects of the use of alcohol. First, its value to mankind which has enabled it to persist against serious opposition; and second, the nature of those dangers inherent in its use which have led to opposition. As a matter of fact, this would be a very sensible kind of request to put to anthropology. Many of the primitive societies studied by the anthropologist are so small and so simply organized that they show us, in almost microscopic form, some of the social and psychological interrelations of different aspects of human life. These are aspects which in our own complex civilization are so overlaid with elaborations and details that most of us have trouble comprehending even some of the major ones. This complexity in our own society, in our own culture, has led us inevitably to specialization in scholarship and research, even to a specialization in understanding. One scholar is an economist. We leave it to him to understand those aspects of our civilization concerned with the production and distribution of goods. Another is a legal specialist. His job is to understand the rules and institutions through which we control our social and economic systems. Another is a psychologist. He is concerned with child welfare and development. Another is a sociologist. He may become the authority on the cause and treatment of crime, juvenile delinquency and marriage problems. Few of us can be authorities in several of these fields simultaneously, and even our experts have trouble in pooling their separate stores of information. Consequently, it is difficult for us to see a social problem in its full relationship to our way of life. We tend to approach any problem from the viewpoint of our special knowledge, and perhaps never do succeed in assessing all of its social, economic, psychological and historical aspects. The need for what one might call a many-angled view of things is, in fact, emphasized by this summer school in its curriculum. You are trying to understand the alcohol problem in its full complexity, starting with physiology and leading right through to economics, law and psychiatry. An anthropological approach which attempts to see in the simple society, in the life habits of simple people like the Indians or the Africans, some of the general patterns of human social behavior, fits in very well with your present approach to the problems of alcohol.

If you ask a native, a member of a primitive or semi-primitive society, why he values alcohol, he will probably say it is because his ancestors found it good, or because the gods gave it to his people; or he might say that the gods gave it to his people and it is also a very good food. He might add that it is good for his health, that it makes people fat and jolly, and that he values it because, when he comes home from a hard day's work in the forest or field, he enjoys his drink. But you would be surprised to find that the majority of them say, "Because it's wonderful to get drunk!"

In point of fact, among primitive peoples and those not so primitive, few drink in moderation as we understand it. Few primitive people drink as moderately as do most Americans. While the individual inebriate is conspicuous by his absence from most primitive communities, the whole community, or at least all of the men, will customarily drink to a degree that we consider to be excessive. Observations on the drinking behavior of primitive peoples have shown that whether the primitive man says that drinking is valued by him because his fathers honored it, or whether he says it is because he likes to get drunk, the fact remains that most of them apparently do drink in order to reach intoxication, for many of them celebrate the glories and happiness of intoxication in song and elegy, as well as in the kind of statement they make to ethnographers.

We know that many native beverages do have a food value, and this is concordant with the statements of many that their alcoholic beverage is a food, and a valued food. Take, for instance, the fermented mare's milk of Central Asia. It certainly has a very considerable food value. So do the beers, which frequently are not strained and are therefore rather thick liquids with a good bit of the original grain in them. We know, then, that the statement that the native beverage does have a food value has some truth in it. We can understand very well its being valued for that reason. We also know that alcohol alleviates the discomforts of fatigue.

A characteristic of most drinking among non-Europeans is that the drinking goes far beyond the requirements for food, or the reduction of fatigue. We note, for instance, that there are communities in which it is customary, whenever there is enough of the native beverage accumulated, to have a beer-drink which may last for several days, in which the men quickly drink themselves into a state of intoxication which they maintain until they go into a stupor. Whenever they wake up, they drink some more and go into another stupor. There are many places in South America where these drinking feasts will last for a week or more. Then there may be a long period of abstinence while new batches are being prepared. Or it may be, among some who are dependent on European liquor, that they can only indulge themselves when the trader comes on his infrequent visits. Then they get as much as they can and drink every drop of it, after which it may be a month or two before they have another drink. But it is quite characteristic that excessive drinking—excessive by our standard—is the normal practice.

ALCOHOL FOR RELIEF OF ANXIETY

This would seem to imply that the appeal to tradition, the religious validation, the food value, are, in a sense, rationalizations. They may have some subsidiary function, but there is something more important than that. Intoxication is the thing. In the state of intoxication, and in what it means to men, apparently lies the answer to the positive value of alcohol. By positive value I mean that this is the thing for which the alcoholic beverage is treasured, honored, preserved as a custom through the ages. The best possible explanation that I can offer you, based on a review of the use of alcohol in a good many primitive societies, is that the value is primarily in its anxiety-reducing function. This is apparently the only explanation which will serve as a key that has universal validity, with which you can begin to understand the use of alcoholic beverages, the customs surrounding their use, the attitudes that people have toward them in any society anywhere in the world, whether it is a highly sophisticated and civilized society or a very simple society of hunters and gatherers of seeds and berries.

We do not have to seek very far for a justification of this hypothesis. As you already know from previous lectures, alcohol is an effective sedative. Among its sedative effects is that of reducing the activity of those physiological mechanisms that produce anxiety. Anxiety, or fear, a state of tension, is a painful condition. Any man who is anxious, who is in a state of anxiety, is actually faced with a problem. In anthropology we frequently find that it is very useful to try to analyze a custom in terms of problems and the solution of problems. If we say to ourselves, "Now, to what problem could this custom be a solution?—how could it be solving a difficulty?—how could it be resolving some kind of conflict for the primitive society in which we find it?"—then we begin to get further insight into the meaning of the custom which, on the surface, might be quite mysterious to us. I suggest that when you have a state of anxiety existing in any individual, or in all the members of the population, you have a problem, an unresolved situation, a tension, which seeks to be reduced. You have a need which has to be met, even though at times it may be unconscious—the people who have this state of tension may not be aware of it. We know that anxiety is a universal phenomenon because it is a very simple thing in its functions. It is merely the anticipation of danger, as when a man has experienced pain or has been exposed to a danger. Thereafter, whenever he comes into the presence of the same danger, whenever it is suggested to him, he will have a slight rise in tension, he will have this anxiety, which warns him that the danger is close and prepares him to evade or avoid or counteract it in some way.

Human life is full of dangers of all kinds. Among primitive peoples there is the danger of external enemies, the enemies who surround the tribe. Remember that in many societies, especially prior to the coming of the European government, when one man kills another it is incumbent on the family, the father, brothers and near relatives of the murdered man, to exact vengeance, to kill the killer. Sometimes these feuds would become automatic and reciprocal, so that once a feud started it would never end, because when the killer was killed his family would, in turn, avenge his death, and so on. In many societies there is a constant state of tension due to the operation of this mechanism, because all people are potential enemies to everyone except close kinsmen.

This method of law and order involves a certain anxiety toward everybody, because it means that each individual is a potential victim of somebody else's crime, the potential victim of the thing that his brother or father does, and so on. Of course, there were peculiar customs which were not universal by any means. Thus, in many societies in many places in the world, head-hunting was a custom. That meant that if there was a tribe of head-hunters, then all other tribes in the surrounding region had to be constantly on guard against the raids of these head-hunters, and there was constant anxiety in that respect. These are not universal things, but much more universal is the fact that being a primitive man, a member of a society on a very primitive level, means being subject to instability of food supply, to famine, and to the dangers of an undeveloped productive technique. The primitive man is always very close to the margin of existence. There is never a very great supply of food ahead. He is rather helpless in the face of such dangers as, say, a grasshopper plague which may eat the garden crop, insects of various kinds, floods and droughts. There is no secure water supply, there are only limited facilities for meeting a drought. The primitive man is helpless in the face of unpredictable seasonal variations in the yield of his crops; or, if he is a hunter, he is faced with the danger that wild life may suddenly disappear, the game animals on which he depends may be decimated by one of the mysterious epidemic diseases that sweep among game animals. Then there are the mysterious migrations of animals that very frequently cause great distress to hunting peoples—migrations that for generations move back and forth each year on a set course and then suddenly desert that route for no apparent reason and follow a new one, hundreds of miles away, leaving the people who had been dependent upon them for a food supply stranded.

Then, consider the constant danger of sickness and epidemics to all people who do not have our medical science. Now, there is a special danger to primitive peoples which has to be mentioned in this regard, and that is the danger of contact with us. Almost universally, contact between native peoples and Europeans —Americans or other Europeans—has been an experience which, in some way or other, destroyed, damaged or harmed their own way of life, sometimes creating hardships and unhappiness for them merely in producing changes; even, though rarely, changes which objectively are for the best. The characteristic thing is that in this contact between the natives and the Europeans the native suffers in very tangible ways. If he depends upon game, the Europeans come in and settle the forest, and the game is driven out. An example is our destruction of the buffalo and, consequently, the life and culture of all the Indians of the plains. Or the European comes in and, in various ways, interferes with the established native way of life and thus creates the potentialities of hardship and unhappiness. This is one of the most common sources of the anxiety, the tensions, of native peoples.

The degree of anxiety aroused in an individual by such threats as these is proportional in a general way to the nature of the threat, its intensity, and the amount of damage that is potentially involved. But of course the actual danger is a function not only of the objective situation, the objective danger itself, but of the competence of native institutions, of the native way of life, to meet the threat—for even a very great threat can be met readily by a competent society. But regardless of the fact that this anxiety, with which man suffers the world over, is a relative thing, there is always some anxiety present. There is always some source of danger to which men are reacting.

The use of alcoholic beverages to reduce this anxiety is, of course, not the only thing that the primitive man does. His reaction, in the first place, is one of practical activity. He tries to overcome the difficulties, to escape from the danger, by doing something sensible which will reduce the danger. Primitive men are by no means fools. Testimony to this is the fact that we ourselves have borrowed and made a part of our culture, even if a minor part, many of the things that they invented. No European goes to the region north of the Arctic Circle without wearing the clothes that were invented by the Eskimos for this purpose. We have never been able to invent anything better than the snowshoe which, in its present form, was the invention of the American Indian, or the dogsledge, which was also an Eskimo invention. These are practical and sensible and very clever ways of overcoming the dangers which produce anxiety.

Furthermore, primitive man has still other means, and magic is one of them. When the practical effort is still not successful in reducing the threat, he takes recourse to something over and above his practical activity. He performs comforting magical ritual which gives him a sense of control over the great danger. Or, in his primitive religious practices, he will sacrifice or offer libations to the Spirits, the Bad Spirit as well as the Good Spirit, in an effort to ward off the danger which he can no longer completely control by his own means. Then, of course, he has all kinds of social responses to dangers. One of them, the most obvious, is that he lives in a closely knit community, that he develops between himself and the other people of his community strong ties of friendship and support. The primitive community is therefore a much more intimate kind of organization than the kind of social organization that we generally rely on. Each of us lives separately in his own house; we come together only on specified occasions. But in the primitive society, people live together in a very close, huddled way, as it seems to us. This close contact and constant daily association with one another gives them strength and support and encouragement in the face of all the innumerable dangers over which they have so little control. Of course, they have not only their religious rituals and ceremonies but their purely social entertainments, their dances, and so forth.

Alcohol is only one of the substances capable of fulfilling the anxiety-reducing function. Among the Asiatic people, for instance, many prefer opium. It is characteristic of some parts of the Asiatic world that where alcohol is not used, opium is used, and where opium is not used, alcohol is. Among the American Indians there are many who seem to prefer certain drugs such as peyote, the fruit of a certain cactus from which they get a trancelike effect with visual hallucinations, color visions, and so forth. It is characteristic of these Indians, too, that those who use peyote do not use alcohol, and vice versa. Others use various other drugs. The Jimson weed, for example, is very common throughout California and Mexico.

ALCOHOL AS A SEDATIVE

Alcohol has a special virtue for primitive peoples as a sedative inasmuch as it has relatively few or no harmful physiological effects and thus there is no necessary interference with productive activities. It does not put the drinker in a semicoma, so to speak, for an indefinite period, and recovery is not accompanied by a long period of illness, as in the case of some drugs. It can be indulged in for an evening, one can obtain a sedation which reduces anxiety, and yet the next day the drinker can perform his daily tasks without any serious hang-over effect. Another factor is that the materials for the production of alcohol are universal. All this great variety of fruits and berries and tubers and cereals which I have already mentioned makes it possible for practically every people in the world to produce an alcoholic beverage. In the case of the drugs, they are limited by the fact that they occur only in certain places and that in many places such drugs are not available. Furthermore, not only are the materials abundant and the technique for the production of alcohol simple and easily mastered, but the process itself is cheap. It does not take a great deal of labor to produce fairly large quantities of an alcoholic beverage.

Another important consideration, it seems to me, is the fact that its effects can be enjoyed along with other gratifications. I have never particularly studied the use of opium, but my impression is that to use it, one has to withdraw somewhat from society. It is a kind of private practice, and you cannot very well conceive of smoking or eating it in an ordinary social gathering as you can use alcohol in the course of a normal social event. Alcohol has the advantage of reducing those tensions that arise among the members of a society when they get together. Inasmuch as people always stand in a slightly competitive relationship with one another in regard to their functions in life, the goods they need, and so on, their relationships are always fairly complicated and subject to the possibility of getting out of kilter. A slight tension can and frequently does arise when certain people get together in a social situation. It is not the kind of thing that makes them enemies by any means, but it is there, and the alcoholic beverage, because it can be used in a social situation, can reduce these tensions and thus actually facilitate the social intercourse which is a part of and the desirable end of the occasion.

THE NEED FOR ALCOHOL

In summary, then, alcohol appears to have the very important function throughout the world, in all kinds and levels of human social activity, of reducing the inevitable anxieties of human life. We find, in fact, that there is a general tendency for the amount of drinking, as measured by the degree of drunkenness obtained, to be roughly proportional to the strength of the dangers threatening the society. The range of variation is, of course, very great—from societies in which there is only slight intoxication as the usual thing, to others, and many of them, in which what we would describe as debauchery is the common thing. The worst cases, inevitably, are in those societies which are undergoing a process of destruction at the hands of Europeans. There, always, we find the ultimate in the excessive use of alcohol, because there the anxieties are very powerful.

In other words, alcohol solves the problem of anxiety-reduction. For every human being who is anxious there is the problem of reducing the anxiety, whether he knows it or not, and eventually something must be done toward reducing it. From that time on, that something will become customary with the individual, become a habit, because it succeeded in relieving him of some pain, succeeded in releasing him from some tension of his anxiety. In other words, alcohol satisfies a need, the consciously or unconsciously felt need for relief from anxiety, and when this is obtained a deep, though temporary, gratification ensues. This makes the use of alcohol a desired end and gives the beverage that contains it an economic value. Upon this function of anxiety-reduction, which may be unconscious, are built other, secondary functions. Of course the food value of many alcoholic beverages used in primitive societies is undoubtedly real, and so we might regard this as an additional function. But then there are secondary functions which can only exist because of the fact that psychologically alcohol has a deep meaning and, therefore, a value.

The general category of its economic functions, its economic value, exists only because it has a psychological value. But once a substance like this has a psychological value, it rapidly develops an exchange value. It can be used, as it is invariably used by primitive societies, in the reciprocal exchanges which are a very important part of their life. I refer to that very primitive form of commerce in which people do not get together in the market and exchange their goods for money, but one gives to the other gifts which he himself does not need, and he expects that sometime later he will receive a gift of something that this other does not need, and in this way surpluses are gradually distributed throughout the population. On a more advanced level there is actual barter, where people come together and exchange directly. Still further, on a somewhat more complex level, is the market for exchange with money, cowry shells, and so on. The native alcoholic beverage becomes an economic value. It can then be used as a medium of trade and can become a part of important economic transactions, can be a way of disposing of surplus food products—fruit that cannot be stored because there is no refrigeration, materials that would spoil unless they were immediately brewed. Then, of course, all of these values can be used as an incentive to labor, as the alcoholic beverage frequently is in many African societies when people get together for joint labor in their mutual interest, in the building of a house or garden. The pay they receive from the man in whose interest they are working is usually food and drink, and the more drink he gives, the more liberal he is, the higher his prestige. As a matter of fact, having started with a psychological value and then developed an economic value, it is only natural that the beverage take on the function of social ostentation, the display of wealth, and the obtaining of prestige, so that the man who can give the largest feast with the most to drink, and who can permit the most people to get the most drunk, becomes the great man of the community. Of course, he has to do other things as well, but this is one of his attributes.

Naturally, anything which has become of value is pleasing and acceptable to the gods and becomes one of the most valued of sacrifices, the most valued of offerings. Where a native beverage is of old standing, that is, has been a part of the native way of life for a good many generations, it has generally worked its way throughout the whole way of life until it appears in the context of every kind of human activity. It then becomes an integral part of the system of religious observances, and no one would think of drinking without first offering a few drops in the proper way to satisfy, in a spiritual sense, the needs of the spiritual beings who are watching over us. Thus these various derived values and secondary elaborations of the whole system exist on the basis of the fundamental psychological value of alcohol which is, as I see it, primarily the reduction of anxiety and fatigue.

The final derived value from all these others is the fact that drinking becomes a necessary part of the system of life. Since it has been from time immemorial, and has all of these ramifications throughout the whole system, it becomes one of those things the absence of which would interfere with all other life habits into which it is integrated. Each of these subsidiary functions obviously could be replaced with a substitute. That is, there could be a substitute in exchanges, a substitute as an offering to the gods, a substitute liquid for giving libation. But the one thing for which there can be no substitute is not the beverage, but the alcohol in it. Again the alcohol seems to be the significant thing; it is what alcohol does which is the crux of the whole matter.

In retrospect, we are now in a position to understand better our first generalization, namely, that the custom of drinking alcoholic beverages has been a highly successful one in that it has survived and has spread in competition with other customs. We can see now that this is probably due to the universality of anxiety and of conditions producing anxiety among semiprimitive peoples, and to the facts that in all of these societies the technique, the scientific knowledge and the ability to meet danger are relatively limited, that there are some dangers which apparently these people cannot meet in any rational, practical way, and that the anxieties arising from these dangers are temporarily successfully reduced by the use of alcoholic beverages.

ALCOHOL AND AGGRESSION

Now, what about the other generalization, that there are almost universal manifestations of opposition to, or concern about, the use of alcohol? To analyze this problem we must again return to the psychological effects of alcohol.

We have said that alcohol reduces anxiety and that anxiety is a signal of danger, that it is a response to danger of some kind. But some of the dangers to which men learn to respond with anxiety are internal dangers, dangers within themselves. That is to say, over and above the dangers involved in the threats from external enemies or failure of the food supply, there are also dangers which take the form of antisocial impulses within the individual himself. On frequent occasions he may be in a situation in which he has the momentary impulse to harm someone, to be aggressive, to strike a blow, to damage, even to kill. Everywhere, to some extent, the aggressive impulse is forbidden and punished when it occurs within the cooperating social group, particularly within the family group, within the clan, within the village, or even within the tribe.

This group—the family, the clan or village group—must work together, must have a harmonious system of social relations, must have a minimum of conflicts, in order to survive, for all the people in the group are dependent upon one another for their survival. Impulses of aggression toward the members of one's own group must therefore be inhibited. They must be inhibited during childhood. The child must learn that when he has such impulses they must be stifled. This is a part of the process of making a child into a social human being.

A child starts out as a mere organism without social character, without culture, without habits to fit him for human life. To this child must be imparted all the behavior that will be required of him as an adult member of the particular society into which he was born. As part of this process of becoming a human being capable of carrying on joint social activities which will enable him and the other members of the community to survive in the face of dangers in nature, the child must learn, among other things, to suppress all his constant impulses to respond with aggression, with hostility, to those who temporarily frustrate him, forbid him to do what he wants to do. Especially will he be punished for aggression toward his parents, because his relations with them must be maintained in a certain form, otherwise the parents may fail in making the child into a productive member of society. The parents must have absolute authority. Parents who have the wisdom of their culture, inherited in turn from their parents, must have control over the child's life. No hostility on the part of the child may be tolerated for long.

From the very beginning every individual in any society learns to control his aggressive impulses, and eventually he forces them down to the point where he is no longer aware of the fact that these impulses are being generated and being repressed. To be sure, some forms of aggression are permitted him. He may be given an opportunity to release all the stored-up aggressive impulses which he has felt toward parents, neighbors and close associates, against some permitted objects, against enemies in warfare, in head-hunting, and against evildoers and criminals. He may be permitted to take part in their punishment. He is always permitted to exercise his aggression against those who are regarded as public enemies. Or he may take it out against those individuals who merely turn out to be queer, who turn out to be not like others; against these he may express his aggression in the form of ridicule. Or there may be some very special forms of physical contests, sports, games of a warlike variety, gladiatorial in character, and he may release some of his aggression in this way. But these various exceptional ways in which aggression may be relieved in a socially accepted form merely emphasize the fact that the taboo on aggression within the society is absolutely universal.

Now the strength of the aggressive impulses arising out of social experience depends largely on how much frustration and thwarting of hopes and ambitions occurs within the group. Some societies produce a human character which is highly aggressive, in which you find an aggressive response occurring in all members of the society very frequently in day-to-day situations. This is especially present in those societies in which the whole nature of the society is solely competitive, in which people are accustomed to striving to get the best of one another, to be superior to one another. There are some societies in which the highest social achievement is to be able to shame your rival by showing that you can accumulate a greater mass of property than he, and then destroying it in front of his eyes. The rival is challenged to accumulate as much property as you were able to get and destroy it. Greatness is manifested by the ability to achieve great things and then to destroy them. In other societies we find that a man's advancement along the road of life and his achievement of distinction and power depend entirely on the good will of certain older people who stand in a particular relationship to him. If these older people choose, they can forever thwart his hopes of attaining the highest status to which he might aspire. In a situation such as that, a tremendous amount of aggression may be accumulated. On the other hand, there are societies in which there is no ruthlessness toward weaker members, in which there is very little competition, in which there are very slight inequalities in wealth, in which opportunity is a matter of no importance between men, where corporate activities are the order of the day, and where anybody who chooses to be too self-seeking is frowned upon. In such societies there is very little evidence of the hidden aggression which has been repressed.

The expectation of punishment for the aggressive impulse arouses anxiety. The psychological mechanism is fairly simple. Punishment is a danger; whether it is direct corporal punishment or a matter of being excluded from some special occasion which is valued very highly, it is a punishment. This punishment, when first perceived, gives rise to anxiety. To escape the anxiety the aggressive impulse is inhibited or repressed. If alcohol has been consumed, this mechanism fails, because it depends upon anxiety. The anxiety is reduced and the aggression is aroused. There is nothing to prevent it, nothing to inhibit it, nothing to repress the aggressive thought, and it then manifests itself in action. In point of fact, aggressive behavior under the influence of intoxication is almost universal. Among primitive societies it ranges from its very mildest form, which is simply the exchange of insults and harsh words, to its extreme form in which assault and murder occur.

RELEASE OF AGGRESSION

As an example of the first case we may take the Lepcha, a people of about 25,000, who live on the slopes of Mt. Kinchinjunga in the Himalayas in northeastern India. These are among the most peaceful people ever reported in the anthropological literature. Their life is almost without conflicts. It does not run to ostentation, display or the accumulation of wealth. It is a life that involves a year-round series of operations in the fields, growing rice and millet, and religious rituals. These go on year after year in their accustomed way—everybody has enough, nobody has too little and nobody has too much. There are no sharp distinctions with respect to class or wealth. These people, who have a calm and even temperament, have a beer called chi, which is made from millet. They have it in abundance because they have enough millet to supply their food needs and to make as much beer as they want. They customarily drink until they are pretty well intoxicated, but this intoxication takes the form of increased jollification and loquacity. Some of them will show slightly heightened sexual behavior, but nothing serious, and in the end the men will gradually go to sleep under the effects of the beverage.

For a contrast, we may take the Indians of the northeastern part of North America—the Indians of eastern Canada. These were a people—they have now been destroyed—who, at the time the Europeans first came here, were living what we would call a marginal existence. They were exclusively hunters, with no other source of food than the game they were able to kill, the berries and seeds that they were able to gather, and the fish that they caught in the rivers and along the Atlantic shore. These people were constantly subject to the dangers of their existence. Game would frequently fail, the fish would fail to run up a certain river and the berry crop would not be abundant. There were many small tribes and they were constantly at war with one another over the hunting grounds, because game frequently became too scarce to support their populations. There was also great competition among the tribes to see who could reach and hold the best hunting grounds, who could surround the largest herd of caribou and fight off all comers. These people were very simple and they had a formal social organization that involved no real government. They had learned for their own good to keep under control all the aggression that arose among them as a result of the thwarting conditions of their natural life. They took out their aggression on their enemies and on their captives. This was one way they had of releasing the terrific aggressions that were built up in them as a result of the frustrations of their daily life. It is interesting, too, that this was accepted by all of the Indians, so that each man knew what to expect if he were captured by another tribe. It was accepted and regarded as a duty to show fortitude and stoicism and not to give one's enemies the gratification of hearing him scream. A man would, if possible, go to his death, perhaps eventually torn into shreds, without letting out a whimper. This was the accepted way of things and it had a deep psychological meaning for these people which was probably important to them. It is hard for us to evaluate, now that we have only the historical records about them, but, at any rate, this was the case. These people had managed, in one way or another, to keep their aggression under control, to give it outlet in warfare and in various ceremonies and rituals.

There was another form that their aggression took and that was that they practised sorcery against one another or believed that sorcery was being practised. This was a kind of projection of their own aggressive impulses. When alcohol was brought into the situation, these people were overcome by it because the aggression that was released was something they could not cope with. They had no institution for handling this effect; they had no police, they had no government, the Chief had only nominal power. When a warrior was given his first bottle of gin by a trader, and then became a maniac and went about killing people, who was to stop him, who would organize the people to stop him? They were not accustomed to dealing with this type of situation. When the whole community got gin and all the able-bodied men began to fight, to kill one another as well as their wives and children, there was just no power available to bring the situation under control. Thus some of these tribes actually were destroyed more by their own behavior as a result of the alcohol than by the direct assault of the Europeans. Of course this situation was complicated by the fact that when the Europeans came, the game became even more scarce, and the Europeans gave firearms to some tribes so that they were able to behave much more arrogantly and successfully in their own interests against others. The whole situation became much more tense.

I have cited these two extreme examples to show the different kinds of effect that one can get with the difference in psychological conditions. We see, next, that in solving the problem of anxiety by the use of alcohol, people may create for themselves a new problem, and this is the problem of dealing with aggression, with the drunken aggression which follows the reduction of anxiety. In the case of the Lepcha this second problem does not arise, so that for them the use of alcohol to reduce their relatively moderate anxiety does not have the social consequences which would create a new problem. But in the case of many other primitive peoples the new problem emerges very sharply.

A similar situation exists with regard to the sexual impulse. In every society the sexual impulse is restricted to some degree. Every society about which we have ever heard, and we know of thousands, has had the basic incest taboo which prohibits, under the severest penalties, sexual relations between parents and children, or between siblings (brothers and sisters of the same parents). This is an absolutely universal taboo, but in many societies it now extends in various other directions. In one society, the taboo will mean that a man cannot have sexual relations with or marry any girl who is related to his mother's family, or all the families that are related to his mother's family, or to his father's family, and so forth. In some extreme cases this will mean that perhaps two-thirds of all the women in his tribe are women whom he may not approach sexually, women whom he may never marry, so that his choice is severely restricted. In other societies, the incest taboo is very much like our own, applying to members of the immediate family and, sometimes, to first cousins. Few societies are as rigid as ours with regard to sex, speaking not merely of the incest taboo but with regard to sexual activities in general, forbidding sexual activity until the time of marriage and then insisting on absolute monogamy, so that, according to our standards, a man should have sexual relations with only one woman in the course of his life. While there are few primitive societies in which the sexual regulations are as severe as this, there are few that are actually promiscuous, and none absolutely promiscuous. A characteristic in most primitive societies is that a certain amount of sexual activity is permitted before marriage, and in some it starts very early. Children are permitted to have sexual play, which gradually becomes serious sexual activity and interest, without any interference as long as it does not transgress the incest lines. Thus a little boy might be permitted to play sexually with all the little girls of a certain clan but not with those of his own clan.

There are various forms of marriage among primitive peoples. Some of these look like monogamy, superficially, but they are monogamous only in a particular sense. There may be a series of spouses but the individual must be faithful to the spouse of the moment. However, the marriage is easily dissolved, each seeks a new partner, and then faithfulness to that partner is required. There are societies, also, in which such practices as wife-lending are permissible; and there are societies in which polygamy is practised, where a man of sufficient wealth may have several wives. But in any case, even with all these variations and relative freedoms as compared to the rigidity of our own system in this regard, any man attending a social gathering in any society in the world will always be in the presence of some attractive women who are forbidden objects to him. If his sexual impulse toward these women is aroused, it must be stopped, it must be inhibited, just as his aggressive impulse toward those members of the social gathering who stand in a competitive or thwarting relationship to him must be stopped. One can very easily see why this must be so. A society that permitted these impulses to come out with absolute freedom would soon be riven by antagonisms and jealousies.

We have seen how primitive societies control the sexual impulses of their members. If there is drinking, however, the reduction of the anxiety which inhibits the sexual impulse will, as in the case of aggression, permit the thwarted impulse to come to life in the form of action. Again in the drinking situation a new problem arises: the problem of restraining the sexual impulses that may be temporarily set off before drinking goes so far that the general anesthetic effect represses them, as it eventually does. We can say, thus, that using alcohol to solve one problem raises two new ones.

There are various ways of solving these problems of aggression and sex. In many societies the aggression loosed is controlled by removing the offender. He is expelled from the drinking situation when he becomes aggressive. In others, he may be rendered incapable of expressing his aggression. Very frequently, and this is a rather amusing thing, one finds, particularly in some of the very primitive tribes of the South African jungles, that the women, who are forbidden to drink at all, or permitted to drink very little, are given the role of policing the drinking bout, and if a man gets aggressive, the women just set on him, tie him up, put him in a hammock, and there he stays until he sobers up. In other instances the women go around the day preceding the party and make sure that all the spears and bows and arrows are gathered up and hidden in some place known only to them, so that nobody can get his hands on a dangerous weapon. Then, when the drinking begins, if anybody gets obstreperous he can fight it out with his fists. They consider that to be relatively superficial, with no danger of anybody being harmed. Removing the offender, or simply removing his weapons, or punishing him afterward, and usually the punishment is only for those who are extremely aggressive, really means that aggression is being given a certain amount of permission: You can be aggressive, provided you do not use weapons and provided it does not go too far. So very frequently these drinking bouts will end up in a brawl in which a lot of people get pushed around but no harm is done. Then it becomes a convention not to hold a grudge against the man who assaulted you, because it is understood that this is one of the effects of the particular drink.

Of course, primitive peoples do not know that there is alcohol in their drinks. All they know is that they have certain beverages which they regard as God-given, remarkable, and very valuable, which have the effect of producing a certain degree of happiness, and occasionally this happiness somehow mysteriously becomes transformed into fighting and somebody perhaps gets hurt a little, but you cannot help that. That is an inherent quality of this particular beverage, so that no grudge is held for it afterward.

They control the aggression problem by limiting it, not trying to prevent it entirely, but giving it a certain permission and always steering it along certain channels. Very frequently the sexual impulse is treated in the same way. It becomes recognized by the society that you can do things in the drinking situation which you may not do at any other time without being punished, so that this again becomes a permitted form of activity as long as it is kept within certain limits. Or it may be prohibited entirely, and in that case the problem is to punish the offender so severely that the next time he will not be able to reduce his anxiety to the point where this behavior will emerge. Another method, very nearly universal, is to exclude women from the drinking situation. If they are not permitted to drink, they are not permitted to be present, and this naturally reduces the instigation to sexual activity.

How successful these measures are will depend on local conditions. Absolute punishment for such behavior can only be successful where there is a fairly strong government with police powers. Many primitive societies lack these institutions, so that their forms of punishment are more like ostracism and other social penalties for bad behavior. In a very few instances, the only solution that the people have found for the problems of aggression and sex is to do without alcohol. This is quite remarkable, because very few primitive societies have been able to do this. Among the few are some of the Pueblo societies of the southwestern United States—the Hopi and the Zuni. They had their chance at alcohol. When the Spaniards came in, both of these tribes learned to drink distilled liquor and wine. Although their historical record has never been carefully analyzed from this point of view, I know that there are indications that the effect of drinking was to release these tensions, to produce aggression and sex behavior which was dangerous to them. But in their case they had something special at stake. They had a society which had lived in a desert situation for hundreds of years, and they had been able to maintain themselves in that desert environment only by demanding a degree of social cohesiveness and solidarity and cooperation which is remarkable even for a primitive society. These people were so closely bound together, and their whole culture depended so much on this question of cooperation, that they had made the nonaggressive, cooperative man their ideal, and they could not tolerate any deviation from this ideal. For them, it was a sheer matter of survival. Not only that, but they did not have to depend on the slow process of trial and error in applying social controls. They had a very highly cultivated system of governmental and priestly authority which included men of no mean philosophical achievement, men who were real thinkers, who actually perceived the problem. This again is a rare occurrence among a primitive people—they generally do not have the techniques of thinking which would enable them to see their social problems in a clear light. The Hopi and Zuni, however, saw their problems, and therefore passed a decree that thenceforward no member of their community could drink. This rule is breaking down somewhat. It is still forbidden to drink in the pueblos, but the young people who go out into American society—to boarding schools in American cities or to work on the railways or in the factories in the surrounding region—do occasionally become drinkers. Usually they give it up when they go back to their homes, because they know that it will not be tolerated there. I mention this last to show that the anxiety which would motivate drinking is present. There is a drive which can be satisfied with alcohol, and in a certain situation they will use it, but in their home community it is taboo. Usually, however, the solution of the primitives is to isolate the drinking situation from the other activities of social cooperation so that these things can happen without doing too much damage to the social structure. When drinking is done in a special ceremonial context—all the other cares and work of the day have been finished, the special arrangements have been made, the weapons put away, and the women excluded—then it is safe to drink to that degree of intoxication which apparently is always the goal of the primitive drinkers.

SOCIAL NEED AND SOCIAL DANGER

Now we are in a position, it seems to me, to understand why this valued thing—the alcoholic beverage—is used with so much concern; why the stories of its origin, the myths that account for its development, usually imply in some way or other that an evil spirit was involved as well as a good spirit, that it is a gift, but a gift with the sting of the scorpion in it. Now we understand why, very frequently, before drinking begins rituals are performed; prayers are made to the gods to see that nothing happens, to keep the alcohol demon from seizing people, to keep evil spirits from taking advantage of their drunken condition to enter into them and to create trouble. We understand why, among the Ifugaos of the Philippines, the special rite of tying up the stomach of a newborn child, designed to control the spirits in him, is performed so that when he grows up he will not be able to liberate these spirits when he drinks. The same ritual, or a modification of it, is performed before each drinking ceremony, just before each party. In other words, the social need for relief from pain, tension, fatigue, anxiety, stands in opposition to the social dangers that inhere in the reduction of certain anxieties. To the extent that the conditions of life are frustrating, frightening, we have the development of anxiety and, at the same time, the development of aggressive impulses. When it is attempted to solve this set of complex problems by means of alcohol, new problems arise.

In general, however, our observation of the peoples of the world indicates that almost invariably, with the exception of people like the Hopi, the Palaung of Indo-China, and a few others, the need for alcohol, the need for anxiety-reduction, overrides the dangers inherent in the release of aggression, and all kinds of compensatory mechanisms are developed to take care of the subsidiary problems which arise. In other words, people will endure the small ills of drunken aggression and sexuality in return for getting rid of anxiety-tensions.

ALCOHOL AND CULTURE

From this concept of the universal function of alcohol, it seems to me, there are some obvious implications that might be useful to us. Here, of course, I step out of my role as an anthropologist reporting to you what goes on in primitive societies, and really venture a few steps as a social philosopher.

First of all, it is quite apparent, as one reviews this field, that drinking behavior is not determined by such qualities as race. We have heavy drinkers and light drinkers, we have fighting drinkers and passive and peaceful drinkers, within every known race. Evidently there could be very little determination here by constitution. While constitutional differences might account for one man's ability to drink more than another before going into a stupor, we know that culture does not follow any constitutional line. The same people racially, genetically, may be divided into different groups with different cultures, and thus behave very differently in similar situations. One feels, in reviewing these data, that drinking habits are rather a question of the social conditions which are reflected through the individual and his behavior.

The anthropological view of the relation of individual behavior to society is something like this: In the first place, a man is what he learns to be. He comes into this world knowing nothing, and he has the potentialities for being any kind of a man that he is taught to become. This teaching we understand not as the formal education of the schoolroom. That is only part of it. His whole life experience teaches him. It rewards him for doing certain things and punishes him for doing others. Through this process over the years he eventually becomes the man who does the things that are proper and rewarded in his society. From infancy, those who have preceded him and who are therefore the standard bearers of the society, who have themselves learned from their ancestors what is right, shape him into an individual who is acceptable to his society. Those who guide him through his infancy and make him into a social being impart an unconscious system of habits, attitudes and opinions which they can change very little as they transmit them to him. They change them somewhat; each generation acts a little differently from the preceding generation. In modern societies, of course, we see this process more strikingly, because in our society change is much more rapid and there are greater differences from one generation to another, while in primitive societies the trend is a uniform one with only slow variations in time. As we look back through the anthropological records we can see that some societies have gone for hundreds of years changing only very, very slightly from one generation to another, so that, over a period of centuries, changes are still what we would regard as minor. We know, too, that you can take an individual from one culture into another—if he has not gone too far in the development of his personality, in the development of that whole system of habits which marks him as a member of the first society—you can take him in infancy, or even in childhood, put him in a new society, and make of him an entirely different creature than he would have become. You can take an Indian, put him in a Mission school and make him psychologically—and in terms of all his habits, in everything except his actual physical appearance—into an American, and of course this is being done all the time.

This system of standards of behavior, of habits, of norms of conduct, we anthropologists call the culture of a people. Each society has its own culture, its own way of life. Each individual learns to incorporate these traditional habits into his own system of behavior. When danger threatens him in his relations with other people; or when it threatens him in facing the crises of life—illness and death; when external dangers face him—the threat of starvation or the threat of enemies; his reactions will be those which his culture demands of him. If he makes any spontaneous reactions which are not acceptable by the culture they will usually be stopped, prohibited in some way.

In primitive societies the culture is fairly uniform. The society is little, the population is usually small, and individuals are much more alike in their behavior than in our society. There are, in primitive societies, relatively few differentiated groups and there is no great differentiation of labor skill. You do not have the teacher on the one hand and the ditch digger on the other. Each man is something of a teacher to his son. Each is able to take what measures are necessary. Each labors in the same industry. Where there is a division of labor, it is usually in certain minor specialties. There will be the priest, the medicine man; there will be the few expert craftsmen who have a peculiar natural talent for making carved wooden objects or dugout canoes, or something like that. But, in general, there will be relatively few differences in culture. There will be no class differences, no great economic differences, so that there is no opportunity for the development of divergent personality types. That is why we are accustomed to say in anthropology that in primitive society the personality, the psychology of individuals, is likely to be fairly uniform for all members of the same sex. There will be differences between the sexes, and slight differences due to age, but, in general, all the mature men will be very much alike in their inner psychological development and structure because they have all experienced the same things, they have had the same teachers, they have grown up under the force of the same tradition.

In our society, obviously, things are very different. We have a tremendous diversification of functions, roles and activities. We have the basic differences of occupations. We have differences in wealth, all kinds of differences of opportunity, differences in national background, and racial differences. All of these make our society infinitely more complex than the primitive society. There is more opportunity for individuals to deviate from the norm because there are certain conflicting norms. Even a criminal, who in a primitive society would be immediately exposed and punished for his crime, may, in our society, seek out a society of criminals in which it is normal to be abnormal, in which one can flout the standards of society and yet be among people who approve the flouting attempt. Of course, such a thing is unheard of among primitive societies. In our society, if one has sexual abnormalities, it is possible to join a society of perverts in our big cities, consisting of a small group of people who agree that because they are perverted they will allow their practices, they will not take the attitude toward their abnormalities that society at large does. And as long as they act within their protected precincts, and do not go so far as to come into conflict with the other members of society, they can manage. In other words, the possibility of deviation is much greater, and the conflicts which give rise to tension within the individual are much greater and much more diverse, and can express themselves in more varied kinds of actual deviation from the norm.

In our society it is much more difficult, merely by an examination, to relate the behavior of an individual to his social context. It is much more difficult to study an insane man and state the social conditions which produced his insanity, yet we know that they must exist unless the insanity is due to an organic disturbance. In the case of psychiatric disorders for which there is no organic basis, however, we know of only one possibility—those disorders came out of the individual's experiences with society. But the society is so complex in this individual's experience, it has carried him through so many different competing situations, situations in which there were conflicting standards of behavior and conflicting attitudes, that it becomes a major job of the psychoanalyst to try to reconstruct the life experience of this individual and to see at what points his contacts with society have produced in him the reactions which now express themselves in a symptom that requires psychiatric treatment.

For us, then, this problem of personality in relation to culture is a far more complicated matter than it might be in a primitive society in which there is much greater uniformity and in which the experiences of all individuals are seen to be very similar if their effects are studied. But some of the larger issues are the same, even though we cannot take, say, the alcohol addict and immediately refer, merely by an examination of the society, to the specific conditions which would give rise to alcohol addiction. We would need a special technique of psychiatry to analyze the character structure in relation to experience, and then experience in relation to mode of life. Nevertheless, it seems to me that we can recognize certain relationships, again speaking of the social philosophy of alcohol addiction. It seems clear to me from all this that certain large factors must be implicated— factors of poverty, of insecurity, of a type of job situation that so often prevails in which employment is uncertain and old age represents the threat of dependency and even starvation, factors of jealous strivings among people for power and security. In all these characteristics of our society, and in the rapid changes which are going on in our culture between the generations, we can see some of the necessary background for the development of the alcohol problem as we know it.

There are general psychological conditions arising out of the conditions created and transmitted by our culture which it is now the task of the psychiatrist and the social psychologist to analyze for us. If we carry over what we have learned about primitive societies to our own society, we certainly cannot regard our problem as specifically the problem of alcohol—because alcohol is merely the agent. The problem is first seen as the use of alcohol, but from there we are led back directly to the anxiety, tension, unhappiness and frustration which led to the use of alcohol and which make it rewarding to the individual. The reduction of excessive anxiety may be tackled as a problem of individual therapy, and that is the standard way of doing it. But if I were asked to give one over-all statement, on the basis of my survey of primitive societies and the reference of this survey to our own society, it would be that the fundamental problem is one of social engineering rather than of individual therapy.

DISCUSSION

Chairman (E. M. Jellinek): You have heard the language of the physiologist and of the psychiatrist and you have found, perhaps, that certain words have different meanings in those languages than they have in everyday language. Now a new language has been introduced by the anthropologist. The sociologist as well as the anthropologist uses words which we use in everyday language but for them they have a different connotation. Experience has shown me that the words "need" and "value" as used by the anthropologists and sociologists give rise to misunderstandings and even antagonistic feelings. In everyday language little distinction is made between "need" and "necessity." Would you care to say a few words, Dr. Horton, on the sense in which you and your profession use the words "need" and "value"?

Lecturer: I don't use the word "need" in the sense of a consciously recognized goal, as is the common usage, but rather in the sense that where there is a state of tension—which may not even be recognized by the individual, so that it might be said that he is in the market for something and does not know what—there is a state of need. And when something happens to reduce this tension, we say that the need has been satisfied. Now the individual may not become conscious of this process until it has actually occurred, so that what happens, for instance, might be this: When the individual is in a state of tension due to anxiety, and all he knows is that somehow he is restless, we say that he has the need for anxiety-reduction, and yet he may not know that this is so at all. What he knows is that he feels uncomfortable. If, at the moment, you offer him his first drink, and if it has the effect of making him suddenly feel relaxed, thus satisfying his need for anxiety-reduction, then he may say to himself, "I was feeling uneasy and they gave me that beverage and now I feel fine; henceforth, when I'm feeling uneasy I'll ask for that beverage." Very soon he may say, "I need that drink because I'm feeling uneasy and tense." Now he has taken the same word and used it to define his objective, but this objective, of course, is related to his subjective state, his subjective condition. He uses it to imply a goal as well as to refer to a condition, whereas I've been using it merely to define a condition of human behavior where there is a tension and the reduction of that tension establishes a habit—say, the habit of drinking.

In one context I used the word "value" with reference to activities on the part of the individual which he himself has now begun to consider as a necessary thing for him, which represents a goal for which he will make sacrifices. If it's an object, it's something that he will exchange other objects for; he will work in order to attain it. This we call "value." The object has value in the economic sense, in forms of exchange; in a psychological sense, that the individual will strive consciously for it; and perhaps in a still more fundamental sense, in that this is the thing that satisfies the need. Each society creates its standards for itself. In most of these primitive societies which I have been describing, intoxication is a value. A man who gives a party without supplying enough liquor so that all the men can drink themselves into a state of stupefaction is a pinchpenny, a miser, who does not know how to give a party. That's one standard of values. But in another society, like the Pueblo, drinking has no affirmative value whatsoever; it's a negative value, a dangerous thing.

Chairman: One fact seems to me particularly significant and that is that for all practical purposes no individual alcoholism occurs in these primitive societies but it is more of a communal affair.

Lecturer: Only a very few instances of individual alcohol addiction or excessive drinking, over, above and beyond the normal, have been observed. Of course in those societies in which it is customary for all adult men to drink to excess, to drink whenever possible to a state of stupor, it would be very hard for an individual to deviate except by being an abstainer. Occasionally, you'll find that; but that's about the only direction in which one could deviate. In most societies, however, where you don't have such an extreme thing, everybody drinks to about the same degree. Solitary drinking is absolutely unheard of.

Chairman: You said that in all these primitive societies they drink excessively. By that you meant that they drink large quantities at a time, but it does not imply excess in the terms of frequency?

Lecturer: Generally, no.

Chairman: Isn't it more a matter of drinking today and perhaps 6 weeks or even 3 months later? It would seem that in these societies the anxiety-reduction is communal rather than individual. This is only possible because in these societies there is great solidarity, much greater than in a complex society. Furthermore, the anxieties are largely of the same type, largely generated by the same stimulus, such as the threat of a bad crop or the threat of a hostile invasion.

Lecturer: Yes, because they are all responding to the same condition in the same way.

Chairman: Another fact of great interest is that in these primitive societies this custom of reducing tension by intoxication has persisted for hundreds and thousands of years in the absence of any organized supply of alcoholic beverages.

Lecturer: In connection with this, it is very interesting to note that when bottled liquors were first brought to the Indians of North America, their first response was to start drinking right away as individuals. Those Indian societies which were successful in handling the problem that arose from liquor did it by developing a pattern of group drinking. There was one tribe, I think it was the Omaha, who finally got the situation under control by putting all the liquors bought in the hands of the Chief, and all purchases of liquor by the barrel, rather than by the bottle, were negotiated by the Chief. Each of the adult men contributed his share to the cause. But the Chief then had control over the barrels and they could use the liquor only at the time he dictated. Then all sorts of preparations would be made. In that way they defeated the tendency to individual drinking.

Campbell: I don't know whether you'll want to answer this as an anthropologist or as a social philosopher, but getting back to primitive society, the Hebrew people, the record of whose conduct we have in the Old Testament, were not accused of indulging in alcohol to a great extent. We read that Noah was drunk and something was said about the abuse of wine, but on the whole, that was not one of their major faults. If you study the history of the Hebrew people over the centuries, I think you will agree that they have shown remarkable control in the use of alcohol. In my own experience, which is limited, I don't think I've ever met an alcoholic member of the Jewish race. If the reduction of anxiety is the basis for the use of alcohol, how do you explain the fact that a race that has been subjected to anxiety shows such a high degree of control over the use of alcohol?

Lecturer: I think the answer to this question is that the situation of the Jews is much like that of the Pueblo Indians of whom I spoke. You will remember that I said these people, living in a semi-desert region, forced to face the possibility of starvation at any moment due to the type of primitive desert agriculture that they have to rely on, have given themselves strength by organizing a community which is more closely knit, more solidly bound by social and individual ties than many other societies that we can compare with it, and that they have done this in self-defense. It seems to me perfectly reasonable to suppose that the Jews, in the face of a world which is and has been hostile to them, with a world that has persecuted them, would have to give up the excessive use of alcohol, even though their need for some form of anxiety-reduction might be great, because in the excessive use of alcohol they would be exposing themselves to a danger which they could not tolerate. And for the Jews this is a multiple danger. It is the danger that with the release of aggression, consequent on drinking, their own ties to one another would be loosened. They cannot tolerate aggression toward one another which would weaken them in the face of the enemy. In the life of the ghetto, people cannot afford to express hostility toward one another. Furthermore, since they have to compete with people who are looking for a chance to disqualify them on some grounds, the mere fact of being a heavy drinker can in itself be used as a basis for disqualification. For these two reasons, if for no others, you have a situation in which, for the Jew, the gratification which he might get from reducing his anxiety by drinking would be much less than the punishment he would receive and that his whole people would be receiving.

Question: Is there much abstinence among Jews?

Lecturer: I've never heard that there was much abstinence. They use alcohol, but always in moderation.

Anderson: You speak of these tensions and fears on the part of primitive peoples that are relieved periodically by drinking. Some of us would like to know if it's just pure coincidence that they have to relieve these tensions about the time that a boatload of liquor comes around the bend.

Lecturer: If people are dependent upon the liquor that's brought to them by boat, they have to wait until it gets there, and their tensions will accumulate until the boat does get there.

Anderson: Pursuing this subject a little further, the same thing would apply, would it not, to the fact that they drink collectively rather than individually to relieve this tension? Isn't it an odd fact that these individuals all restrain these temptations to drink until the whole tribe decides to go on a drunk?

Lecturer: That sometimes occurs, but generally it becomes a tradition, a pattern, for them to drink together, just as it becomes a pattern in our society for people to drink and eat together. In others, drinking occurs with the meals, for instance, so that a man, his wife and children will have some of their beer or wine with every meal that they eat. The beer- or wine-drinking occasion is more than mere drinking; it is elaborated into a whole ceremony, a social occasion, as when old friends meet, when a business deal is closed, when religious ceremonies are performed. All of this gets tied up into a kind of complex performance of which drinking is only the core but perhaps not a particularly obvious core.

Gross: You said that drinking in primitive societies is done mainly in groups and very far apart, say weeks apart. Is there anything that could be compared with chronic alcoholism?

Lecturer: What is chronic alcoholism?

Chairman: Do you mean actual physical changes, such as the diseases of chronic alcoholism?

Gross: Yes.

Lecturer: Is it not generally felt that these extreme disorders occur only as a result of the drinking of distilled liquors? Aren't these disorders connected with food deprivation and avitaminosis? I don't know of any instance in a primitive society that drinking has gone to the point where people no longer eat enough food and rely almost entirely on the beverage. My information is gathered from the observations of anthropologists who themselves are not particularly interested in the problems of alcohol. Therefore, they describe, for the most part, the normal behavior, and if anybody is very queer, they note him, and say something about him. But no special studies have been made of the subject of drinking among primitives. It hasn't become the focus of extensive research. I know of only one instance in the literature that I've read in which there's any reference to an alcoholic disease. The Mongols, it is reported, have a distilled liquor which has an alcohol content of 80 per cent, and after drinking this to excess they very frequently suffer from a stomach disorder which actually can lead to starvation. The lining of the stomach is injured to such a point that it cannot hold the food and people actually die as a result of this. For the rest, I can't answer. I just don't have the data.

Hoover: While these primitive tribes have done something with alcohol, have worked out certain techniques to limit injurious aggression by removing the weapons and women, what techniques are practical to civilized society?

Lecturer: I don't profess to give the answer, but I simply say to the questioner, "Examine the drinking in our society." If you focus your attention on those relatively few chronic drunks that you stumble on, the fights that they have, and so on, you say that we don't restrain aggression. But consider the moderate drinkers—millions of them. How do they do it? You'll find that there are all sorts of social conventions, pressures, rules and ultimate punishment that control aggression in our own society. You could make a study of that.

Question: The Democratic National Convention for presidential nomination, now in progress, is not allowing drinks to be sold. Can this action be explained on the basis of lack of anxiety?

Lecturer: I think the answer is undoubtedly yes.

Lecture 14

Alcohol and Complex Society

Selden D. Bacon

ONE of the foundations for a more penetrating insight into the problems of alcohol is an appreciation of the many diverse origins from which the problems arise and of the many diverse channels in which they make themselves felt. It is my purpose to present one view of the nature and functions of alcohol from a broad, sociological framework. I say "one" view since there are many sociological approaches and I am not pretending to touch them all.

Let us start with the idea that alcohol has certain effects on the individual and certain effects on the over-all group of individuals. Some of these effects seem to have value for the individual and for society, a conclusion buttressed by the observed fact that, as a custom, the drinking of alcoholic beverages has spread to almost all groups of men ever known, and has enjoyed a long life in almost every society of which we have knowledge. It is equally clear that some of the effects of alcohol on individuals and on groups have been disadvantageous.

Let me mention very briefly some of the outstanding effects. For the individual, alcohol can reduce tension, guilt, anxiety and frustration. For the individual, alcohol can also reduce operational efficiency below the minimum necessary for social existence, or even for existence at all. In relation to the total society, alcohol can make possible association and interpersonal activity which may ordinarily be barred; it can permit variations in ideas and activities also, although this is a minor point; and it can allow an escape valve for socially frustrated individuals, an escape which can be relatively safe. Alcohol can also break down individual participation in associations, thus weakening them. It can impair the exactitude and rhythm of behavior patterns and socially valuable ideas, and it can impair foresight and the results of previous foresight.

We may thus liken alcohol to other discoveries or inventions of dynamic character, such as the wheel, electricity, techniques of organization, political and scientific concepts, dynamite, gases, and so on. It is a human artifact of great power. How it is used or misused is, of course, a very different matter.

I shall discuss the relationship of social structure to the functions—to the potentialities—of alcohol. You have heard a discussion of alcohol and simple societies. What is the effect of social complexity on the functions of this phenomenon?

SIMPLICITY AND COMPLEXITY IN SOCIAL STRUCTURE

Simplicity and complexity as characteristics of a society are generally related not to end goals or final purposes but to the means of attaining those goals, the numbers and divisions of society and their interrelations. The end goals of the Trobriand Islander or of the totality of Trobriand Islanders are not basically different from those of the Manhattan Islanders. All these individuals want food, shelter, and clothing; they all want protection from enemies within and without their groups and from the unknown which is potentially dangerous; they all want pleasurable interaction with others—love, affection, prestige; they all want a certain degree of control over themselves and over their situation, both current and future. The way in which these wishes are concretely expressed or attained will vary, of course, in different societies, although there will be for all a minimum core of similarity determined by the biological similarity of all mankind.

The needs of the societies are: first, a minimal satisfaction of the individual needs; second, perpetuation of the species; third, internal unity and order; and fourth, protection from outside groups. The achievement of these ends can be relatively simple or relatively complex. For example, a group of 50 families, comprising perhaps 300 people, can maintain itself by what we could call simple social processes. The members of each family could serve as a unit for production and consumption, grow their own crops, store them, prepare them, and eat them; they could build their own dwellings, make their own clothes, utensils, and weapons. They could worship their ancestral spirits through avoidance, sacrifice, prayer, and other ritual at their home. Division of labor could be based on sex, age, and talent, but the latter would be only occasional; that is, on a hunt or in constructing a dwelling, one function might invariably be activated by a given individual, but the others would be capable of doing it. Except for age and sex differences, almost any member of the group could fulfill almost any of the activities of the group. Property ownership would vary with talent, application, and luck, but would not vary in as great a degree as in our society, since the possibility of exchange, the range of types of production and the quantity of durable goods would be limited. Defense of one's physical self and of one's social prestige would be largely a familial and individual matter.

In contrast to this picture, consider the industrial, commercial, service, or professional worker in the large contemporary city. He does not produce his own food, shelter, clothing, utensils. He does not distribute or store them. He may, in the case of food, do something about final or immediate preparation. Yet he must obtain food, clothing and shelter, and he does so, but by totally different life activities. The steps by which this behavioral revolution occurred are highly complex, are the result of changes taking place during scores of generations. I will present a sweeping description of the process. Specialization of economic function had the results of allowing more production, a greater variety of production, quicker production, and finer output. These are great values for group survival. To take the simplest sort of an example: in order to make metal weapons one needs metals, a forge, hammers, fuel, skill, and time. Everybody in the group wants metal weapons. Everybody in the group also must tend his garden, mingle with others, and so on. Further, not everyone in the group has the same dexterity and imagination; it takes William, an excellent farmer, 7 hours to make a third-rate scythe blade; Joseph, a poor farmer, can make a marvelous scythe blade in 2 hours. If William sticks to farming and Joseph to forging, and they exchange, there will be more and better food and more and better blades, both scythe and sword. It is necessary, however, that there be considerable numbers to allow Joseph to do nothing but make tools. And it is through continual operation that his skill, ingenuity and speed will increase. It is easy to see that Joseph may soon be similar to our city worker in that he will not need to produce his own food, clothing and shelter.

Specialization continued to increase not only in production of goods, but also in the rendering of services. Note that the basic needs and the answers to those needs are not particularly changed. Everybody wants food, clothing and shelter. Everybody is getting some food, some clothing, and some shelter, probably more and of a better quality than before. The means, however, have changed. How far this specialization process has gone in contemporary society almost defies description. As an indication of its extent I may cite the following: (*1*) There are so many specialized occupations that a dictionary has been published which explains the names of the *industrial* types of jobs alone; it contains 25,000 different titles. (*2*) The personnel of a factory, consisting of men classified into all sorts of different workers who could not substitute for one another, makes products which, in turn, are only small parts of a product which is assembled elsewhere; the then assembled unit is shipped to still a third place to be part of a building, a boat, or a laboratory, which none of the workers ever heard of or used. (*3*) The specialized nature of the work can be little more than turning a crank a half turn four times a minute, or pushing a stamp against a piece of cloth. (*4*) On some farms producing dairy products and fresh vegetables the workers receive only canned milk and canned vegetables for their meals, the fresh product being regarded only as an exchange value.

Specialization has occurred not only in the realm of mechanical acts but also in the realms of foresight and imagination, organization, responsibility, and the giving of orders. There are all manner of gradations and specialties along these lines within the specialized economic categories.

Not that specialization is limited to the economic sphere. Recreation, education, medication, protection from personal attack, from disease, from poverty in old age, from fire, religious activities, to mention the most obvious, have, to a very large extent, been taken over by specialists. Once these functions were activated in the home by a member of the family or by the person involved. Now we have professions, businesses, industries, services, institutions, and so on, to do these things for us. The same values of specialization apply here as in the economic sphere. Variety, quality, quantity and speed are mightily enhanced.

It should be mentioned that this specialization process has been speeded, refined and enlarged by the development of a machine technology.

Results of Specialization

From this extraordinary specialization has sprung the greatest amount and variety of food, shelter and clothing the world has ever experienced. There is protection against sickness, there are facilities for recreation and many other values which go beyond anything even imagined by the sages of primitive groups. There are also some other results of or concomitants to this process which have not been an unmixed blessing. I have placed these under several headings which will first be described and then related to the functions of alcoholic beverage consumption.

Social Stratification

One result of this extraordinary specialization has been the appearance of a social stratification system. Without stating the reasons for it, let me merely postulate the process that like tends to cluster with like. Carpenters mix with carpenters, college professors with college professors, the unemployed with the unemployed, hobos with hobos, actors with actors. The like is true of persons who have the same religion, enjoy the same hobbies, admire the same person or music or philosophy. Furthermore, this clustering of people according to one interest tends to make all of them more similar in other aspects and, consequently, more different from members of other clusters.

A second concomitant of this specialization is an hierarchical form of stratification. What we may call the horizontal stratification just discussed is accompanied by varying degrees of prestige, responsibility, training, and monetary reward. Since the amount of money determines the variety, amount and quality of goods and services, and since, because of the efficiency of the specialized society, there is an enormous amount of goods and services, the more-moneyed groups become more and more different from the less-moneyed groups—a process enhanced, as in the other instance, by the process of like clustering with like. Further hierarchical or vertical stratification occurs because of conquest or because of immigration of foreign groups, and also because of other lesser processes.

Interdependence

A third result of this specialization is that persons are equipped with only a vague perception of the interests, ideas, habits, problems, likes and dislikes of those not in their group. To speak bluntly, specialization is commonly related to ignorance. Very few factory workers know anything about farm work, dentistry, international relations, wholesale distribution, geology, or soap making. Nor do these others know much about factory work. This is not true in the simpler societies. The economic activities, recreations, religious activities and beliefs of all are fairly common knowledge. There are those who are more skillful, more energetic, luckier, but the difference is of degree rather than of kind. The smith and the priest may be exceptions and there are certain activities limited to only one sex, but that is about all.

A further result of the horizontal and vertical stratification, and of the consequent ignorance, is extreme interdependence. This might seem almost paradoxical. The more independent people become, the more dependent they become. However, this is just a loose use of the word "independent"; there is a difference between independence and specialization. Each one of these specialists needs the goods and services of many of the others and wishes for the goods and services of most of them. Yet if the doctor and the banker and the street cleaner could not get food and shelter, then the food and shelter specialists could not get medical, financial, and sanitary services. All the specialists are mutually dependent.

Without considering the reasons for it, we may merely observe that many groups, if not most, deplore this idea of dependence, and either deny its reality or state that it is a very bad thing. They are able to push its existence further from consciousness by utilizing their symbolic translation of goods and services, money.

Role of Money

Money is a very important concomitant of increased specialization; it is needed because of the great difference between the specialists and because all the specialists need the goods and services of the others. This problem is *immediately*, but only *immediately*, settled by two steps: one, the translation of every object and service into terms of a common denominator, an invention in the realm of ideas; two, a material invention, a representation of that symbolic denominator by tangible objects. In other words, running an elevator, preparing a person to meet death, growing corn, telling jokes, and organizing public health measures, must all have a common denominator, and that denominator must be represented by a tangible and transferable and carefully trade-marked object. The immediate answer is money, but although this is a brilliant adjustment, it carries problems in its wake—problems unknown to less specialized societies and also problems known of old but enhanced and complicated because of money.

One use made of money is the denial of intergroup dependence. People refuse to admit they are dependent on other groups and individuals and nature. The only thing they depend on is money. Rather than organize their lives and their efforts to satisfy their needs around activities and interpersonal relationships, many individuals attempt to organize their lives around an adjustment between themselves and money.

Lest anyone underestimate what I mean by individuals organizing their lives around money, let me illustrate. As basic needs of man I first suggested food, shelter, and clothing; I take it for granted that you realize that we Americans, about 95 per cent of us at least, meet these needs through money—not only city apartment dwellers, but farmers and cattlemen and fishermen. They buy equipment and pay taxes and get clothes and medical service and paint and nails and seed and education for their children, and food and shelter, and much else, with money.

But there are other needs. Affection, friendship and prestige, pleasant interpersonal relations. We get these primarily through family and friendship groups. In complex society, money plays a tremendous role in maintaining position in such groups. Its function in this role is largely a limiting, negative force rather than a determining, positive force. That is, even enormous amounts of money cannot guarantee entrance into groups, but just small decreases can force one out. Friendship and clique membership is a two-way affair. If the Joneses serve food to you at their house, you have to reciprocate. If the Joneses' daughter takes your daughter to the movies or buys her an ice cream cone, your daughter has to reciprocate. If your friends and neighbors keep their places in good order, which requires money, you have to do likewise. Amongst your friends you cannot be the only one who does not have a car, send the children to a private school, invite the others to a meal, have a clean shirt every morning, or participate in the ways of the clique whatever they may be. Studies made of the unemployed during the depression show that the threat to or actual loss of social position was one of the most painful blows suffered. It was felt by the husband, the wife, and the children. They lost their friends.

Still another very important value to the individual is that of maintaining some degree of control over his own existence and of the situation immediately pressing him. That money has influenced the satisfaction of this desire is obvious. But to what degree does it operate? The answer is that it exerts a controlling interest. An enormous number of persons in our commercial, industrial and personal-service life can exert control of their own lives only through a weekly or daily wage. Whether or not they will receive that wage is dependent upon forces beyond their understanding and control. Effort and ability are important, but are not controlling. For the member of the less specialized society, this situation does not exist. Food and shelter and respect of others are subject, of course, to outside, uncontrollable factors (weather, fire, insects, personal and group enemies, disappearance or diminution of species of food animals and fish, and the like), but there is no danger of having perfectly satisfactory environmental conditions plus willingness and ability to work accompanied by the inability to get food, shelter, and protection. Our millions of unemployed were quite unable to live and support families by farming, hunting or fishing. Nor could the millions whose standards were lowered by receiving $20 a week rather than $30 make up the difference by return to such direct ways of existence. Their way of directing their lives is by acquiring wages. They get the wages from persons over whom they have little control, with whom they have little in common. Furthermore, the wage payers are often quite uncertain as to how much money will come in from which they can pay wages. The complexities of the flow of money need only to be recognized by us as existing. The relevant point now is that in the specialized world the worker's control of his life is, to a great extent, controlled by money, and he cannot control money. Moreover, he faces this problem every week, every day. It can control his whole life continuously. He cannot plan ahead without it, and he cannot be assured of what he will have.

This utilization of money in the specialized society has two important aspects for our consideration. The first is that different groups of persons who are heavily dependent on each other are enabled to avoid contact and to avoid mutual understanding and cooperation. To put it conversely, it allows mutually dependent groups to fight each other bitterly in a completely impersonal way. To dramatize this possibility let us note how money can allow persons to hold utterly incompatible ideas. The example is purposefully extreme. If one man should go to another man's house, a member of the group but a stranger and an unoffensive one to him, and should take away his food, his furnishings, ruin his friendships, force his children to stop school, prevent his family from having medical care and recreation, we would violently disapprove, no matter how the story was told. If this one man, by manipulating prices, credit and wages, achieves the same result on many other men, strangers and unoffensive to him, but makes money for himself and some others, then, depending on how the story was told, we might feel he was a very able person. This incompatibility of ideas is one of the great questions to be solved in American life today. Note that the interposition of the idea of money between the two parties makes an extraordinary difference. This magic symbol is able to relieve the guilt, is able to take away the viciousness and aggressiveness which otherwise would be observed. Many writers have pointed this out in contemporary literature: When the farmer is pushed off his land, when the city tenant is evicted, when the borrower of small loans is forced to pay three to four times the amount he received, it always appears that no one is being aggressive or unpleasant; it is just fate, the magical turn of the financial wheel. Nor can the aggrieved party find out who hurt him. The sheriff points to the finance company, the finance company to the bank, the bank to financial holding companies, the latter to stockholders, and all of them are terribly sorry if they happen to hear about it.

This brings us to the second point, which is that money is an artificial, that is, a humanly invented idea, represented by paper and metal objects. Like all powerful and brilliant ideas or inventions—dynamite, political parties, electricity, unions, the family—it is very, very useful, and very, very dangerous. Instead of always insuring that specialized effort will be possible and that all the specialists will get all the specialized goods and services, it sometimes happens that it has very different results. It gets completely out of control. A lot of people can have no money at all and no prospect of getting any. A much larger number suddenly may have a great deal less than usual. And nobody knows what to do about it, although many are certain that the other fellow's ideas are crazy.

Individualism

A sixth, and for present purposes the final, concomitant of this process of specialization is individualism. To describe this process we must consider another facet of complexity, namely, mobility. The physical possibility of mobility was enormously increased by the technological revolution of the last 150 years. The need for such mobility rose from the specialization process and its concomitants.

Individualism refers, first, to the increased value of each individual to other individuals. Association is always of great value to every human being, and so other persons are always valuable, but in a world of specialists this value is extended and enhanced. For example, when bakeries first emerged in the colonies, the specialist baker was hardly an indispensable person. If one did not have cash or did not like shop-made products, one made one's own bread at home. This was possible because one had flour and other ingredients sufficient for the purpose at hand, one had utensils, basic equipment, oven space, a kitchen; one had the skill, the time, and the feeling that it was right, proper, and natural to bake one's own bread. Specialization has its values, however, and bakeries became integrated into the way of life. Nowadays many, many persons do not have the ingredients, would not have place for them anyway; they do not have the utensils; they have only the minimum of basic equipment, quite likely not enough for baking unless other uses of the stove are given up; they lack the skills—a marriageable girl of 150 years ago who could not bake would have been a rare exception; the day is arranged very differently, and the time required would probably demand sacrificing some other activity; and finally, the feeling that baking one's own bread is right, proper and natural is gone.

The baker has become indispensable if you want breadstuffs. If you have no money, you get no bread. If you do not like the baker, you can only go to another baker. You may not know the baker personally, but he is very important to you. So are the telephone linesman, the personnel at the sewage disposal plant, the shoemaker, the laundryman, the bus driver. This means that power adheres to individuals which was not present in the simpler society. If, in the more primitive group, John Jones decided to quit work, it was not just a matter of his starving to death; it did break up the pattern of life considerably, especially for John's family, but it did not directly and immediately threaten a large percentage of the group, and it was possible, although irritating, for someone else to take up the slack. John's work was as hard and as easy, as dignified and as undignified, as most other persons' work. Not many of us, however, could take on someone else's job today. Nowadays the Jack-of-all-trades is further characterized as being master of none. Furthermore, there are many jobs we would consider as below our respective dignities. More and more individuals have become clothed with a type of power unknown before. This aspect has a reverse side also. If the specialty becomes outmoded or if the specialty requires almost no skill or training at all, then the person seems to have less power than any individual in the more primitive group. For the most part, however, the individual's social power has been increased by specialization just as the individual's physical power has been increased by the automobile and the gun.

A second consideration on this score is that the individual specialists or participants in a particular specialty have worked hard to extend this automatic importance and power. The bakers, the doctors, the tool-and-dye workers, the teachers, the shoemakers, and so on have endeavored to enhance and to guarantee their positions. They have a private stake in this process.

Another aspect of individualism is the person's lessened need for close social participation. The rise of money and mobility has had a great deal to do with the emancipation of individuals from tight, all-encompassing social organizations. Not having to depend on the parents, on the priest, on the neighbors, as did the member of the more primitive society, the individual can withdraw from their control. He can look forward to making money, living in another place, having radically different ideas, doing what he wants without their meddling. For the member of the primitive society such attitudes or actions meant death. Without father, brothers, cousins, children, who would do business with you, who would back your side of an argument, who would protect you? The answer was clarion clear—"No one." That was why banishment was such a terrible sentence. It meant some form of death, not quite determined how, when, or where, but fairly soon and very sure. Today the young man leaves his home town "to make something of himself." He will adjust to strangers through money, through his drive and skill and luck in his specialty. He is "on his own," a great value in our society, although a death penalty among primitive groups. Not that he stays "on his own" very long. He joins groups, but more and more they tend to be specialized groups. Whereas the person in the simpler society worked, played, worshiped, gossiped, and, in general, lived with about the same group of persons, the individual in the modern complex society may belong to several groups with different personnel. The church group, the school group, the neighbors, the men at the shop, office or store, the three or four close friends, may form half a dozen groups with varying personnel. These, in turn, may have slightly, even greatly, different ideas of what is proper, permissible, interesting or desirable. Most important, the individual can shift from one group to another. This means that a wider range of behavior is open to him. The sanctioning power of any one group is, of course, potentially weakened by the varying norms of the others. What is of greater importance is the fact that these are specialized organizations and that a group having over-all societal interests does not command the individual's loyalty, as it could in a simple society. One result of this situation is the commonly observed fact of a single individual following incompatible moral codes. A man can show aggressiveness, slyness, laziness in his occupational morality which he would bitterly reject in his home circle. He can pray in one direction and vote in another. His life being somewhat compartmentalized, such relative variety of behavior is possible. This emancipation from a solid, unified, omnipresent group sanction has many assets for both individual and society. It also has many liabilities. There is a loss of security in personal relationships. A wide field is opened up for fraud. Many groups are exceedingly shortlived and competition between them is continuous, often bitter. A strong, widespread morality is more difficult to maintain. The greater freedom of action for the individual puts a heavy burden upon him; he has to face questions and problems that hardly exist in a simpler, uniform, less specialized society.

Major Needs

I have now sketched certain major attributes of a complex society which distinguish it from a simpler society. Let me repeat my introductory statement. The end goals, the major needs of both individuals and of total societies, are not much changed by a greater or lesser complexity of society. The difference is in methods, subgoals, organization, numbers. The major aspect of complexity has been defined as a specialization of form and function. For modern Western civilization this specialization has been primarily economic. That is, changes in the economic structure have forced adjustments on the other major institutions —family, church, government, caste—while changes by those institutions were not necessarily adjusted to by the economic structure. Do not think that ours is the only complex social structure or that the economic institution must always dominate in a complex world. The religious or the familistic can be the dominant interest and can involve tremendous specialization.

The specialization was seen to result in the greatest production of goods and services yet attained by any society. It had also the following effects, although it alone may not have been responsible: (1) horizontal stratification; (2) vertical stratification; (3) less and less knowledge of the whole society, its ways, subgroups and ideas; (4) extreme mutual dependence of subgroups and individuals; (5) a utilization of money which allowed impersonal contact between individuals and resulted in a new life orientation for all individuals, but which defied human control and resulted at times in the inability of masses of people to avail themselves even of the extraordinary amount of goods and services at hand; and (6) a great increase in the social potentiality of the individual and a decrease both in the unity of the society as a whole and in the enduring strength of any of its subgroups.

SOCIAL COMPLEXITY AND ALCOHOL

With these attributes of complex society described, we may consider the significance of social complexity for the part played by alcohol both in relation to society as a whole and in relation to the life of the individual.

Dr. Horton, in his description of primitive societies, pointed out certain individual needs which are answered, more or less, by alcohol. One of these is the satisfaction of hunger and thirst, a very minor factor; another is a medicinal need, also very minor. Let us consider the effect of our complex societies on these two needs. I think it can be said that in the society where increased complexity is dominated by the economic institution, beverage alcohol is not used for these needs. Goods and services have become so refined, so tested in competition, and are so plentiful, that such a second-rate food and fourth-rate medicine as beverage alcohol will tend in these regards to die out or be limited to those rare instances where alcohol has some special value. There will be a lag in ideas, however. Old ideas of the nutritional and medicinal values of alcohol will persist long after the best knowledge and experience will have shown them to be mistaken.

Another function of alcohol mentioned by Dr. Horton was its use in attaining religious ecstasy. Here alcohol must compete with fasting, purposefully induced exhaustion, self-laceration, drugs, autohypnosis, and the like. Religious ecstasy, however, must be a generally approved and prestigeful affair before any of these techniques will be utilized. In our highly specialized economic life there is small place for religious ecstasy. Moreover, the mental state achieved by alcohol intake has been considered for many generations as ludicrous or disgusting rather than mysterious. Catalepsy, automatic writing and conversion hysteria may still inspire some awe in the more superstitious, but even the most confirmed crystal gazers are scornful of alcohol-induced spiritual experiences. In this complex society, that function of alcohol may be safely forgotten.

Another function of alcohol has been its use in social jollification. Although the distinction between the needs of the society as separate from those of the individual is occasionally difficult to perceive, in this instance a fairly clear discrimination can be made. The maintenance of order and of unity within the society is imperative for the survival of the society. The feeling that the individuals are a "we-group" as opposed to "others," the feeling that it is pleasurable to be one of "us," the restatement of the fundamental mutuality of the members, these values are attained by meetings of pleasurable purpose. In any society there will be stresses and strains which tend to break the unity; certain individuals will be unsatisfied, will be more ambitious than achieving; certain groups will be antagonistic. Meetings in which such ambitions and frustrations and resentments are irrelevant, in which purely rewarding pursuits are at hand, will help restore or enhance the integrating principles.

As we have seen, one of the concomitants of complexity is stratification, another is ignorance of other subgroups, a third is the increased aggression allowed by the widespread utilization of money, a fourth is increased individualism. The need for integrating mechanisms in a more and more complex society is a phenomenon whose existence can hardly be challenged. The difficulty of effecting such mechanisms is apparent. One of the best ways, aside from great external danger, is through amusements. They present an activity or interest which can be neutral to conflicting interests and personalities; they can be stimulating, they can be rewarding, and they hold small threat of punishment.

Theoretically we would expect an increase of pleasure meetings in a complex, competitive, individualistic civilization, and in our society this theoretical expectancy is fully met. There has been a development of both commercialized and noncommercialized pleasure rituals which would seem extraordinary to the members of the simpler society. From organized spectacles which operate 8 to 16 hours a day every day to the informal tea, cocktail, and card-game gatherings, the members of our society are almost surfeited with recreational association. As would be expected, activities connected with occupational specialty are generally held taboo at these meetings. Specialization and specialists, however, have infiltrated this area of behavior as they have almost all others.

With this extension and elaboration of recreation, alcohol's part in jollification or in pleasure association has become enhanced. Note the role of alcohol in these situations. We have, on the one hand, a society whose individuals are often (1) more self-contained and independent, (2) more ignorant of each other's interests and activities, (3) more separate from each other, (4) more prone to aggressive and competitive relationships; on the other hand, there is a need for unsuspicious, pleasant, relatively effortless joint activity. How can one put these together? One way is to transfer the ordinary, diverse, specialized attentions of the individuals to one neutral object interesting to all—a spectacle, for example, or a chess game. The trouble with this adjustment is that it does not allow much interpersonal activity. Another way is to relax all the people. All of us here have undoubtedly experienced meetings intended to be recreational and found them stiff, uncertain, tense. Intermixture does not take place. Despite the need to spread interaction, individuals remain aloof, or little groups of previous acquaintance maintain their own safe little cliques. The organizers have to break down the hostilities, the indifference, the ignorance, and the suspicions. To do this they try to get the individuals to relax. Alcohol is a quick, easy, fairly sure means of accomplishing this end. It may have other, less desirable effects; at the moment, that is irrelevant.

The conclusion on this point, whether reached by deduction from principles or by observation of our own society, is that the stratification, individualism, intergroup ignorance, and internal competitive tradition, all engendered by the complexity of society, enhance the function of alcohol. Complexity results in a need for greater integrative functioning; relaxation of tension, uncertainty and suspicion is necessary for this function; alcohol has been found useful in its accomplishment.

In addition to the need of the society for greater integration, there is also the need of the individual to make contacts, both occupational and recreational. In a mobile, multistratified world, this is more difficult than in a stable, less-stratified world. In a specialized, competitive world, recreational devices for the individual seem more essential. Yet the factors just discussed make difficult the attainment of that easy, trustworthy, noncompetitive friendship situation which is requisite for interpersonal relaxation. The traveling salesman is an extreme example. His role is highly competitive and is lived in a world of strangers. Alcohol is obviously functional for achieving the relaxation of suspicion, of competitive tension, of the barriers usually present in our society between strangers.

In contrast, then, to the effect of a complex society on the medical, food, and religious-exaltation functions of alcohol is the effect of the complex society on alcohol's function of promoting recreational and other association. This function is definitely enhanced.

ALCOHOL AND TENSION

We now approach the more important, perhaps the fundamental function of alcohol for individuals. As you are all aware, alcohol is a depressant. Alcohol allows, through its depressing function, a relaxation of tension, of inhibition, of anxiety, of guilt. There is no need to define narrowly the meanings incorporated in these words. You have heard a good deal about them and are aware of the sort of behavior and attitude which is implied. I will consider, however, the areas of behavior and attitude which are most commonly colored with these emotional characteristics. The listing I shall present is only suggestive, grows out of reading, training and observation; the order of appearance is quite arbitrary. Around what personal problems of adjustment do anxiety, tension, guilt, and the like, arise?

I would suggest the following: (1) the individual's opinion of himself; (2) gaining and holding the respect and the affections of others; (3) conflicting with others, through self-assertion, through criticism, through out-and-out aggressions; (4) over-all security, as to ownership, prestige, personal safety, as they are tied up with money; (5) responsibilities accepted in the achievement of specific goals; (6) sexual matters.

This is a purely descriptive listing. It may seem to imply that these six are totally separate matters. They are not! The list is merely a convenient set of handles by which one can pick up and examine the package labeled "one human being." The handles alone are meaningless.

In a complex society these areas of behavior and attitude are more greatly challenged, are more difficult to live through or adjust to than they are in a simpler society. For a very simple example, take the matter of self-assertion or the exhibition of aggression. In a world of extraordinary dependence on others, aggression is very dangerous. To make an oversimplified analogy—an airplane engine in which the cylinders are at war with each other or with the spark plugs is a dead engine. You may want to tell your client, your parishioner, your landlord, or your boss, what you think of him. But it is very, very dangerous. So you refrain from doing it. You have been trained since infancy not to do it. We have all been trained not to lose control of our tempers, not to attack others, not to be too self-assertive. Does that mean that we do not feel aggressive? It does not. We just cover it up. Sometimes we can train ourselves so well that we do not even recognize that we are angry, but our emotions do not stop operating. In a complex, specialized, stratified society we are continually in situations where we are dependent on others and the others do not seem to care much about us. Elevator operators, waiters, salespeople, clients, partners, all of them have it in their power to frustrate us. By the very nature of the system they must frustrate us somewhat, since they serve 50 or 500 other people in addition to us, and we must take our turn; that is ineradicable in association. So we get angry. But we cover it up. The complexity of society increases the incidence of aggression-provoking situations. The complexity of society renders the expression of aggression ever more dangerous.

Consider the matter of prestige, of recognition from others. In a society in which there is great homogeneity of activity, where most people do about the same things in the same way, the range of prestige is smaller. Either you are a good or a mediocre or a bad workman. Furthermore, in a simple society the tangible marks of success, such as conspicuous consumption or ownership, are also limited in variety and quantity. But in a complex society the situation is dramatically different. There is an extraordinarily refined hierarchy of prestige. Much of the prestige goes with the position rather than with the individual's talent or exertion of effort or pleasing personality.

Furthermore, recognition and prestige depend more and more on obvious, often tangible, symbols. In the simple society, it is easy to tell who is an efficient, pleasant person. In the stratified, specialized society, it is not easy. People are more and more inclined to give recognition according to conspicuousness and wealth. There is not the time, there is not the knowledge, there is not the personal interaction on a variety of levels of experience, for people to judge.

Let me give an example of this that took place at football practice on the Yale field when I was a freshman; probably it occurred many years earlier and surely has been going on ever since. One of the players, utilizing the accepted technique of "talking it up," was always calling his roommate's name whenever the latter did anything that was even passably good. "Come on Johnson," "Attaboy Johnson," "Take him out, Johnson," and so on, and so on. The only purpose was to fix the name Johnson in the coach's mind. In any other situation he called his roommate Brad. The coaches were faced with about 140 persons from whom they would pick 25 for the first team. They very soon were aware of Johnson. Even though the coaches know of this system, it still works. It works in the army, it works in the factory, it works in getting into Who's Who. In a simpler society, it just will not work.

Yet, despite this weakness, the need to get good persons for specialized positions is pressing and in this impersonalized competitive society the goal of gaining prestige is enhanced. The result, of course, is increased apprehension, increased sensitivity, increased tension.

In a complex society where personal relationships are more and more specialized, impersonal and competitive, and where various specialties are not understood by others, recognition and respect and prestige are more intensely desired, are more difficult to attain, and are, perhaps, more suspect, than in simpler societies. This results in frustration, envy, aggression and anxiety which do not appear in such marked form from this source in simpler societies.

The increased complexity of our social existence has increased social responsibilities. As a simple example, consider General Eisenhower or the president of a large corporation. One of the outstanding characteristics of high position in any of our ways of life is increase in responsibilities. For many hierarchies we may say that the taking on of higher office is matched by an increase in the anxieties a person carries. One of the earmarks of the executive is his ability to assume anxiety with understanding and with poise. The person in the lowest rank carries very little anxiety about the function of the organization. At 5 P.M. he quits work and forgets about it, although he still carries personal anxieties. The high-ranking man carries his anxiety concerning the whole organization all the time. The one has little or no prestige and little or no anxiety on this score; the other has much prestige and much anxiety.

The general over-all security represented by money in a complex society has already been dealt with. The increased anxiety from this source reflects through all of the significant emotional areas that were listed, in addition to possessing a ranking of its own. Although it weighs most obviously on the people in the lowest economic ranks or in marginal positions, it can be equally oppressive to people who, while not threatened with starvation, are threatened as to their social position and prestige.

Time forbids dealing with the other emotional areas. It is, or should be, sufficiently clear that interpersonal relationships and personal satisfactions are more difficult, are more anxiety-provoking, are more exhausting, in a complex society.

The advantages of a complex society are manifest. But there is a price to pay. That price is intangible, difficult to measure or define. It can be roughly labeled as emotional insecurity for the individual. Since alcohol can reduce the impact, can allow escape from the tensions, fears, sensitivities, feelings of frustration, which constitute this insecurity, its role will be more highly valued.

I shall mention one more view of the enhanced importance or power of the alcohol-drinking custom due to social complexity. The most obvious aspect of complexity has been described as specialization. Specialization occurred in the activation of this custom as in all the others. Specialized crops, specialized industries, specialized distribution, advertising and financing, specialized retailing, all occur in the realm of alcoholic beverages just as in that of railroading, of dairy products, of education, or of men's clothing. Just as the function of clothing is extraordinarily expanded and enmeshed in other social organizations, beliefs and activities because of specialized institutionalization, so is that of alcohol production and distribution and consumption. For example, when one makes one's own clothes or one's own wine or whisky, there is a great deal of pressure, of anxiety, about not using the product unless it is really needed. Under conditions of specialized production, where there is competition, a monetary basis, and impersonal relations between producer, distributor, retailer and consumer, this pressure is completely reversed. The more consumption, the more success. This process is heavily reinforced by the fact that unit costs tend to go down as the number of units produced goes up.

The effect of this concomitant of social complexity is to equip the whole constellation of alcoholic beverage activities, ideas, material objects and organizations with motives, mechanisms and functions which are utterly disconnected with the physiological and psychological functions of alcohol. The same distinction, of course, is true for all other specialized institutions.

DYSFUNCTIONAL ASPECTS

Now we come to the results of societal complexity on what might be called the socially and individually dysfunctional aspects of alcohol. The potentialities of alcoholic beverage consumption remain the same but are to be viewed in a different light. We could speak of dynamite in the same way; its properties do not change, but its effects on human beings can be of a tremendously constructive or tremendously destructive nature.

The complex society presents great rewards to individuals; two factors balance these rewards, are a sort of fixed charge: (1) break-down of any part is far more dangerous than in the simple society; (2) there must be a more exact fulfillment of function than was previously necessary on the part of every subgroup and every individual. To put this in a more general way: the need for imagination and perception, for control over responses, for timing and balance, is greatly increased by the complex culture; just to get things done is a more delicate task, and the penalty for not getting things done has far greater social implications than in the simpler society. Do not illustrate this in your minds by the sole picture of a person driving a car or tending a machine. One tendency of our material culture has been to dominate our thinking in just such a narrow way. Think rather of relations between groups of people, employer and employee, principle and agent, people of different social classes; think rather of the foresight necessary in a production schedule, in bringing up children, in establishing governmental procedures. These activities in a complex society demand greater sensitivity, greater efficiency in action, greater imagination and greater caution than in a simpler society. Alcohol lowers sensitivity, efficiency, and caution. It deteriorates balance and timing. Personal aggression and irresponsibility are far more dangerous in a complex society, and, as an adjustment to this, child-training in complex society lays heavy emphasis on self-control, indoctrinates inhibitions and repressions on aggression and irresponsibility; alcohol allows release of these inhibitions. Regularity of behavior is as essential in a complex society as in a complex machine. Alcohol can wreck regularity of behavior. I need not expand on this point. The conclusion is apparent. The need of the society for regularity, precision, individual responsibility, and integration through self-control and cooperation, is increased by complexity. The achievement of these values is directly threatened by alcohol in proportion to its depressant action.

A further societal complication is to be seen in the means of control. It has been pointed out that specialized and formal groups have become more powerful and have extended their functions while all-purpose and intimate groups have been weakened. If the drinking of alcohol and its effects were limited to the area of one of these specialized groups, sanctions could be efficient. Or if the society were simpler, more homogeneous, more dominated by some all-purpose, personally intimate and significant association, sanctions could be significant. The drinking of alcohol and its effects, however, infiltrate all manner of acts and associations and ideas. The attempt to exert sanctions over this wide, loosely organized area will be met with opposition, argument, and relatively unabashed violation. The sanctioning authority will not be recognized. The ideology behind the attempt will be challenged. Social classes, minority groups, religious groups, locality groups, and other categories will not have the identity of purpose, understanding and experience which would allow such action to proceed smoothly. The complexity of society is of manifest significance on this point. Furthermore, the question of control can itself create further disorganization in the society. This, of course, is quite irrelevant to the physical and psychological properties of alcohol.

In a society already impersonal, competitive, individualistic and stratified, the effect of excessive drinking on the individual is dramatic. You have heard, and presumably will hear, sufficient on this subject to make any treatment here quite superfluous. I would only draw attention to the fact that the complexity of the society, and the concomitants of that complexity as here described, exaggerate and speed the deterioration process in the maladjusted person.

SUMMATION

Now let us recapitulate the particular sociological viewpoint on alcohol here presented: Social complexity, in the case of Western civilization a complexity dominated by economic specialization, has enormously increased the number and variety of goods and services, has improved quality beyond measurement, and can produce with unparalleled speed. This is as true of alcoholic goods and services as of others. Complexity has also resulted in horizontal and vertical stratification, in mutual ignorance and disinterest of societal subgroups, in extreme interdependence of subgroups and of individuals, in the emergence of money as a controlling factor in human life, and in an individualism marked by the increased power of each person and the decreased power of such all-purpose intimate groups as the family and the small neighborhood.

In relation to alcohol these concomitants of social complexity have had the following seven effects:

1. They have practically eliminated three functions of alcohol which were of minor importance in primitive society, namely, food value, medicinal value, and religious-ecstasy value.

2. They have enhanced the need for integrative mechanisms in the society which are personally significant; the pleasure group is important here, but other meetings are not excluded. The function of alcohol in depressing certain inhibitions, anxieties, aggressions and tensions, thus allowing relaxation, has increased significance since it can help in this process.

3. These concomitants of complex society have increased, compared to simpler societies, the weight of anxieties of most individuals, and have added new anxieties. The depressant function of alcohol thus becomes more significant, especially since these anxieties are directly related to the most basic human drives.

4. The very nature of the specialization process has created a network of relationships, activities, wealth, social position, and so on, which revolve around the business of alcohol, thus bringing into existence a set of factors not present in the simpler society, a set of factors unrelated to the physiological or psychological properties of alcohol.

5. The complexity of society increases the needs, if the society is to exist, for sharp discrimination, caution, accurate responses, timing, cooperation, and the acceptance of responsibilities. Alcohol, taken excessively, can deteriorate all of these.

6. The nature of the complex society makes social controls over behavior that is not strictly compartmentalized into one or another institution an extremely difficult task. The drinking of alcohol and its effects are not in any one institution or pattern of behavior but infiltrate throughout; the drinking itself is largely in the loosely organized area of individual recreation. Control of drinking behavior in the complex society is therefore a more difficult problem than in the simpler society.

7. The individual in the complex society has a far more formidable task in integrating himself to groups and ideas in a satisfying way, is equipped with more personal choice, and belongs to looser, more specialized, less personally satisfying associations. The excessive use of alcohol can more rapidly and thoroughly destroy such participation in complex societies than it can in the simpler, more general, more intimate groups of primitive societies. The power of alcohol to deteriorate personality is thus enhanced in complex society.

It can be seen, thus, that the complexity of society is a significant factor in the relations of alcohol and man. It obviously enhances the uses of alcohol for man. It obviously increases the dangers of alcohol for man. Social complexity has added new forces and motivations for the production and distribution of alcohol. It has taken away the power from agencies of control which could once be efficiently used.

A complex society has great advantages, but, like all real advantages, complexity demands a price. The problems of alcohol are not insoluble. But in our complex world their solution is going to demand sensitivity, discrimination, effort, experience and cooperation which may well tax our patience and energy and honesty to the utmost. Solving this complex problem will be hard, the price will be high, but it can be done.

DISCUSSION

Shepherd: It is estimated that there are 40 to 45 million users of alcoholic beverages in the United States. Would it be your opinion that the number of users could be reduced if our society were less competitive?

Lecturer: My remarks concerned compulsive drinking—excessive drinking—and not the ordinary moderate use of alcoholic beverages. There are not 40 to 45 million excessive drinkers in the United States, but only 2 to 2½ million. If you could reduce the competition and reduce the basic anxiety, one would expect that fewer people would, in fright and compulsively, turn to the excessive use of alcohol. Many people would find alcohol in society just as any ordinary experience, but they would not feel that they had to have it. But if you reduce the competition in our society, what are you going to do to the whole society? It might be a fine thing for alcohol problems, let us say, but a great many people feel that competition is an integral part of this whole specialization process through which we have attained so many goods and services. So, although it is an interesting question, I am afraid that at the same time it is really an academic question because so many of our people feel that in all matters—social, business, athletic and even romantic—competition is at the very heart of what might be called the American way.

Mrs. Sloan: Is the use of alcohol to reduce anxiety, instead of overcoming the threatened danger, a sign of human weakness? If so, would the increasing use of alcohol in our complex society point to a weakness that may, in time, destroy it?

Lecturer: I will answer that question in what might be called a sociological way. In the first place, alcohol is not going to overcome, realistically, many of the dangers that people face. That must be obvious. But is the excessive use of alcohol a sign of human weakness? I have been trying to point out that the social structure is tremendously important in its effect on human beings. Human beings can do all manner of things. From the point of view of behavior, they are the most malleable of all forms of life. You can, perhaps, direct them all to become extreme alcoholics, or you can direct them to become, perhaps, the opposite. The social structure, I would say, is very important in determining in what direction they will go. Now, rather than call it a human weakness, I would say that excessive drinking can more usefully be viewed as a resultant of social factors in their impact on each individual. The latter part of your question is whether the increasing use of alcohol may, in time, destroy society. That would call for a very subjective answer. Taken to extremes, why, of course. If everybody in our society got and stayed quite drunk, it is obvious what would happen. You wouldn't have any water, or any food; you wouldn't have any milk, or any doctors; you wouldn't have anything. But that is going to such an extreme that I certainly don't foresee anything of that sort.

Davies: Would it be correct to say that our society has deteriorated because of our inability to control excessive drinking on the part of individuals, whereas, in primitive societies, they control the alcohol drinking?

Lecturer: In a certain sense this question answers itself. Our inability to control excessive drinking is obvious enough, and, in part, this has come about because of our lack of an over-all, homogeneous group with strong controls. A simple society would exert such control with greater ease. However, I would reverse your statement somewhat by saying that our control of drinking is less apt, because our social homogeneity, in purpose, in behavior, and in organization, has deteriorated.

Hoover: If primitive tribes using alcohol have worked out certain techniques to limit injurious aggression by removing weapons and excluding women from the drinking bouts, what techniques are practical in civilized society?

Lecturer: I do not think it was by the removal of weapons and the exclusion of women that alcohol became less injurious among primitive people. That is a final-end technique to remove an immediate cause of violent aggression, of violent activities which are proscribed by the mores. The problem is not that. The problem is basically the over-all, commonly accepted morality and belief structure. We cannot deal with little bits of this. To take a matter such as excessive drinking, you can't do too much by manipulating a little thing here and a little thing there. You have to go to the over-all morality of your group. Then the little techniques will of themselves appear. They will not be difficult to find. As to what such techniques will be in our society, your guess is as good as mine.

Question: What is needed, then, is good intention?

Lecturer: Yes, without that good intention, without that over-all belief, any technique can be very nicely got around. Various techniques have been tried. For instance, in order to get people to stop drinking so much in saloons, legislation was passed which made everyone stand up. "Take all the chairs and tables out, and people won't hang around so long." It appeared a good idea, but when they tried it, it didn't seem to work. The customers seemed to stand around and drink more, just because they were standing up. Then laws were passed so that nobody could stand up at the bar. "Everybody must sit down"—just another technique. Well, here in Connecticut, for instance, to get around this technique, they placed little tables about a foot wide in front of the bar at a height so that it was like sitting on a long stool. You were practically standing at the bar, but not actually—you were really at a little table. It is easy to work out techniques like this, but unless there is good will, belief, and conviction behind the purpose, there are always ways to get around them.

Moorey: If both the skilled and the unskilled worker, employed by the same business firm, used alcohol, which of the two would show the greatest tendency toward becoming diseased through the excessive use of alcohol? Both men have the same physical and mental characteristics and both use equal amounts of alcohol.

Lecturer: You use the term "become diseased through the excessive use of alcohol." I am going to take that as meaning "become compulsive drinkers." Your question then is: of these two men, under the conditions described, which is in greater danger of becoming a compulsive drinker? This question relates directly, I suppose, to a comment I made when I said that the higher up a person gets, the greater are his anxieties, his responsibilities, and, at the same time, his need of precision. That is the skilled worker. On the other hand, you have the man who doesn't need all this precision, who doesn't have the carry-over of responsibility and anxiety. One of these men gets pretty good pay and has prestige and position in the community; the other has a much lower position and much less economic security in the community. And the question is, Which one is the alcohol going to affect the more severely? Well, we are just dealing with intangibles here. We know that alcohol hits individuals; it does not hit specific positions or roles. I can't say that alcohol will affect dangerously a man in trade A before it will do so in trade B. Although these two men have, perhaps, different types of responsibilities to face, different types of anxieties, I don't think that the economic position would be so dominant in most people's lives that it could control the answer to the question. The man's family situation, his feelings of prestige and satisfaction and ease in dealing with other people, his respect for himself—these things make a tremendous difference. We know that a person on the low economic level can often be a mature, easy, responsible, pleasant person, relatively free from anxiety, while a person higher up can be very anxious and scared indeed. This one characterization is probably insufficient evidence from which to make any general statement, particularly since the distinction between skilled and unskilled has become more and more difficult to define.

Shattuck: Alcohol is reported as being one of the four leading causes of the downfall of France. Would you say that this is an over-statement?

Lecturer: That is such an enormous question that I think I can give an enormous answer. I'll say, yes, I think it is an over-statement. I am not qualified to speak on what the situation was in France, and I presume you are asking me as a person who has read the newspapers. I certainly would not have picked that as a leading cause. I don't know what I would have picked, but that sounds just like one of many rather rash statements. I do not say this as a sociologist, but rather as a private person with no special knowledge of the particular situation.

Stoneburner: In your opinion, would the reduction of competition in the sale of alcoholic beverages, by the limiting of licenses to a larger population-numeral, reduce excessive drinking? Would it not allow more room for morals on the part of those who are in highly competitive areas?

Lecturer: I don't think that changes of practices in that specific institution—retail trade—are going to have a very great effect on the morals of the group as a whole. Are you going to increase the morals because you keep retailers from selling liquor to all the people, or make them sell less liquor, or control the types of liquor? I don't believe that morality is going to be turned on and off for the great mass of people because they can or cannot get liquor. The greatest sanctioning power for morality is within each individual, resulting from the training that he has received in childhood and the closeness with which that training meets social conditions—so that he can accept that training and believe in it and carry it out. That is what is going to have the greatest *moral* effect. On the technical side, there are probably people who know more than I do about how such restrictions might work by their knowledge of the experience of specific countries.

Stoneburner: In asking that question, I was looking for something tangible to take home with me from this School and was wondering if the strong competition that exists between the licensees does not reduce the margin of their own morals.

Lecturer: You are thinking of the economic morals of the retailers?

Stoneburner: Yes, of their morals in their attitude toward the people who come into their places. That is the import of the question. I know that in other businesses, when competition becomes too strong, people are pressed to do things they otherwise would not do. And I am wondering if it would not raise the caliber of licensees if there were fewer of them and a larger population left to support them than presently exists. A larger population for each particular licensee.

Chairman (E. M. Jellinek): This limitation on the number of licensees for a given population has been used in several countries, especially in Holland where they determine a maximum as well as a minimum ratio. It seems that one does not get an entirely straight-line relation, that is, one cannot say that the more customers per licensee the less the incentive to violate rules—or the greater incentive to be satisfied with what the licensee can get legitimately. That works in a straight line up to a certain point only. Past that point, the licensee might not be able to cater adequately to an increasing number of customers, or a limited kind of monopoly might result with its attendant dangers. Anyway, the utility of increasing the number of potential customers per licensee grows to a certain point and after that the utility ceases. Thus a minimum as well as a maximum ratio may have to be stipulated. Furthermore, in Holland they did not have a rigid rule for the number of population per licensee, but they had given ratios for towns of a certain size, and different ratios for smaller towns. In rural areas, special ratios were applied. There is much more sense in relating the ratio to those social factors which are roughly reflected in the size of the community.

Lecturer: Following such a determination of general policy, you can go on to a method of control. Anybody who has a sincere, honest method of control, particularly one which has been tested by experience, has an adequate instrument especially as it concerns technical terms. But will it work in this or that community? That is very hard to predict.

Brown: Is competition between the specialized groups in our society necessary in order to have the goods and services which these give us?

Lecturer: That, of course, is a question that has been argued and argued and argued over the last 15 or 20 years. A great deal of emotion is shown on this point. If you take one side, you are a horrible capitalist; if you take the other side, you are a horrible communist. Whatever you are, you are certainly an "ist" of one sort or another. Historically speaking, the weight of the evidence would seem to be that the competition, the competitive spirit, did a great deal to achieve the extraordinary material progress and wealth in our particular hemisphere. I don't think that there would be very much denial of that point. It produced an incentive, an extraordinary incentive, which, in turn, resulted in one of the miracles of the world. On the other hand, it is true that the conditions have changed. Just take the simplest fact, the matter of population—people per square mile—and the number of available square miles. That's just one simple example, and there can be no question but that the situation of 1925–1950 is very different from that of 1875–1900. Certainly some of the values of competition which existed in 1875 have not survived. There is obviously still value in competition. There is also danger in it. Those values must be recognized in the social situation in which they are taking part, in which they exist, not in the situation of another era. Can we do away with competition and still maintain the values? That is the question. The middle path seems to consist of exerting more and more governmental control on those parts of competition which lead to the most drastic pains, in those fields which affect the most people. And we still seem to be getting pretty good service in those fields. I wouldn't say whether it was better, or worse. It is apparently possible for society to go on with control of some of this competition. A great many people are terrified—really very frightened—that if you reduce the need for competition beyond a certain point, you are going to change the basic personality structure of people in our society. This is one of the great questions of our day.

Robinson: In our society, aren't there other and better ways of reducing anxieties and tensions from a physical efficiency standpoint than by using alcohol?

Lecturer: The previous questions have approached the general problem, "How do we reduce basic anxiety?" And to many people the answer is, let us say, revolution, change everything, take out all competition, take away all dependency, and so on. This question is of a different nature. What is there to substitute in place of alcohol? I think there is a great deal. I think the substitutes will have to play a role in those areas which I spoke of as being emotionally very significant. One conclusion is that the answer will not be found through the great spectacle. I don't believe that a person can get sufficient personal reward, sufficient interpersonal activity, to satisfy the need for prestige and for affection and personal relationships of all kinds, through watching a moving picture production, that is, through substitutes which are largely on the escapist side. Now, neither can we expect everybody in society to start playing chess. We have got to achieve something which will allow people to get together on grounds that are not highly competitive, that are not emotionally frightening, but which allow personal activity. And it can't be just those same little groups that always stick together. It is going to have to be an association that can cut across these barriers that have been set up between different groups. This is going to demand organization and imagination. It means putting something rewarding into our national life on a group level instead of on a simple individual striving level. And I think very many things can do better than alcohol, many things, indeed. But it means that many of us will have to participate in those activities, get behind them and give them a feeling of "this-is-our-way-of-doing-things," "it's us," "it isn't just something they tell us to do." We are going to have to find activities and beliefs that are apart from this intense individualism in our country, and you don't have to give up all individualism to do that. Those are the broad lines in which such activity can take place.

Edwards: You spoke of the great power inherent in alcohol, depending upon how it is used. Will you comment further upon means by which alcohol may be used in constructive ways?

Lecturer: "In constructive ways?" That is changing the tenor of the remark somewhat. I don't believe that I spoke of the great constructive values of alcohol. I think the functions were spoken of as relaxing and depressing; I also pointed out that relaxation and the depression of tension seemed to be called for more in our society and that alcohol as a quick, cheap way of getting this, was used more and more.

Shepherd: If the over-all social morality is important in control, would you care to suggest some possible normative standards for that morality in relation to alcoholic beverages?

Lecturer: This is really a question to be answered by one of two people, I think: either the social engineer (which is, I should say, a potential position in society, although I've never seen one); or a person versed in ethics. I don't think there is any question but that the over-all social morality is important. It is a dominating factor. What are the standards for that morality? You can find them in any great social system, any great religious system—those factors which hold people together, keep them in control, and yet satisfy their basic needs. All I could do would be to read some of the great slogans of history. They haven't changed in fundamentals very much. The other possibility is for me to give you a blueprint, and certainly I don't pretend to have that.

Lecture 15

Some Economic Aspects of Inebriety

Benson Y. Landis

MANY questions in economics could be raised in connection with inebriety. One could investigate the effect of business depressions and booms on the consumption of alcoholic beverages; the influence of foreign-trade agreements on the kind of beverages consumed; the effect of taxation on bootlegging, and so forth. The economist would not run out of questions emanating from his field and relevant to the problems of alcohol.

Obviously a large number of lectures would be required to answer these questions. Thus we must limit ourselves to a few questions which seem to us to be of special interest.

The expenditures involved in inebriety—the particular question selected for discussion—have been the subject of much guessing but of little systematic estimation. Also, the guessing has served the purpose of furnishing fuel for indignation rather than data for economic solutions.

In the present inquiry an attempt is made to arrive at a reasonable estimate of certain annual expenditures due to inebriety in the United States for the year 1940; and to consider these expenditures in relation to the public revenues from the alcoholic-beverage industry and to the allocations of certain of these funds. The year 1940 was selected because the best statistics are available for that year. This study is devoted mainly to a review and synthesis of scattered information found in the literature, but in some instances critical evaluation of available but hitherto not utilized sources has been made.

Only a rough approximation can be secured by this method. The state of present knowledge about costs is such that only the most evident factors could be considered. Further, in some of the categories to be considered, an estimate could be arrived at only from original assumptions. In other categories, statistical presentations of the annual costs of inebriety cannot be made at all.

In this discussion the term inebriety will be used to mean habitual excessive drinking. I shall take as the basis for this study the estimate of Haggard and Jellinek that of some 44,000,000 users of alcoholic beverages, there were approximately 2,400,000 excessive drinkers in the United States in 1940, and, of these, about 600,000 were chronic alcoholics. We shall be concerned *mainly* with the 2,400,000 excessive drinkers.

ALCOHOLIC MENTAL DISORDERS

In forming an estimate of the costs of alcoholic mental disorders a sharp distinction must be made between the mental disorders attendant upon the prolonged excessive use of alcoholic beverages and those in which excessive drinking is incidental and cannot even be regarded as one of the contributory factors.

At the onset of schizophrenia, of general paresis, and of manic-depressive psychosis, quite frequently excessive drinking appears as a prodromal symptom. Since the excessive drinking does not precede the onset of the psychosis it cannot be regarded as a contributory factor, and exception must be taken to those estimates which include the cost of care of those patients who are diagnosed with other than alcoholic psychoses but who are recorded as "intemperate drinkers." In our estimates, therefore, only patients diagnosed as having an alcoholic mental disorder will be considered.

In order to obtain satisfactory estimates of the cost of the care of alcoholics in mental hospitals in 1940 it is necessary to know the average daily number of alcoholics under care in these hospitals. For 1940, however, only the number of first admissions, readmissions, discharges and deaths are recorded. The number of alcoholics in mental hospitals at the beginning and at the end of the year is not stated. Such figures are available, however, for the year 1933 for all hospitals in the United States, and for other years for Massachusetts and New York. From these statistics it appears rather consistently that the ratio of all admissions (first admissions plus readmissions) with alcoholic psychoses to the average daily number of patients with alcoholic psychoses is approximately 0.49, and the ratio of all admissions for alcoholism without psychosis to the average daily number of alcoholics without psychosis is 3.4. Utilizing these ratios we can compute the approximate average daily number of alcoholics in mental hospitals. The estimates are shown in Table 1.

The per-patient cost in state mental hospitals for the year 1940 was $361.50. For veterans', city, and county hospitals, the cost is not stated, but may be taken as approximately 30 per cent higher than in state hospitals, that is, $469. The rates in private institutions range more or less from $30 to $100 per week, with a probable average of $50 or a yearly average of $2,600. The estimated cost of care of all alcoholic patients in mental hospitals in 1940 is shown in Table 1. The total cost is nearly $13,000,000.

TABLE 1. *Estimated Cost of Care of Alcoholics in Mental Hospitals, U.S., 1940*

Type of Hospital	Average Daily Number of Patients	Annual Per-Patient Cost	Total Cost
State	11,000	$ 361.50	$ 4,013,000
Veterans', city, county	2,200	469.00	1,032,000
Private	3,000	2,600.00	7,800,000
Totals	16,200		$12,845,000

A significant commentary on the economic aspects of this situation comes from those familiar with the results of treatment of those suffering from alcoholic mental disorders. Novick concludes that "the state hospital has failed to cure the alcoholic," and that in these institutions little has been learned about the problem of alcoholism. He contends that "separate institutions giving special treatment" are needed, and further, that treatment is especially needed by the patient in the 10-year period prior to the onset of the alcoholic psychosis, because alcoholic mental disorder results from many years of very excessive drinking.

If there is to be a wise social policy with respect to treatment of alcoholic mental disorders, including prudent use of public and private funds, these opinions need to be taken into account. I shall return to this consideration later in the discussion of uses of public funds.

BODILY DISEASES

To arrive at an estimate of expenditures for the treatment of bodily diseases associated with inebriety is a much more difficult matter than that for mental illness. Haggard and Jellinek sum up available data as follows:

Perhaps the most striking fact in regard to the bodily diseases of chronic alcoholism is that none is specifically limited to individuals who use alcohol in excess; the diseases may, and do, occur in those who use no alcohol. . . . The diseases of chronic alcoholism are essentially nutritional disturbances.

There are a few clues in some data from the general hospitals, but these are limited to cities in which investigations have been made. Moore and Gray found for the Boston City Hospital, 1927 to 1937 inclusive, that between 4.5 per cent and 8.0 per cent of the total cost of the Haymarket Square Relief Station was for the care of alcoholic patients. The average cost for treatment of alcoholics per year for the period investigated was 5.6 per cent of all cost; but the alcoholic patients were only 2.8 per cent of all patients. Thus the cost of treatment of alcoholics was twice that of the average patient in this one station.

For New York, in 1933, Deardorff and Fraenkel, in a study of discharges from the general local hospitals, both voluntary and public, found that 2.7 per cent of all patients discharged received treatment for alcoholism. (Hospital treatment is largely given for bodily diseases only, not for addiction.) There were 15,576 such patients out of a total of 576,623, and of these, 85.7 per cent were male. Seventy-three per cent of the alcoholics treated stayed 2 weeks or less; this was, comparatively speaking, one of the conditions for "short-stay."

In general, the treatment of alcoholics in hospitals in the larger cities tends to be concentrated in a few of the public institutions; private general hospitals usually will not admit alcoholics. The relatively few alcoholics who do receive treatment in the voluntary hospitals do so only because of special intercession on the part of their physicians.

According to Falk, total expenditures for all medical care by the people of the United States in 1940 amounted to about $3,500,000,000. The population resident in the continental United States, according to the Bureau of the Census, was 131,669,275 persons. The over-all expenditure per person per year was $26 plus. If we eliminate expenditures for treatment of mental illness and dental care, the expenditure per person averaged, probably, about $23. Repeated investigations have shown the uneven distribution of expenditures for medical care by income groups; in general, the lower the income the lower the expenditure for medical care. Large numbers of persons have inadequate medical care; and some have almost none.

There were, in 1940, about 2,400,000 excessive drinkers in the population, of whom about 600,000 were chronic alcoholics. Habitual excessive drinking usually takes place among persons at least in middle age. And such persons, present knowledge indicates, are more prone to certain diseases, as mentioned above, than the general population. It seems reasonable to assume that the expenditures for medical care of the inebriates, as made either by themselves, or for them by others, or at public expense, are somewhat higher than the per capita expenditures. Therefore, for the habitually excessive drinkers, all adults, we may estimate that expenditures for bodily diseases were about 33⅓ per cent higher than the average of about $23, or $30.70 per person. For 2,400,000 persons, the excess over the normally expected cost of illness is $18,480,000. Only this excess can be charged to the costs of inebriety since it is not to be assumed that the inebriate, if he were not an inebriate, would not share in the average expectancy of illness and its cost.

ACCIDENTS

Much has been written on the role of alcoholic intoxication in accident causation. Yet no quantitative estimates have been made on the contributions of intoxication to accidents in the home, at work and in public places (excluding motor-traffic accidents), although guesses have been ventured. Some of these guesses—anything from a 5- to 75-per-cent contribution of inebriety—have been quoted as if they had been estimates.

Reports on occupational accidents have pointed out that on Mondays the number of accidents is considerably higher than on other days of the week and the assumption has been made that this is due to week-end drinking. At least a part of the increase in Monday accidents may be ascribed to alcoholic binges, but no inference can be made from these data as to the possible number of accidents due to intoxication, or to the effects of "hang-over."

Reports have also dealt with comparisons of the per-thousand rate of industrial accidents for excessive drinkers on the one hand and moderate drinkers and abstainers on the other hand, but in no case was the number of excessive drinkers stated. All these investigations tend to show that inebriates are more liable to accidents than noninebriates, but they do not give an idea of how many inebriates there are among industrial workers.

As to motor-traffic accidents, some partial estimates have been offered but no general estimate has been presented, although arbitrary percentages have been used.

For 1940, and for several years prior to that, the National Safety Council stated that in 20 per cent of the fatal traffic accidents described by state and local authorities the driver or pedestrian was reported as "having been drinking." Relative to drinking drivers the Council's publication, *Accident Facts*, said: "State summaries showed that 11 per cent of the drivers involved in fatal accidents had been drinking. These drivers were involved in 1 out of 6 accidents." Thus drivers who had been drinking were involved in 16.7 per cent of all fatal motor-traffic accidents. Berry summed up available knowledge of the entire traffic situation by writing that "alcohol is an important primary cause of many traffic accidents," but that "it is difficult to say how many."

It is generally acknowledged that fatal accidents are investigated more thoroughly for intoxication of persons involved than the nonfatal accidents. Also, local reporting varies greatly. Some cities report no one was drinking; others report high percentages. Again, the use of chemical tests of blood, urine, and breath is becoming more widespread. In 1940, 57 cities of over 10,000 population reported using the tests. Berry reports that in 1942 the laws generally made it a criminal offense to drive while "under the influence of intoxicating liquor"; but that the courts in many places have held that there is a difference between "under the influence" and "being intoxicated." He also says that in many jurisdictions it is difficult to secure convictions on charges of this criminal offense.

But apparently no investigator has been willing to assign precise percentages to alcohol as an important factor in motor-vehicle accidents, except for fatal injuries. At one time the National Safety Council used the figures of "5 to 10 per cent" of all traffic accidents referable to alcohol, but has not done so during recent years.

While it may not be safe to estimate separately the cost of home, public, occupational, and automobile accidents of inebriates, there appears to be a body of data which permits of an estimate of the number of inebriates involved in all accidents and consequently of their share in the costs of all accidents. On the one hand there are the statistics of the National Safety Council on the number of fatal and nonfatal injuries for all categories of accidents as well as on the property damage, cost of medical care, wage loss, and overhead cost of insurance involved in these accidents. On the other hand there is available a reliable estimate of the number of fatal accidents among inebriates based on statistics of the Bureau of the Census and Jellinek's corrections for incomplete reporting. Since the relation of nonfatal to fatal accidents is known for the entire population, it is possible to obtain an estimate of the number of nonfatal accidents of inebriates by applying the national ratio to the fatal accidents. Since death from chronic alcoholism occurs in chronic alcoholics only, these estimates may be designated as estimates for the chronic alcoholic population.

For the year 1940 the Bureau of the Census reported 2,531 deaths from alcoholism as a primary cause and 3,109 deaths from other causes to which alcoholism was a secondary cause of death, a total of 5,640 deaths, including 769 deaths from accidents associated with alcoholism as a primary or secondary cause. This means that of persons reported to have died from alcoholism as a primary or secondary cause of death 13.6 per cent were involved in fatal accidents. In comparing this with statistics for the general population, two points must be considered. First, since for "inebriates' accidents" primary as well as secondary causes have been taken into account, the same procedure must be followed for the general population. Thus, to the 96,885 deaths from accidents as a primary cause there must be added 2,875 deaths from other causes associated with accidents, giving a total of 99,760. Second, since for practical purposes inebriety does not occur in persons under 15 years of age, the general death statistics as well as the statistics of death from accidents must be limited to the population of 15 years and older. In 1940 all deaths in the population of 15 years and over amounted to 1,258,344 and for the same ages the total fatal accidents—primary and secondary causes—were 86,049. In the general population of 15 years and over, fatal accidents formed 6.8 per cent of all deaths. It is thus seen that fatal accidents in 1940 were twice as great a source of deaths among chronic alcoholics as among the general population.

The Bureau of the Census states that the reported deaths from alcoholism may be doubled, since a special study has shown that deaths from this cause are under-reported by 50 per cent because of the reluctance of many physicians to certify alcoholism as a cause of death. Furthermore, Jellinek has pointed out that "death from alcoholism" does not include "death from cirrhosis of the liver with mention of alcohol," and that alcoholism is involved in 35 per cent of deaths from cirrhosis of the liver in which alcoholism is not mentioned. Making all these corrections, Jellinek arrived, for the year 1940, at a total of 15,250 deaths from alcoholism and cirrhosis of the liver in which alcoholism was involved. Applying to this the rate of 13.6 per cent, the fatal accidents in the chronic alcoholic population may be estimated at 2,074. Since the inebriate population is 4 times as great as the chronic alcoholic population, the fatal accidents among all inebriates may be put at 8,296 for the year 1940.

In that year the ratio of nonfatal accidents to fatal accidents in the population of 15 years and over was 90 to 1 and since, in other years, this ratio has shown only a few points of variation it may be applied as a rather characteristic ratio to the fatal accidents of inebriates. A total of 698,130 nonfatal accidents and a grand total of 706,426 nonfatal and fatal accidents is thus obtained for the entire inebriate population. This is 9 per cent of the 7,843,049 nonfatal and fatal accident total of the general population of 15 years and over.

The 2,400,000 inebriates, including the 600,000 chronic alcoholics, formed 2.43 per cent, let us say 2.4 per cent, of the 98,620,000 persons 15 years and over of the 1940 population. There is no reason to assume that these 2,400,000 persons would have had no accidents at all if they had not been inebriates. The reasonable assumption is that they would have shared in the accidents of the nation at the rate of 2.4 per cent. Thus not more than 6.6 per cent of the total accident cost can be debited to inebriety.

Certain adjustments for age must be made of the costs given by the National Safety Council for home and public accidents, but not for occupational and motor-traffic accidents. Except for a fractional percentage of the occupational accidents, only persons of 15 years and over are involved in them. In the case of motor-traffic accidents the cost does not require adjustment for age since injuries to children below 15 years of age are caused by drivers above that age, even though in many instances the children may be at fault. Except for loss of wages, which applies only to persons of 15 years and over, the cost of home accidents must be adjusted for 21 per cent of the accidents by persons less than 15 years of age, and the cost of public accidents for 16 per cent of accidents below that age. Of the overhead cost of insurance, only that part is adjusted which pertains to medical cost.

The National Safety Council estimate and the costs adjusted on the basis of the principles given above are shown in Table 2.

As the wage losses are dealt with separately in the present study, we shall consider now only the $1,351,000,000 remaining after deduction of wage losses. The net contribution of inebriety to this is 6.6 per cent, amounting to $89,170,000.

TABLE 2. *Cost of Accidents for the Year 1940*

	National Safety Council Estimate	Estimate Adjusted for Age
Medical expense	$ 300,000,000	$ 257,000,000
Overhead cost of insurance	300,000,000	294,000,000
Property damage (motor vehicle)	800,000,000	800,000,000
Wage loss	1,800,000,000	1,800,000,000
Totals	$3,200,000,000	$3,151,000,000

CRIME

With the exception of a small percentage of offenders committed to Federal and state prisons and reformatories for misdemeanors, these institutions house prisoners sentenced for felonies, while the jails, with the exception of a small percentage bound over for felonies, usually house prisoners sentenced for misdemeanors. This is a distinction which merits close attention.

Drunkenness is a misdemeanor if not accompanied by anything graver than disorderly conduct or disturbing the peace, and persons arrested for these misdemeanors are committed to jails; they are not classed as felons. In the statistics of the Bureau of the Census this distinction is consistently observed, but unofficial statistics and the public mind rarely make this distinction. Consequently the large percentage of drunkards among the jail population frequently leads to excessive estimates of the role of inebriety in the causation of felonies.

In the following analysis the contribution of inebriety to misdemeanors, and thus to the jail population, will be kept apart from the contribution to felonies and the prison and reformatory population.

In the matter of arrests for drunkenness in numerous American cities, we have at least a well-recognized type of expenditure on account of inebriety. The problem of refining the data and of stating their significance is, however, difficult, because in most instances we have only gross figures of total arrests and no information about the number of repeaters.

It is often stated that "drunks on the streets" absorb "too much" of the time and energy of the municipal police. Miller reports, for example, that in 1940 in the city of Cleveland, arrests for intoxication were about 19 times as high as in the same municipality in 1910, although the population had not quite doubled in that interval. A preliminary statement on "Drunkenness in Wartime Connecticut," a report of the Connecticut Crime Survey, revealed 9,516 arrests for drunkenness in Hartford in 1940, the figure being an increase of 27 per cent over that of 7,490 in 1939. The Committee to Investigate Crime found that there was an increase of 32.5 per cent in offenses of every kind in the larger towns and cities, particularly in the defense centers, during the 12 months following July 1940; and that "the great bulk of these offenses, aside from traffic violations, consisted of drunkenness cases. . . ."

In a special study over a period of 5 weeks early in 1942, the Committee found there were 2,000 arrests in Hartford, Bridgeport and New Haven, and

1,529 of these were for drunkenness. At this rate there were probably 20,000 arrests for drunkenness a year in those 3 cities alone. About "two-thirds of all nontraffic arrests are for drunkenness," and a "great burden" is thus placed on law enforcement agencies. In the 3 cities "there is a minimum expectancy of 123,000 lost working days because of the arrested drunks."

Of the 1,529 persons arrested for drunkenness in Connecticut, 66 per cent were given their freedom by discharge; 22 per cent were given short jail sentences, usually 10 to 30 days; small fines were imposed on 11 per cent; and the small portion remaining was otherwise dealt with. The means of dealing with the problem, said the investigators, produced practically no useful result, and did nothing about prevention. The most hopeful discovery was a practice, in New Haven, of sending some of the inebriates to jail to do useful work. Recommendations were made for a systematic approach to the problem, including adequate records, and a beginning of rehabilitation through special treatment of selected individuals.

The Federal Bureau of Investigation reported for 1940 that in 1,212 cities with a total population of 41,146,894, 11.81 per cent of all "persons charged," that is, held for prosecution, were detained for "drunkenness"; 3 per cent for "disorderly conduct" (a term which includes drunkenness in certain cities); 1.68 per cent for "vagrancy"; and 0.76 per cent for "driving while intoxicated." Of all arrests, 73.11 per cent were for traffic violations and the remainder were in various other categories. In the same year in 79 cities with a total population of 13,493,387, 155,528 persons were found guilty of drunkenness, disorderly conduct and vagrancy, and 7,267 of driving while intoxicated.

The majority of investigators agree that persons arrested and held for drunkenness probably account for 70 per cent of the annual costs of maintaining about 3,000 county and local jails. Some investigators place this figure at only 50 per cent, but published statistics indicate that 70 per cent is a conservative estimate.

MacCormick says that the cost for an average daily jail population of about 100,000 amounts to $36,500,000 a year. Seventy per cent of this amount, or $25,550,000, will be included in our estimate of the cost of inebriety.

Police magistrates, probation officers and penologists in general have come more and more to see that the enforced abstinence in jails is usually of no benefit to the inebriate. Such opinions were expressed at the discussion in the Summer School of Alcohol Studies at Yale University on the penal handling of inebriates. This opinion has been voiced by MacCormick and also by Robinson in his recent book on jails.

The relation of excessive use of alcoholic beverages to other aspects of crime statistics is much more complicated. Koren, who did investigations for the Committee of Fifty, organized in 1893, wrote in a book of his own in 1916: "The assurance with which intemperance is held responsible for the mass of criminality has at any rate the merit of being quite natural. When any offense is committed in a state of intoxication or by an habitual user of strong drink, the causal relations seem unmistakable, even inevitable, no matter how infinitely complicated the problem appears to the criminologist." But Adler concluded, "We now believe that the hope of finding specific causes of any of the major behavior disorders, such as crime and delinquency, is likely to be a futile one." He pointed out that criminals generally are intemperate with respect to sex, alcohol, narcotic drugs and gambling.

An intensive study has been made by Banay. As chief psychiatrist of Sing Sing Prison, he made careful studies of 1,576 first admissions in 1938–39 and 1,559 in 1939–40. Centering attention upon those persons whose criminal acts *followed* long periods of drinking, he summed up as follows: "In 25 per cent of the total offenders, alcoholism was closely related to the commission of the crime, or was directly responsible for it." But from the combined tables of his study it appears that the percentage is 22 rather than 25. We do not know, of course, whether such conditions are general throughout the United States. Banay says that very little effort is made in prisons to remedy tendencies toward alcoholism. Banay did not include in his data persons whose alcoholism appeared only after numerous criminal acts, or as a sequence to a dissolute life, or seemed to serve only as an agent to give false courage or to dispel scruples.

Some students of this question believe that there is a persistent tendency on the part of criminals, and more especially of their relatives, to single out excessive drinking as an explanation of crime, rather than to consider the whole social milieu and the influence of early delinquent activities. When is excessive drinking incidental? When is it a concomitant of other unsocial and antisocial conduct? When is it the "precipitating cause"? Criminals follow a general pattern of "low living," a prominent social worker asserts, in which excessive drinking is often present. Criminals are often persons who develop aggressive tendencies after long periods of frustration. Economic competition and economic insecurity are also sometimes cited as important causative factors in the development of criminal careers.

The study of 13,402 convicts made for the Committee of Fifty indicated that intemperance alone helped to explain the criminal careers of 16.87 per cent of that group; this was about the same proportion as those for whom no cause could be ascertained. Other factors cited were unfavorable environment and lack of vocational training. Farnam wrote, however, in the same survey, that "the study of crime offers peculiar difficulties. . . . Crime cannot . . . be attributed to a single cause."

The National Commission on Law Observance and Enforcement, reporting in 1931 on "The Cost of Crime and Criminal Justice in the U.S.," stated that total economic loss was impossible to determine. The Commission did note that various investigators had set the total costs of crime per year at figures varying from $1,000,000,000 to $18,000,000,000 and recorded that an estimate appearing in the report of the White House Conference on Child Welfare in 1930 set the figure at $16,000,000,000. The Commission made estimates, however, of a number of evident items. The Federal Government was spending about $52,000,000 per year for administration of criminal law; the states were spending for penal agencies, including parole and police, $53,500,000; cities of over 25,000 were spending $247,000,000; private expenditures were $3,900,000 —these items being grouped as "in excess of $350,000,000." The cost of insurance against criminal acts was put at $106,000,000; losses in connection with use of the mails to defraud were $68,000,000. The cost of maintaining an average daily prison population (not including local jails) of 145,000 in 1930 was over $51,000,000. The loss of productive labor on the part of 170,000 persons engaged in full-time law enforcement was set at $300,000,000 a year, and the loss of productive labor of the state and Federal prisoners was set at $235,000,000. No item for property damage was included. The sum of all these items, minus wage loss of prisoners considered later, was $875,000,000 in terms of 1930 conditions.

In 1940, the daily population of state and Federal prisons was over 165,000 compared with about 145,000 in 1930, an increase of 13.8 per cent. It seems altogether probable that the annual cost of all the items mentioned in the National Commission's Report was at least 10 per cent higher in 1940 than in 1930, or $962,500,000.

We have not found an investigator ready to assign any definite percentage of these costs as referable, in large part, to excessive use of alcohol. We cannot know, for example, whether if by some miracle there were no drunks on the streets for a year, the costs of maintaining county and local jails would be reduced by one-half. It seems entirely likely, however, that if inebriety could be drastically reduced, through prevention and effective therapy, tendencies toward criminal acts would likewise be reduced; but such prevention and therapy would obviously have to be carried on in the broad terms of personal and social adjustment.

Taking the 22-per-cent incidence of primary inebriety in Banay's study as the basis, at least 2.4 per cent allowance must be made for the fact that the 2,400,000 inebriates represent that percentage in the population of 15 years and older and therefore may be expected to share to that extent in crime even in the absence of inebriety. Thus $188,650,000, or 19.6 per cent of the total costs of $962,500,000 for the several items involved in crime, mentioned above, is included as probably in large part referable to excessive use of alcoholic beverages.

SOME GENERAL CONSIDERATIONS

"The alcoholic is usually successful in involving his family and himself in a series of dramatic and distressing crises that demand attention from the agency and community," writes Lewis in a systematic discussion of nine case records. In one of these a wife was quoted as saying of her alcoholic husband that he was puzzling and contradictory, noisy, yet when sober she could not ask for a better husband. A "melee of opposing forces" is noted by this social worker.

Intemperance appears "frequently" in the records of persons aided by social agencies, that is, those aiding families in the cities. But case records are confidential and we have found no recent statistical reports. Case workers are known for their thorough work, case by case, and they hesitate to generalize about the role of alcohol in dependency, as the psychiatrists and criminologists hesitate to generalize in referring to crime statistics. Nevertheless, some approximations on this question have been made. The director of the Catholic charities of Cleveland, Ohio, has mentioned several statistics which indicate that inebriety may be a contributing factor in 18 per cent of charity cases.

Expenditures for assistance for various dependent, handicapped and neglected persons are large. The Department of Commerce estimated, in its *Survey of*

Current Business (October, 1942) that in 1940 local voluntary social agencies expended $117,900,000. Of this amount 18 per cent, or $21,220,000, may be included as the estimated share caused by inebriety. Public funds spent for general relief, such as W.P.A. funds, cannot be considered here, and probably are not greatly affected by the factor of inebriety.

Juvenile delinquency has been frequently related to inebriety, but it would appear that it is more the case of a common parent factor than of an actual contingency. About the rise of juvenile delinquency in 1940 and during the later war conditions many social workers have said that the high mobility of the population, working mothers, poor housing, night work shifts, lack of adequate recreation, lack of total community responsibility, all were probably in part responsible for a complicated social situation in which drinking was also a noticeable factor.

Since habitual excessive drinking usually follows years of drinking, the attitudes of youth are important. The American Youth Commission of the American Council on Education queried 13,528 young people in Maryland between the ages of 16 and 24 and published the results in 1938. Of these persons, 52.9 per cent reported that they drank alcoholic beverages; 19.3 per cent that they were generally opposed to drinking liquor; and 27.8 per cent that while they did not personally use liquor, they were not opposed to others doing so. Of the males, 60.7 per cent reported they drank; of the females, 44.7 per cent. Liquors of all kinds were legally available to persons 21 years of age and over.

The Northwestern National Life Insurance Company of Minneapolis is apparently the only company that releases data on the use of alcoholic beverages by applicants and the importance of this factor in rejections. In 1938 this Company reported that 2 out of 5 men and 1 out of 12 women under 30 among applicants stated that they used alcoholic beverages. In the age group of 30 to 45, 3 out of 5 men and 1 out of every 3 women stated that they were users. Over age 45, 2 out of 3 men and 1 out of 6 women said they were users. The data were based on 16,000 applications. Of these, 1,000 were rejected. Of the rejections, 24 per cent were not granted insurance because of evidence of the excessive use of alcohol. The Company reported that the proportion of rejections because of excessive use of alcohol had been practically stationary since 1936; but that the general use of alcoholic beverages had become more widespread "during recent years."

POTENTIAL WAGE LOSS

One of the items of cost is an indirect one—the loss of earnings because of disability on the part of those who drink to excess. This is considered separately because it is a "potential" loss. It is not known whether all the persons idle because of disability would have become earners in any given year, if and when they became well. It would probably depend largely upon the year. The year 1929 or 1943 would probably require one answer; the year 1932, another; and the year 1940, still another. However, the year 1940 was one of relatively high economic activity. There was an expansion of enterprise, the national defense program was shifting to high gear during the latter half of the year, so that there probably would have been good opportunities for employment and earnings for the ill and injured if they had been well and able to work.

Inebriates under care and treatment in public and private mental institutions numbered 16,300, as noted previously. Of these persons, approximately 85 per cent are males, judging by the trend of first admissions to the state hospitals. Median earnings for 1939 were reported as $1,038 for males and $610 for females; and according to Keim there was a wage increase of 7.5 per cent on these earnings in 1940. Taking, therefore, $1,116 for males and $656 for females, a total wage loss of $17,060,000 is found for this category in 1940.

For loss of time on account of bodily diseases, only a very rough computation seems possible. Falk estimated a potential wage loss for all illness, during 1940, of $1,500,000,000. For some 50,000,000 persons gainfully employed, this would amount to $30 per person per year. On the basis of 2,400,000 excessive drinkers, it has been assumed above that their expenses for illness were probably one-third higher than the national per capita expense. If that is applicable, then these persons would probably have an average wage loss per person of $10 more than the average earner, and this may be designated as the net loss due to inebriety. This sum, for the 2,400,000 persons, would be $24,000,000.

For the "floating drunks," probably a daily average of 70,000 who move in and out of the county and local jails, the wage loss is more difficult to estimate. They are mostly males of the underemployed type. Even under 1942 conditions they did not work steadily, according to the previously mentioned Connecticut survey. But it is not possible to say definitely that they would have been unemployed even in the absence of inebriety. Thus we cannot but assume a potential wage loss of $1,116 for each of the 70,000, or $78,120,000.

The National Safety Council assigned $1,800,000,000 as the potential wage loss of the persons involved in accidents. As seen before, the net contribution of inebriety to accidents was 6.6 per cent and thus the wage loss in this category must be taken as $118,800,000.

For figuring loss of time of prisoners in Federal and state institutions 19.6 per cent of the total number of about 165,000 must be taken, or 32,340 prisoners whose inebriety was an important contributory factor. Of prisoners released in 1940, about 5 per cent were female. It may be estimated, then, that 1,617 females had an average wage loss of $656 or $1,060,000; and 30,723 males an average wage loss of $1,116 a year, or $34,288,000, a total of $35,348,000.

Excessive drinking as a cause of absenteeism in industry is often noted, and we have already referred to days lost in 3 Connecticut cities early in 1942. Week-end dissipations and pay-day sprees were undoubtedly one reason among many. Haggard and Jellinek stated that in 1 factory of 18,000 employees, 2.6 per cent "lost time on 1 or more occasions because of acute alcoholic intoxication." In another establishment with about 20,000 employees, about 4 per cent lost time for this cause. The number of workdays lost through acute intoxication can hardly be ascertained from factory records. At the Yale Plan Clinics it was found that inebriate factory workers lost, on the average, 3 days per month, or 36 days per year.

Taking an average of several surveys it may be said that 65 per cent of the inebriate population are skilled and unskilled workers. Thus, we can assume that of the 2,400,000 inebriates in 1940, 1,560,000 were workers in industry. Applying the 36-day-per-year loss and the median annual earning of $1,116, the wage loss from this source in 1940 may be estimated at $169,632,000.

The total potential wage loss of the groups considered is $442,960,000.

RECAPITULATION

The main expenditures and potential wage losses because of inebriety during 1940 have been estimated as follows:

Expenditures Probably Referable to Inebriety—1940

Mental-hospital care and treatment	$12,845,000
Bodily diseases—care and treatment	18,480,000
Accidents—injury, property damages, etc.	89,170,000
Maintenance of drunken persons in county jails	25,550,000
Crime—various items	188,650,000
Support of dependent persons (private)	21,220,000
Total	355,915,000
Less correction for probable duplications, 2.5 per cent	8,898,000
Net total	347,017,000

Potential Wage Loss in 1940—Certain Groups

Persons mentally ill	$ 17,060,000
Bodily illness of wage earners	24,000,000
Mobile inebriates in county jails	78,120,000
Persons involved in accidents	118,800,000
Prisoners, Federal and state	35,348,000
Absentees in industry	169,632,000
Total	442,960,000
Less correction for probable duplications, 2.5 per cent	11,074,000
Net total	431,886,000

This gives a grand total of $778,903,000.

This is, to reiterate, a crude estimate, subject to correction after further study. It applies only to the well-recognized items enumerated in the preceding text and considered by review of the literature. It applies mainly to the approximately 2,400,000 persons in the population in 1940 who drank to excess. It is obviously not an estimate of the social costs of all drinking. While the costs estimated here are far below the multibillion products of fantasy, they represent a very large sum, indeed. Not even the $56,875,000 spent in one year on mental-hospital care, treatment of bodily diseases and temporary segregation in jails contribute constructively toward the rehabilitation of inebriates. Expenditure for treatment of the inebriate habit is conspicuously absent. It is not far-fetched to hope that investment in the treatment of compulsive drinking and research on inebriety might cut down the costs due to present-day policies to a practically negligible amount.

In order to ascertain the possible sources for such a proposed investment, a survey will now be made of the status of the alcoholic-beverage industry and of public revenues from the consumption of its products.

CONSUMPTION, MANUFACTURE AND DISTRIBUTION OF BEVERAGES

In 1944 the Department of Commerce published estimates of the total value of alcoholic beverages purchased by the people of the United States from 1934 to 1943. The total amount estimated as spent in 1940, the year considered in this study, was $3,595,000,000; that for 1934, $2,003,000,000; and for 1943, $6,083,000,000. During the same period the national income increased rapidly and the rate of taxation generally increased. These reported expenditures for alcoholic beverages have apparently been equal to between 4 and 5 per cent of the total income of all the people in the years 1934–43. In 1940, the estimated expenditure for alcoholic beverages was slightly less than 5 per cent of the total income of all the people from all sources. For the 131,669,275 persons resident in the United States, the expenditure of $3,595,000,000 in 1940 was the equivalent of about $27 plus per capita. For the approximately 44,000,000 users of alcoholic beverages, it was an average of about $81 per person. The proportions of these expenditures that became revenues for governments will be referred to later. For the manufacture of alcoholic beverages in 1940, use was made of about 3.2 per cent of the total volume of the corn, barley, rice and rye crops; also of about 60 per cent of the grapes grown commercially.

For the manufacture of alcoholic beverages, the latest official figures are for the year 1939, published as part of the 16th (1940) Census of the United States. Five branches of manufacturing were reported, as follows: malt liquors, malt, wines, distilled liquors, rectifying and blending of liquors. The malt manufacturing industry simply produces malt, mainly from barley, which is used by other manufacturers in the industry. These 5 branches reported a total of 1,241 establishments with 76,585 employees drawing wages and salaries, and a total payroll of $145,564,387. The total value of manufactured products was $722,561,399; this is the value at the factory, and is not to be confused with the value of products sold at retail. Table 3 shows the division of items for the various branches and has been constructed from the census report.

The Federal Trade Commission, as part of its Industrial Corporation Reports in 1941, presented an analysis of financial operations of six of the "more important concerns" in the distilled-liquor industry. Their total sales in 1939 were valued at $290,699,253; net income after taxes was $17,083,626; dividends paid totaled $1,126,333 on preferred shares of stock and $6,253,776 on common shares—equivalent to 4.9 per cent of the "equity value" of $150,-646,987 of the six corporations. They spent for advertising an amount equivalent to 4.8 per cent of sales, or $13,984,494. More comprehensive data on expenditures for advertising of alcoholic beverages will be given later.

The Federal Trade Commission also reported on 21 of the "more important" corporations manufacturing malt beverages—those having about 44.4 per cent of the total value of all products as given in the 1940 Census of Manufacturers for 1939. Their sales in 1939 amounted to $203,496,279; net income after taxes was $23,732,813; dividends paid were $1,069,821 on preferred shares, $12,011,120 on common, equivalent to 10.4 per cent of the equity value of $125,763,115. Expenditures for advertising totaled $14,157,477, equal to 6.94 per cent of total sales.

The Securities and Exchange Commission reported "data on profits and operations" of certain corporations whose stocks were listed on exchanges for 1940. For distillers, 10 corporations were listed, having total sales of $349,-965,000 in 1940; their net profits after taxes were $24,617,000, equal to 7 per cent of sales, and to 11.4 per cent of net worth.

TABLE 3. *Some Economic Data on the Alcoholic-Beverage Industries*

Industry	Manufacturing Establishments	Wage Earners Employed	Salaries and Wages Paid	Value of Manufactured Products
Malt liquors	605	61,185	$122,264,690	$526,076,938
Malt	52	1,902	4,136,702	58,478,581
Wines	301	3,491	4,550,868	32,782,080
Liquors, distilled	135	5,752	8,258,731	56,080,195
Liquors, rectified and blended	148	4,235	6,353,396	49,143,605
Totals	1,241	76,565	$145,564,387	$722,561,399

The S.E.C. reported in 1940 on 5 distillery corporations in the United States with assets of over $10,000,000 each on June 30, 1939. These owned the major portion of the total assets of the 15 corporations of this industry that had registered securities with the S.E.C. The total value of the sales of these 5 corporations was $308,000,000 during the year ending in 1939. Their profits, after all charges, were $23,100,000, or 7.5 per cent of sales. They paid dividends of $12,800,000 during the year ending in 1939.

The S.E.C. presented data for 27 breweries with listed stocks for 1940. Their total sales were $78,489,000; the net profits after taxes were $7,503,-000, equal to 9.6 per cent of sales and 11.8 per cent of net worth.

As for the distributive process in this business, the most comprehensive recent figures are for 1939, appearing in the 1940 Census of Distribution. In that census there were reported 135,594 "drinking places," that is, places primarily so operating, such as bars, beer gardens, cabarets, night clubs, saloons, tap-rooms and taverns. Their total sales were reported as $1,385,032,000, or 3.3 per cent of all retail sales for all purposes reported in the census. At a portion of these "drinking places" meals are also served. Their total payroll was $159,689,000 for 212,235 employees, and there were enumerated 136,-217 "active proprietors of unincorporated businesses."

For retail liquor stores selling packaged goods there were reported 19,136 outlets, with $586,351,000 worth of sales, 25,676 employees, and a payroll of

$30,782,000. Their total sales were 1.4 per cent of all retail business reported in the nation for that year. Alcoholic beverages were also sold, to some extent, at establishments listed as primarily "eating places," which numbered 169,792; and at food stores, which totaled 560,549; but it is not known what proportion of these businesses is in the form of alcoholic beverages.

The most inclusive available estimate of advertising is the one for national advertisers using the four important media of radio, newspapers, magazines, and farm journals, made for 1940 by the Bureau of Advertising of the American Newspaper Publishers' Association. The total spent by national advertisers in 1940 in these media amounted to $420,479,424. Among the highest categories was "alcoholic beverages," which stood fifth on the list, with expenditures of $27,920,643. In the newspaper field alone, expenditures for alcoholic-beverage advertising amounted to $19,533,136, the third on the list, and exceeded only by automobile and grocery advertisers.

Printers' Ink published an item in 1942 to the effect that the brewing industry alone had spent $170,000,000 for advertising since 1933. The estimated total of brewers' advertising in 1940 was $21,058,000 through the following six media: daily newspapers, weekly newspapers, magazines, radio, out-door, and "point-of-sale." The data were compiled by the research staff of the Brewing Industry Foundation.

PUBLIC REVENUES AND THEIR USES

We are here discussing a heavily taxed industry. In most periods of our history the alcoholic beverage industry has paid high proportions of all Federal revenue. Between 1911 and 1917, for example, the Federal revenues from alcoholic beverages each year amounted to over one-third of the total receipts from taxes levied by the National Government. The Tax Institute of the University of Pennsylvania, which has made informing reports on many aspects of taxation, has compiled comprehensive data on public revenues received from alcoholic beverages in 1940. Total Federal tax receipts for 1940 were $4,860,-524,000, of which $624,253,000 came from the levies on alcoholic beverages. To this must be added customs receipts of $32,340,000. Total state tax revenues were $3,267,165,886, of which $243,776,068 was from alcoholic beverages. To this total must be added the net profits in the "monopoly states," amounting to $66,057,520 in 1940. The revenues collected by local governments were estimated by the Tax Institute at $3,500,000 out of total local receipts of $4,745,000,000. Others use a considerably higher figure. Thus the revenues from alcoholic beverages totaled $969,926,588 of total public revenues of $12,872,689,886, not including payroll taxes, equivalent to almost 8 per cent of all tax revenues. The Distilled Spirits Institute published a somewhat higher estimate of $1,140,110,006.

As far as can be learned there is no specific designation for the use of Federal receipts; it is also the general practice to retain local receipts from licenses for the general purposes of local governments. But the state revenues of $243,-776,068 in license states, and net profits of $66,057,520 in monopoly states are, in many instances, designated for specific purposes. The following state allocations, for example, may be noted:

Alabama: Ten per cent of state sales profits to state public welfare fund; 10 per cent to the public welfare funds of 67 counties.

Colorado: Of state license fees and excise taxes, 5 per cent for administration, 85 per cent of remainder to old age pension fund, and 15 per cent to public welfare fund up to $870,000; balance to state general fund. Of county and municipal license fees, 85 per cent to old age pension fund.

Florida: Of state license fees and excise taxes, 7 per cent for administration; first $3,400,000 of remainder to old age assistance; next $400,000 to crippled and disadvantaged children; balance, if any, to general fund for distribution to public schools.

Georgia: All license fees and excise taxes go to common schools, with minor exceptions.

Idaho: Under certain conditions, 50 per cent of any money received by a county from state allocation must be paid to "a junior college district." A recent revision of this act assigns a percentage to research on narcotics.

Indiana: Of retail permit fees, one-third to tuition funds of the school taxing units of the state.

Iowa: State beer license fees and taxes to emergency relief fund; of state sales tax, first $1,000,000 to old age assistance fund.

Kansas: Retail sales tax distributed, among other purposes, for general public welfare and state school aid.

Louisiana: Portion of spirits and wine license fees must be used exclusively for homestead tax exemptions; beer license fees and excise taxes apportioned to public schools, and, conditionally, to various charitable institutions.

Maryland: State receipts to general fund which is used, among others, for old age assistance, dependent children, needy blind, general public assistance.

Massachusetts: A portion of revenue from state license fees and excise taxes is distributed to cities and towns for certain old age pensions.

Missouri: Proceeds from seizures and confiscations to county treasuries for benefit of schools.

Montana: Of state monopoly profits, 5 per cent to teachers' retirement fund, and up to $5,000 to Temperance Commission fund; of state license fees, 50 per cent to public school fund, and portion of remainder to public welfare fund.

Nebraska: State license fees to state school fund; state registration and excise taxes to state assistance fund for child welfare, crippled children, public relief, old age assistance, and other public welfare.

Nevada: Of state license fees and excise taxes, major portions to state distributive school fund and university contingent fund.

New Mexico: Major portions of state revenues to social security, aid for dependent children, needy blind, and for emergency school fund.

North Carolina: Sales tax receipts on beer and wine to emergency fund for support of schools.

Ohio: Most of sales tax on beer to poor relief and workmen's compensation fund.

Oklahoma: Most of state license fees and excise taxes distributed to county school districts.

Oregon: Portion of state sales profit and excise taxes to mothers' aid, old age pensions, aid of indigent.

Pennsylvania: Under certain conditions, payments for public assistance may be made from liquor revenues.

South Dakota: About one-half of receipts from beer and wine license fees and excise taxes to counties for relief and hospitalization and indigent.

Texas: State license fees to old age assistance fund; of state excise taxes, one-fourth to state school funds, three-fourths to old age assistance.

Utah: State sales tax receipts to state emergency relief fund to be used for schools and old age assistance.

Washington: Over one-half of state sales tax receipts to state current school fund.

West Virginia: Sales tax receipts to school fund.

Wisconsin: Portion of state excise taxes on spirits and wine to state aid of public schools.

There is thus a tendency for the states to use portions of the public revenues from alcoholic beverages specifically for certain educational and social purposes. Other undesignated funds are, of course, also used for the purposes enumerated above, and for other needs, too. The states pay much toward the support of mental illness, for example. Thus general state funds go toward the custodial care of alcoholics among the mentally ill. Relatively small sums are also designated for educational work by state liquor control authorities. No information could be obtained in this inquiry, however, of any specific designation of revenues received from the alcoholic-beverage industry for other care and treatment of the alcoholic, although a careful search was made for such data.

The Committee on Inter-Governmental Fiscal Relations reported to the Secretary of the Treasury on January 1, 1943, that "the liquor tax field is characterized by such diversity of legislation and administration . . . that it would be unwise to attempt a uniform national program." However, other informed persons have thought otherwise. Some of these have thought that a constructive beginning might be made by a system of graduated taxation, particularly of distilled spirits, by proportion of content of alcohol—the higher the proof, the higher the rate of tax. The Federal Government, since 1940, has applied this principle to the taxation of wines. This policy would furnish an incentive of tax reduction for the purveyor of the more dilute product. A second recommendation, particularly applicable to wartime, was made by the late Professor Yandell Henderson, who had drafted a bill which would have limited the sale of spirits to a maximum content of 80 proof, or 40 per cent alcohol. The proposed bill was modeled after the Food and Drugs Act, and was "designed to control the hazards to life and health" due to the use of distilled spirits.

A use of state funds, that may be of economic and social significance, by the state of Virginia is worth noting here. In February, 1944, the Virginia Legislature authorized the Alcoholic Beverage Control Board to purchase 29,200 shares of the common stock of the American Distilling Company. By this transaction the State received a dividend "in kind" of 27,740 barrels of whisky—

over 525,000 cases—a portion of 237,000 barrels being distributed as a dividend by this Company to its stockholders. The transaction at least raises questions of social and public policy. Virginia is known as a "monopoly state." Its public authority became, for the time being, an owner of a corporation established for the purpose of making private profits.

SUMMARY AND CONCLUSIONS

We have noted a probable minimum expenditure of $778,903,000 because of certain antisocial behavior of inebriates and of conditions due to inebriety in 1940; and the figure might have been higher if one could make a detailed statistical computation of some other factors which might bring the estimate up to or somewhat over the one-billion-dollar mark.

Also, we have found that the heavily taxed alcoholic-beverage industry produced for public treasuries in 1940 the sum of about $969,926,588. The 1943 revenue from this source amounted to $1,423,647,000. These revenues are an important aspect of public finance. In many instances the states designate portions of these public revenues for social purposes. Except for the use of public funds for care and treatment of alcoholics who are mentally ill and for some educational work by public liquor authorities, however, it was not found that any of these large revenues are designated for discovery of ways and means of preventing inebriety, or for reducing the large social costs that result from the behavior of those who drink to excess. In recent months, however, the legislatures of Connecticut, Indiana, New Jersey and Massachusetts have considered proposals to use revenues from alcoholic beverages for treatment and research.

Thus the total effect of these policies is that the public has a socially irresponsible attitude toward the serious questions under consideration. If the industry may freely advertise alcoholic beverages for sale, and if large public revenues accrue, it seems that, as a minimum procedure, considerable funds should be designated for discovery of more effective means than now exist for dealing with the personal and social problems arising from the policy. Such designations might properly provide for experimental research, for the training of medical and other personnel, and for clinics and hospitals that would specialize in specific measures of prevention and treatment that would promise improvements in the current situation.

Preliminary reports of the operations of the Yale Plan Clinics, begun early in 1944, indicate that promising results in the treatment of alcoholics can be obtained by the expenditure of about $60 to $100 per person. The Clinics, one at New Haven and one at Hartford, were established through the cooperation of the Connecticut Prison Association and the Laboratory of Applied Physiology of Yale University. There is a medical committee, appointed by the State Medical Society, and the policies of that Society are safeguarded. The aim is to aid the alcoholic to find his way back to useful participation in the community. Every patient is given a physical examination and is studied on several occasions by a psychiatrist and a social worker. The Clinics provide only simple ambulatory treatment for persons unable to pay for the services. It is believed, however, that the methods used thus far might be employed to reach perhaps 85 per cent of the alcoholics in the community. More than one-third of the patients have come on their own initiative. Others have been referred by probation officers, the prosecuting attorney, social agencies, and friends and relatives.

The extension of these special methods of therapy, at a cost of about $100 per patient, to the 600,000 chronic alcoholics in the United States would cost $60,000,000. This amount would be a relatively small portion of the public revenues received from the industry. Such an expenditure for prevention and therapy would seem to be wise in the light of the social costs of about one billion dollars paid annually by the people because of inebriety.

DISCUSSION

Question: Does your figure on drunkards in jails include also the cost of prosecution and conviction?

Lecturer: My memory is that it does not. It is simply limited to maintenance of these persons in the jails.

Weil: Have you any figures as to economic loss due to drunkenness in the Army and Navy?

Lecturer: No, there aren't any figures so far as I know. There was one study in Boston of rejections because of alcoholism, but my understanding is that the standards of the Selective Service Administration on this point were not very rigid, namely, a man had to be pretty much of an alcoholic—unmistakably a chronic alcoholic—to be rejected. We haven't much of any indication from the Selective Service figures. As to the loss of manpower and so on in the Army and Navy—I don't know that any figures have been published.

Smoot: You said that the cost of the liquor was three and a half billion for 1940 and that one billion of that was tax. Is that about the proportion that it usually runs?

Lecturer: Taxes in 1940 ran considerably higher than in preprohibition days, and since 1940 the tax rates have been increased on two occasions. At present the tax rates on distilled spirits are higher than in any other industry.

Smoot: What I was wondering about is the comparison here between the cost of the liquor at three and a half billion and the tax of one billion. That would make it about 35 per cent of consumer expenditure on liquor, wouldn't it?

Lecturer: Yes, that was the proportion of the tax in 1940. I cannot say offhand what it was for other years. There has been a search for public revenues. Governments are assuming more functions and this industry has produced a considerable amount of revenue. I have enumerated some of the purposes for which that revenue is being used when it is specified in the various states. It is all a part of the search for more revenues to cover more government functions.

Question: Does your figure of three and a half billion for 1940 include distilled spirits and beer and wine?

Lecturer: Yes. The Department of Commerce estimate is an over-all estimate. It is the best knowledge of consumer expenditure for these purposes—a part of a study of all consumer expenditure. That is why I gave it to you. I think it is a very important study. It obviously ought to include an estimate of illegal consumption. My understanding is that in the case of distilled spirits there is still enough bootlegging, black markets, whatever you want to call it, to account for up to 50 per cent of the consumption. I do not know whether that is correct or not, but it is apparently an important factor in the case of distilled spirits. The testimony from the brewing and wine industries is that bootlegging or the black market is *not* an important factor.

One other thing on taxation. One of the difficult questions of policy involved is at what rate should you tax in order to discourage illegal traffic? If you levy high taxes, there are those who say you encourage the illicit traffic. A good many people feel that a relatively moderate tax rate is better for discouraging the illicit traffic than a high one because the high tax rate provides an incentive to the bootlegger.

Mrs. Lewis: Have the high taxes paid by the liquor industry been used by them as a reason for continuance in business as against prohibition?

Lecturer: Yes, to some extent. The industry points to these uses and it is part of the public relations program of the industry. I think it is an important part of their argument.

Olson: I refer to the charge that the present Administration has shown favoritism to this industry in the rationing regulations. Would the search of the Government for revenue and the lucrative business of the liquor industry have any effect upon the attitude of the Government toward such a business, that is, would it tend to be favorable to the liquor industry, to encourage indirectly the consumption of liquor?

Lecturer: When you are getting public revenues, it is a competition between, let us say, income taxes and consumption taxes. We might get a little perspective on this by considering the gasoline tax. That is reported to be a relatively painless tax. The public paid it rather readily with very little complaint. For one thing, in most cases, the revenue, until recently, was used for a specific purpose. Originally, you remember, it was to be used for roads and the fellow who paid his gasoline bill at the filling station felt that the tax was going for road improvement and he was rather willing to pay it. Now, in the controversy as between corporation taxes and income taxes and these consumption taxes, the states and the Federal Government have found taxes on these beverages also somewhat painless to extract. Public opinion being what it is, the public pays these taxes rather readily. In 1943, the public got much less liquor for its money than it did in 1942, but in these times of surplus incomes apparently paid it very willingly. So I would think that public opinion being what it is, the legislature has a somewhat favorable attitude toward the encouragement of the consumption of liquor because there are these revenues to be secured. But, if you're going to change that, you've got to change public attitudes. You've got to have people willing to pay other kinds of taxes if you're going to carry the government expenditures that are now being carried in the states.

Excessive Drinking and the Institution of the Family

Selden D. Bacon

MY previous lecture considered the many and varied functions of the custom of drinking as it affects complex societies. The same method may be followed in the consideration of the use of alcohol as it affects a particular institution within a complex society: Just as new needs for greater integration are apparent in the total complex society, so they may be seen in specific institutions within that totality; just as dangers from inaccuracy or bitter competition are enhanced in the total complex society, so they appear exaggerated in the specific institution. The use of alcoholic beverages plays its part in meeting these needs and in activating these dangers. The functions of the many and diverse activities included in the phrase "drinking customs" as they touch upon the institution of the family are not, however, the subject of the present discussion. Rather than an elaboration of the previous approach within the sphere of a single institution, I propose to present an approach which is not only different but also definitely restricted. It is restricted because only excessive or pathological drinking is to be considered. The question to be posed concerns the relationship of a particular activity, excessive drinking, to a social institution, the family—or, more accurately, marriage and the family. The usual writings or declamations on this topic are confined to a portrayal of the havoc which excessive drinking wreaks upon the family. I think it will become apparent that such a limited description of the relationship between these two phenomena is quite inadequate for efficient understanding, whether that understanding be desired for purposes of therapy, for purposes of prevention, or for the more general purpose of a keener and more broadly oriented appreciation of the problems of alcohol.

THE AMERICAN FAMILY: STRUCTURE AND FUNCTION

The first subject to be discussed will have to be the family. One might think that a definition of the family would be a simple matter. It is not. If you ever tried to count families, or to decide to what family every person belonged, you would soon discover the difficulties. If you were to look to the census, for example, you might be surprised to find the category "one-person families," surely a strange phenomenon. Is a servant who "lives in" part of the family? Is a 20-year-old son who goes to college 500 miles away from home and has a summer job, also away from home, part of the family? We are forcibly reminded of Humpty Dumpty's remarks on the definition of words.

The family is a social phenomenon. This needs emphasis because it is sometimes thought to be a biological phenomenon. The family, however, is in no sense a biological entity, any more than a bowling club or an industrial union. One can be born, grow up, maintain life, procreate new life, and die, without a family. The family is an association of persons, its form determined by traditional usage. It rose in answer to human needs. It has probably been the most useful technique of association known to man. In one form or another it has existed at all times in every society of which we have record.

We may briefly consider the form of the family. Basically it is an association of one or more adult men with one or more adult women and their offspring. In America we have a modified monogamy. If husband, wife and children are the only roles included in the family, it is called a *kleine* family, but if nieces and nephews, uncles and aunts, servants, apprentices and adopted strangers are added, it is called a *grosse* family. In the last century in America the family has more and more changed from the *grosse* type to the *kleine* type. The American *kleine* family has also become smaller in size, the 3-person and 4-person family today being the usual type, a decided change from 1800–1840. For those who like averages, the American family averaged 6 persons in 1840, and only 4 persons in 1940. According to the way of determining descent, families are patrilineal, matrilineal, or bilateral; the American family is partly patrilineal, partly bilateral. According to the relative amount of power adhering to husband or wife, the family can be classified in a range extending from patriarchal to matriarchal. The American family is still on the patriarchal side, but there has been a steady change in the last hundred years decreasing the husband's influence.

Other labels to describe the form of the family could be presented. I would draw your attention not to the types, however, but to the fact of change in almost every category of formal description of the American family in the last 150 years.

As to the functions of the family, these also have undergone great changes since our country was founded. I shall list these functions under 12 headings:

1) procreation
2) physical care and socialization of
    a) infants
    b) children
    c) adolescents
3) answering sexual drive of husband and wife
4) answering affectional needs of all members
5) establishing social status
6) serving as the unit of economic consumption
7) protection of all sorts
8) distribution of goods (especially durable) and services
9) production of goods and services
10) serving as a religious unit
11) serving as a recreational unit
12) a societal function of reinforcing other institutions, ideals, customs, order, and security

In modern American society some of these functions have almost completely left the family, others have partly left it. It has been stated, and not without considerable justification, that the primary function of the American family has come to be the satisfaction of the personality needs of affection, prestige, self-respect, and sexual expression. It is certainly apparent that the economic institution has taken large areas of function from the family, that the educational institution has done the same, and that governmental and recreational organizations have expanded, at the expense of the family, to a greater and greater extent.

This loss of function has resulted quite naturally in the loss of power and prestige. Compared to most societies of which we have knowledge, ours has a relatively weak family institution. The family is, of course, still of dominant importance. Consequently, these changes in its form and function may be regarded as important, if not more important than any development in American history; this, despite the fact that history books never mention the subject. One reason for this significance is the fact that personality is formed in the family: ideas, ideals, attitudes, satisfaction of inherited drives, mechanical aptitudes, language, taboos, restraints, basic anxieties, ability to manipulate and appreciate material objects, the learning of interpersonal relationships, the orientation of the self, all these occur in, with, and under the control of the family. A society is made up of individuals; and of the institutions which mould the individual, the family is, beyond question, the most important.

A few descriptive facts: The family is the most widespread of all institutions in American life, appearing everywhere and at all times; the one or two dramatic exceptions, which usually are temporary, are of minor significance.

The family includes persons of all ages and both sexes, cuts across all caste, class, economic and geographic lines.

Perhaps 99 per cent of the population over 10 years of age has spent, at the minimum, 10 years in the family. Of those over 20 years of age, 80 to 85 per cent are or have been married; of the remainder, many will be married. It is the most continual, widespread, and universal of all our institutions, and its impact upon the individual is not only tremendous during the most formative years, but also throughout life.

The family institution has one aspect which differentiates it from the other major institutions—religion, the economic organization, and government. Only in this institution is it usual for every individual to fulfill every role, sex differences excepted, during the normal course of life.

From my previous lecture you will remember the enormous specialization which has occurred in our complex society. The most obvious example, perhaps, was to be found in the economic organization, but the same process was apparent in government, religion, recreation, education, and so on. This has not been true of the family. One of the aspects of specialization is the separation of activities, powers, privileges and responsibilities, with its consequent hierarchy, a hierarchy with few positions at the top. I hope I need not argue that Horatio Alger is a myth. Most of the personnel of the Army has not been, is not, and will never be in the bracket of generals, in fact, will never reach the rank of lieutenant. In industry the vast majority will not rise to be chairman of the board, in fact, will not even become shop foremen. The same thing follows in the church, in recreational associations, and in government. The great mass of persons are participants or workers without much authority or prestige. And so they will remain. You cannot have an army made up of generals or a bank made up of vice-presidents.

In the family, however, the opposite situation exists. Almost everyone is an infant, child, and adolescent in a family. Almost everyone becomes a husband or wife and then father or mother, may then expect to see his or her children leave the home to set up families of their own, and finally may become a grandparent with a particular role to play at that stage.

Horatio or Henrietta Alger in a familial sense is not a myth. The family is the one institution in which every person can expect to change his or her position from that of dependence to independence, from that of taking orders to that of giving orders, from that of small prestige to that of great prestige. Furthermore, it is a regular transition directly correlated with age, with obviously gratifying marks of status advance. Except for a small minority this process of automatic progression does not exist in any other institution.

To turn to another very important aspect of the family in a specialized society: As pointed out in the lecture on complex society, associations have multiplied in numbers and have become specialized around particular interests, have become impersonal, have become lax as to membership (both as to admission and as to withdrawal), and have less control over the individual member. For example, the factory is interested in the man as a factory worker rather than as a total personality; the garden club is interested in flowers and in the members as persons interested in flowers; likewise, the political party, the bowling club, and the lodge have their interests in one or two facets of the person. They tend to exert control over a person only in those aspects of the person's life, not in others. Furthermore, one can join or retire from such groups with a fair amount of ease. Concomitant with these factors, perhaps most important, is the fact that one can be a member without forming intimate, personal ties. There can be areas of the personality kept aloof from the other members. There can be a formal façade protecting emotionally significant matters from other persons. This is a very useful device for some purposes, so much so, that some organizations strive to maintain an impersonal character. But it does not allow that personal security and ease and satisfaction and warm acceptance by others which the human being craves.

In our society this very significant need of the human individual is met primarily by two groups: one, the small friendship clique; and two, more importantly, the family. And as other organizations have taken up more and more of the individual's time and effort, and as they have maintained, even increased, their specialized, impersonal nature, the family, especially the marital family, has become more and more important in satisfying these profound human wants.

In considering the family and excessive drinking, let us accentuate those functions of the family which allow a sense of personal ease in a broad range of interests: It is a group in which the members are given respect and affection not because of competitive success or great talent but just because of themselves; it is a group which automatically gives the individual a feeling of self-respect; it is a group which will rally to one's side no matter what the cause; it is a group in which one can relax without fear of gossip, demotion, or attack.

INCOMPATIBILITY OF MARRIAGE AND EXCESSIVE DRINKING

What is the relation of excessive drinking to the family? I shall confine my remarks to the marital rather than the parental family and shall direct attention to the roles of husband and father since, in our country, excessive drinking is largely a masculine affair. My thesis shall be that excessive drinking and the marital association are incompatible, more incompatible than excessive drinking and any of the other institutions.

I shall treat of the relationship between these two phenomena from three points of view. The first of these may be stated as a proposition: Excessive drinking and the factors in personality leading to excessive drinking tend to preclude or debar marriage.

This situation is closely related to the present structural condition of the marital institution which we have just considered. The contemporary American man can get along without marriage far, far better than could his counterpart 150 years ago; in most primitive societies, bachelorhood was almost impossible. In our society, production, consumption, protection of all sorts, recreation, and a multitude of associations are available for the single man. In addition to the lesser need of marriage is the fact that several of our institutions favor the postponement of marriage, while some occupations definitely bar it. Furthermore, the over-all social pressures directing, almost forcing men into marriage, are not so powerful as they once were.

As indicated, however, the changes in form and function of the family have not only minimized some aspects of family life, they have also maximized others. The functions of satisfying close interpersonal relationships, needs of affection and sexual release, the function of presenting a situation in which there can be close, reciprocal, continuing intimacy covering the widest variety of attitudes and activities, these functions have been greatly enhanced.

Just as the withdrawal of certain functions and the loss of over-all sanctions have made marriage less essential and less compelling for the individual man, so the enhancement of the personality factors listed makes marriage less attractive, even threatening, to certain types of people. What are the characteristics of such types?

One type is represented by the man who has been heavily dependent on an older person, very likely his mother, perhaps his father; this is the man who, because of his dependence on an older person or persons, found it unnecessary to join play groups or school groups or groups of his contemporaries except in a most superficial way, superficial from the point of view of emotional involvement; this is the man who had never needed to surrender himself in part to others and who feared close, mutual relationships on a basis approaching equality.

Another type would be the selfish and aggressive and, perhaps, cynical man who may have joined groups of his equals but only to domineer them, who was both aware of his individual ability and also afraid to put himself in anyone else's power. If such a man can make great achievements, he will get great respect; if not, not; but in neither case will he get love and affection. He may get slavish adoration.

Still a third type may have solved many of his needs without utilizing other persons. He depends on himself for love and admiration and respect. He may get the thrill of achievement from his daydreams, his great ideals. His emotional life is carefully protected from the potential wounds and frustrations of the reality world.

To men such as these, marriage is threatening, threatening because of those now so important aspects of marriage—affection, intimate contact, and relaxed, trusting reciprocity over a wide range of life. And to these men of our modern, complex society, marriage is not so important an association for economic, protective, recreational and other functions. The three types might be called the immature man, the aggressive individualist, and the unsocial dreamer. The reaction to mature sexual response may be especially fearsome for the first and last types. For the first, it means surrender of his dependent boyish position. For the dreamer, it means acting and living with another person, a person who cannot achieve the model of his dream existence, and it means that he will be subject to someone else's ideas, perhaps criticism, or ridicule. The aggressive individual type is more likely to be the Don Juan who uses sex merely to dominate or to exploit his reputation or notoriety.

I believe that our stratified, competitive, romantic, individualistic society of small families and impersonal associations tends to produce more of these types than are to be found in a simpler, less stratified, less competitive, less impersonal society.

Some of you may be wondering what this has to do with excessive drinking, although those familiar with the descriptive literature on alcoholics have probably foreseen the path of the argument. The types described are the very types which the psychiatrist or student of alcohol portrays as constituting the largest group of alcoholics. The academic and therapeutic experts are joined on this point by the ex-alcoholics who have described themselves and their experiences. I cannot list all the personality descriptions of alcoholics that have been given, but the following are characteristic: dreamers, immature, frightened of the opposite sex, aggressive, asocial, without close friends, suspicious, impossibly idealistic, generally introverted, escapist, emotionally childish, and so on. Alcoholics Anonymous, in its very successful program of social rehabilitation, attacks just these characteristics in warning against violent individualism as manifested in hate, envy and fear on the one hand, and in unrealistic dreams of self-importance on the other; it attacks these same characteristics in presenting a group which offers intimate, reciprocating, unspecialized and mature roles for the member to play; and it attacks these characteristics in getting the person to *do something* constructive and *do something* with others.

A word should be said about the relationship between the factors described and the habit of excessive drinking. In our society the adult man who is immature and dependent, or who is aggressive and domineering, or who is a socially isolated dreamer, is subject to great emotional insecurity. He has the same basic drives as others; he wants affection, recognition, and relaxed personal relationships; he has sexual impulses. But he finds it almost impossible to attain such satisfactions since they demand surrendering his immaturity, aggression, and secure isolation. In other words, he is faced with incompatible needs. Only under very favorable circumstances can he achieve a happy life. In our society, where the great majority of adult men are introduced to alcohol, it is not surprising that many such men find release from their often almost insoluble problem through alcohol. Many find alcohol a magical solution to such personal problems and use it for just that purpose and for that purpose alone. Whether they are drinking with a friend, with 100 acquaintances, or alone, makes no difference. There is no social purpose here; there is the complete opposite—an individual purpose, asocial in motive and antisocial in result.

The proposition that the factors underlying inebriety tend to preclude marriage is now explained: (1) Marriage has become less imperative for men in our culture; (2) the institution of marriage has become more important as an association for establishing intimate, affectional relationships of a reciprocal nature; (3) certain types, such as the immature man, the aggressive individualist, the unsocial dreamer, are afraid of the close associational ties of marriage; (4) the pressure on them to marry is less; and (5) such types are very susceptible to alcoholism.

Alcoholism itself tends to enhance the very factors which are correlated with its onset. It makes close interpersonal relations—in fact, any personal relationships—far more difficult; it increases suspicions; it provides a safe retreat, temporarily, from the world of reality; it allows immaturity, cynicism, aggressiveness, egoism, and self-pity even fuller play. That alcoholism tends to preclude marriage is sufficiently evident so that further explanation is unnecessary.

To conclude this argument, it may be stated that among male inebriates who have been arrested and among those in mental institutions the incidence of bachelorhood is far greater than in the comparable general population. This will be illustrated later.

INCOMPATIBILITY OF MARRIED LIFE AND EXCESSIVE DRINKING

So much for excessive drinking and some of its most common background factors as precluders of marriage. Now let us consider excessive drinking and the marital family. If there was any question as to the incompatibility of these two phenomena after a consideration of nonmarriage, it will have to become a very shriveled little doubt indeed, when the facts about married excessive drinkers are observed.

In a recent survey of 1,200 arrested male inebriates in Connecticut towns it was found that whereas 72 per cent of the ordinary male population (of the same ages as the inebriates) were married and living with their wives, only 23 per cent of the arrested male inebriates were in this category. More than half of the inebriates were single, which was true of less than a fifth of the general male population of the same ages. Of those men in the general population who had been married, about nine-tenths were living with their wives; this was true of less than half of the inebriates. The latter were divorced 12 times as often, separated 6 times as often, and widowed more than twice as often as were men of the same age in the general population. The following tables describe (a) the observed marital status of the inebriate group and (b) the marital status of all men in the same state (corrected to ages similar to those of the inebriates), expressed in terms of a total of 1,200; this is entitled "expectancy."

*Normal Expectancy of Marital Status and Observed Marital Status of
1,196 Arrested Inebriates*

	NUMBERS		PERCENTAGES	
Marital Status	Observed	Expectancy	Observed	Expectancy
Single	649	234	53.1	19.6
Married	280	860	22.9	71.9
Separated	141	42	11.5	3.5
Divorced	92	14	7.5	1.2
Widowed	61	46	5.0	3.8
Totals	1,223	1,196*	100.0	100.0

*Difference is caused by 27 men being of unknown age.

*Observed and Expected Proportion of Divorced, Widowed, Separated,
and Married Among Married Inebriates Only*

	NUMBERS		PERCENTAGES	
Marital Status	Observed	Expectancy	Observed	Expectancy
Married	280	860	48.8	89.4
Separated	141	42	24.6	4.4
Divorced	92	14	16.0	1.4
Widowed	61	46	10.6	4.8
Totals	574	962	100.0	100.0

The explanation that excessive drinking breaks marriage and upsets the family suggests itself, but it gives a picture which is not only oversimplified but also fallacious. I think it can be shown that just as excessive drinking may cause the breakdown of marriage and consequent divorce or separation, so may marriage cause the breakdown of sobriety and the consequent alcoholism. If men similar to the types described get married, the incompatibilities which previously were threatened by the idea of marriage have now become actual. The dependent, immature, boyish character finds himself in the role of an independent adult. The egocentric dreamer finds himself in an unavoidable reality situation with a real person. The domineering, aggressive individualist finds himself in a cooperative, intimate, self-denying, and continuing association.

That two-fifths of these marriages are completely disrupted is hardly surprising. However, there are marital situations which could fit these personalities. Suppose that the domineering, aggressive, perhaps secretive, perhaps cynical, type marries a woman who likes to be domineered, who fits into a role of wife which might suit an extreme patriarchal type of family. Or, suppose that the immature, dependent man marries an older, motherly sort of woman who treats him more like a son than like a husband.

These are possibilities, but they are still likely to be marriages of minimal satisfactions. The reason for this is that the American family is constructed differently, not only in form and function, but also in the ideas, in the climate of opinion in which all of us live. When people live out traditional roles in an untraditional manner, they are subject to all sorts of insecurity and punitive sanction, especially gossip and ridicule. In the sort of marriage suggested for the immature man, or in the marriage which links a socially timid, dreamy, outwardly mild husband with an executive, practical, socially competent wife, this ridicule and gossip is even stylized, so common is its application. The domineered, uncomplaining, belittled wife is also a social anachronism, but since the background of our family institution, in popular theory at least, is more compatible with that role, it is not so obviously maladjusted.

Now marriage is only part of the institution we are discussing. When there are children, the structural aspect of the institution is more complete. Then husband and wife also fulfill the roles of father and mother. But the father role is likely to increase the personality difficulties of the types of men we have been describing. The husband who has been emotionally playing the role of little boy to his wife's role of mother is rudely shocked. Now there is a real child and, willy-nilly, he is the adult. Do not think of the man logically figuring all this out for himself. He only knows that he is unhappy, that he is upset, that he is excited, that he is fearful. He may get headaches, he may suddenly find that he has to go far away on a business trip. He also may be terribly anxious about the safety and comfort of the child; no wonder, for he may dimly perceive that he does not want the child, a socially evil and sinful attitude from which he will recoil with some horror, and in his trepidation he may well rush to the opposite extreme.

For the dreamer, the actuality situation becomes even more pressing and real.

As for the aggressive, domineering individualist, he is finally trapped into a social world. In spite of himself he has given hostages, not to fortune but to society. Unless he is willing and able to flout some of the strongest moral views and some of the most compelling customs of our society, he is going to have to behave, or seem to behave, in a manner inconsistent with his major personality traits. Furthermore, the status of his wife is going to change; she is going to become a more important person in his family.

To persons of the type we have been discussing, alcohol is a very likely refuge or crutch. Obviously, all unhappy people do not become alcoholics, but the man with a deep personality problem of the sort here portrayed is not unlikely to make use of alcohol to ease or to forget his dilemmas, especially those which he does not understand.

Now let us turn to the effect of excessive drinking on the family. On this point we need not spend much time, since it has often been abstracted from the total picture of the problems of alcohol and treated in lurid terms.

The alcoholic can use drinking to attack his family, to gain attention and mothering, to test their love for him, to excuse his not being a responsible husband or father. It is well to remember that being known as an alcoholic may be a lesser stigma than being thought a weakling, a fool, a wife-hater or wife-fearer, a mentally disturbed person, a little boy masquerading as a man, and so on.

Or let us merely consider the effects of the drinking without noticing such motives. Let the man have become a drinker by mere chance (although to a student of the problem this would be an inadmissible hypothesis). Excessive drinking will not only wreck the economic and prestige structure of the family, it will also deteriorate the normal social roles of husband and wife as they exist in our society. Excessive drinking makes inroads on the learned attitudes and activities which allow close, personal relationships. It allows selfishness, carelessness, and aggression. In other associations which are only of limited purposes and functions, this is bad enough. For the close, continuing, all-purpose, intimate association which is the family, it is catastrophic.

If separation or divorce or death does not occur, the family will have to limp along in a fashion unlike that of the expected familial unit. The role of wife and mother will differ from the norm; the role of the father toward the children will differ from the norm, and the position of the children in relation to the father will vary from the norm. A vicious circle is set up, since these variations from the socially expected pattern can only increase the man's anxieties, and, to these, he adjusts through more drinking.

I have stated the thesis that excessive drinking and family life are incompatible. Very much the same story is true of excessive drinking and close friendship. But without close, continuing personal ties, life is very difficult. How can one build up the personality traits which are compatible with the formation of such ties? One of the major techniques is to teach the individual the rewarding elements in close associations. So we come to the apparently paradoxical result of proposing that membership in the very groups which increase anxieties and drinking is also the means of retraining the person for living with reduced anxieties and no drinking. For such lessons cannot be learned in an institution, in an ivory tower, or in a desert. Mere intellectual appreciation will not be enough.

For the common type of alcoholic here considered, for the personality type described, nothing can be more helpful than a wife or one or two close friends, but they must be wise beyond the point expected of the ordinary wife or the ordinary friend. The wife must distinguish between being a wife to a mature man and being either a doting mother or an adoring slave. The friend must distinguish between being a mature friend and being host to a parasite or audience to an exhibitionist. And this is hard, very hard. It would seem to demand experience, knowledge, deep sympathy, great self-control, patience, and a tremendous drive to help the afflicted person. Moreover, it would appear that two or three such persons may be necessary rather than just one.

Before concluding the argument that family life and excessive drinking are incompatible, it is worth while considering the female alcoholic. Although she is outnumbered six or seven to one by the male alcoholic, the female's adjustment, or lack of adjustment, to the institution of marriage is quite relevant to our subject. At first glance it would seem that the hypothesis that marriage and excessive drinking (or the factors often underlying excessive drinking) are incompatible is untenable: Women alcoholics get married in just about the same proportions as do other women. On the other hand, women alcoholics show the same extraordinary rates of separation and divorce as do the men alcoholics.

Explanation of this difference between men and women alcoholics calls for renewed consideration of the changes which have occurred in the last century in the structure and functions of the family. These changes have not been the same for both men and women. Just as social pressure against alcoholism is stronger on women than on men, so social pressure to marry seems greater in its impact on women. It may be proposed, as a tentative explanation of the difference between the marrying rates of the two groups, that although each is ill-suited for marital life, the imperative character of the sanctions calling for marriage has weakened more for men than it has for women. The incompatibility of marriage with excessive drinking or with factors commonly correlated with its appearance holds for both men and women. The difference is caused by the variation in social pressure which allows the precluding effect to operate with men but not with women. After marriage the incompatibility is as obvious among women as among men; in fact, in the handful of women cases appearing in a recent survey of arrested inebriates, the rates of divorce and separation were decidedly greater than among the men.

Excessive Drinking and the Widowed

One more relationship between the institution of marriage and excessive drinking remains to be considered. We have noted that excessive drinking and factors leading to it tend to preclude marriage and, if marriage occurs, are likely to result in its dissolution. Not explained are the figures on widowers presented in the tables. Among all men of the same area as that from which the arrested inebriates came, who were of comparable age and who had been married, only 4.8 per cent were widowers. Among the married inebriates, 10.6 per cent were widowers, a highly significant difference. Malzberg, reporting on psychotics, found the same situation:

It is a matter of significance that widows and widowers had higher rates of mental diseases than the married. Since, broadly speaking, both groups probably had similar mental characteristics to begin with, the differences in rates of mental disease must be due to the sorrows and tribulations consequent upon the death of a closely related individual, and the subsequent difficulties of economic readjustment on the part of widows. That widowhood entails a severe shock is seen from the fact that in some of the important groups of psychoses, widows had higher rates than the unmarried population. In fact, they had the highest standardized rate of first admissions with alcoholic psychoses.

The incidence of inebriety is exceptionally high among widowers. In this phenomenon we do not find proof of the hypothesis that excessive drinking and marriage are incompatible, but explanations of this high rate fit well with the hypothesis and, in an indirect manner, lend it some support.

In viewing this relationship between excessive drinking and widowhood it should be carefully noted that all widowers do not become excessive drinkers. In attempting to account for the unexpectedly large proportion who do become alcoholics it has been suggested that among all widowers there is a certain percentage who were abnormally dependent upon their wives for emotional security, for instigation to action, and for control of impulse and activity. Such men would have few interests outside the home, would participate but little in groups or activities not essential to the maintenance of their home, and would be unused to forming close associations or to gaining satisfactions from them. With the irreparable collapse of their all-important and only form of interpersonal activity, their whole life pattern is destroyed and, with the rigid and limited form of adjustment to which they are by long use restricted, their chances of reorganizing their life are scant indeed. For a man of this nature and experience the situation is not too different from that of the immature or asocial types earlier described: He is suffering; he can see no way out; he is inhibited from forming intimate and meaningful associations which might help to answer his needs for affection, recognition, self-respect, and personal orientation. If introduced to alcohol, this sort of widower is all too likely to try to use it as a crutch and may soon come to depend upon it as a means of facing an unhappy and rather meaningless existence.

We have in this situation something similar to a converse of the original proposition. In the one instance there are those who, because of aggressive individualism or general immaturity or an unrealistic and almost asocial character, are unable to enter into intimate association with others on a reciprocal basis and thereby gain the normal satisfactions of life; they are unlikely to marry, likely to dissolve any marriage they enter, and are prime candidates for alcoholism. On the other hand, there are those who have utilized a single intimate association for almost all their individual and social needs. They have, so to speak, put all their eggs in one basket, and on the collapse of that association are left bewildered, suffering, and both unprepared and unwilling to adjust to the new world in which they are situated. In this situation they exhibit a sort of social immaturity or regression, tend to relapse into a sort of dream world, and develop what might be called a passive egocentrism. They also are prime candidates for alcoholism. Such an explanation of the high incidence of alcoholism or excessive drinking among the widowed lends support to the hypothesis that excessive drinking and the sociopsychological factors correlated with its background are incompatible with marriage and the family in that, as the latter is destroyed, the incidence of the former exhibits a marked increase.

Conclusion

This approach to an understanding of excessive drinking and the effects which it has upon the institution of marriage and the family, as well as the effects which that institution has upon excessive drinking, should sharpen our perception that the problems of alcohol are not a separate sphere for understanding either therapeutic or preventive activity, but that they are intimately and completely related to factors of personality and to the myriad aspects of societal form and function.

It should also be apparent from even this brief discussion that glib, single-cause explanations of human behavior are almost invariably wrong. Few are those who have not heard that excessive drinking is the cause of a large percentage of divorces and separations. The fundamental error in thought in this proposition is the age-old tendency to think that because one event precedes another, it is necessarily the cause of the later event. In the present instance a more reasonable explanation would be that both marital discord and excessive drinking are products of a complex of social and psychological factors. That each symptom aggravates the other is obvious. In this discussion the sort of background factors leading to both maladjustments were exemplified by brief descriptions of three types of individual. These are not the only background factors in the etiology of the broken family, or of inebriety, or of the combination. They are, however, very common occurrences in a large proportion of excessive drinkers and play a significant part in the development of the habit of excessive drinking.

This form of approach also illustrates the impact of cultural changes upon the individual and upon his adjustments to the world in which he lives. The decreasing importance of some functions of the family and the increasing importance of others have created new psychological stresses and have allowed wider individual scope; that these changes are closely related to the problem of alcoholism is fairly apparent. The increased significance of the family as the only major association in which status is almost automatically elevated and in which intimate and emotionally significant reciprocal interpersonal relations are, in contrast to other institutions, of primary importance, makes adjustment of the individual to the marital family a key factor in the total structure of the personality. The incompatibility of marital adjustment and excessive drinking is suggestive not only for a clearer understanding of inebriety but also for an analysis of the problems of family life.

Finally, this description of the relationship of some of the factors behind excessive drinking and of excessive drinking itself to the institution of marriage and the family emphasizes again the fact that inebriety is a product of social and psychological and historical forces. It underlines the necessity of a broadly oriented approach if we are to achieve a more successful social adjustment to the problems of alcohol.

DISCUSSION

Stoneburner: A man (one of my cases) had married a woman beyond his own status financially and socially, which was the beginning of some difficulty, although there was a true basis of love on her part. My first contact with him was when he was in a state of intoxication. The drinking began when his wife, on the death of his mother, discovered papers to the effect that he was an adopted child, which fact he never knew. That was the second strike against him. They moved away from the city in which they were living and he proceeded to become a real alcoholic, even hitting the bottom, as Alcoholics Anonymous say. After several efforts to stop his drinking had been made, she returned to her home town, and over a period of months he continued to be intoxicated, losing good positions and places to stay until he came into our office one January day dressed in a Palm Beach suit and white shoes—the only clothes he hadn't pawned. After a period of months, by cooperating with the Alcoholics Anonymous group and by offering what the church had to present for his rehabilitation, we were able to get him back on his feet again, to prevent his wife from divorcing him, and to reestablish the family. I undertook this as an amateur. I should be glad if you would analyze this case and tell us what were the therapeutic features.

Lecturer: From your selection of facts to describe this case, it is clear that you recognize the relevance of certain social factors in this man's turn toward alcoholism. I can do no more than repeat some of the facts which you have just stated. This man was placed in an embarrassing position within this important association; he could not play the role of husband in the traditional and expected manner with any feeling of reality since, as you have stated, he was socially and financially subordinate to his wife. This fact alone would probably not knock the man off his emotional balance; it could threaten his self-respect. The loss of his mother may have been a great shock; there is insufficient evidence to state whether this was important or not. Then came a further threat both to his social position and to his evaluation of himself, the recognition that just as he really was a subordinate member, almost on trial, so to speak, within his marital family, so he had been a subordinate, not a wholly real member, of his parental family. Even this would not necessarily throw him off balance, since I assume that he had friends and acquaintances who judged him by his character and talents and through their mutual experiences. But then he was deprived of this buttress to self-esteem and of this social support by moving to another locality. I don't think that even this is a sufficient explanation. One would want to know something of the personality development of the man in order to appreciate why he reacted to these blows as he did; indeed, why he put himself in the position of being so isolated from his earlier social contacts. Also, of course, one would need to know something of his first contacts with drinking. That his wife left him was, of course, an extremely aggravating factor. From his own point of view, he may well have seemed to be a forlorn and banished soul, tossed out by his parents, both literally and figuratively, by his friends, by his home town, and by his wife.

You say that you undertook this case as an amateur. May I state that I wish there were more such amateurs. For your actions could be described as performing a sociopsychological reorientation for that man, reestablishing a friendship group, a sense of self-respect and self-interest, and finally, a marriage. Naturally this is a most speculative discussion, since I have heard only a 2-minute description of an unknown individual, but the case certainly seems relevant to today's subject and is suggestive for our consideration of the relationships of family factors to excessive drinking. It is worth while considering these situational and formal factors, that is, marriage, loss of parent, social-class change, community departure, knowledge of adoption status. They are suggestive; they are imperative for adequate understanding, but it must be remembered that they are the outward manifestations only. The personality development and emotional characteristics of the individual must also be described.

Squires: My thought is not so much the father or the mother who might be incapacitated by excessive drinking, but would drinking to any extent, even the occasional moderate use of alcohol in a home where there are small children, have any detrimental effect upon the moral and spiritual teaching which that home should offer to those children as they grow up? This is the thought in my mind. How can a mother, who is supposed to be a Christian mother and believe in the teachings of Christ, and so forth, teach her children, bring them up to an idea of the American freedom of life and also of normal wholesome living, and still be a user of alcoholic beverages? I am not talking about smoking. Of course, in my limited circle, if there is a mother who smokes you put a question mark right there. Of course there are many mothers who smoke and who are, I suppose, very earnest Christian people, but my thought is that there are many thousands of homes where liquor is used a little, used casually by the father and mother, and this has an unfortunate effect upon the children, by way of example, so that Christian teachings all the way up from babyhood, childhood, are thereby, to a large degree, negatived by such indulgence.

Lecturer: In answering this question I think one would first have to know what the situation is for most people in the wider society. If, in the wider society, the thought of drinking, no matter what the amount, is bad, is by definition immoral, then the occurrence of any drinking at all means that there will be a certain hypocrisy involved both at that time and also when the child has grown up. Because if the child has to believe in this badness, and yet it believes that the very source of morality, which is the father and mother, has been acting behind or underneath or sliding by real morality, then it undoubtedly will be weakening to morals; it can't help but be. But that statement only holds when such a belief is truly prevalent in the society. In an abstinent society, I think it undoubtedly would have such an effect. Suppose, however, that drinking is accepted as a social value, or that there is uncertainty or even conflict about the practice. Then I think the situation is quite different. If the child sees its parents doing those things which are normally considered to be all right—by normally considered I mean beliefs of the people with whom it is going to live—then seeing its parents acting that way can hardly set up fears, threats, suspicions, challenges to father and mother as if they were evil people. An adequate answer to the question depends upon the perception that our culture determines in the last analysis what is moral and what is immoral.

Robinson: What is the relative percentage of divorce in which alcohol usage may be a cause? This has to do with our general society and not with alcoholics.

Lecturer: I don't believe anybody can answer that question. People can only give judgments from their experience in a given court or in given cases of divorce. The reason for this is not too difficult to see. In the first place, we have increased the amount of divorce enormously and rapidly, while our ideas, our theories, our stated, formal beliefs have not changed with the same speed. Therefore, when we go to a court and say, "Mr. and Mrs. Jones want a divorce," we do not give the real reason. We are not allowed by law to give the real reason. In your divorce statistics you will find that in one jurisdiction, in the State of New York, for example, 97 per cent of the divorces are on the grounds of adultery; whereas you can go to another state and find that the percentage for adultery is down to about 10 per cent. It doesn't mean that the people have been behaving differently at all. It is just that the official reasons given for divorce are made to fit artificial legal reasons. That is one reason for believing that we cannot know the real percentage of cases in which excessive drinking is the cause. The second is, that divorces are generally sought not for one reason but for many reasons. There are social prestige reasons; there may be reasons to do with smoking or drinking or some other such habit; there are reasons concerned with the sex relationship of the people. It may have to do with the fact that the people really didn't know each other before they were married. It may have to do with something like a personality change in one of them. The reasons given in court, especially those appearing in court records and statistics, are legally significant, not emotionally significant.

Davies: Were the subjects of your study excessive drinkers?

Lecturer: Yes. Of these 1,200-odd people, I think 57 per cent had a record of 7 or more arrests for drunkenness. You can be sure that they have been drunk many more times than that. Another 26 or 27 per cent had a record of 3 or more arrests for drunkenness. These are the arrests that they admitted to. In some instances, we know that they understated by far. They had all the reason in the world to do so because they thought they might get a lesser sentence, even though we told them that this had nothing to do with the sentence; nevertheless, they saw us with the judge, and they were anxious to cut the record down. There are about 12 per cent who said that they had had 2 previous arrests; and, altogether, 8 per cent claimed that this was either their first or their second appearance. Something over 90 per cent had an official record of being arrested for drunkenness, and 75 per cent of them had shown up many times. I think there can be little doubt that the overwhelming majority were excessive drinkers. There may be 30 or 40 of them who were not. We would know pretty definitely if it were just a kid who got gay and began throwing beer bottles around as a college stunt, or something of that sort. They were not included in the study.

Weil: Why is it that so many wives of drinking husbands start divorce proceedings, or say they wish to leave their husbands, only to go back to them?

Lecturer: If you ever go to an Alcoholics Anonymous meeting I think that you will invariably hear at least one man say, "I can't understand why my wife ever stood by me." I must say that most of the nonalcoholics who are listening have the same question. Why did they? I cannot answer this. I don't know. There are one or two general factors that could be suggested. I think that in our society, today, marriage means emotionally more to women than to men. In other words, not only when they are 20, 25 or 30, but even when they are little children, more of their life is directed toward fulfilling a specific role—the role of mother and wife; their whole life may well be centered around the fact of marriage. As a result, there may be an emotional tie not only to the man but also to the marriage itself, to the very idea of marriage. Another factor to consider is the smaller and narrower contacts to which many women are limited: They are not meeting customers, fellow workers, lunch partners, union members, lodge brothers, and so on, as are their husbands. Having fewer associations, the danger of losing the main one may well be magnified. Training for the role of woman and mother may have its effect on the wife's attitude to the erring husband. These are rather superficial explanations but if they are suggestive, they may serve a purpose. If one were really going to study this matter, one would first have to determine whether this reaction of planning to break up the marriage, followed by strenuous efforts to revive it, were really very common and, if so, if it were a real intention to break the marriage or merely a cry for help, a threat, a bid for glamor, or what.

Lecture 17

Alcohol and Pauperism

Rev. A. J. Murphy

I AM going to start, as my mother told me years ago to start, by telling a story. The story was told by Dr. Phelps, a beloved memory on this campus, rest his good soul. I think it will illustrate, probably as well as anything, some of the problems which confronted me in my effort to draw to a synthesis some of the wide variety of data that lay before me on this question.

Dr. Phelps told this story over the radio. I presume that it attracted my attention because it concerned a divinity student. He said there was a divinity student, some time ago, in the class of a professor of Scripture who was getting a little old. The professor, for some years, had invariably asked the question, "Mention the twelve kings of Israel" in the examination. One year, one of the other professors said to him, "Now, Reverend, I wonder if some students aren't becoming a bit familiar with that question. Wouldn't it be possible for you to change it around a bit, or, better still, substitute another question?" The professor of Scripture said, "Yes, that's a good idea." So the next morning, lo and behold! to the amazement of the class, who expected the old question of the twelve kings of Israel, there, at the bottom of the blackboard, was a new one that puzzled them no end, and it was: "Distinguish between the major and the minor prophets." Most of the students were filled with consternation, except one. A little more ingenious than the rest, he began to scribble furiously. Looking over his shoulder, you would have seen this: "Who am I to distinguish between the great and holy men of God? However, the twelve kings of Israel are as follows . . ."

Frankly, I thought at the outset of this subject of mine that I was going to discuss the twelve kings of Israel. I got farther into it and found that I had to do a lot of distinguishing between the major and the minor prophets; and now I am not sure whether it is a combination of both or whether it does not refer to either.

First of all, I am going to take the liberty, at the outset, of indicating that I shall speak of "poverty" and "pauperism" pretty much in relative terms. I am doing this because, pauperism, to my mind, seems to be a rather specific term with antecedents dating back to the Elizabethan poor laws, with special reference to a particular class of people that now is not very numerous in our society. It does not seem right to confine my observations to the question of pauperism. Similarly, when I speak of the problem of alcohol, I am speaking in general terms of excessive drinking, the drinker, the alcoholic, the problem of alcohol, without precise or detailed reference to the scientific delineation of the special categories under which some of these alcoholics fall. I am not, for instance, referring at any point to the psychotic drinker, the neurotic drinker, the occasional drinker, or to any other. When I speak of the excessive drinker I mean just that—the excessive drinker of alcoholic beverages.

Excessive drinking as a destructive factor in the economic life of families and the nation has never seriously been questioned by observers on the matter. The extent of its incidence and its exact cause or effect relationship have frequently been the subject for wide debate. Benjamin Franklin's first summarization of the effect of drinking in its economic aspects probably epitomizes the viewpoint of most men long after his time. He said: "Some of the domestic evils of drunkenness are houses without windows, gardens without fences, fields without tilling, barns without roofs, children without clothing, principles, morals or manners." One of the interesting things to observe about this comment is the simplicity of its socioeconomic framework. He is speaking of pioneer folk with their strong family loyalty as a barrier against any widespread poverty, with their isolation, with their ability to get along independently of the wage system, with their reliance on nature for their livelihood, with their far-reaching mores, sanctions, folkways as governing factors in their daily experience. As a consequence, the impact of heavy drinking and the heavy drinker upon society at large would naturally result in no such broad and serious implication as would be felt later on.

At about this time in England, on the other hand, comments on the relationship between alcohol and poverty were beginning to derive their force from observations centering around the economic status of the drinker as a wage earner and producer in the then early stages of the industrial system. Adam Smith, in *The Wealth of Nations,* wrote "that all the labor expended producing strong drink is utterly unproductive, it adds nothing to the wealth of the community. A wise man works and earns wages and spends his wages that he may work again." In similar vein, a member of the British Parliament stated the problem more graphically when he observed: "I saw a man in the gutter, he was dirty and hence the soap trade was suffering; his hat was broken and hence the hat trade was suffering; his toes had broken through his boots, hence the boot trade was suffering."

In parallel to this reaction was the changed economy of advancing times in our own country; observers began to direct more thought, from a wide variety of viewpoints, to the relationship between poverty and excessive drinking. Many of these approaches, although segmented, erratic, based on meager data, in some instances lacking the objectivity of a true appraisal, nevertheless served as useful instruments in preparing the ground.

STUDIES OF CONDITIONS IN THE PAST

It was not until the nineteenth century, however, that any comprehensive attempt to measure the correlation of heavy drinking and economic life was made here at home. In 1893 the Committee of Fifty was formed for the purpose of studying the problem of alcohol in its various aspects. With Scott Booth's study of London poverty made 17 years earlier providing something of a background, a subcommittee on the economic aspects of the problem brought forward data to show the close relationship existing between poverty and excessive drinking. These data were gathered from the files of 33 charity organizations and societies, 11 children's aid agencies, 60 almshouses, and 17 prisons and reformatories. The summary indicated that 37 per cent of all pauperism in almshouses,

45.8 per cent of all destitution among children, 25 per cent of all poverty requiring relief, and 50 per cent of all crime was brought about either directly
or indirectly through excessive drinking. I mention this study only because it is
important in the literature on the question and not because I believe too seriously
any of the facts that have been brought forward by it. Since then, few attempts
have been made over a wide area to trace any of the significant relationships
thought to exist between poverty and alcohol. Three major reasons may perhaps
be submitted for this. It was asserted, even at the time the investigation of the
Committee of Fifty was contemplated, and by a rather imposing number of leading authorities, that a work of such magnitude as was then proposed would add
little to the sum total of effective information on the question. These men
pointed out that much of the material to be gathered on this question over a
long period of time and at considerable expense belabored the obvious; and that
the matter required little elaboration and statistical data for the purposes in hand.
Perhaps a more practical reason for lack of further research in this field has been
the intervention of the Paul-Mission movement and its lulling effect upon many
who might otherwise have felt the need for further inquiries. Studies comparable
in magnitude to those of the Committee of Fifty would require considerable
time for planning, a high degree of skill in organizing personnel and resources
for the task, and a determination of the need for such studies, but all these have
been far from conspicuous amid the confusing pressures of wider problems confronting the nation since 1932. The third reason, and perhaps the greatest reason
for failure to advance further in our knowledge of the relationship between
poverty and inebriety, has been the changed emphasis brought into the discussion
of the problem by the rise of the mental hygiene movement.

Efforts of this movement, particularly insistence on the psychiatric method,
with its diagnostic findings and intimate case recordings, have done a great deal
toward turning the attention of men toward individual therapy. This influence
has effected a profound change in attitude among practitioners in the field of
human relations. It has brought us increasingly to understand that in almost
every situation in which excessive drinking is a factor, complex, delicately involved, deeply tangled and badly obscured motivations may possibly defy tabulation at this time and may even be too elusive for really worth while, constructive, statistical analysis. However, from time to time, other studies in no sense as
exhaustive as the Committee of Fifty's work, and far from conclusive, have
been attempted as a means of gaining further knowledge. These efforts have
frequently resorted to broad sweeping strokes of propaganda and, as a consequence, they sometimes lack the validity desirable in studies of this type. Some
of these efforts have fallen into the snare of lumping together statistics concerning heavy drinkers and statistics concerning moderate or occasional drinkers.
And from these statistics they have at least hinted a causal relationship between
poverty and drink. Thus, it seems to add little to the solution of any problem to
assert that the per capita consumption of liquor has risen from 1.8 gallons in any
year to 8.7 gallons in another year. Population trends over the corresponding
period of time need to be analyzed likewise before such data can become meaningful. Nor, frequently, does the information provided by social-agency records
greatly clarify viewpoints on the question. These records, although significant

for other purposes, touch upon only one phase of the problem and leave a vast area of inquiry still uncovered. Nor do mortality rates provide too much conclusive evidence, again because of the need for more careful analysis of population trends in connection with the subject under discussion.

That large studies, such as the Committee of Fifty study, would be of eminent value can scarcely be questioned in the light of advances achieved recently through studies on other phases of the problem. Such studies would undoubtedly help to reorient the thinking of large groups toward important aspects of the evils of heavy drinking. They would confirm or allay suspicions, generalizations and deductions which now rightly or wrongly dominate our approach in the absence of more systematized data. Such studies would almost inevitably stimulate greater interest on the part of society itself in customs, in fashions, in attitudes and in laws on the problems of alcohol and the problem of the alcoholic. Such studies might turn on new light even for the patient himself, groping for help in his plight.

ECONOMIC STATUS OF THE INEBRIATE

One of the more fruitful fields of inquiry on this question, at present and possibly for the future, would appear to be in the ranks of industry. The postwar disruptions, disorganization and divisions now loom up before us almost as a matter of moment, with industry adjusting its sights to the long hall of peace. The alcoholic will undoubtedly find himself no better off in the future, so far as his economic status is concerned, than he has ever been traditionally. He will be dependent upon an economic system which in our day sets great store by mechanized skills, insists upon the regularity, stability, and efficiency vital to a proper gearing of the industrial process, and through its pressures and tensions crowds out with cold and deadly precision the inefficient, the casual, and the poorly adjusted. It can be readily seen that the personality characteristics of the alcoholic will drive him to an unsound economic status fraught with peril both for his family and himself, and extremely burdensome to society as a whole.

What evidence is at hand points quite strongly to the fact that the alcoholic fits into the wage system as disjointedly as he fits into any other phase of social life. He is unpredictable and irregular; and insufficient attention to his job will undoubtedly become a more severe obstacle to steady employment as time and industrial progress move forward. His work is characterized by irritability and overaggressiveness toward employer and fellow employee alike. His feeling of inferiority, of not belonging, of restlessness, make him difficult to get along with in a system requiring smooth working relationships within a highly complex mechanism. He becomes an object of irritation to his employer because of the danger of frequent garnishing of his wages and his need for incessant advances on his pay, with the additional bookkeeping which this involves.

For the union, also, he is the source of unmistakable anxiety. He is irregular in paying his dues, he shows little interest in internal union matters, he throws an additional burden onto other members of the union in their relation to the system of sick benefits, insurances, and the like. To the shop steward, on whose shoulders falls the responsibility of many delicate and involved negotiations with the heads of industry, he is a source of irritability, looked upon with increasing resentment.

As a wage earner he tends to move toward the status of the marginal employee more frequently than in the direction of advancement, promotion, and further responsibility which other employees come to enjoy. He is a bad financial risk. At a time when approximately 47 per cent of all merchandizing in this country rests on credit, his inadequacy throws him irresistibly over onto a cash level or, what is worse, he is thrust willy-nilly into the hands of the borderline credit system with the long, sharp, high interest rates, with the prospect of foreclosure meeting him at every turn. He can seldom fall back upon unemployment compensation because of his regular unemployment. He becomes all too often the victim of exploitation, even among his friends, because of his irregular habits with money. He has likewise little interest in any of the informal systems set up among employees or neighbors to carry them over the periodic stresses of life. Even the door of his own wider family relationships has been shut against him in those crises that fall upon ordinary families at birth, at death, in sickness and in those ever-recurring milestones in life, when families normally assist one another. The oft-repeated instability in the past has placed him in the unhappy position of moving toward the financial future alone and unassisted. That his home and family life thus heads for the saddest of poverty is evidenced in many ways. Home ownership, perhaps one of the strongest stabilizing influences in the life of the family, is almost permanently beyond his grasp, and the rent experience is characterized by frequent skipping, narrowing the circle of new rent opportunities. The neighborhood in which he is to be found will ordinarily be permeated with a sense of frustration, of hopelessness, and an air of soggy indifference to the better things of life. It will be a neighborhood in which the incidence of ill health, of delinquency, of transiency, of divorce and kindred social evils, is high.

The Alcoholic as Social-Agency Client

His home, his family, and his children will be subjected to the contagion of these conditions, and where his problems have gotten beyond him, the social agency will find itself dealing with perhaps its most complicated and exasperating client. For the social agency there will be the initial difficulty of trying to determine whether he is a relief client, as such, or a family case-work client with a larger possibility of rehabilitation and reform. The agency, despite long experience with such situations, can never quite satisfactorily establish a policy as to where he fits into the scheme of things. The agency contact with him will reveal the need for periodic relief despite the fact that his wages at a given time may be relatively high. His work record is spotty, and where his wage goes will be a mystery to the social agency. Looking at him as an individual the agency is frequently tempted to feel that the family situation would be much better were he permanently out of the home. There will be instances where his habit of intemperance has finally placed him in the correctional institution, the workhouse, for short periods of time. And in those interludes the agency will see a vast improvement in the home, almost from the moment he has left. It will note that the children are clean, more regular in their school attendance, and conform to the discipline of the home in a more satisfactory fashion. The wife will have lost something of her hopelessness and will begin to have taken on a new interest in life.

Plans of the agency, hitherto destroyed by the turmoils and confusions which the man's drinking has produced, will flow now with considerable success toward constructive objectives and, as a shortsighted policy, it might seem advisable to the agency to work for his long-time elimination from the home which they are now finding themselves able to service rather satisfactorily. Anyone, however, who has seen the strong relationship existing between the wife, the children and the alcoholic will recognize this overanxiety toward taking shortcuts on the part of the agency as an illusory gain. Despite the excessive drinker's manifold inconsistency it must be confessed that he does provide some sort of emotional supplementation for the home and the family. His wife, feeling the need for his presence in the home, will more often than not protect him and his shortcomings from the more rigid scrutiny of agency personnel. She is very frequently an unstable person herself and, despite his recognized weaknesses, he nevertheless provides at many points in life something of strength for her toward the confusing future.

Faced frequently with this additional perplexity which the situation reveals, the agency is very often at a loss to determine what policy to pursue. The excessive drinker and his family in most instances find need for the services of innumerable social agencies. The familiar picture of the clearings on this type of problem will reveal contacts with from 3 to 12 different agencies. Because of frequent colds among the children, suspected tuberculosis, eye and ear difficulties, nutritional deficiency, vocational dispensary services, hospital services and other health needs, many of the health agencies will be called into play. Probation service will be needed very frequently; psychological tests will be resorted to in other instances. The family, in other words, runs the gamut of services provided at either public or private expense in almost any community.

It has been necessary in some instances for the community to protect the children of such families by withdrawing them from the home. Here the excessive drinker is again one of the important and unfortunate forces which the agency finds it necessary to work with. The family's relationship with the agency is then characterized by irregularity in payment for the children's care, in overaggressiveness toward the agency, toward the foster parents, and even toward the children on the part of the delinquent member of the family. He upsets the foster parents and his children alike. He seems to take an unnatural delight in disturbing them by visiting at odd hours of the day and under the influence of liquor. He disturbs his children emotionally by alternately raising their hopes, embarrassing them, and showing grave inconsistencies either in his affection or in his indifference. Occasionally he becomes involved in multiple marriages, with several sets of children further to complicate the future. More and more he moves toward new responsibilities, fresh crises, additional tensions, without having extricated himself from the perils of the old. His disordered familial relationships become an extremely disheartening task for the agency with which he has to deal. Excessive drinking, together with other disturbing forces at play at other fronts along his life, have perhaps finally placed him in the familiar jungle of the large city, and here it becomes even more of a challenge to the community seeking to determine what is best for him in the way of constructive treatment. In most cities, at this point, the workhouse or the house of correction becomes the only resource available for his custody.

One commentator on this phase of the problem has recently observed that the present handling of inebriates involves extraordinary and unnecessary expenditures through police efforts. No exact studies of such costs in this country are known, but investigations abroad have shown that a repeater may occasion, in some instances, a cost of several hundred dollars in a single year. Other phases of this problem draw our attention unmistakably to the relationships between either public or private expenditures and the evil of inebriety. The National Safety Council, for instance, tells us that in 1940, 34,500 persons were killed in the United States in traffic accidents. It further asserts that 1 out of every 5 of these fatal accidents report the driver or pedestrian as having been drinking. Again, in 1938, chronic alcoholism and alcoholic psychoses accounted for 11.5 per cent of first admissions to all mental hospitals in the United States. One authority has estimated the economic loss due to hospitalization for alcoholism among mental patients in one year at 100 million dollars. Of the 40 million persons who are commonly accepted as drinkers in this country, probably not more than 6 per cent can be recorded as problem drinkers. Almost every place one turns, one finds indisputable evidence that these problem drinkers, at this proportionate range, are upon the country's resources in a multiplicity of ways.

DISCUSSION

Chairman (E. M. Jellinek): I am perhaps talking out of school if I mention that on our way up from the class I asked you about some information on the experience of charity agencies with cases in which alcoholism was involved. I know that you did not attribute much accuracy to these figures; nevertheless, they are of certain interest. I wonder whether you would care to say a few words on this question.

Lecturer: One of the places where you turn in seeking data on this question of the relationship between poverty and alcohol is the social agency. I attempted to gather some of these data in one locality and I presume the over-all picture would indicate that in the neighborhood of 18 per cent of the clients involved excessive drinking habits. One agency said that of 2,000 cases there were something like 311 in which alcoholism or excessive drinking was a major factor. In another agency, we found that of something like 295 cases, in the neighborhood of 85 involved excessive drinking. In still another agency, I forget the exact figures but I believe it was around 275 or 280 cases, a similar percentage was noted.

Again I think that one of the reasons why this doesn't seem too significant is that the wide variation in social agency figures depends, to a large extent, upon the policy of the agency itself. As between public and private family agencies, you have your more hopeful cases coming to the private group. When they get to the dead end, in many instances they will be public cases, and there you get over just a bit into the poor-law concept of the Elizabethan period. In children's agencies, similarly, you will find the short-time placement coming to the private agencies. The long-time, less hopeful cases will be the responsibility of the public agencies. Between those and between the differences in various localities you find yourself in great difficulty in trying to gather comparable statistics.

Carl: How does 18 per cent of clients related to excessive drinking correspond with 37 per cent or 45 per cent destitution among children and 50 per cent crime?

Lecturer: Those were the figures which were gathered in the Committee of Fifty study started in 1893 and then continued in 1905.

Carl: I understood that. But I wondered how their figures related to your actual experiences in your field in Cleveland.

Lecturer: I would say that their figures are quite high. First of all, when you talk of almshouses, you are talking about a system that has experienced distinct changes from the almshouse of the early century. You're talking about the number of men who possibly might have been in the almshouse now were it not for the Old Age Insurance benefits and many of the other new benefits. In talking about destitution among children, I think the reason why you can't compare the figures too well is that in those days you probably had a greater absorptive power of relatives to take the children.

Shattuck: Is it your opinion that industry is less severe on the drinker now than it was just before the last World War?

Lecturer: My experience, limited as it is, is that industry is much more lenient with drinking today because of the manpower problem. I've heard of instances where employers have been at the workhouse, waiting with open arms for the man who probably had been placed there 2 or 3 days before. I think any probation officer in this gathering will testify to the fact that employers come down quite frequently either to bail their employees out or plead for them, or make use of any of the other expedients whereby they can get them released more quickly. And I say that, by and large, industry, in this most unique and unusual cycle which is merely temporary, is much more lenient than it was back in 1918. I think (this is just my opinion) that the heavy drinker needs to be very, very alarmed about what is going to happen to him in this highly complicated mechanistic system toward which we are moving.

Mrs. Colvin: Isn't the moderate use of alcohol by a minimum wage earner a factor in bringing down the standard of living of the entire family and does it not tend to poverty?

Lecturer: I'm going to be awfully cautious about that question because it gets us into a tiny area. I sometimes think of the automobile and wonder just how many facts and figures you could bring forward to show that the automobile has been a diabolical invention when you get over into one particular area of discussion about it. When we discuss even the moderate use of alcohol in relation to the whole wage earner, I wish to think of it in terms of what emotional stimulation it may provide for him, what recreational opportunities it may open up for him which, if they weren't present, might lead him at certain points to deviate from norms that are helpful in other respects. In other words, if we do hold (I'm not too sure that we need to and I'm not too sure we all do) that the moderate use of alcohol is not, per se, something wrong, then I think you have to leave the individual himself to determine just how much he feels he can afford to spend on alcohol if he doesn't have a problem in his own drinking. For us to come out and say that by drinking moderately he takes away from some of the things in the family, I think we'd have to know, in that particular situation, whether the things that he has taken away from that family would be more conducive to its happiness than his drinking.

Question: What is meant by excessive drinking? What is the line one has to cross to leave the moderate-drinker class and be classed as an excessive drinker?

Lecturer: When we speak of excessive drinking, I've come to be very, very cautious about definitions and hard and fast designations. My general description of excessive drinking would be that a man has taken sufficient drink to destroy, at least for the time being, the faculties that God has planted in him as a human being as distinct from the rest of the animals. In other words, he has disturbed his emotions, he has beclouded his faculties of thinking, he has disturbed the power of will. He has done that which almighty God never intended he should do when He created the two things—man and drink—and permitted them to come together.

Miss Cox: Is it true, as has been suggested by some people, that children are better off in very inferior homes, perhaps those in which excessive drinking is prominent, than when put in a large institution?

Lecturer: I'm not institutionally minded. I think that again we get the second problem of what is excessive drinking. If it's so demoralizing to the home that the home cannot remain together, then the community itself will break up the home and place the children. But if the home, according to the minds of the community, can persevere, I think the children are better off in that home, despite all its limitations, than they would be in an institution.

Watson: Do you find any significant relationship in the city of Cleveland between low educational standards and inebriety?

Lecturer: We probably could answer that; that's a very good question, but it's difficult to pull it apart. Here's what I'm going to attempt to say as a generalization. The more educated one becomes (I hope) in the future, the more we'll move toward sobriety and toward the moderate use of alcohol. The corollary to that would be, naturally, that the less educated people might be more addicted to excessive use of alcohol; but in following such a corollary I think we should wander all over wide open pastures. For instance, you find excessive drinking where you have the lowest incidence of education; you'll find it again where you have the low economic group; you'll find it in the group that comes from the vitiated, "less-chance" neighborhood; you'll find it among groups where the economic level of existence does not enable people to hope for higher education for their children. Now, how would we untangle all of those various strands, so as to see the real direction and importance of any one of them? I would say, off-hand, that in a neighborhood that is characterized by poverty, that is, a "less-chance" neighborhood, you undoubtedly would find more unrestricted drinking than you would in the upper-stratum neighborhood. Similarly, in that lower-stratum neighborhood you'd find a lower degree of education than you would find in any other neighborhood.

Hall: Hasn't alcohol been an opiate of the people in that, as an escape mechanism, it has drained off the worker's protest against unjust industrial and economic conditions?

Lecturer: You mean the bread-and-circuses idea, only in reverse? My observation is a very limited one, but, such as it is, it has been my impression that the leaders of the organized labor movement are men of general sobriety.

Hall: We have been emphasizing in these days and weeks that the use of alcohol may be an escape from tensions or frustrations, economic disability or serious inhibiting circumstances. If a man uses alcohol, he forgets, and uses that as one way of adjusting himself to an inhibiting economic environment.

Lecturer: We have been discussing this economic situation that you described as if it were something that is terrifically inhibiting for the rank and file of men. Isn't it probable that if we took actual figures we might find that we were speaking of a very, very small group in relation to the total number that is actually involved in the industrial system? As a consequence, I wonder how much your facts would weigh in relation to the total? We'd possibly find that the person you describe as having been given the so-called narcosis to tension and frustration is in reality in such a minority, in relation to the group which is engaged in a similar process, that one would question very seriously whether it has had any deep significance.

Hall: The theory advanced here over these weeks as to why people continued to drink is that alcohol is a psychological crutch which makes more tolerable what the individual would otherwise feel as an intolerable situation. I believe that there is innate in every human being at least a dormant sense of justice. However inarticulate this sense of justice may be, it will be brought out by the impinging circumstances of unjust industrial conditions. Following, then, our theory of why we use alcohol, won't some people try to forget through the use of alcohol this sense of injustice in which they live, just as others may resolve their tensions by trying to change the economic conditions under which they and their fellow workers live?

Lecturer: I think your viewpoint, as far as my own personal observation goes, has a tendency to give the drinker too much insight into the whole economic system and its injustice and into some other deep spiritual and intangible realities that crowd around life. My experience with both the laboring man and with the drinker has never fully convinced me that they are sufficiently concerned about justice as a metaphysical entity to take to drink.

Hall: Is there any more reason why a man might take to drink because of a nagging wife than because of a hard, unjust employer? Is that analogous?

Lecturer: As I see it, there's a difference of about 8 hours. He is on the job 8 hours, but he has 16 hours in which he lives off the job and considerable of that time is going to be spent with his wife.

Chairman: Vandervelde, a Belgian socialist, has written an essay on the socialist view and maintains that every worker who is won over for abstinence is won over for the cause of socialism, because alcohol makes one forget, and the laborer cannot afford to forget. This is the classical attitude of Belgian socialism, which greatly differs from the original Marxian as well as the later German socialist standpoint which calls it a matter of too minor importance to receive the attention of the party. There is no unitary socialistic view of the question.

Question: Talking about the socialist viewpoint, I read in the *Call*, just before coming here, an article by a commentator who writes regularly for the socialist press. He was talking about this Yale School and there was a little sarcasm in the article. He said that his solution of the problem of alcoholism was to change the economic order so as to get a little more justice into it, and thus remove a great many of the tensions which the workingman has to face today and which come from the factory set-up, long hours, poor wages, and the insecurity of his job. It seemed to me that he had hit upon a very important factor. It does seem to me that if we could have a more just economic order, we would relieve a number of tensions and we would greatly decrease the alcohol problem. That's just an opinion. I don't know if you want to comment or not.

Lecturer: I'd like to comment on it, for we're getting some place. To me, the attitude of the last speaker seems to be entirely too much that of throwing out the baby with the bath. I think this whole question of tension in industry is something that is a very, very small and insignificant causal factor of drinking. I think (this is only my personal impression) that by and large many of these so-called terrific tensions that we speak of in connection with the assembly line, with the speeding-up process and other things—and stories are written about it—are exaggerated. I think that many a young man will go out after what is called a terrific day of tension at the assembly line, and will play a game or two of baseball, or will work out in the garden, and thus get sufficient relief from these tensions in normal ways to prove that others could do likewise. I think many of those who allege the excuse of the complicated industrial system as a factor leading toward excessive drinking probably had many of those tensions inside them before they punched the time clock. They're individuals who are pretty much like those you will find in these social-agency records. I wouldn't take such evidence from the foreman and I wouldn't take that from anyone. It just doesn't ring true.

Mrs. Colvin: If it takes higher intelligence to learn to drink moderately, would a little more intelligence lead one to abstain entirely?

Lecturer: I think, personally, my attitude there would be that we shouldn't talk so much of the higher forms of intelligence leading toward sobriety, as unfortunately the lesser forms of intelligence lead to insobriety. The emphasis is in that direction.

Mrs. Colvin: I'll agree with your statement that "lower intelligence leads to excessive drinking." If you'll include "leads to moderate and excessive drinking" then I'll agree with you completely. You said your statement the other way, that lower intelligence leads to excessive drinking, but if you'll just take the step in between, which comes before excessive, which is moderate drinking, then I'll agree with you.

Lecturer: I think that much of our evidence would probably prove that lower educational opportunities, lower mentality, and probably more disorganized emotional systems, do lead to excessive drinking. However, I wonder if the converse or the reverse is true? It does not follow that if you move counterclockwise toward the point where the higher intelligence and greater emotional stability are, that you should find more abstinence from drinking. I can't see that. I think that moderation in the use of drink is probably a higher state of perfection—and I know that you won't agree with me there —and indicates a more reasonable, rational, and generally well-organized emotional system, probably, than the one who never touches a drop. A man who can drink moderately and can use it as one of the forces that contribute toward life is, to my notion, probably better organized than the other.

Alcohol and Traffic

Donald S. Berry

A S most of you know, the National Safety Council has been interested for many years in the alcohol problem. This interest is not in moral or other social aspects of the problem, however, but only in alcohol as it relates to accidents. My discussion here today will be limited to the subject of alcohol as a factor in traffic accidents, and means of dealing with the problem.

I feel sure that all of you are aware that highway traffic control is one of our biggest social problems. There are in this country today over 3 million miles of highways and many more miles of city streets. Operating over these streets and highways are 24½ million passenger cars and about 5 million trucks, buses and other commercial vehicles.

This vast highway transportation system must be operated for the public good. All of us can visualize what would happen if each person were allowed to do what he pleased—with some driving on the right side of the streets, others on the left side, at speeds of their own choosing, and with no control at intersections. The results in accidents and congestion would be terrific. To avoid this, it is necessary that the individual, desiring to do as he pleases, be controlled as far as driving or walking on public highways is concerned.

It is for this reason that we have rules—traffic laws. For this reason, also, we have traffic signs, traffic signals, and other devices for regulating and controlling traffic for the greatest good of the greatest number. Likewise, we have licenses to control the privilege of driving, education and training on safe driving and walking practices, and enforcement for those who will not conform voluntarily.

THE GENERAL TRAFFIC ACCIDENT TOLL

Even with all of these controls, however, the picture is not bright. During the year 1943, motor vehicle accidents killed 23,400 persons. This is the lowest total since 1926, when an equal number were killed. This total represents a 17-per-cent decrease from 1942, a 41-per-cent decrease from prewar 1941, and a 25-per-cent decrease from 10 years ago.

In addition to the death toll, there were 800,000 non-fatal injuries during the year from traffic accidents. Deaths and injuries together are estimated to have cost the nation 700 million dollars in lost income, medical expense, and insurance costs, and another 550 million dollars in property damage, making a total of 1¼ billion dollars economic loss from traffic accidents in a single year. During the same year the nation's workers lost a total of 13 million man-days from motor vehicle accidents, of which 10 million were off-the-job accidents and 3 million were from injuries sustained in the course of their occupations. Other delays caused by absence from work, together with the hours lost by less seriously injured persons, hampered production to the extent of 19 million more man-days. Thus a total of 32 million man-days of production were lost through motor vehicle accidents alone. This is equivalent to more than a month's time of a million workers—it would have been enough to build approximately 2,500 heavy bombers or 5 battleships.

A careful study of the 1943 traffic death toll, in comparison with 1941 and 1942, shows that the decrease is due almost entirely to reduction in travel. When the necessary adjustments have been made for comparability of death totals in terms of miles traveled, there is actually an 8-per-cent increase indicated for 1943 over that in 1942. The death total for 1943 under the same exposure conditions as 1941 would have been identical with that year.

Reductions in travel are due not only to limitations on gasoline and tires, but are affected also by the number of vehicles going off the roads. At the end of 1943 there were only 24½ million automobiles registered in the United States, a decrease of 5 million from the peak in 1941. Thus passenger vehicles have been going off the road at the rate of more than 7,000 per day. Furthermore, of those that remain, 54 per cent are 7 years old or older. It is apparent, therefore, that a concerted effort must be made to keep transportation rolling with a minimum loss of manpower and equipment through accidents.

Some of you may ask about the experience for the first part of 1944. Traffic accidents for the first 5 months of this year cost 9,400 lives. This is 11 per cent, or almost 1,000 lives, higher than the toll for the same period last year.

The month of May was the eighth consecutive month in which traffic deaths were higher than for the comparable months of the previous year. It is apparent from this steady increase, which is not due entirely to increases in travel, that we are now reaching a point where the effectiveness of patriotic appeals for conservative practices is decreasing.

It is a general impression and belief of traffic observers and others that war workers and other drivers have become increasingly indifferent to past appeals for conservation of gasoline, tires, vehicles, and even lives; that speeding and other wasteful driving practices, both around war plants and elsewhere, are on the increase. This impression is borne out by the speed checks reported by the U.S. Public Roads Administration, showing a gradual nationwide increase in average speeds since the low point attained in the fall of 1942 following promulgation of the 35-mile speed limit by the Office of Defense Transportation.

TRAFFIC ACCIDENTS—POSTWAR

After the war, the urge to take it easy, to save tires, gasoline, and the vehicles, will be gone. Vehicles in poor operating condition may be driven at higher speeds by drivers accustomed to relatively low wartime speeds. This may well lead to a much higher accident rate. In addition, the spirit of release from wartime tension and the probable easier availability of liquor are sure to add to the problem.

Later, after the automotive industry has retooled and is again engaged in full-scale production of passenger cars, we may expect that vehicle use will go up by leaps and bounds. Some have estimated that the vehicle miles of travel in 1960 will be double the travel in 1940—and 34,000 persons were killed in traffic accidents in 1940.

With this in mind, I predict a traffic death toll of 50,000 annually by 1950, with the possibility of an annual toll of 75,000 persons by 1960, unless vigorous preventive action is taken promptly by all concerned—police, engineers, driver licensing officials, educators, and all organizations and agencies with an interest in public welfare and safety.

Active steps are being taken right now in the field of postwar traffic safety planning. On August 2, 1944, a comprehensive report on the subject will be issued with the joint sponsorship of 40 different associations having an interest in traffic accident prevention. This report contains a summary of an action program not only for officials but for others interested in the problem.

ALCOHOL AND ACCIDENTS

Alcoholic intoxication is one of many factors contributing to traffic accidents. The factors contributing to accidents may be classified in the following four general categories: (1) driver factors, (2) road factors, (3) vehicle factors, and (4) pedestrian factors.

Driver factors are especially important, and are made up of three classes: deficiencies in physical condition, lack of knowledge or skill, and improper attitude. Physical deficiencies include not only permanent physical deficiencies, such as a lost arm or leg, but also such temporary deficiencies as those resulting from fatigue or the influence of alcohol. Many drivers with permanent physical deficiencies compensate for them, but it is difficult to compensate for a temporary deficiency such as the influence of alcohol.

Knowledge of road and driving laws and of safe driving practices is important, as is skill in executing safe driving practices.

It is possible to go into great detail regarding the other factors: attitude; road factors, including sharp curves, etc.; and vehicle factors, which include deficiencies of brakes, lights, and steering equipment. However, you are interested primarily in the factor of the influence of alcohol, which is extremely important in affecting not only drivers but also pedestrians.

INFORMATION ON ACCIDENT REPORTS

Most of the information on alcohol as a factor in accidents comes from the accident reports which are made out by drivers and police officers who investigate accidents. The accuracy of the reported figures is dependent upon (1) the accuracy of the information contained in these reports and (2) the system used in summarizing the information.

As many of you undoubtedly are aware, the accuracy of the information reported by drivers is none too good. A driver may hesitate to indicate that he himself had been drinking. However, if there has been a collision and the other driver's breath has the slightest odor of liquor, the first driver might report that the other was intoxicated.

In many cities and states, however, most of the serious traffic accidents are investigated by police officers trained in the techniques of accident investigation. Each accident is investigated at the scene, and the officer makes an impartial analysis of all factors involved and fills out an official accident-report form. Information summarized from such reports is much more accurate than that summarized from the usual driver reports.

In using information which has been summarized by the officials of any state, care should be taken to determine just how the information is tabulated in that state. In some states the tabulations are made on the basis of those who are reported as "had been drinking." In others, the only persons tallied are those who are reported as "intoxicated" or "drunk." Thus, the figures on the monthly and annual summaries can be expected to vary considerably from state to state.

In the State of New York, for example, only 0.3 per cent of the drivers involved in injury accidents in 1942 were reported as intoxicated. In contrast, the annual report for the same year in Minnesota reported 20 per cent of the drivers involved in fatal accidents as "had been drinking." Obviously, these figures are not comparable. Because of such difference there has been considerable misquoting of figures from state reports. For purposes of comparison, it is preferable to use information on fatal accidents because we have the most complete information on such accidents, and to report both the percentages involving "had been drinking" and "under the influence."

Now, as to what the summaries show: If we consider as a whole the annual accident summaries for all states for 1943, the summary tabulations show that 13 per cent of the drivers involved in fatal accidents were reported as "had been drinking." This compares with the figure of 11 per cent reported for 1942. On the other hand, drivers reported as "under the influence" at the time of the accident decreased from 7 per cent in 1942 to 6 per cent in 1943.

The above figures are for drivers—not pedestrians. The figures for reported drinking on the part of pedestrians killed in traffic accidents show a slight decrease—from 15 per cent in 1942 to 14 per cent in 1943. Considering adult pedestrians only, one in every five adult pedestrians killed was reported as "had been drinking."

When we consider together the reported incidence of drinking by drivers and pedestrians, the statistics show that a driver or a pedestrian who had been drinking was reported involved in one out of every five fatal accidents during 1943. This is approximately the same as that reported for 1942.

A year ago I reported here the trend in reported drinking in fatal traffic accidents in urban centers of war activity. A similar study was made again this year, using reports from eight cities: Cleveland, Dallas, Louisville, Philadelphia, Portland, San Diego, San Francisco and Seattle. Results showed that while there had been an increase in reported drinking by fatal-accident drivers in the year 1942, as compared with 1941, there was quite a drop in reported drinking of those involved in fatal accidents in 1943. These eight cities, however, may be too small a sample to use the results as representative for all centers of war activity.

Reported as "Had Been Drinking"

	1941 Per cent	1942 Per cent	1943 Per cent
Drivers	10.3	10.8	5.9
Pedestrians	10.2	13.0	10.0

The data in the preceding table are rather general and are not of much help in identifying the circumstances of accidents involving reported drinking. It is necessary to go back 4 years in order to get detailed information on special circumstances of such accidents. A special study of the experience for four states for the year 1939 showed that the frequency of reported drinking on the part of drivers and pedestrians is, as might be expected, much higher at night and over week-ends. Eighty-six per cent of all fatal accidents involving reported drinking by drivers occurred during the hours of darkness. About one in every three fatal accidents at night involved reported drinking on the part of a driver or a pedestrian.

Drinking is also reported more frequently for rural accidents than for those occurring in urban areas. A special study of the fatal accident experience of six states during 1939 showed that the incidence of reported drinking on the part of drivers and pedestrians involved in such accidents was about 50 per cent higher in rural areas than in urban communities.

CASE STUDIES OF ACCIDENT VICTIMS

Most traffic authorities agree that the data from official accident reports do not give a true picture and that in general they reflect underreporting. Results of special studies bear this out. Chemical tests of body fluids or breath of drivers and pedestrians injured or killed in traffic accidents have revealed that the percentage of accidents involving drinking is higher than indicated on the official accident summaries. These studies were made of accident victims taken to hospitals or morgues. Specimens of blood or other body materials were analyzed to determine the percentage of alcohol in each person's system. This method obviously is more accurate than personal observation in determining whether a person involved in an accident had been drinking or was under the influence of intoxicating liquor.

Results of surveys made in four cities are shown in the following table. In each instance, the percentage of drivers reported as "had been drinking" and the percentage found to be "under the influence" according to usual standards are shown.

Chemical-Test Surveys of Drivers

Location of Tests	"Had Been Drinking" Per cent	"Under the Influence" Per cent
Evanston, Ill.	38	21
Uniontown, Pa.	48	37
Cleveland, Ohio	56	38
New York, N.Y.	51	42

These figures indicate that half of the drivers tested after having been injured or killed in traffic accidents were found to have had alcohol in their systems. About one-third had sufficient alcohol to be under its influence. These figures are considerably higher than those found in official accident summaries of states.

Just this past week I received a special tabulation from the toxicological chemist of Hennepin County, Minneapolis, Minn. He reported that during the year 1943, 54 persons were killed in traffic in that county, with 32 persons dying either immediately or within a few hours after the accident. Of these 32, 9 (28 per cent) showed 0.15 per cent or more of alcohol in the blood. Obviously this is a small sample, but it falls in line with the results of the 4 chemical test surveys just described.

The study which was made at Evanston, Ill., was somewhat more comprehensive than that made in any other locality. In this study, tests were made of drivers on the street, as well as drivers involved in accidents, so as to permit the making of estimates of the comparative danger with various blood alcohol concentrations.

One thousand seven hundred and fifty nonaccident drivers were tested in carefully selected locations in the city at different times throughout a week so as to obtain an accurate picture of the drinking habits of the driving population. During the preceding 2 years, tests had been made on 270 drivers who had been involved in accidents and brought to local hospitals.

A comparison of the percentages of accident and nonaccident drivers by content of alcohol in the blood revealed some very significant facts. Only 12 per cent of the drivers in the normal driving population showed alcohol in the blood, whereas about 47 per cent of the drivers involved in accidents had been drinking. There were 33 times as many drivers whose blood contained 0.15 per cent alcohol or more in the group of accident drivers as in a similar-sized control group of drivers from the normal driving population.

Results showed that the greater the concentration of alcohol, the greater the danger. A person with an alcohol concentration in the blood of about 0.15 per cent has a relatively poor chance of staying out of an accident. The average driver in this range is 55 times more likely to be involved in a personal-injury accident than drivers with no alcohol.

The study further indicated that the average driver with any alcohol in his blood is certainly more likely to be involved in an accident than if he had no alcohol at all. More studies of this type are needed.

LAWS ON DRUNKEN DRIVING

The hazard of driving a motor vehicle while intoxicated or under the influence of intoxicating liquor is recognized in the laws of every state. Each state has a law providing penalties for driving or operating a motor vehicle in such a condition. I shall discuss briefly some of the variations in these laws, the difficulties in enforcing them, and shall describe some of the procedures used in enforcement and education.

Drunken-driving legislation varies in different states. The two major differences in such legislation are in the definitions of the terms used, and in the penalties which are prescribed.

The two most commonly used terms in such legislation are "under the influence of intoxicating liquor" and "intoxicated." In 42 states it is unlawful to drive while under the influence of intoxicating liquor. In the other 6 states the term "intoxicated" is used instead. I mention this difference because some state supreme courts have held that there is a difference between the terms. According to definitions of such courts, a driver may be "under the influence of intoxicating liquor" and yet not be "intoxicated."

Penalties for driving while intoxicated or under the influence of intoxicating liquor vary considerably. In some places the penalty may be only a $25 fine for the first offense. In contrast, the penalty in a nearby area for the first offense may be a penitentiary sentence. In Missouri, for example, the offense of driving while intoxicated is a felony under state law, with a penitentiary sentence. In Kansas City, however, such drivers are prosecuted under a city ordinance which provides a $50 fine for the first offense.

Recommended legislation on driving while "under the influence of intoxicating liquor" is contained in Act V of the *Uniform Vehicle Code* of the National Conference on Street and Highway Safety. The first edition of the *Uniform Vehicle Code* was prepared in 1926 by officials of the association and other organizations represented on the Conference. It was reviewed and revised in 1930, in 1934, and again in 1938. In each case the revisions were based upon thorough study which considered the experience with the various provisions and the changed conditions.

Section 54 of Act V provides as follows:

a. It is unlawful and punishable as provided in subdivision (b) of this section for any person who is an habitual user of narcotic drugs or any person who is under the influence of intoxicating liquor or narcotic drugs to drive or be in actual physical control of any vehicle within the state.

b. Every person who is convicted of a violation of this section shall be punished by imprisonment for not less than 10 days nor more than one year, *or*, by a fine of not less than $100 nor more than $1,000, *or*, by both such fine and imprisonment. On a second or subsequent conviction he shall be punished by imprisonment for not less than 90 days or more than one year, *and*, in the discretion of the court, a fine of not more than $1,000. The Commissioner shall revoke the operator's or chauffeur's license of any person convicted under this section.

A majority of the states have state laws containing substantially these provisions. In a number of states, however, revocation of driver's license is discretionary rather than mandatory as provided above.

DIFFICULTIES IN ENFORCING THE LAWS

Enforcement of such laws is possible only to the extent that the public will support it. However, there are many practical difficulties which reduce the efficiency of enforcement even below the standards of what the public would support in most places.

The three elements in establishing a case of driving while under the influence are as follows: (*1*) The suspected person was driving or operating a motor vehicle; (*2*) his driving ability was impaired; and (*3*) his impairment was due to the effects of alcoholic liquor.

Difficulties may arise in establishing any one of the three elements. All must be established beyond reasonable doubt to warrant a conviction.

Proof of element number *2* usually can be obtained by testimony of officers and witnesses on appearances, actions and conditions of the suspected drivers. However, this element is often difficult to establish in court, partly because of the fact that alcohol affects people in so many different ways. Furthermore, many persons who are definitely under the influence but not "dead drunk" can "pull themselves together" when under observation and appear to be normal. In accident cases, particularly, the shock of the accident sometimes seems to "sober" the driver temporarily, and it is extremely difficult to obtain any evidence that drinking had impaired the driving ability, using normal observation tests. In many cases, after the person has been examined and has completed his test, he then will relax and, not knowing that he is under observation, display many of the usual symptoms of alcoholic intoxication.

Another difficulty that occasionally arises is the establishment of element number *1*, proving driving. The suspected person may admit influence of alcohol but will insist that he was not driving the car. Unless witnesses can be found, the case is lost.

In other cases the suspected person will admit being slightly under the influence, but states, "Certainly I had something to drink, but someone came along just after I had the accident and offered me a couple of drinks to settle my nerves. I was not drunk at the time of the accident."

The main stumbling block in many cases is the difficulty of proving the influence of alcohol. It may be evident from the testimony of officers and witnesses that the ability of a driver was impaired, but the case may be lost because of failure to prove that this impairment was due to alcoholic liquor. The defense may present testimony showing that the suspected driver received a blow on the head in the accident, and that the impairment may have been the result of the injury rather than the alcohol. In some cases it is pointed out that each symptom might be a pathological condition resulting from illness or the taking of medicine. For example, the defense may present testimony that the person has diabetes and that the impairment may have resulted from an overdose of insulin.

Examples of other testimony introduced in an effort to explain abnormal actions or conditions include the following:

The reason my car was weaving as it went down the street was that the steering gear was out of commission.

I had just been to a dentist who had given me a shot to quiet my nerves.

I had just had an alcoholic mouthwash.

I had been driving all night and did not have enough sleep.

Methods of Improving Enforcement

The difficulties enumerated above may be overcome in most cases through the use of modern procedures for obtaining evidence of the influence of alcohol. Many cities using such procedures have greatly improved their records in securing convictions of intoxicated drivers.

The essential features of this procedure include the following:

1. Thorough police examination at the scene of the accident or violation, using a special examination report form for recording the information obtained.

2. Chemical tests or medical examinations for cases involving illness or injury and for cases not showing pronounced physical symptoms.

3. Proper presentation of evidence in court, including adequate case preparation by the police, the prosecutor's office and any experts who are to testify.

Many possible false defenses can be refuted successfully if the police officers carefully question the suspected person before time is given to develop alibis. Samples of questions and spaces for recording the answers are given on the *Alcoholic Influence Report Form,* developed by the National Safety Council's Committee on Tests for Intoxication. The form also includes space for checking evidence of abnormal actions and conditions and results of performance tests. This type of examination should always be given, regardless of whether or not it is supplemented by chemical tests.

The National Safety Council has furnished initial supplies of these forms free to those police departments that desired to try them.

In many cases of suspected driving while under the influence, police officers call in physicians for physical examinations. Even in these instances, however, there are many difficulties. Many physicians hesitate to handle such cases because of the possible detrimental effect on their private practice.

Chemical Tests Furnish Needed Additional Evidence

Results of chemical tests of the body fluids or breath of suspected persons can show definitely whether or not there was sufficient alcohol in the person's blood stream to produce the impairment noted in the performance tests. Thus chemical tests for alcohol furnish the badly needed additional evidence to prove the third factor in establishing the fact that the suspected driver was under the influence of intoxicating liquor. When used properly, such tests also eliminate many of the other difficulties discussed previously.

Methods for making chemical tests, and possible variations to be expected in tolerance to alcohol, have been covered in other lectures. It is known, however, that there is a fairly definite relationship between the concentration of alcohol in the person's blood and the degree of intoxication. This has been recognized not only by committees of the American Medical Association and of the National Safety Council, but also by the legislatures of the states of Indiana, Maine and New York, which have adopted laws officially setting forth a definition of "under the influence" in terms of alcohol concentration in the blood.

The Committee's recommendations and the laws of these three states provide for two blood-alcohol values or limits, rather than selecting one arbitrary dividing line for distinguishing between those under the influence and those not in that classification. These values are 0.15 per cent and 0.05 per cent alcohol in the blood, the second being just one-third of the first. Drinking drivers thus are divided into three classifications: (1) Blood alcohol from 0 to 0.05 per cent; (2) blood alcohol from 0.05 per cent to 0.15 per cent; and (3) blood alcohol of 0.15 per cent and above.

In the range below 0.05 per cent alcohol in the blood, practically no person would be sufficiently under the influence to be an unsafe driver. No driver should be prosecuted for being under the influence of alcohol in this range. The use of alcohol tests thus would permit the nondrinker and the mild drinker to avoid the embarrassment of an unjust arrest.

In the range between 0.05 and 0.15 per cent alcohol in the blood, some people would be definitely under the influence. The percentage of people affected would be greater at the higher concentrations of alcohol. This evidence would be used only when other symptoms warrant prosecution.

In the range above 0.15 per cent alcohol in the blood, every driver is definitely influenced by his accumulated alcohol. The state laws of Indiana, Maine and New York provide that such concentrations are prima facie evidence of the driver's being under the influence of alcohol. This presumption in effect puts the burden of proof on the defense to show that the driver was not under the influence. The defense has an opportunity to refute the evidence by showing that the subject has a tissue tolerance sufficient to withstand the alcohol concentration above 0.15 per cent. This would be extremely difficult, however, as has been shown by many scientific investigators.

Some investigators feel that this upper limit should be 0.10 per cent rather than 0.15 per cent, since there are few, if any, drivers with concentrations above 0.10 per cent who do not show some impairment in special tests. Possibly the 0.15-per-cent limit may be lowered to 0.10 per cent as chemical tests become more widely accepted and more evidence becomes available on tolerance to alcohol.

USE OF CHEMICAL TESTS IN COURT

Chemical tests for intoxication have been used successfully in court in many places throughout the country. Recent information from state police departments and from cities of over 10,000 population indicates that such tests were used for enforcement purposes in at least 26 states during 1943.

Sixteen state police departments reported use of chemical tests for enforcement purposes during the year. Those in Indiana, Vermont, Iowa, Ohio and Minnesota reported definite arrangements providing for the use of chemical tests in different areas throughout the states. In Indiana the test equipment is located in every state police post, with trained technicians for performing the tests.

Cleveland and Milwaukee are the 2 largest of the 55 cities reporting the use of chemical tests. These 2 cities use such tests on a routine basis for enforcement purposes. In Cleveland, urine specimens are taken by police officers with the analyses being made by trained chemists in the police laboratory. A physician attached to the laboratory handles the expert testimony. In Milwaukee, the chemical tests are made in the City Health Department, with the health commissioners and Dr. H. A. Heise handling the expert testimony when needed.

Chemical tests have been a very effective aid to the police in dealing with suspected drivers. In Milwaukee, for comparable periods, convictions for driving while under the influence more than doubled after the tests were started, while convictions for reckless driving decreased 40 per cent. Similarly, there was a marked improvement in the 1939 conviction record of cases handled by the Cleveland Police Department and the Indiana State Police.

In addition to aiding in obtaining convictions, chemical tests also aid in exonerating innocent persons. There are many cases on record in which persons who were suffering from a blow on the head or from some other injury were exonerated as the result of chemical tests for intoxication.

LEGAL PROBLEMS IN USE OF CHEMICAL TESTS

The use of the evidence obtained through chemical tests of body fluids or breath involves such questions as (1) proving that specimens were given voluntarily, were handled properly and were analyzed accurately; (2) getting results of tests interpreted properly in court by a qualified expert; (3) obtaining special laws to aid in getting courts to admit such evidence; and (4) overcoming the constitutional prohibitions against self-incrimination so as to permit the taking of specimens without the consent of the accused person.

Although tabulations show that evidence obtained from chemical tests for intoxication has been admitted in the courts of 32 states, some courts have refused to permit the results of such tests to be used as evidence. This situation is due partly to the fact that the use of such tests for enforcement purposes is relatively new, and in many states there is a lack of legal precedent in court decisions. This is being overcome rapidly as the tests are used in more and more places, and precedents are established in decisions of various courts.

Some of the difficulties of getting such evidence admitted in court have resulted from questionable procedures used in the taking of specimens, their handling, their analysis, and the presentation of evidence in court.

For example, many cases have been lost because of questions of doubt regarding identification of specimens. In others, accuracy of analysis was questionable. There have been a few cases also in which the chemist who made the test was not available to appear in court. In one case, test results were questioned when it was admitted that the suspected person's arm might have been sterilized with alcohol prior to taking a blood specimen.

Many cases have been lost because of the lack of properly qualified testimony on the interpretation of test results in terms of the state law. Unless the state law contains an interpretation of the phrase "under the influence of intoxicating liquor" in terms of the per cent of alcohol in a person's blood or other body fluid, it is necessary that a properly qualified expert appear in court and testify in this matter. Such experts include physicians, toxicologists, pathologists, medical technologists, and others who have had considerable training and experience in the effects of different concentrations of alcohol upon the human system. Of course, such testimony is not necessary when there is a plea of guilty.

Many of these difficulties can be avoided by following instructions based upon the experience of enforcement agencies which have used such tests for a long period of time. The Committee on Tests for Intoxication of the National Safety Council has collected information concerning these practices and has issued a manual of instructions, *Public Safety Memo No. 29*, designed to avoid all possible difficulties which might arise from the collection of specimens, their handling and analysis, and the presentation of evidence in court.

These instructions include procedures in obtaining the consent of the accused person, the proper taking of the specimen, the use of preservatives, proper sealing, identification and storage, transfer to the chemist, analysis by the chemist, preparation of evidence for court, including the qualifications of the chemist and the expert, and presentation of testimony by all persons connected with the case. It is essential that an expert who can interpret the results of chemical tests be available in the event the case goes to trial.

Supreme courts of several states have rendered decisions on the admissibility of the evidence. In Arizona, for example, a driver was brought to a doctor and asked to give a urine specimen. The urine specimen was tested and the results used in court to aid in convicting him for a drunken driving offense. The driver appealed on the grounds that he did not know why he was asked to give the specimen and that the use of evidence obtained from the specimen violated the constitutional guarantee against self-incrimination. The Arizona Supreme Court upheld the admissibility of the evidence, ruling that failure to inform the driver of the use to be made of the specimen did not violate his constitutional rights. The case reference is *State vs. Duguid* 72 Pac. (2d) 435 (Ariz. 1937). Other cases of a similar nature include *Commonwealth vs. Capalbo* 32 N.E. (2d) 325 (Mass. 1941), and *State vs. Cash* 15 S.E. (2d) 277 (N.C. 1941).

Practically every court will admit evidence obtained through chemical tests for intoxication if the following procedures are followed.

1. Specimens are obtained with knowledge and consent of accused person.

2. Specimens are taken according to accepted techniques by qualified persons in presence of witnesses.

3. Specimens are preserved, sealed, labeled, transported, and stored properly, with care taken to record all facts so that there will be no question of identification or tampering.

4. Specimens are analyzed properly by a qualified chemist, using an acceptable chemical method.

5. All witnesses are available for testifying in court, including a physician or other qualified person who can present expert testimony in court on the meaning of the test results in terms of degree of intoxication.

6. The prosecutor is informed of the procedures used and plans his questioning to bring out the evidence properly.

A public educational program on the value of chemical tests in freeing the innocent and convicting the guilty helps greatly in obtaining acceptance. It is helpful also to conduct demonstrations of the testing procedures for the benefit of judges, prosecutors, other officials and leading citizens of a community prior to the first use of such tests for enforcement purposes.

Police have had little difficulty in getting suspected persons to give specimens voluntarily. Generally, a person who is under the influence of intoxicating liquor is glad to cooperate to "prove his innocence."

CHEMICAL-TEST LEGISLATION

Legislation dealing with evidence obtained through the use of chemical tests for intoxication is extremely helpful in getting wider use and acceptance of the scientific procedures. Four states now have such laws: Indiana, Maine, Oregon and New York. These laws deal not only with the admissibility of such evidence, but, as stated previously, most of them interpret the results of certain concentrations of alcohol in the blood or body fluids in terms of influence of intoxicating liquor.

The advantages of such laws are numerous. Summarizing the more important advantages in states having such legislation:

1. It is easier to get the evidence admitted in court.

2. It avoids the need for expert testimony in most cases.

3. It usually results in a marked increase in the number of cases in which there are pleas of guilty.

4. Since the number of contested cases is reduced, court costs are lower.

5. It provides for greater uniformity within the states in enforcement of drunken-driving legislation.

The latest development in the field of chemical-test legislation has been the inclusion of a model provision in Act V of the *Uniform Vehicle Code.* This model provision, which contains the same blood-alcohol percentages or limits as does the Indiana law, was approved by the Committee on Uniform Traffic Laws and Ordinances of the National Conference on Street and Highway Safety in June 1944.

SETTING UP A CHEMICAL-TEST PROGRAM

Before starting to make use of chemical tests for enforcement purposes in a locality, all details of the procedure should be worked out in advance, and the public "sold" on the program. The organization of a local committee to investigate thoroughly all possible arrangements for making chemical tests is helpful in starting the program. This committee should be composed of interested officials, citizens and professional persons.

The forms to be used should be prepared and printed, and the chemists and police officers should be trained in their part of the program. The officers should be given special training in observing objective symptoms and in questioning suspected drivers, and in using the *Alcoholic Influence Report Form.* Chemists should perform a series of control tests so as to be sure of their accuracy. Many specimens from suspected drivers and pedestrians should be taken and analyzed before the first case involving chemical tests is taken to court.

Finally, a carefully planned educational program should be carried on for some time to stimulate interest and obtain support from the judges, prosecutors, police officials and the public in the new program. Demonstrations, sound slide films, newspaper stories, speeches and radio should be used in the educational program.

After all arrangements have been made, the training completed, the experimental tests run, and the officials and the public sold on the value of chemical tests, the first case involving the test can be taken to court.

Detailed information regarding this procedure in setting up a chemical-test program is contained in *Public Safety Memo No. 30* of the National Safety Council, entitled *Setting Up a Chemical Testing Program*.

PUBLIC EDUCATIONAL PROGRAM

Since public attitude has a great deal to do with individual behavior, it follows naturally that educational programs can be very helpful in obtaining greater voluntary conformance to laws dealing with driving while under the influence of intoxicating liquor. Public officials, safety councils, tavern operators, state liquor control commissions and civic associations can cooperate in carrying on public educational programs directed at the hazards of driving after drinking, and to develop public support for the enforcement program.

Media through which such educational programs can reach the public include radio, newspapers, films, posters, leaflets, meetings, exhibits, schools and routine contacts by enforcement officers.

Aids to those desiring to carry on such public educational programs, available from the National Safety Council, include the following:

1. Exploded Alibis, a 15-minute radio interview script on the value of chemical tests for intoxication.

2. A sound slide film, *Testing the Drinking Driver,* on the value of police examination and chemical tests in dealing with drinking drivers.

3. Traffic posters with such messages as "Don't Drive After Drinking" and "Drink —Speed—Death."

It is imperative that all agencies and individuals work together to keep this important problem under control. Persons associated with alcohol education can help by carrying on educational programs and supporting the work of state and local officials and other agencies active in accident prevention.

DISCUSSION

Jackson: How widespread is the use of movies of persons involved in accidents as compared with the use of chemical testing procedure? How highly do you recommend the institution of the system?

Lecturer: As far as movies are concerned, there have been three or four cities in California which have set them up for use on a routine basis. Fresno, California has used them quite a bit. One or two other cities in California have used them some. I believe that Wichita, Kansas, uses them to some extent. But their use is not nearly so prevalent as is the use of chemical tests. As for recommending them or not recommending them, they do provide additional evidence, and if facilities are available, I certainly would recommend their use. However, in most places that use chemical tests they also make careful physical examinations and, furthermore, they are sure to get all of their witnesses who can testify on the person's appearance. In general, the additional expense of movies in these latter cases would not be warranted.

Miss Moon: Are the forms for police reports which you mentioned provided by the Safety Council?

Lecturer: They are available from the National Safety Council; as a matter of fact, they are glad to send a supply to any police department that will request them. Then, if they need additional forms, they can print them themselves with their own department name on them or, if they still want to get them from us, they are available at a low price.

Hoover: In speaking of the educational phases in prevention of traffic accidents you stress the importance of groups cooperating. Have you any record of the cooperation of tavernkeepers?

Lecturer: Yes. In El Paso, Texas, for example, the tavern owners have cooperated considerably in a program relating to drunken driving. As a matter of fact, they have cooperated to the extent that when a person reaches the stage where he appears to be intoxicated they will refuse to sell him any more liquor and advise that someone else be called in to drive his car home.

About 3 years ago I had the opportunity of talking to the association which represents the State Liquor Control Commissions. At that time I went into the subject in some detail and discussed various ways and means by which liquor control commissions, tavern associations and others can cooperate. The Michigan Control Commission had done quite a bit in the field of education working with the various tavern owners. There is a new association located in New York. It's an association of tavern associations. The Conference of Alcoholic Beverage Industries recently started to get into this field and have put out a circular designed to aid in the controlling of parking in and around taverns. They have said that they would be perfectly willing to cooperate in a more extensive program designed to get people to avoid excessive drinking and then driving.

Davies: Do you have any records tabulated to show the number of arrests for drunken driving in the Wet states and in the Dry states? If so, are the figures available?

Lecturer: We have tabulations available for about 42 of the states on driving while under the influence. We have never broken them down as to Wet or Dry states and furthermore I doubt that we would release those figures for that purpose. The figures were reported to us on a confidential basis by the various states and a good many state officials do not like to have their individual performance figures reported because it might reflect upon their own political administration.

Davies: In a record from Washington it appears that in New York State, and practically every other state where liquor is licensed, there was a 224-per-cent increase in drunken driving over the first year of National Prohibition. I was just wondering if that might correlate with any figures that you might have.

Lecturer: I can't see any definite correlation between those and the other figures here. It would be interesting, of course, to make a more comprehensive study of arrests, convictions and reported drinking on the part of drivers in accidents in states with various types of liquor control. We have never done that. I imagine it could be done in cooperation with the F.B.I. and some of the other organizations that have complete reports from a lot of these states and cities on arrests and convictions. Outside of our records for 42 states, the only agency that I know of that has complete information on arrests and convictions for most states is the F.B.I.

Rothrock: I'd like to ask about the possibility of using the Alcoholometer in the different states. Could we get it, for instance, to be used in the Ohio State Department?

Lecturer: There are two types of breath tests which have been used for enforcement purposes more than any others. One is the type developed at Yale by the Laboratory of Applied Physiology. The second is the so-called Drunkometer developed in Indiana. I don't know of the availability of the Alcoholometer developed at Yale commercially. I doubt if it would be available until after the war because of priorities on parts and equipment. Of the other device, limited quantities are still available.

It happens that the Michigan State Police are experimenting at the present time with the use of one of these devices, and they plan, as soon as the war is over, to equip a good many of their police cars and police posts. As far as Ohio is concerned, the Highway Patrol has used the urine test to quite an extent. Some of the doctors that participated in those programs are now in the armed forces and are not available for civilian services.

Butler: I refer to your report sheets, Dr. Berry, and think they're fine. But is it not true that every individual in the United States does not have to answer any of those questions if he only knew?

Lecturer: That's entirely right. However, the police officer tells the man that everything he says will be used against him, and he is usually in that condition when most of them are glad to answer those questions, particularly in starting out with where he's been and what he's been doing. Those are the routine police questions anyway and the other questions are gradually worked in. Another point in obtaining specimens for chemical tests is that any person has a perfect right to refuse to give a specimen. However, by using the proper approach, particularly when the person is under the influence, he is always glad to give one of these specimens to prove his presumed innocence.

Philosophy of the Temperance Movement

A PANEL DISCUSSION

Harry S. Warner, Rev. Francis W. McPeek and E. M. Jellinek

Jellinek: That the philosophy of the temperance movement should form the subject of discussion in a scientific and entirely objective course on the alcohol problem may cause some astonishment. For certain of those who are here it may cause some anticipatory misunderstandings. Some may think, "So these gentlemen are, after all, Drys," and others may think that "these scientists are now going to take the opportunity to show that these Drys are all wet." The guessers on both sides will find that they are wrong. Scientists form a curious variety of the species man. They may be interested in a matter without having any interests attached to it. For instance, the zoologist may pursue the study of zoology without necessarily liking or disliking animals, but wishing only to derive from their study a greater knowledge of the fundamental processes of life.

We are interested in the temperance movement, but not in its merits or lack of them. In the alcohol problem, total abstinence and the movement around it are as significant a phenomenon as is alcoholism. We have found in one discussion here that alcoholism is not an isolated phenomenon but an element in a vast cultural pattern. Similarly, total abstinence cannot be regarded as an isolated phenomenon, as something floating in a vacuum; it, too, is related to a vast pattern. What we think about alcoholism is meaningless unless we recognize its relation to the many elements which form the pattern; and, on the other hand, our ideas on total abstinence will be distorted unless we see this movement in its relation to a total outlook on life. In the solution of the alcohol problem we are not dealing merely with abstract ideas but with human beings, and we must know their motivations.

I said that we shall discuss the philosophy of the temperance movement. Perhaps I have misused the word "philosophy." What I was thinking of is not philosophy with a capital "P" but with a lower-case "p," meaning by it rather an outlook than a philosophy in the strictest sense of the word. There may be some misunderstandings when we speak about the philosophy of this movement. Some may mean by philosophy the rationale, that is, the overt justification. In all these matters we can speak of rationales, and in back of the rationale may be underlying philosophies and outlooks, and behind those may be psychological undercurrents. Although I have said that the rationale is overt, it is overt in its simplest form only. Its more sophisticated formulations are not quite overt. And then there are the encumberments, such as strategies and techniques, superimposed on the rationales. By the strategies and techniques in this case I mean, for instance, the propaganda activities. The strategies may obscure the rationale. Perhaps in the discussion among the three of us here and, following that, in discussion from the floor, we may not come much further than the formulation of the rationale, but perhaps we shall have an inkling of the more hidden underlying philosophies. The question of the psychological undercurrents we need not even touch upon.

We shall proceed in proper panel fashion. We are not going to quarrel; we shall ask each other questions and try to clarify our ideas. We are not going to quarrel because we are not interested in proving that the total abstinence movement is right or wrong; we are trying to elucidate here what is really behind the temperance movement—the underlying motivations. In the course of that I may ask some questions which may seem to be embarrassing, and which might give the impression that I am trying to prove something, but I can assure you that my questions are not loaded. In discussing a new theory or hypothesis with a scientist friend I often ask embarrassing questions, not because I disbelieve him, but because I want to force him, with such embarrassing questions, to formulate his ideas in the clearest possible way. I might ask him a question to which I know the answer, but I want to hear it from him. Practically always when a scientist proposes a new idea I ask, "How do you know?" I may say it in a nasty way and nevertheless not imply anything derogatory. Please take it for granted that all my questions will be asked in this spirit.

The star of this "Information Please" performance is Mr. Harry Warner, a scholarly exponent of the temperance movement. The Rev. Francis McPeek will help to formulate some of Mr. Warner's exposition in theological terms. I serve merely as the stooge to ask the stupid questions. I shall now turn this session over to Mr. Warner.

Warner: In our efforts in this school to understand the problem of alcohol from the scientific viewpoint, we have come to appreciate the complexity of the problem with a new understanding of its many ramifications and variations. I am interested this morning in helping to bring out an understanding of the temperance movement and I hope it will not be entirely unscientific although it is called philosophic. I wish to give you some idea of what has been in the minds of the people concerned in it who have been active in trying to find solutions.

We speak of the Temperance Movement in America. I think I would give it another name if I could, but that's what it is known by.

HISTORICAL BACKGROUND

First of all, I shall supply a little historical background to it, for the temperance movement is not new. It seems to me that in the United States the origin of the movement was very realistic. It faced a problem as the people found it, as they saw it right at hand. Let me give you some illustrations.

"We shall all become a community of drunkards in this town unless something is done to arrest the progress of intemperance," that was the very realistic statement of three typical pioneers, 136 years ago in a New York village, when they called their neighbors together to form the society that became the first permanent group for organized temperance activity in America. These three, Dr. "Billy" J. Clark, Rev. Lebbeus Armstrong and John H. Smith—physician, minister, farmer—completed their society of 23, with the cooperation of the barkeeper in a tavern with a bar, at Moreau Springs, N.Y., on April 15, 1808.

But 34 years earlier, Anthony Benezet, Quaker teacher and organizer of public schools, published a pamphlet in which he said that any drink "which is liable to steal away a man's senses and render him foolish, irascible, uncontrollable and dangerous," is unsafe as a common drink—a conviction that has been basic in the movement ever since. A pupil of his, Dr. Benjamin Rush, physician and signer of the Declaration of Independence, put the new philosophy into scientific terms in his "Inquiry into the Effects of Ardent Spirits upon the Human Body and Mind," a classic of the movement for a hundred years. And a group of farmers at Litchfield, Conn., founded the first known temperance society for the very practical purpose of changing the community custom which required them to provide whisky for their men in the harvest fields, thereby causing such drunkenness that the harvesting of the crops was seriously delayed.

Thus, out of rough daily experience, without theoretical idealism, but with much practical realism, and scientific and religious background, there grew up among the sturdy middle classes of the early years of the Republic a strong reaction against alcoholic intemperance and a *determination to do something* about it. From these beginnings, a philosophy took shape that, for a century and a half, has questioned seriously alcoholic culture and alcohol as a beverage.

From such realistic beginnings, a great succession of organized temperance movements swept the country; reduced the consumption of "hard likker"; helped popularize beer as a temperance drink, then banned it as itself alcoholic; rescued drunkards by the hundred thousand; started a clear differentiation of the whole people into distinct groups, the drinkers and the nondrinkers; and spread so generally as to include by 1837, for example, one-third of the people of New York City, then as now the metropolis, in organized temperance activities.

The early advocates may not have understood the whole problem of alcohol, but they were determined to do something to solve what they did know of it. Significant is the fact that in the first groups, as outstanding leaders, were physicians, ministers, educators and statesmen. But the active service and the movement of organization that followed were sponsored and led, in largest part, by men and women of the churches. At first, the Quakers, Methodists, and Brethren; then, gradually, nearly all churches. The social philosophy of the new movement was pungently expressed by a conservative statesman, President John Adams, when he said that as a young man he had been "fired with a zeal amounting to enthusiasm against ardent spirits, the multiplication of taverns, retailers, dramshops and tippling houses," because of the "idlers, thieves, sots and consumptive patients made in these infamous seminaries."

Main Trends Established

At its beginning, the temperance movement represented three basic concepts that have been prominent ever since: (*1*) Recognition of the serious community outcroppings of alcohol and its beverage consumption; (*2*) the strengthening of individuals in social groups, and by knowledge and religion, to withstand the attractions of alcohol and its excesses; and (*3*) an organized effort to reduce and to remove sources of intemperance, to "do something," as contrasted with the attitude of those who did not concern themselves with consequences.

In the main, these concepts express the background philosophy that has characterized the movement of a century and a half to "arrest the progress of intemperance," as a personal and community problem. Many variations in understanding, approach and methods of procedure have been prominent from time to time. Sometimes the temperance groups have quarreled with each other almost as much as with their opponents; but the movement has gone steadily forward through the many varying philosophies and arguments that have supported the following definite steps, as one great experiment to solve the problem:

The moderate or temperate use of alcoholic beverages; abstinence from the use of ardent spirits; encouragement of the use of malt brews instead of distilled liquors; abstinence from all alcoholic beverages; pledging children and youth to abstinence; total abstinence as the only safe course for reclaimed drunkards; total abstinence for all as a comprehensive and social-welfare as well as a personal plan; the changing of social customs to insure safety to those unusually susceptible to the influence of alcohol; formation of temperance societies in every community possible, then into great successive waves of national action; pledge-signing in evangelistic style to win drinkers; pledge-signing as an educational technique for children and youth; vast organization of reclaimed drunkards seeking others, as one man who knows to another man; increasing restrictions and limitations on liquor selling; strict licensing of dealers to keep retail sale in reliable hands; movements to make the saloon a club, a "poor man's club," with liquor assigned to a secondary place; local option as to sale by every possible local unit of government, township, town, ward, municipality, county; territorial, state and national prohibition; government ownership, control and monopoly sale, to eliminate private profits. All of these, accompanied continuously by educational and propaganda activity, especially by the churches, were tried to create and strengthen public opinion against liquor as the means to intemperance.

All through this century and a half of trial-and-error experimentation, the basic purposes—to win men from drink, to stop the initiating of drunkards, to protect the home from drunkenness, to train children to accept the natural, non-alcoholic way of life and to promote community safety—have stood out as dominant motivations. It has been a movement largely among the great middle classes of America; it reflects a philosophy of serious concern, community conservation and urgent efforts to remove alcoholic beverages, the essential source of intemperance.

But very early it was noted that many who gave up liquor, quickly slipped back; that the customs of certain groups, uninfluenced by this middle-class movement, continued to initiate youth into drinking habits and to increase the use of liquor among adults who did not, or could not, remain moderate in such use; that those who continued to favor drink gave no attention to the effect of their practice in the community on those who could not avoid excess; that the economic interest of the "liquor traffic" could be counted on to oppose any and all efforts that, directly or indirectly, might lead to reduction in the source of their profits. Antagonism between "the temperance movement" and "the liquor traffic" became conscious, outstanding. It was expressed in a thousand varieties of conflicting ideas and acts, moral, social, civic, and political, in nearly every community and state, extending even to murder, in frequent instances. The saloon became a neighborhood center of degrading association and a community blight, because of the stream of drunken, befuddled men who came from it.

Coordinate with this wider movement, the attitude of the Protestant churches grew increasingly positive. The saloon and the church represented opposite poles as to the role of alcohol in a community. To reduce drunkenness, create opinion against drinking parties, discredit liquor and the saloon, and to condition children against intemperance, were regarded by most church people as battles in a war against sin. The Bible was understood to be against drink, since indulgence easily slipped into drunkenness. To start a course of life that included liquor, was to start sinning. The custom of getting mildly intoxicated at parties, banquets, or the corner saloon, was a custom that gave approval to sin, since it opened a way to loss of self-control, and to loose and unconventional talk and conduct that might easily become immoral and socially corrupting. Therefore, the reaction of many religious leaders and the tenor of official church pronouncements against liquors of all kinds became increasingly strong and persistent.

Impressions of how alcohol affects the personality and group conduct, of how it disrupts mental and spiritual capacities, and the succeeding influence on group attitudes gained by rough, realistic observation, were deeply ingrained arguments and philosophies in the temperance movement long before modern psychologists began to offer explanations of how these results happened, or to verify, as far as they may have done, the knowledge gained by the experience of those who had undertaken to restrain "the evils of intemperance."

SUMMARIZING PAST AND PRESENT

The philosophy of the temperance movement, as it has grown out of a century and a half of experience and been modified by religious, scientific, economic and other information, may be summarized in broad outline:

A positive reaction against alcoholic drunkenness and its results, and an urgent desire to reduce, to remove, and to prevent it.

The basic philosophy of the temperance movement, in the main, has been and is one of action, as against that of no action, the attitude of the many who do not concern themselves with the unfortunate fact and consequences of the alcohol problem, or who prefer the status quo, or are involved in the financial profits of the liquor industry.

The natural, healthy "way of life" is nonalcoholic: the gaining of happiness and of release from unhappiness is by natural means, play, recreation, music, work, a variety of activities, and the emotional and social thrills that accompany such expressions of growth in personality and in living together as social beings.

Such a life from childhood, under ordinary conditions, makes possible the best that is in each individual, through healthy growth, education, religion, and experience in the overcoming of the handicaps and ills of life. It means growth of inner strength. It means enlarging personality without resort to, or dependence upon, any artificial means such as a drug. It assumes that alcoholic pleasure may be "a crutch for lame ducks," but not that the normal duck is lame.

The way of evolutionary growth is toward the nonuse, in healthful living, of such drugs as alcohol; toward their rejection in favor of the natural satisfactions of the desires they serve. The nonalcoholic life should stand out as the one that furnishes the "norm" for a growing civilization. Whether that norm has fully emerged in present-day society, or only in certain sections of society, it is, nevertheless, the natural ideal—more natural, certainly, than that of mass resort to alcohol or any other drug.

When the attitudes and emotions of younger lives are guided educationally toward the overcoming of frustrations—and all ills of life—rather than led to the easy acceptance of drinking customs as a palliation, this social crutch of past generations will be discarded by a generation that prefers to stand free on its own feet.

The "way of life" in which beverage alcohol plays a part is not one of normal, healthy satisfaction of human needs. It offers pleasure—often keen, thrilling, exciting—but pleasure that is short-lived and often followed by a "hang-over," in personal experience and society; a tendency toward slump in personality, mental efficiency and social conduct. The pleasure it offers is a path of illusion; the relief it gives is largely one of delusion, since alcohol can do little to remove any real cause of unhappiness.

The custom of utilizing alcohol for the feelings that it yields has come down from primitive societies and the early days of the race. It has been accepted automatically, from generation to generation, by those groups who do accept it. Its social use is one of unthinking tradition. The customs that give it standing should now be examined in the light of modern conditions and its wider social consequences, since the pleasures of mild intoxication tend to slip, imperceptibly and essentially, into excess. Since alcohol, in more than minor quantities, disturbs the mental processes of a vast proportion of individuals, leading to serious breakdown in some who would otherwise remain useful citizens, the toll of care and cure that it puts on the community is both heavy and needless.

The understanding that alcoholic pleasure is not worth while; that it fails to give the desired release from inferiority and unhappiness; that it gives little other than drug service, the prescribing of which is a matter for specialists; that it cannot be self-prescribed by all sorts of humanity, each for himself, without grave consequences to many; that it is not a reasonable and safe popular beverage, even when handled without immediate excess; that the borderline between excess and moderation is not known; that it cannot be acted upon at the necessary moment even if known; that the popular acceptance of alcohol as a beverage is fraught with degrading tendencies, is, and long has been, basic in the philosophy of the temperance movement.

In taking this basis for his philosophy, the temperance advocate feels that his position has been largely confirmed by scientific research, as, in the early days, it was substantiated by critical observation. As a popular beverage, alcohol has a too-costly influence on modern life, whatever function it may have served in less complex ages; and this notwithstanding the approval given it by many social groups.

The use of alcohol for sociability, to enhance fellowship, add to gaiety, and serve a ceremonial function, has been discarded by a large and intelligent part of society, including many who accept it under conventional pressure. Among all races, in all classes and major groups, there are many who drastically limit or refrain completely from its use. The number and spread of the nondrinking group is so wide and representative as to raise seriously the question whether alcohol would not now be "on the way out," as a cultural element, except for its traditional prestige, its easy accessibility to the unthinking and imitative, and the continued pressure of modern advertising.

The tradition that alcoholic feelings are something to be desired, and the trade promotion of that desire, are primarily responsible for the strong survival of alcohol in present-day life in the face of the wide questioning of its value and the educational, religious and industrial reactions of a century against alcoholic excess. The initiating of alcoholic desire in youth, the creating of habits of dependence upon it, are almost wholly of social group origin. It is in association with others, at the drinking party, the dinner, the tavern or roadhouse, that the first experience of alcoholic "short cuts" is gained, and the desire created for what it offers alike to abnormal inner urges, to outer misfortunes, and to the mere conveniences of daily living. Consequently, many intelligent people treat alcohol as they treat other anesthetics and narcotics that yield similar feelings.

That a public industry should flourish by supplying, for unlimited popular consumption, a brain-confusing, intoxicating article of any kind, with such consequences to personality and in daily living as alcohol is freely conceded to yield, does not make sense to the temperance philosopher. To him it is a traffic in the exploitation of human fears, inferiorities, weaknesses, for profit.

As a minimum, the normal desire for freedom to lead a healthy life would require that the production and distribution of this outstanding source of anesthetic or narcotic release should be classed with the other drugs to which responsible society and government give particular attention. Scientifically, and by experience, it is one of them. The total consequences to personality and in daily living that come from alcohol are vastly greater, quantitatively, in any modern state, than are the corresponding consequences of the more quickly acting, and socially disapproved, drugs.

As a source of gain, the alcoholic desire is deeply established in social recognition. Whatever its origin, the habit often becomes intensely strong, especially in those most susceptible to injury from it. Its economic significance when fully established, consequently, is very great. The desire for alcohol is a source of increasing profits because of its abnormal attractiveness and the tendency toward its more frequent use and in increased amounts. Its "pull" on the purchasing power of the heavy user gives it an unfair advantage over the demand for necessities, good food, clothing, and home furnishings. Where income is low, the deprivation of the children in a drinking home is tragic.

The greater the consumption of alcoholic beverages, the larger the gain to seller and producer. Naturally, as Professor Carver, the Harvard economist, has indicated, the tendency of the trade is to make every nondrinker into a drinker, every moderate drinker into a regular drinker, and every regular drinker into a heavy drinker. This basic trend finds full expression and confirmation in the vast volume of appealing, high-pressure advertising that is constantly put out by the liquor trade.

Largely because of this tendency the high point of conflict over alcohol in the past 60 years has been "the traffic" rather than "the alcoholic." The latter, in temperance philosophy, is an end-product of a wide-spreading, sifting process which selects those who are most susceptible to injury by alcohol and keeps them on the road of increasing indulgence until their meager capacities of resistance are overcome. The liquor business is one that encourages youth and mature men alike to seek release from life's ills in a state of illusion in which an innumerable variety of casualties may take place, from mere conventional indiscretion through petty vice to traffic smash-ups, homicides, and the mental disorders that end in state hospitals and prisons.

That alcoholic pleasure in restrained, moderate degrees is widely sought and socially approved is obvious, in the view of temperance philosophy, but this social practice is regarded as unworkable. Moderation too often is a step toward excess, not away from excess; and essentially so, because of the character of the satisfaction that alcohol offers. Any drink which "is liable to steal away a man's senses," as Anthony Benezet said 175 years ago, is unsafe as a common beverage.

This brings the whole beverage use of alcohol into serious question. Too many people too easily slip into excess. The line between moderation and excess is unknown—cannot be clearly marked. There are too many complicating, interacting factors, personal and social. The ability of the average man or woman to practice strict moderation recedes in proportion as alcohol affects his brain center. His ability to estimate what is happening, to judge how much he can take, his very desire to remain moderate, are disorganized as alcohol "puts to sleep" his centers of discrimination. His ability to stop, no less than his judgment in driving a car, is confused just when most needed. Previous decisions not to cross the danger line are futile in the face of intoxicated desire to go further. He not only cannot recognize the point of excess—he no longer wishes to do so.

While large numbers continue moderate in their use of alcohol throughout life, the number who do not, or cannot, is too much of a public burden and tragedy. The pleasure afforded those who do is not sufficient to offset the excesses of those who do not, and never will, maintain moderation. The alcoholic route of illusion and escapism, since life is filled with many forms of unhappiness to which alcoholic anesthesia gives temporary release, is one of tragic cost to vast numbers.

To understand and remove the sources of alcoholic ill health, mental and physical, wherever found, has been and should be even more, a part of the public health philosophy of temperance activity.

The sources that lie deep in individual personality—heredity and parental neglect—will require, in addition, the aid of the expert, the physician, the psychiatrist, the physiologist, the minister, and the ex-alcoholic. Those that are of community origin, blighted neighborhoods, impoverished homes, and lack of play in childhood, call for neighborhood programs of improvement and the expert leadership of social workers. But those sources that are of cultural origin, social tradition, group practices and profit motives, require changes in public attitude, wide public education, the building of intelligent public opinion and legal restraint or removal, by democratic processes, when educational and health measures are found to be insufficient. For the right and power of a community to protect itself from ethyl alcohol, the essential source of alcoholic disorders and their consequences, have been fully established in constitutional law in the century of temperance experimentation.

The attitudes of the community are vital, both as to cause and as to cure. The majority of all who become intemperate, whatever their background, even the compulsive drinker, who is such because of inner emotional conditions, learned to count on alcohol in some social group, because of social approval, in their younger days. Social invitation and suggestion, the desire to conform to expectations, to be one of the group, especially not to be a "wet blanket," are the starting points of moderate and heavy drinking alike.

Thus youth of all degrees of alcoholic susceptibility, of many shades of mental and emotional make-up, heredity, personality, "problem children," and those without a problem, are exposed continuously to the attractions of alcohol, feel it smart to use it, find release in it, and may come to count on having it again and again until, without knowledge of what is happening, a sense of dependence upon it has been established. Those with a well-rounded childhood may, and usually are, able to resist pressure toward excess; but for many others, in all strata of society, this habit-custom of looking to alcohol for what it gives is usually *not* broken until a stage has been reached at which the aid of a specialist is required.

As a sifting process of those who are inclined to alcoholic excess, local group pressures are a fundamental occasion and source of the alcohol problem. In every group, of course, there are some who are not appreciably affected; they may continue drinking for years. But there are many who are—that is the serious fact.

The voluntary choice of attitudes that tend toward the reduction of alcoholic disorders, rather than the continuation of any particular form of pleasure, is a part that the responsible citizen, who sees no injury to himself from alcoholic beverages, may well consider as his in any comprehensive program for solution of the problem.

In choosing such attitudes, the responsible citizen will be acting and expressing his own social self—the self of his mature personality that sees realistically the working out of influential conduct in the lives and character of a people.

Those who feel that beverage alcohol is desirable or necessary in social intercourse; and that vastly larger number who count on a drink at the end of a day of heavy toil, dust and strain; and all others who usually continue moderate in their use, will only be making a higher choice of satisfaction for themselves when they discontinue practices that in every walk of life have left a blight on the lives of millions. In their relative immunity to excess, they will not forget "the other fellow," who cannot, or never does, and never will, remain moderate. The man of strength is no less strong for choosing not to add to the unhealthy pressures that burden the weaker, the less knowing. Here lies *the heart* of the philosophy of the nonalcohol movement—the readiness of many men and women to set aside an overly attractive custom that they, themselves, may not "abuse," in order that society as a whole—and the less knowing—may have a new freedom.

Jellinek: The presentation which you gave us, Mr. Warner, was very interesting and it was very well rounded. However, as I expected, there was more of the rationale than of the truly underlying philosophy. Nevertheless, in the exposition of the rationale as you gave it there were indications of the underlying philosophy. I would like to ask a few questions which might tend to clarify the matter to a greater degree. Two years ago, in a conversation, somebody mentioned that you had written a book in 1928 which was entitled, "Prohibition, an Adventure in Freedom," and the person who spoke about it ridiculed this title. I didn't find it funny; rather, suddenly it dawned on me what the underlying philosophy might be. The title suggested it. I wonder whether my association of that title with some elements of that philosophy is correct. Will you tell us what you meant by that title, "Prohibition, an Adventure in Freedom"?

Warner: What I meant was that the effort, whether wise or unwise, to remove the burden of excess from the mass of the people who were suffering from it, was a movement toward freeing them rather than toward reducing their liberty; that every effort which sought to set man free from too much subservience to the influence of a drug was a movement for the freedom of the personality; that those who did not need that freedom probably would not be any worse off, they were capable, strong people, and the freedom would come to that great group of society where it would be most effective, where it was needed, where the restrictions were felt.

Jellinek: What the title suggested to me was a medieval outlook. There are great differences in outlook concerning the ideals of freedom and liberty. There was a time in our history when an ideate culture prevailed in which the ideas about liberty and freedom were that freedom consists of the absence of wishes and desires that might interfere with pursuing the spiritual goals of mankind. In the subsequent sensate culture the idea of freedom or liberty was to obtain such gratification as could be reconciled with the smooth working of society. Is it essentially right that the temperance movement has the ideal of freedom which was inherent in the so-called ideate culture of the Middle Ages?

Warner: The idea of freedom as I see it would be understood by most cultured, temperate people as the freedom to live and utilize all of one's native tendencies and instincts in the best and most effective way for the development of his personal and social life. But in utilizing any capacity, any instinct, we reach places where regulations, control, discipline are necessary; beyond that it may go not into freedom but into limitation of freedom, because the excess expression of any one instinct, sex instinct or anything else, means shutting off the freedom to express yourself in other ways in addition to that. For many people who drink heavily, alcohol may come to occupy so prominent a place in their lives that the other satisfactions they might get simply haven't the chance to function, or are greatly reduced.

Jellinek: This more or less confirms my idea of the cultural origins of total abstinence. In your presentation you repeatedly used "the natural way of life." I wonder whether in that philosophy there is inherent the rejection of any means to change or modify the course which is thought of as "natural"?

Warner: No, there could not be, because most of our civilization is artificial, as compared to the ancient days when men lived in the forests.

McPeek: The phrase which kept cropping up in Mr. Warner's presentation is "the gaining of relief from unhappiness" in the sense that alcohol brought about a desired release from inferiority and unhappiness. Since you said we might quarrel, I simply don't like the formulation that freedom consists of the absence of desires.

I don't believe that the temperance movement can be understood in any sense unless the framework in which it developed is understood, and this framework is essentially Christian. The successes of the temperance movement and its characteristic failures are just as much a part of the Christian ideology, the point of view, the way of life. I hesitate to formulate what is a Christian view of life. There's very little to be said for a man who attempts to do it in 10 minutes, and especially when he is in the presence of about 52 Methodist ministers. None-the-less it is necessary, and an integral part of any discussion. We must look back and see what the principal elements in the Christian view of man and his relationship to society are. The New Testament, and I am sure the new theologians who are more informed than I will bear me out, is tremendously realistic about man. It rejects the point of view that he is pure spirit, the old Manichaean heresy; it rejects the point of view that he is imbedded in nature, that he cannot escape from it; but it does assert that he is uniquely a part of the order of created beings. Essentially, he is a social being. Paul says, "For no man liveth to himself and no man dieth to himself." And it is in this connection that moral problems arise. Man's capacity for moral reflection, for choice, are among the surest indications of his uniqueness. Here, again, Paul formulates, "The good that I would, that I do not, and that which I would not do, that I do." This is at once a statement of the necessary social inhibitions and man's conscious or unconscious rebellion against them and the fact that life has to be frustrating in a very large degree. Man must be, in a sense, in a state of rebellion against what he finds by way of the society into which he is born—the conflicts, the disappointments.

We learned two words recently, and they slip into the old Christian point of view just as well as they do into modern sociology—aggression and tension. Paul saw these, as have Christian theologians ever since. Well, it is constantly posed for the individual as the problem of how he can maintain his own dignity and identity in the midst of many external and internal threats. Occasionally, and indeed frequently, men must utterly lose their way. It must come to the man; here comes the central problem of religion as Christianity has seen it: How can I minimize these daily and hourly threats against my integrity, against my very nature? How can I truly be free? There is a difference between escape and freedom which is sometimes lost. How can I be free from the things which limit my powers, everything which belongs to me? How can I live in the internal warfare of the soul, as Paul clearly characterizes and pictures it, particularly in the letters to the Romans? How can I still that internal warfare of the soul, how can I act and live so that there is a deep, even flow toward a horizon which has no limit? This is as I essentially think of it, and it is not accidental that Jesus stated his own mission, in Luke 4, not in terms of anything which was very great and well taken, but in a very simple fashion: He has come "to preach the gospel to the poor; he hath sent me to heal the brokenhearted, to preach deliverance to the captives, and recovering of sight to the blind, to set at liberty them that are bruised."

You cannot formulate Christianity in terms of the pathological personality only, but this is of deep significance—that Christianity understands, it has seen, what is the nature of man and how he can escape, how, rather, he can be free, from the paths in which he is caught and which for naturalistic philosophers have no explanation whatever. You can say that Christianity, the philosophy of the Christian, can be summed up in one way: It is release from those things which cramp and inhibit, which deny, restrain, sicken, and bring to death. It is what William James said, using a phrase which was more familiar to the psychologists of religion of 40 years ago than it is to us, what he calls the "expulsive power of a higher affection,"—this is what religion is, what conversion is.

But there is another matter in this; you use the words "release of growth," and there we go back to the Christian concept of stewardship, which is, very simply put, that God has given to us many remarkable faculties as men—the power of mind, the strength of body, the moral awareness which we have, and the will—not for any idle purpose but so that they may be used. They may be used, and must be used, for the fulfillment of what man understands to be the will of God—"Thou shalt love the Lord thy God with all thy heart, and with all thy soul, and with all thy strength, and with all thy mind." This is to put it not as the absence of desire, but to put it positively in terms of desire. It is not simply, as St. Augustine has said, "Love God and do as you please." This is not absence of desire; this is to have the one desire which means everything. This is my background.

And now, relating it more immediately, there are two things: First, the Pauline doctrine that the body is the temple of the spirit; "Know ye not that your bodies are the temple of the Spirit of God which dwelleth in you and if any man defile the temple of God, him shall God destroy." This is the idea of stewardship: that what you have must constantly be brought into a higher seat of affection; that the faculties of the mind must be sharpened, must be used; there must be a greater growth always toward the moral ideals of conscience. And the will itself must become unified and directed, and these other things will follow. All else is immaterial.

And the second thing is this—it was touched on by Mr. Warner: The concern that one must have for other persons. It has been often stated; Paul put it in several ways. "We then that are strong ought to bear the infirmities of the weak." In the letter to the Galatians he says, "If a man be overtaken in a fault, ye which are spiritual, restore such an one in the spirit of meekness; considering thyself, lest thou also be tempted." In other words, the sense of responsibility would come side by side with the effort to do the best one can with what God has given him. I have not said anything specifically about alcohol. But if one wishes to understand the temperance movement in all its successes, in all its failures, I think that something of this background must be kept in mind.

Jellinek: This theologically oriented formulation was extremely helpful but I still think that we misunderstand each other on the question of desires. When I talk about the idea of ideate versus sensate culture I am naturally not talking about how it should have been but how it was: what seemed to be the outlook. You spoke of the one desire, basic to all human goals.

McPeek: And I also spoke of it in the sense that I was here attempting, and very poorly, to give something of the ideals, but this does not refer to their distortion.

Jellinek: Well, you see, in order that this one necessary, basically oriented desire should function it seemed necessary to the culture of the early Middle Ages that there should be no interfering desires. You have freedom from those desires which interfere with the development of this one basic desire.

McPeek: We're in agreement.

Jellinek: I wonder, when I listen to conversations with exponents of prohibition, whether they really like the word prohibition. It seems to me that they would like to get rid of it. Perhaps what they were after was not prohibition but protection.

Warner: There are many prohibitionists who still have the "don't, don't" attitude, but originally the movement proposed as a basic tenet the protection of others, especially the protection of the home and the family. Criticism of those who drank without causing trouble, at least from their point of view, was unavoidable, but simply an incidental matter. However, from the larger viewpoint, it is clear that excesses do come, and that the protection of the family must come first.

Jellinek: May I pose one of my unkind questions? You said that I was right in my assumption that it was more a question of protection than of forbidding. How can you claim the prerogative of protecting others?

Warner: The right of the mother bear out in the forest to protect her cubs; the right of intelligent men and women in society, who see the effects of a social custom on those who do not understand it, to utilize their knowledge in a way that is socially constructive, rather than setting in operation trends which may ultimately lead to something very different.

Jellinek: Are you sure that you base this on knowledge and not on sentiment?

Warner: Probably both.

McPeek: May I ask a question? Are you speaking of the rationale or of the philosophy?

Jellinek: Both are involved.

McPeek: I have done some reading on the early history of the temperance movement and have been left with the general impression that much of the early work arose because of a concern for the individual alcoholic; he was seen to be a man in need of help. Under the principles I mentioned a moment ago, people felt it was their obligation to help him insofar as it was possible. There has apparently been a transition from that early concern to a concern with the liquor traffic as such. In other words, the individual alcoholic has been lost sight of. Now I can understand that in terms of the way of life, or the philosophic point of view just presented. I understand why it should be there, something of its philosophy. But how is it, in the light of the whole Christian framework and its interest in the individual, that there has been this transition from interest in the individual to interest in things which are apart from the individual? In 1855 Dr. Fellows of the Union Theological Seminary led the fight against some temperance people who objected to the establishment of the New York State Asylum for the Inebriate. He led the fight against them as much as he did against the indifferent, in order to convince them that it was a good part of Christian love. Now I want to know why the temperance movement has excluded the alcoholic and paid very little attention to him, but has dwelt on the other things, although it was originally deeply concerned with the alcoholic.

Warner: I believe that there are two answers. First, I think it is more apparent than real, but it is partly true. In the early days the Washingtonian movement was one of the great ones concerned with the alcoholic. Part of it has been a change due to a matter of strategy. I think it was found that constantly curing alcoholics did not give the desired result, and they did not want to stop there— they wanted to get further back in the social forces and trends. And then those became more spectacular and probably they centered too much attention upon them for a certain period, but it is a part of the program nevertheless and recognized as such, although it may not have been as spectacular in the last 20 or 30 years as it was earlier. Probably our present scientific study will help to turn us back to the individual alcoholic as one of the vital elements which needs renewed emphasis.

Jellinek: When we opened the Yale Plan Clinics for rehabilitation of alcoholics we were told that we were playing into the hands of the liquor trade, that we were getting the drunkards away from the street where they wouldn't be pointed at, and that this was essentially in the interest of the liquor traffic. That is a standpoint which I cannot accept. If the temperance movement is basically humanitarian, how can it exclude the misery of these people merely because the alcoholic-beverage industry might obtain some indirect benefit?

Warner: I certainly wouldn't permit the impression that that is typical of all the temperance movements even during the last 50 years. It may have prevailed, and did, of course, or it wouldn't have got the concrete reactions to specific cases that it did. But back of it all has been the idea of trying to stop it at the sources. The institutions which seemed to profit most from it ought to take care of their own excesses. And there are certain people, too, who, in a propagandistic state of mind opposing an enemy, would like to see him commit hara-kiri rather than have to kill him off. But I do not think that in the temperance philosophy as a whole there is a lack of sympathy with the victim which that understanding would seem to suggest. It is not at all typical, although it may have appeared at times.

McPeek: The religious movements have themselves been responsible for the establishment of many resources for the treatment of alcoholics. I have noticed quite a list of institutions which were developed under church leadership in Germany. The Washingtonian movement was mentioned and that isn't simply a religious movement although it did begin under religious auspices—the church did give it some support. But it seems characteristic of the American temperance movement that its attention has not been toward rehabilitation, the redemption —in religious language—of individuals, while in Europe it has.

Jellinek: Mr. Warner, you made a few statements which were of especial interest to me. For one thing, you said, "The way of life in which alcohol plays a part is not one of healthy satisfaction of human needs." You have come to the same kind of formulation that we find in the exposition of the sociologist, namely, human need on the one side, and alcohol as one of the many ways of satisfying this need, on the other. For me the important thing there is, you do recognize the need as the source of the utilization even if that modus is being rejected. But the interesting thing for me is that you do recognize the problem as coming out of a basic human need instead of out of a bottle of alcohol. Now you also made a statement which, essentially, means that alcoholism is a kind of a self-medication of an ailment, and that one should go to the specialist when one has an ailment instead of attempting self-medication. So we have here, first, the idea that the problem comes from a basic human need and not from a bottle of alcohol; and second, that alcoholism is an attempt at self-medication. Now apparently the temperance movement wants to disregard these connections.

In our sociological discussions here we have found the need to be produced by those tensions which are generated by the structure of society. Is it compatible with the philosophy of the temperance movement to go back to this original source instead of concentrating on the medicine? Might it not be that by taking the medicine away, another undesirable form of satisfying the need might be developed? Would it be compatible with the ideas of the temperance movement to try to remedy the anomalous conditions from which self-medication with alcohol arises?

Warner: I certainly think that it is entirely right to go back to the original instinctive desires and needs and help to satisfy them. But I can't conceive of people in a great mass following the course of life of the processes necessary to produce the releases from tension which are sometimes a little drab, which are not so easy, which require education and study and effort, when the alcoholic short cut is so near at hand and so easily accessible. Most people will take the short cut.

Jellinek: You say that the alcoholic takes the short cut and that the short cut is not good. Is the short cut that the temperance worker proposes any better? That is, is it any safer, any more well-founded?

McPeek: I think every educator would count that as essentially basic. The training and developing of the personality is the only way that does allow natural release.

There always has been some temperance movement within the Christian Church and I think it was well formulated by John Calvin: "If anyone vow abstinence from wine as if there were any holiness in such abstinence he is corrigible with superstition. If this be done to any other end which is not improper no one can disapprove of it." He means by this, I understand, that if one thinks he is going to propitiate God by giving up wine as though the act of denial were itself something important, it is improper and not to be countenanced at all. However, if he does it for any reason which seems good and satisfactory to himself, this is quite all right. But he must not take upon himself an arrogant opinion.

Jellinek: I believe we may close the panel discussion with this quotation from Calvin and open the discussion from the floor.

DISCUSSION

Question: Dr. Jellinek, is not Mr. Warner's statement proof that moderate drinking is actually a step toward excessive drinking? Has that not been brought out by your studies?

Chairman (E. M. Jellinek): I think it could be said that all excessive drinking does start with the drinking of small amounts, although that cannot be equated with moderate drinking. It begins with small amounts, there's no question about that. But our experience is such that we can say that the probabilities of a user of alcoholic beverages becoming an excessive drinker are about 5 in 100. Beyond that, we cannot predict who those 5 are.

Mrs. Colvin: I'd like to speak on the question that you asked about why temperance people aren't interested in the clinics and why they are particularly interested in getting rid of the traffic. The reason is that as early as 1862, immediately after the Government entered the liquor business by licensing and issuing tax receipts, the consumption of liquor in this country doubled for the first time in history. It had always increased each year according to the population, but that year there was a tremendous increase due to the fact that the business became legal and money could be invested in it safely. Large amounts of money went in and the business increased so much that within 4 months after the Internal Revenue Act was passed the first national organization of liquor people, the National Brewery Association, was formed. At their first convention the president of the association said that he wanted temperance people to continue to do gospel temperance work. He wanted them to stay out of politics because temperance should never be taken into politics. Their work should be gospel temperance work because when they cured the drunkard they got him away from the bars; they took him into their society and cleaned up the bar so that he didn't hang around and disgrace the saloonkeeper.

I think it was when women started the crusade, about 10 years later, that, for the first time, they went into the saloon to get the saloonkeeper to stop selling. It wasn't the conversion of the drunkards that were hanging around that they wanted, but the abolition of the saloon. Women believe in prevention rather than cure, and they are not willing to be the mop of the liquor traffic. We're not just going to clean up. We are sympathetic and willing to help any drunkard. But we think it is better to turn off the spigot than to mop up the floor.

Even after we get rid of the alliance of government and business we are always going to have work because anyone can make alcohol out of potato peelings or any other stuff and drink it. But prohibition, by the way, didn't prohibit the use, and the philosophy of prohibition is not against the use, or to prohibit anybody drinking; it does want to prohibit a business that creates appetites. Society has a right to prevent that. When I was a young girl I heard an old preacher explain this; he put it in a vivid way. He said that an old diseased cow might die, lie out in the fields and be exposed for a few days or weeks; a man could go out, take a knife, cut a slice of beefsteak off that cow, go home and eat it and nobody could do anything about it. But as soon as he cut a steak and tried to sell it to his neighbors, society would step in for the protection of public health, and that's just what prohibition was supposed to do. Prohibition and temperance are not the same. Temperance deals with the habit, and prohibition deals with the traffic.

Chairman: The prohibition movement has centered on one or two activities and has no obligation to take on other activities. The question which I raised was not why don't they embrace the treatment of the alcoholic but why do they oppose it? Why do they even criticize our clinic idea? Why object to it when others do it?

Mrs. Colvin: May I say this, there may be individuals, but I don't know of any temperance organization that would oppose any treatment of a drunkard.

Carl: Is there any prospect in this school for the presentation of as strong a statement in behalf of the liquor traffic as Mr. Warner has made in behalf of the temperance movement?

Chairman: Yes, there's no reason why we shouldn't have it. Perhaps it will be possible in one of the seminars; I wouldn't be able to fit it in now into the curriculum. Next year perhaps we'll have a symposium in which four or five of us will sit out here and the liquor trade will be represented. We'll try it.

Allen: The prig and the snob who wish to be moral examples to the unwashed half—are not their examples totally ineffective? Is not the whole argument of moral example invalid?

McPeek: The moral example invalid? I should be the first to declare against that statement in any of its forms. It seems to me that one of the faults in modern educational movements is the failure to recognize the power of influence and example. We can substitute for this the psychiatric term if you wish. You can talk about the power of the father in shaping the ego ideal of the boy, and it becomes the same thing. In other words, I would like to point out that the motivations of conduct are largely found in our attitudes, and attitudes are emotionally conditioned points of view which are largely incorporated uncritically from those adults in earlier life, and from our fellow adults in later life, for whom we have the most affection and to whose group we most wish to belong. It is a compulsive power of influence. But I do not answer to the first part because it is loaded. The prig and the snob I do not recognize.

Campbell: Webster defines temperance as "habitual moderation in the indulgence of the appetites." Why is the name temperance given to the movement whose underlying philosophy is total abstinence? Why not call it the total-abstinence movement?

Warner: The way it got started originally was, of course, as a temperance movement, because it started out with the moderation idea. There have been abstinence factors in it; there are many factors in it yet, and there will continue to be other factors in it. As I said at the beginning, I would change the word from temperance to something else, but I don't know what word to use. Those general words naturally have connotations. Personal abstinence is one thing. They are all a part of the great effort to solve the problem.

Mrs. Mann: Should not the basic principle of the temperance movement, as stated by Mr. Warner, to remove alcohol from all people because of the danger it holds for a few, be measured against our great democratic principle—"I may not agree with what you say, but I'll fight for your right to say it"?

Warner: Certainly, it's part of our democratic right of discussion.

Jackson: Mr. McPeek, you say the temperance movement is rooted in the Christian ethic. Did not Jesus turn water into wine, and did not St. Paul say, "use a little wine for thy stomach's sake"?

McPeek: I'd be glad to respond to it according to my light. The reference, obviously, is to the miracle recorded in John 2 and to the letter of Paul to Timothy, and the passages contained therein. With respect to the miracle at Cana, the oriental experts agree that this was actually beverage wine. If you wish to read an article on that, those of you who are in religion can get Hastings' *Encyclopedia of Religion and Ethics,* the chapter under Wine. It was wine as it was understood in the sense of that day. The Jews had, as a proverb, "What is he likely to ask the young man for wisdom, he is likely to want to drink wine from a basket," by which they meant unfermented wine. So the first point to establish is that it was actually wine. Jesus used wine as did the people of his day. When people wanted to criticize Jesus, they accused him of being a winebibber. They compared him unfavorably with John the Baptist, in eating or drinking. St. Paul said, "a little wine for thy stomach's sake." He is referring, I think in this particular passage, to two things: First, the common belief that wine is of medicinal value; and second, I think he was touching on the same thing I read from John Calvin a moment ago, ". . . if there were any holiness in such abstinence he is corrigible with superstition." The Christian tradition, up until the time of the nineteenth century, has always been in the sense I expressed a moment ago. There has always been a temperance movement, and it has always said that any indulgence to excess is wrong. In Catholic theology it is a mortal sin; in Protestant teaching a very heinous sin. Drunkenness is always wrong in the Christian tradition. Moderation has been a personal matter through all Christian history.

I have a statement here from Tertullian in *The Apologetica* in which he repudiates the charge of drunkenness by saying, "We who are Christians drink only as much as the rest . . . and we dine not so much on dinner as upon discipline." There has always been a temperance movement in the Church in this sense, and that is reflected in the Bible.

Jackson: Does not the forbidding of drinking of beverage alcohol create in a normal individual the desire to drink?

Warner: The forbidding may create a desire to drink in some, but the presenting of alcoholic beverages in a socially attractive way may create the desire in a great many others. It probably works both ways, but the continual pressure of social customs is much more sweeping.

Miss Perry: Does not the freedom of an individual to drink as he pleases impose restrictions on the possibilities of the way of living of other individuals?

McPeek: If that means that the excessive use of liquor may, and often does, mean deprivation for others, that is, removing from them the possibility of realizing those things which are legitimate to them, their desires and needs, I should say yes. As a matter of fact, in my personal opinion, excessive use of alcoholic beverages almost inevitably does, for the reason which I mentioned. "For none of us liveth to himself, and no man dieth to himself." In the case of the alcoholic father, because of the very fact of his illness, it means that the children, the family, are necessarily denied those things that are essential for their proper nourishment and welfare. I don't think there's any question of this; but I would not accept the question as stated here, because it is stated in terms of "yes" or "no," and the answer is not in those terms.

Mrs. Bolland: I am a member of the Oregon Educational Advisory Committee to the Liquor Commission, the committee that was created by an act of the legislature to further education to reduce the consumption of alcohol in Oregon. We prepared a little single leaf, a very attractive pamphlet with a few facts, some questions, and attractive cartoons so that it would be read. At the time we prepared it (a Bishop Astor was on the committee and sent some designs, and now Dr. Shannon is on the committee) we thought we were doing a very good piece of work, and we had one included with the bottle when the purchaser came to buy. This meant that the indulger got the pamphlet and not somebody who was already Dry. Yet we have received from church conventions and from W.C.T.U. groups so many resolutions, or other types of complaints, against that piece of work, that it has disturbed me. I wonder if, at this time, I could ask if this sort of activity is really a part of the program of the temperance worker and the prohibition worker, or if that was incidental, and decide why they would oppose action of that kind when our purpose is to do the very thing that in the end they claim that prohibition would do. Why would they not be glad that we were doing that kind of thing with the actual drinker?

Warner: That seems to have been a variation from an original temperance pamphlet which was worded like this, "Alcohol peps you up, but it always lets you down." The variation came from putting in the words "excessive use lets you down." This is probably the cause of the criticism. I don't know.

McPeek: Mrs. Bolland, was the objection made against this type of literature or was it made against this specific pamphlet mentioned by Mr. Warner?

Mrs. Bolland: The objection was made both against this pamphlet and against the existence of the committee which was created by the legislature for the purpose of carrying on education to decrease the excessive use of alcohol.

The Churches and Alcohol

Rev. Roland H. Bainton

THE motion picture "Going My Way" offers a striking illustration of the difference between Catholic and Protestant clerical mores as to sex and drink. In the story, a young priest, by a vow of celibacy, wounds a heart. An old priest has concealed in a bookcase, behind the works of General Grant, a whisky flask. A Protestant clergyman would have married the girl, but in many denominations he would never have been able to grow old in the ministry if he were caught with the flask. The Protestant clergyman is expected to be abstinent, the Catholic to be celibate. Of course, each is free to emulate the virtues expected of the other, but the pressures are differently weighted. The Catholic priest is subject to obligatory celibacy. The Protestant clergy is well-nigh subject to obligatory matrimony. Such differences in practice make one wonder whether Protestant rigorism may not be directed to drink and Catholic rigorism to sex.

If this be true, the explanation might be that Catholicism is prevalent among southern peoples more prone to sexual excess, and Protestantism in northern climes more disposed to intemperance in drink. The mores required of the clergy represent, in each case, a recoil against abuses. This explanation, although plausible, is at every step too simple. To begin with, Catholicism and Protestantism are not to be neatly equated with south and north, for Catholicism has a great hold in Ireland and Poland, and Protestantism was once strong in France. Neither can we be too confident that excess in sex is southern and excess in drink is northern. Statistics for the year 1927 reveal that in the total consumption of alcoholic beverages France was first, Spain second, Italy third and Germany in the twenty-first place.

On the other hand, the generalization may be defensible for the days in which the Catholic and Protestant ethics were formulated. In the time of St. Augustine, who did so much to fashion the Catholic view, the Germanic invaders were reputed to be more chaste than the Romans. The Vandals were lauded by the vanquished for having closed the brothels of Carthage, whereas in the period when the Protestant ethic was taking shape at the hands of Martin Luther in Germany, this people was notorious for drunkenness. These considerations perhaps support an explanation ultimately in terms of climate. But this again is too simple. Religious ideas mould conduct even in defiance of climate.

A more serious difficulty is that the lines do not fall neatly between Protestant and Catholic on the matter of drink. The Lutheran and the Anglican churches on this point have preserved the Catholic attitude. Not even Puritanism in its formative period espoused total abstinence and prohibition. The initiative came from the Methodists and Quakers, with the churches of the Puritan tradition rallying to their support. If one would understand how all this came to be, a little historical sketch of the attitude of the churches toward the consumption of alcoholic beverages is in order.

THE JEWISH ATTITUDE

The starting point must be the attitude of Judaism, which was taken over by the early Church, as to the use of fermented drinks. This attitude was conditioned by the essential character of Jewish religion, which is neither ascetic nor orgiastic. The former type repudiates drink altogether along with all the delights of life. The latter utilizes drink in order to stimulate religious emotion. Ascetic religions regard the material world as evil and seek wherever possible to avoid contact with matter. They commonly proscribe contacts with women, war and wine, because sexual relations, killing and intoxication are all defiling. Of this attitude there is scarcely a trace in the Old Testament. Judaism is an affirmative religion. God created the world and saw that it was good. The Psalmist praises the Lord for "He causeth the grass to grow for the cattle and herb for the service of man . . . and wine that maketh glad the heart of man" (Ps. 104: 13–15).

Judaism, on the other hand, is not an orgiastic nature religion, discovering particular evidence of the divine in the processes of fertilization, vegetation and fermentation and seeking communion with God through the excitements of sex and drink. This type of religion was found in Canaan in the Baal cult, and in the Hellenistic world in the rites of Dionysus. Against all such orgies the prophets of Israel were flint, even to the point of slaughtering the priests of Baal. Drunkenness in Judaism, whether connected or unconnected with religion, met with the sternest rebuke. Noah, Lot and Nabal were subjected to reprobation for their lapses. Incidentally, one of the problems for Biblical commentators has been to explain how Noah could be sober for 601 years and then get drunk. The classical denunciations of drunkenness in the Old Testament are to be found in the Book of Proverbs: "Wine is a mocker and strong drink a brawler. . . . Look not upon the wine when it is red, when it sparkleth in the cup, when it goeth down smoothly: at the last it biteth like a serpent and stingeth like an adder" (Prov. 20: 1 and 23:31).

The only cure for drunkenness contemplated in the Old Testament is moderation. We do hear, however, of two groups of total abstainers, the Nazirites and the Rechabites. The Nazirites, in the interests of holiness, vowed to hold themselves aloof for a limited period from razors, corpses and wine (Num. 6: 1–6). Here, there is a suggestion of ascetic religion. In the case of the Rechabites abstinence was a survival of nomadic mores. The Israelites, before their invasion of Canaan, had been desert tribes for whom liquor was difficult to manufacture. On entering Canaan they adopted the agricultural pursuits and the drinking habits of the Canaanites. The Rechabites held out sternly for the good old ways, refusing to build houses, sow the soil, plant vineyards or drink wine (Jer. 35: 1–11). This point is worthy of note because not infrequently in Christian history reformatory movements have been couched in terms of cultural primitivism, a return to some simpler mode of existence. Commonly in our day, however, the cry is from the city to the country, not from the country to the desert.

To sum up: Judaism steers a middle ground between an ascetic religion renouncing wine as evil *per se*, and a nature religion using wine to produce religious ecstasy. Drunkenness is reproved, moderation is commended. Total abstinence is represented only by rigoristic minorities.

EARLY CHRISTIANITY

Christianity inherited this ethic and very largely reproduced its pattern. Jesus was no Nazirite or Rechabite like John the Baptist, for "the Son of Man came eating and drinking," and could be slandered as "a winebibber and a glutton" (Mat. 11: 18–19). At the same time Jesus upbraided the drunken stewards (Mat. 24: 49) and introduced an ethical rigorism more exacting than that of Judaism in that an offending eye is to be plucked out and an offending hand is to be cut off (Mat. 5: 27–29). The Apostle Paul is more explicit because he was confronted with actual drunkenness within the Christian congregations at a very dangerous point, the celebration of the Lord's Supper. Here was the peril that Christianity might degenerate into an orgiastic nature cult (I Cor. 11: 21). The Apostle sternly rebuked inebriety. "Let us walk becomingly as in the day, not in revelling and drunkenness" (Rom. 13: 12). Among the offenses which exclude from the Kingdom of God is drunkenness (I Cor. 6: 10). The antidote in the New Testament is not total abstinence, for Timothy may take a little wine for his stomach's sake (I Tim. 5: 23), but first the avoidance of evil company. With the drunkard the Christian should not eat (I Cor. 5: 11). The real cure is that "ye be not drunken with wine . . . but filled with the Spirit" (Eph. 5: 18). As a rule for conduct Paul formulates a principle destined to play a great role in the temperance movement, the principle of consideration for the weaker brother. "Let no man put a stumbling block in his brother's way. . . . All things indeed are clean . . . but it is good not to eat flesh, nor to drink wine, nor to do anything whereby thy brother stumbleth" (Rom. 14: 13–23).

The ethic of the New Testament was appropriated by the early Church and modified occasionally in the direction of a greater rigorism as a safeguard to Christian morale in the period of persecution. Total abstinence, however, was not enjoined as a general practice. The normal attitude is represented by Clement of Alexandria in a book called *The Instructor*, in which he inveighs against all excesses and indelicacies in eating and drinking and especially upbraids drunkenness, while recognizing that a moderate use of wine rejoices the heart. Incidentally, in the course of his discussion, he displays a rather broad acquaintance with at least the names of the choicest varieties. At the same time voluntary abstinence is commendable, especially in the young.

Total abstinence was made obligatory in the early Church only by ascetic heretics who, in an age of persecution, readily fell into the error of regarding the material world as evil. Various Gnostics abstained from contact with women, war and wine for the sake of holiness, and in the celebration of the Lord's Supper substituted water for wine. Hence they were nicknamed Aquarians. The same practice prevailed for a time in the orthodox churches of northern Africa where the motive appears to have been not asceticism but the fear that in persecution the Christian would betray himself through the smell of wine on his breath at an unusually early hour of the morning. Bishop Cyprian replied, "Are you ashamed of the blood of Christ?" The sacramental use of wine soon displaced that of water. The danger that actual intoxication might receive a religious sanction was obviated by sublimation into a spiritual intoxication, a *sobria inebrietas*, which runs all through the works of the Greek and Latin fathers to reappear in the great medieval mystic, Bernard of Clairvaux.

THE CATHOLIC ETHIC

The reconciliation of Christianity with the state made the new religion popular and led to accessions with unseemly haste and all too little preparation. The way was made easier by relaxing the standards. St. Augustine tells us that frequently, when the heathen hesitated to embrace the faith for fear of having to renounce the tippling of pagan festivals, the Church relaxed and countenanced drinking in commemoration of the martyrs. Augustine was doing his best to stamp out the practice in his diocese of northern Africa. St. Basil was similarly outraged by the revelry accompanying the celebration of Easter. But neither enjoined a total abstinence. St. Basil, even in his monastic rule, recommended only self-discipline and variation in practice according to individual need. St. Augustine, writing against a new variety of religious ascetics, the Manichaeans, defended wine as a gift of God.

The rise of monasticism introduced no essential change. The movement was a protest against the corruption of secular and even of ecclesiastical society. To escape contamination the monks fled to the desert. So great was their despair of any Christian society upon earth that they renounced propagation and lived in segregated communities of men and women. In consequence, the quelling of sexual desire became, for a period, a positive obsession, and the means employed was mortification of the flesh by fasting and abstinence. Yet the Rule of St. Benedict did not prohibit wine and the earlier rigor was soon so far relaxed that the Benedictines and the Chartreuses became famous for their vintages.

The Middle Ages offered nothing new in principle, only a constant recurrence of the ancient abuses and the traditional correctives. The holy days of the Church were celebrated with conviviality. There were church-ales, Whitsun ales. What we now call a bridal party was then a bride-ale. The Church inveighed against all such abuses. Occasional drunkenness was branded as a venial sin and habitual drunkenness as a mortal sin. The drunkard was pilloried from the pulpit. All of the burlesques of the English stage and novel have their prototypes in the medieval satires of the pulpit. The drunkard was ridiculed who, seeing two candles and extinguishing one as superfluous, was amazed to find the other disappear as well. More serious was the situation of the inebriate who came home to find four children instead of two. He accused his wife of irregularity and called upon her to demonstrate her innocence by holding a plowshare which he heated red hot in the fireplace. She consented if he would hand it to her, which he did. The preacher assured his auditors that the Virgin would turn away her face from the prayer of a monk whose breath was redolent of wine. The ideal of temperance was at least so well established that satires on clerical intemperance were as funny then as they have been ever since. No more blasphemous piece of buffoonery could be conceived than a parody called *The Mass of the Drunkards*. The lines of the mass, which read *per Dominum nostrum qui vivit et regnat per saecula saeculorum* (through our Lord who lives and reigns through the ages and ages), were turned into *per dominum nostrum reum Bacchum, qui bibit et poculat per omnia pocula poculorum* (through our lord Bacchus who drinks and guzzles through the cups of the cups). As an example of the same type of literature in modern times we have the skit of Alphonse Daudet concerning Père Gaucher, who imperils his immortal soul to invent a choicer cordial for the profit of the monastery; or the hilarity of Dickens in the *Pickwick Papers* over the exploits of the red-nosed Pastor Stiggins at the session of the Brick Lane Branch of the United Grand Junction Ebenezer Temperance Association.

But to return to the earlier centuries. A new possibility was introduced when the Roman Empire gave its patronage to the Church. Christian ideals could then be embodied in secular legislation to be enforced by the state. In other words, the door was open for prohibition. No ruler attempted it in the Christian Roman Empire, nor in the west during the Middle Ages, but regulation of the sale and consumption of liquor by rulers, whether ecclesiastical or secular, was very common during this period. Sumptuary legislation was frequent enough long before the period of the Protestant Reformation.

During the Middle Ages instances of total abstinence are hard to find. The end of that period saw the resurgence of ascetic sects such as the Cathari, resembling the ancient Gnostics. They may have been total abstainers. Bernard of Clairvaux says of them that their faces were pale with fasting. One may perhaps infer that their noses were not red with tippling. But that they were complete abstainers is not clear, since they allowed the use of wine in the sacrament.

EARLY PROTESTANTISM

The Protestant Reformation brought at first no great change in the picture. Martin Luther, when he abolished monasticism and inaugurated that attitude which was to make matrimony almost a prerequisite for a Protestant clergyman, did not compensate by rigorism as to drink. On the contrary, he was somewhat convivial. Once, when at table with his colleagues, he pointed to a stein girt with three rings. The top one, he said, stood for the Ten Commandments, the middle ring for the Apostles' Creed, and the bottom for the Lord's Prayer. Then Luther drained the stein at a draught and refilling it handed it to his friend Agricola who, to Luther's intense amusement, could not get beyond the Ten Commandments. But Luther was no drunkard. Melanchthon testified that he was abstemious and, under the stress of work, would often fast for days. Luther had no use for drunkenness and scathingly denounced his fellow Germans and even his own prince for lapses. Luther's matured attitude is well expressed in his commentary on the miracle at Cana. Jesus turned water into wine. Let us not be scandalized, commented Luther, if some one should take a little more than was necessary for thirst and grow merry, but alas! in our day we drink until we are soused; we are swine, not men.

Not to Luther nor to Lutheranism are we to look for the origin of the modern

Protestant campaign against all drink. Nor is the source to be found in the Anglican Church. On this point Lutheranism and Anglicanism are at one with Catholicism. The reason is that they are all churches of the masses, including in their membership, wherever possible, all the babies born into the community and baptized into the church. Any church whose membership is not more selective cannot be too rigoristic in ethics.

Another type of Protestantism arose, in the sixteenth century, which insisted that the Church should be a city of the saints no matter how small, and should exclude the unworthy from her membership. The code of conduct demanded of the saints was exacting. This has been the pattern of English and American sectarianism. Its prototype in the Germany of the Reformation was Anabaptism. The movement was not ascetic in the sense of the ancient Gnostics. The Anabaptists did not eschew marriage, and required only moderation in food and drink, but they were ethical rigorists who criticized the Lutheran Reformation for failure to produce a manifest change in moral demeanor. One of the marks of the true Christian is sobriety. The rule of the Hutterian Brethren (1545) forbade any member of the society to be a public innkeeper or to sell wine and beer. The Lutheran Formula of Concord enumerated among the errors of the Anabaptists that a Christian might not keep an inn. A Lutheran minister in 1531 testified that the best way for a suspected Anabaptist to clear himself was to indulge in frequent drinking bouts. These people were ruthlessly suppressed in Germany, and one of the tragedies of the German people is that they have deprived themselves of that sectarian Protestantism which has been such a stimulus to English and American culture.

But the Anabaptists were not without their influence. Their memory afforded an impetus to German Pietism, which, in turn, affected English Methodism. The sectarian Protestantism of Germany likewise made itself felt in the English sectarianism of the seventeenth century among the Quakers. In view of such connections we need feel no surprise to discover the Methodists and the Quakers as the pioneers in the modern temperance crusade.

They were to enlist the support of the churches of Calvinist derivation, and Calvinism itself owes much to its competition with Anabaptism. In order to meet the Anabaptist criticism Calvin adopted a strict discipline. His whole demeanor was more austere than that of the convivial Luther. To be sure, Calvin was no teetotaler. He allowed wine in moderation and did not decline the present of a cask from the town council. At the same time he revived and went beyond the sumptuary legislation of the late Middle Ages. Taverns were suppressed in favor of hostels where food and drink were served only to those who looked as though they would be able to say grace after as well as before partaking, and who agreed to depart from the premises at 9 P.M. Even though the hostels lasted but 3 months, the Genevans were proud of their austerity. A satire, composed by Calvin's colleague Theodore Beza, pictured a Catholic spy coming to Geneva to discover to his amazement how pale were the faces of the heretics. Beza was not slow to point the contrast with the leader of persecution against the Protestants in France, whose nose was the hue of a cardinal's hat. Calvinism contributed to the ultimate temperance campaign a deep moral earnestness, and a readiness, not characteristic of Anabaptism, to make use of the state to institute and enforce a code of conduct. But initial Calvinism was not committed to total abstinence. The modern movement of prohibition is really a combination of the Anabaptist code with the Calvinist program.

But the modern movement did not come until the late eighteenth century. Calvinism was a long time in adopting the Anabaptist code. The Calvinism of Scotland under Knox was no different from that of Geneva under Calvin. Knox had his wine cellar. The Calvinism of English Puritanism exhibited the same general pattern. The Roundheads, indeed, stigmatized the Cavaliers as rowdy and dissolute, but the worst of their offenses appear to have been Sabbath breaking and "God-damn-me oaths," together with pillaging. When King James promulgated a "Book of Lawful Sports" to be played on Sunday afternoons in order to wean the people from "filthy tippling and drunkenness" the Puritans were so outraged by this proposed profanation of the Lord's day that the "Book of Sports" was burned.

New England Puritanism exhibits no marked change. A housewarming had reference to the use of ardent spirits. Even the ordinations of ministers were often unseemly occasions. The shepherd of souls was sore tried to do justice to the hospitality of his flock and get home with the aid only of his crook. Ministers such as the Mathers inveighed against drunkenness. Colonial assemblies regulated the hours of taverns, the quality of beer and the sale to domestics and the Indians, among whom rum wrought havoc. The name Manhattan, by the way, is said to be a corruption of a sentence in the language of the Delawares meaning, "Here we got drunk," referring to their first experience of the hospitality of Hendrik Hudson. Despite all regulation, excessive drinking continued even among churchmen in New England until the reform movement of the early nineteenth century.

THE TEMPERANCE CRUSADE

The initiative in the temperance crusade came from the Methodists and the Quakers, with the Calvinist churches swinging later into line. The Catholics, Lutherans and Episcopalians were reluctant to demand one practice only of their constituents, let alone of society at large. The first temperance reformers were not ascetics fleeing contamination, nor saints aspiring to perfection. Their motivation might rather be called sociological. The evil of drink had grown worse in the eighteenth century due to the displacement of fermented by distilled liquors. A report to His Majesty's Justices of the Peace in 1735–36 lamented the surprising increase of gin-drinking in London in which whole families were involved, parents, children and servants. No one was better acquainted with the prevalent excesses than John Wesley. In the campaign for correction, the alliance of religion with medicine is noteworthy. The inaugurator of the American reform was Benjamin Rush, the Quaker doctor of Philadelphia.

If the program of the reformers became ever more drastic, the reason lay not in any ascetic presuppositions but in the lessons of experience. First came total abstinence from hard liquors, coupled with moderation as to beer and ale. But when it was found that drunkards on the way to reform could lapse as readily on the mild as on the hard, the ban was placed on both, and those who might be able to drink in moderation were urged to refrain entirely out of consideration for the weaker brother. The same moral was deduced from the failure of the Duke of Wellington's attempt to oust hard liquor in Britain through the encouragement of beer. Inebriety was only increased by the Free Beer policy of 1830–69. The failures of regulation likewise drove the temperance movement to the advocacy of prohibition. The course of the movement was very similar in England, Germany and the United States, except that prohibition was achieved only here.

In England the Methodists took the lead. John Wesley, who so well knew the debauchery of the English countryside, lashed out against the sellers of spirituous liquors as poisoners of the people. The Rules of the Society called Methodists, in 1743, required members "to avoid buying or selling spirituous liquors, or drinking them, unless in cases of extreme necessity."

In the United States the Quakers were the most notable exponents of reform. The reputed father of the temperance movement in this country was the Philadelphia doctor, Benjamin Rush. Having observed all too well the evils of excessive drinking in the Revolutionary Army he published a tract entitled *An Inquiry into the Effects of Ardent Spirits* (1785). His objection was only to the use of distilled liquors. As a substitute he recommended first water, and if that did not suffice, then cider or light wine. Much medical observation was introduced. He closed with a ringing plea to all the churches to join in the crusade. In the following 6 decades his tract circulated 200,000 copies. Another notable Quaker pioneer was Neal Dow, one of the fathers of American prohibition. He was a citizen of Maine. His first enunciation of the principle of prohibition was in 1839. He lived to see it embodied in the law of his state in 1851. Thereafter the cry of the temperance reformers was, "Remember the Maine Liquor Law."

Among the churches of the Calvinist tradition which rallied to the support of the Methodists and the Friends come first the Congregationalists, who were the leaders of the movement in New England from 1810 until the formation of the Temperance Society in 1826. The year 1810 was marked by the indignation of Lyman Beecher when, at his ordination, the sideboard was loaded with decanters containing every liquor in vogue. The talk was jocose and convivial. This, said he, "woke me up for the war." He was ardently seconded by Leonard Bacon who, in New Haven in 1829, preached his sermon on "Total Abstinence from Ardent Spirits." By ardent spirits he meant distilled liquors. Beer and wine were not discussed.

With regard to other churches of the Calvinist tradition we may note that the Presbyterians in 1827–30 took a strong stand for total abstinence, and in 1854 endorsed prohibition. The pronouncements of the Baptists were the most rigoristic. The New Jersey Association in 1835 declared that "It is morally wrong in all, and especially in a professor of religion, to manufacture, vend or use such liquors [alcoholic, whether distilled or fermented] as a common article of luxury or living."

The churches with the more inclusive membership, the Catholic, Lutheran and Episcopalian, have been less disposed to general requirements binding upon all members, although of course perfectly ready to bless total abstinence movements within their folds. The approval given by Pope Leo XIII to the Catholic abstinents was similar to a papal sanction of a vow of celibacy or poverty, which is commendable in those who take it, but not required of all. The zeal and effectiveness of thousands of Catholics who did espouse the cause are by no means to be minimized. One thinks of the Confraternity of the Sacred Thirst, and the vigorous support of Cardinal Gibbons and Bishop Ireland who declared that, "to Irishmen particularly, because of their comparative native powerlessness to resist alcohol . . . I will never cease pointing out with undeviating finger, the harbor of peace and security—total abstinence." One may question his appraisal of the Irish, for prior to the great famine Father Mathew well-nigh dried up the island.

The Lutherans have generally confined themselves to the advocacy of temperance, although various synods have taken strong stands against the liquor traffic.

The Episcopalian Church has had a Temperance Society in which moderates and total abstainers alike participated. Episcopalians accepted Prohibition because it was the law of the land, but the majority of the clergy desired modification or repeal of the Volstead Act. They stoutly and very properly resisted the efforts of the teetotalers to impose their code upon the Bible by interpreting the "wine that maketh glad the heart of man" as unfermented, and the wine into which the water was turned at Cana as grape juice.

The Protestant sects with the strong ethical rigorism led the campaign for prohibition by government of the manufacture and sale of intoxicating liquors. The Holy Experiment came and went, and like most lost causes, now is memorialized by a wreath of sneers. The knell was sounded in *The Rubaiyat of Ohow Dryyam,* which concludes with the verse:

> When thyself at last shall come to trip
> Down that dim dock where Charon loads his ship,
> I'll meet thee on the other wharf if thou
> Wilt promise to have something on thy hip.

Prohibition is gone, but the problem of inebriety confronts us still in no less acute form. The attitudes of the churches throughout the centuries provide us with no absolute rule. The only fixed principles are self-control and consideration for the weak. The concrete application of these principles may vary in accord with circumstances. A very good case can be made for a more rigoristic attitude in modern than in ancient times because mechanization has increased both the evil and the danger. The discovery of distillation has produced much more potent liquors; at the same time the mechanization of travel and manufacture has introduced hazards which can be avoided only by the speediest reactions of the eye, hand, ear and foot. Earlier generations ran less risk through moderate indulgence than do we.

An interesting parallel to the attitudes of the churches toward the drinking of alcoholic beverages is afforded in their attitudes toward slavery. Here, too, there was no agitation for abolition until comparatively recent times. The anti-slavery movement began only in the eighteenth century. The reason was very largely that slavery in the Christian Roman Empire and during the Middle Ages in Europe was in no sense so vicious as the Negro slavery introduced only after the discovery and colonization of the Americas. More serious diseases may require more drastic cures.

The Bible and the teaching of the Church, then, afford us no absolute rules, only certain guiding principles. The churches are not of one mind as to their application, although a large number of Protestants in the United States have come to feel that in our land and time these principles are best exemplified through total abstinence.

DISCUSSION

Heimburger: Are there two Greek words which mean wine, one meaning "the fermented" and the other "nonfermented"? If so, which one did Paul use in writing to Timothy?

Lecturer: There are two words, *gleukos* and *oinos;* the one used was *oinos.* The difference between them is not that one is intoxicating and the other nonintoxicating. The same thing is true with *yayin* and *tirosh* in the Hebrew. They are both intoxicating.

Question: If the movement of total abstinence began with the use of distilled spirits, what would have been the attitude of Bible writers if they had dealt with the problem of whisky?

Lecturer: That, of course, has back of it the implication that the attitude taken in the Biblical period was conditioned by the particular offense with which they had to deal and that they were not legislating for all time. That is perfectly sound. Had they lived in a later period and been confronted by a different problem they might well have spoken differently with regard to it.

Stoneburner: I am a Lutheran minister. I am sure that Dr. Bainton did not mean to imply that there was no social consciousness on the part of the Lutheran denomination. In its social relationships in America, however, I think it operates on a different basis than it has in any of the constituents of any of the countries from which it has emanated. But for the Lutheran Church to have sounded its voice in the prohibition movement would have meant a violation of principle which it has always maintained, that is, separation of church and state in America. It has never pronounced its selected views on any social issues.

Lecturer: I did not mean to imply that the Lutheran Church had no social consciousness by any means. As far as the separation of church and state is concerned, that can hardly be the rule in Lutheranism in view of the situation in Germany and Sweden.

Stoneburner: I qualified that.

Lecturer: You mean in the United States. Well, I can see that if the Lutheran Church is committed to that principle they wouldn't want the state to put over a program in the name of the church but they might individually support that program nevertheless. The Baptists are also committed to the separation of church and state but, as citizens, they give advice to the state or even let the church give it without violating the principle of separation, don't you think?

Stoneburner: To my knowledge, even in the North and South, although many of our faith gave their lives for the cause of liberating the slaves, yet there was no church statement on the subject.

Lecturer: The only statement on that by the Lutherans was not with reference to slavery but with reference to the maintenance of the Union. On the question of the war, the Lutherans in this country took the traditional attitude that government is to be supported in the maintenance of its authority, and that rebellion is to be put down, but they did not call on the Government to emancipate the slaves. They supported the war on the grounds that it was a just war instituted by government for the suppression of an insurrection, rather than that it was for a social cause—the emancipation of the slaves. There is a recent very good book by Dunham on "The Attitude of the Church to the Civil War" in which the Lutheran and various other attitudes are described.

Stoneburner: When it comes, though, to the subject of participation as a denomination in movements of that kind, our church just doesn't do it.

Lecturer: Even if you did not endorse prohibition, you might have enjoined total abstinence on all church members, as some other groups have done. But the Lutherans haven't done that either—they have made it optional. Is that right? There has been total abstinence, but it isn't universal.

Stoneburner: There is still a lot of denunciation of the use of alcohol.

Lecturer: Oh, certainly.

Stoneburner: But no demands that you can't be a Lutheran unless you are a total abstainer, whereas the Methodists and the Baptists make a stand on that.

Bosse: How do you account for the seeming contradiction of the Bible with respect to abstinence? There seem to be places in the Bible where the writer thinks it is all right to use alcoholic beverages moderately, then there are places where it says, "look not upon the wine when it is red in the cup," not to use it at all.

Lecturer: In Psalms, "wine maketh glad the heart of man." In Proverbs, "Wine is a mocker and strong drink is a brawler." I am not sure that even Proverbs wants to do away with it completely; that might be merely a warning against taking too much. But if there are differences in the Bible, that doesn't trouble me, because the Bible is not one book but many.

Stoneburner: Are we wrong, then, in taking our view toward total abstinence from the Bible?

Lecturer: Not wrong, but I don't see how you can get total abstinence out of the Bible very easily.

Stoneburner: That is what I mean.

Lecturer: I think the temperance movement did two things. It appealed to Paul's principle of consideration for the weaker brother. The other thing was to wrest scripture to its purpose by making the distinction between the two Hebrew words and the two Greek words for wine, interpreting one as nonintoxicating and the other as intoxicating, which I think really does violence to the context. It would seem to me that ethical courses of action are to be based upon the spirit of Christianity which is to be worked out in the light of continually changing circumstances rather than on a set of rules laid down for all time.

Shattuck: Is there any relationship between the Industrial Revolution and the attitude of the church toward total abstinence?

Lecturer: Yes, there are indications of such a connection. In the first place, distilled liquors are, in part, a product of the Industrial Revolution; they are a product of the improvement in the mechanized process for producing liquor. In the second place, the degradation of the working people in the Industrial Revolution may very readily have prompted them to drink as an outlet.

Shattuck: I wonder if there is also a relationship in the fact that the person becomes a victim of a traffic that is interested in making profits out of the sale of liquor to the person purchasing it?

Lecturer: That may well be. Wesley thought so, and denounced sellers as poisoners of the people. The organized traffic certainly led the reformers to become more and more drastic in their demands and more and more despairing of anything short of prohibition.

Davies: Getting back to the Bible again in this matter of wine, most ministers have the idea, and rightly so from their training, that the Bible is a way of life, and such it seems. And all that tends to disintegrate such a life is an evil. As far as the ministers have been taught, the alcohol problem is a problem of the disintegration of life in various forms, drunkenness, suicide, destruction of the home life, destruction of oneself, and so forth. Going to the Pauline story, Paul comes along and admonishes us and all people to keep away from everything that has the appearance of evil, not that it is evil in itself, but anything that appears to be evil. On the basis of that, putting it over against the fact that ministers are opposed to anything and everything that will destroy life, I wonder what argument we could put up if there is no record or no argument for total abstinence when total abstinence will clear the way for a purer life?

Lecturer: I am in agreement with you that the Bible is a guide to life, but not in a legalistic sense. I should agree with you also that drunkenness is a great social evil, and of course the Bible teaches that it should be eliminated. The only question is whether to eliminate it by total abstinence or by moderate use, and the Bible lays down no legalistic word on that subject.

I remember having supper one day with a friend and ordering coffee while he ordered beer. He said, "You know, coffee would stimulate me so that I couldn't sleep tonight, but beer will relax me and I'll have a good sleep." Well, I didn't feel that I was holier than he because I was taking coffee and he was taking beer. Nevertheless, coffee at its worst is not going to have the same dangerous consequences as liquor at its worst. I feel it is much more discreet for young people who haven't tried themselves out not to bother to find out, because they'll get along perfectly well without it, and that certainly, for the sake of the example, it is wiser to refrain entirely. But, you see, that is not a legalistic ethic derived from the text of the Bible. If anything, it is rather a prudential ethic coupled with an attempt to exemplify a spirit, and it is open to discussion with a man like my friend who takes his glass of beer in preference to my coffee and says that coffee would be a worse debauch for him.

Controlled Consumption of Alcoholic Beverages

Edward G. Baird

EVEN excluding the topic Prohibition, my subject is broad enough to cover nearly all the law there is. Few people comprehend the vast extent to which rules and laws concerning alcoholic beverages have permeated the body of Anglo-Saxon jurisprudence. Most of us are in the habit of regarding the liquor control statutes adopted since the 21st Amendment as containing all the law on the subject.

I assure you that such is not the fact. The liquor control statutes of today contain only a fraction of the total quantity of law that has to do with the alcohol problem, even explicitly. It would be difficult to point to any part of the body of American law that has not been affected by problems arising from the use of alcoholic beverages. It is not possible to mark off any part as free from such effects, nor to regard any liquor statute as not within the scope of the subject which is assigned to me today.

One does not know just how to begin such a task. Unless he begins with some comprehension of the frame within which the alcohol law has its place in the social scheme, there is very little chance of demonstrating that order does exist, or that there are sequences and relations between statutes. I do not hope to demonstrate that there is a form and logical sequence to the sum total of law that has to do with the alcohol problem in all its aspects. In fact, after raking all this law together from all of the various fields one will see, at the first glance, no order at all. It seems to be just one big, amorphous heap of rules, regulations, statutes and decisions.

There must be some sense to the business. So let us keep looking at it for a moment to see whether there is anything we might do to bring order into all this chaos.

It is no small job to read the 48 state codes on this subject. If they were placed end to end they might reach from here to Oregon. After reading the statutes, it is necessary to read the court decisions, because there the judges tell you what the statutes mean and that is the only way of finding out.

Let me illustrate this complexity by selecting the common provision of the control law that forbids sale of liquor to certain persons. An examination of the statutes of the 48 states will disclose a unanimity on the question of whether intoxicating liquor should be sold to minors. All the states forbid it. But there the unanimity stops. The states differ as to the age of majority and also on the question of whether marriage terminates minority. Thus, in some states a girl of 12 or 14 can be legally married. In those states would the statute be violated by sale to such a wife? This question takes the reader afield from the liquor control acts. He must go to the local judge-made law on the subject of domestic relations and emancipation of minors.

Thirty-eight of the states have statutes which prohibit the sale of alcoholic liquor to a person who is "visibly intoxicated." When is a person "visibly intoxicated"? If you should attempt to read all of the court opinions on this question you might never get back to reading the control acts.

Nor does it follow that in the other 10 states it is legal to sell a drink to an intoxicated person. It may be that there was already a statute on the books which prohibited such sales, and therefore the drafters of the control acts did not think it necessary to include such a section. Perhaps it was simply forgotten. I am convinced that many of the state control acts were adopted in such haste after the repeal of the 18th Amendment that the job was not altogether well done. Many things were left out that could properly have been included.

Thirty-six states forbid the sale of liquor to habitual drunkards, but there is no unanimity of opinion as to what constitutes habitual drunkenness. Eighteen states forbid sales to insane persons. Is insanity to be defined according to the several meanings of psychiatry, or by reference to the legal distinction of whether the purchaser knows the difference between right and wrong? Sixteen states have barred sales to Indians. Some Indians are United States citizens, and no longer are wards of the Government. May liquor be sold to citizen Indians? Can you tell, by looking at them, whether they are citizens or not? Ten states impose a penalty on whosoever sells liquor to prisoners and inmates of state institutions. Five states forbid sales to prostitutes. Two states, Delaware and Kentucky, forbid sales to persons convicted of drunken driving. Delaware prohibits sale to university students within 2 miles of the State University; Minnesota does likewise, but does not add the 2-mile limit. Louisiana forbids sales to women and girls. Massachusetts prohibits sales to women at bars unless they sit on stools. Men are permitted to stand to drink in Connecticut bars; women are not. Michigan punishes retailers who sell to truck drivers on duty.

Why do not all states forbid all of these sales, or why do they forbid any? Why do the statutes differ so much on these matters? Is there actually a difference of opinion among the people who command these governments? If so, why do such differences exist? When did they start, and what caused them?

It is quite obvious that random selection of topics, or even an attempted explanation of the meaning of the various provisions of the control act of a typical license, monopoly, or "open" state, is not the way to go about obtaining a comprehensive picture of alcohol control law. It is also quite certain that I could not describe all of this law, even if I knew all the answers, which I do not. Legal abstractions and fine distinctions, which may be enjoyable to lawyers as exercises in mental gymnastics, even valuable in a monetary sense as technicalities when used to cover the strategy of opposing counsel in a lawsuit, or in a criminal trial, should have no currency here, and could serve only to confuse rather than to clarify the larger issues before you. The alternative is to lay out the legal material in as broad outline as I can so that you may see it in such form and perspective as it has.

I have discovered that the only way I can see these matters in outline, and with any degree of significance, is to examine them as historical categories. One not only learns in that way to give full meaning to these statutes, but the process is decidedly helpful in eliminating ideas that have no basis in fact, which, if not eliminated, would lead to errors of judgment in appraising the correctness of statutory construction by the courts.

Do you remember Artemus Ward's definition of ignorance? "Ignorance," he said, "does not mean not knowing the answers, but in knowing so many things that ain't so." I have found the historical approach to the study of the alcohol law very helpful in unlearning some of the ideas that "ain't so."

For example: In 1935 the Wisconsin Supreme Court had before it the appeal of a man who had been convicted of drunkenness in the privacy of his own home. The Wisconsin statute made no express distinction between public and private drunkenness. Other state courts which had passed on the question were unanimous in holding that to sustain a conviction the offense must have been committed in public. The reasoning behind the distinction was said to have come from the common law preceding the statutes, on an analogy with public nuisance. The Wisconsin Court sustained the conviction anyway, but felt obliged to justify what it conceded to be an unorthodox view by arguing in its opinion that protection of the family interest was at stake. The point is, that if the Court had known the history of the law against drunkenness, there would have been no necessity to invent an argument or justification for its position. There was no common-law rule which confined drunkenness to a public environment, nor should the offense be regarded as growing out of the idea of public nuisance. The first American court that said there was such a rule was overly optimistic, or perhaps remembering a misspent youth. The common law actually made no distinction between public and private drunkenness, as I shall presently demonstrate.

One more preliminary matter must be attended to before I attempt to describe some of the existing statutes. That is the question of what we mean by the word "law." Let us define law as a secular command to do or to refrain from doing something, with a penalty annexed. The penalty may be physical punishment, imprisonment, a fine, or the awarding or refusal to award a judgment for money or a decree for specific performance. There are other sanctions. This definition is far from being complete, but it is adequate for our purpose.

Let us think of the control laws as classifiable into eight rough groups. Obviously, some statutes can be classified in more than one category. These groups or categories are: (1) the statutes against drunkenness and disorder; (2) the price-fixing, quality and measures statutes; (3) the license laws; (4) the revenue acts; (5) the trade laws; (6) various items of discriminatory legislation; (7) the judge-made law that relates to criminal and civil capacity and responsibility; and (8) the state-store acts. These are listed in the approximate order of their first appearance in the law books, and I shall discuss them in that order, selecting the first and second groups for somewhat more detailed discussion than will be given to the others, in order to demonstrate the relation between categories and to show you that there is an over-all form and pattern to the alcohol law.

Statutes against Drunkenness

One would expect to find that the earliest laws were those that fixed prices and measures for ale, beer, and wine. It is probable, however, that the drunkenness statutes or laws came first, that is, in the English law. At a synod held in Canterbury in A.D. 670 or 673 Archbishop Theodore promulgated rules which imposed penances on priests and laymen guilty of drunkenness. Whether it is correct to regard these canons as "secular" law under our definition is arguable. Later archbishops exercised temporal powers under charters of the ninth and tenth centuries. It is certain that the Church claimed jurisdiction over drunkenness as a moral offense. Just when it was first exercised is not known, unless Theodore began it. William the Conqueror confirmed a general power of the Church over moral offenses in 1072, but that old charter does not name any of the offenses that were then so regarded. The collection of decretals by Gratian, in the twelfth century, names these offenses, and drunkenness was included as a venial sin, increasing in importance to that of a cardinal sin if occurring often enough and carried on long enough to amount to gluttony, one of the seven cardinal sins. It is interesting to note that exuberant drunkenness, especially if at Christmas time, was not so regarded. Some actual records have survived, and I have read some that date from the period 1491 to 1638. It is said that there are more such records in England, that go back even farther, of penalties imposed by the ecclesiastical courts, then called the courts-christian. From 1102 to 1603 there were several church synods at which canons were adopted against moral offenses. It appears that adultery, procuration, incontinency, fornication, incest, defamation, sorcery, witchcraft, misbehavior in church, neglect to attend church, swearing, profaning the Sabbath, blasphemy, drunkenness, haunting taverns, heretical opinions, usury, and perhaps others, were offenses within the jurisdiction of the courts-christian. Just when these powers were first exercised is probably beyond the efforts of research people to demonstrate. Whatever may be the answers, it is unquestionable that two parliamentary statutes of 1534 and 1545 during the reign of Henry VIII authorized the courts-christian to impose penalties for moral offenses. Those statutes would make the church regulations "secular" enough to satisfy our definition. These statutes, then, made the matter *de jure*. I believe they were *de facto* secular law from the time of William the Conqueror, if not before, but I cannot prove it.

The first parliamentary statute authorizing the secular courts to fine persons guilty of drunkenness or tippling was adopted in 1606. The language of the preamble is significant:

Whereas the loathsom and odious Sin of Drunkenness is of late grown into common Use within this Realm, being the Root and Foundation of many other enormous Sins, as Bloodshed, Stabbing, Murder, Swearing, Fornication, Adultery, and such like, to the great Dishonour of God, and of our Nation, the Overthrow of many good Arts and manual Trades, the Disabling of Divers Workmen, and the general Impoverishing of many good Subjects, abusively wasting the good Creatures of God: Be it therefore Enacted . . .

I shall not read the remainder of that statute. It has significance for four reasons for this present discussion. First, notice the language of "sin." Second, the statute made no mention or distinction between public and private drunkenness, and indeed, it is difficult to believe that these people thought private drunkenness less sinful than public, or less wasteful, in an economic sense, or less provocative of other and more serious offenses. Third, the statute itself saved the jurisdiction over this offense which had been exercised by the courts-christian. And fourth, the statute not only punished drunkenness by a fine of 5 shillings; it also punished tippling, defined as sitting over-long (more than an hour) at drinking, by a fine of 3 shillings and 4 pence.

The statutes against drunkenness and tippling were to remain law until 1872, when they were replaced by a new act which punished drunkenness only, and only in public places. In 1879 Parliament adopted a more modern solution of this problem by providing for commitment of the confirmed inebriate and assigning his property to conservators for protection.

Now how is this brief glimpse of history to have usefulness for our purposes here? How will it help us to discover order and form in this chaos?

1. The statute of 1606 served as the model for colonial legislation. The original words have been lost as the states have recompiled and revised and restated their statutes a great many times since Plymouth Rock and Jamestown. But to this day, in a surprising number of our states, the crime of drunkenness is classified as an offense against morality. And if it is so classified, logic would seem to demand that these states follow the Wisconsin rule. For example, in the revision of 1930 of the General Laws of Connecticut, drunkenness is in section 6248 of chapter 329 entitled "Offenses against Humanity and Morality." It is common to find the same law in other states grouped along with blasphemy, profaning the Sabbath, adultery, fornication and sodomy. Thus, it is not inaccurate to call drunkenness a crime—although a minor one—of a nature *malum in se*—bad in itself, a deed carrying the connotation of moral turpitude, while it is small enough to be called a misdemeanor. It is not accurate in a historical sense to describe it as a crime *malum prohibita*, in the meaning of a rule against doing something that would have injurious social consequences, like driving through a red light, or conducting a public nuisance. Nevertheless, it is commonly so described, even in those states that classify the offense as one against morals.

2. We "unlearned" something. We see that there was no common-law rule which confined the offense to public places.

3. This may best be expressed in the form of questions. In the light of what we know today about the alcohol addict, about the natural curiosity and exuberance of youth, about the social acceptance of alcoholic beverages by 40 million or more of the American people, is it expedient to describe drunkenness as a moral offense? Would it be more socially and politically desirable to make further distinctions about it in the law books? Is it a matter in which the law has kept pace with the points of view of our people? Is not the problem too complex for the law alone? Is it not time for our students in matters of morality, our churchmen, our sociologists, to draft a "restatement" of morals—to give us a modern axiology, a table of relative values?

4. Notice that the seventeenth-century point of view toward drunkenness as a sin did not apply to drinking. If you should study this matter you would learn that total abstinence, as a rule of morals or conduct, developed in the United States, and furthermore, that its acceptance is today confined to certain groups. It is obviously not shared by all groups. So far as I am able to determine, there has never been a statute against drinking. Even the tippling provision of the statute of 1606—defined as sitting over-long at drinking—did not last, unless by stretching our imaginations a bit we can see the present provisions against loitering as a surviving element of this old offense. Even if that were so —and I do not believe it is—the loiterer is not punished, only the permittee may be punished by loss of his license. There is more reason to regard the loitering provisions as aimed at petty thieves, prostitutes and vagrants. There is a long and respectable line of statutes aimed at these creatures since the time of Hammurabi, over 4,000 years ago.

In other words, let me point it out, we may have, individually, certain notions as to the motivations and purposes of these laws. Our notions are also amorphous. The study of the history of each provision will allow us to select those that probably explain it. When we are through with our examination we will know that we have been guessing, but guessing intelligently, and it is possible that we may be in a position to demonstrate that an earlier guesser—opposing counsel or judge—had guessed less intelligently.

5. Of greatest importance is the knowledge, gathered from the historical method of study, that a particular law has different meanings at different times, that its purposes change when the factors which brought it into being are disclosed and identified and its relations to other laws are made manifest. It is at this point that we find ourselves in a position to comprehend the social significance of the law as one mechanism functioning in the larger—and as yet relatively uncharted—panorama of civilization.

As we trace a specific statute backward through time, each of its provisions may fall away, one by one, or we will discover old and different provisions. We learn that each such provision may have been added, or subtracted, as difficulties in the administration of the statute had become manifest and new controls or slightly different controls were thought to be desirable. We are thus directed to search times and places for the motivations which were responsible for the adoption or subtraction of each provision.

The motivations are seen to be many and complicated. But a surprising number of them can be isolated and identified. Thus, we learn to think of the law as the result of ethical, economic, and political views and attitudes of people and groups, which have been articulated or verbalized and systematically set down as statutes or decisions and opinions of the judges.

The statutes are commonly expressed in words of command, or as limitations upon interest. The judicial opinions are invariably given a logical formulation, simply because more flies are caught with honey than with vinegar. The statutes may be wise or they may be foolish, they may work well or they may fail as tools for social engineering. The judicial opinions may be logical or they may be something else. Depending on your philosophy, the law may express immutable and universal principles, or rules of only temporary significance. We are not at this moment concerned with a search for the philosopher's stone, although a man who says he is not interested in the greatest of mysteries is kidding himself, and his listeners. The important thing to notice, at this minute, is the legal process, the dynamic character of the law as a part of the going concern we encompass by the word civilization. We are now observing a phenomenon, not philosophizing about it.

We see a dynamic process, then, a forward-looking, a growing law. Each time a judge applies a statute to the case before him, he in effect redefines the statute. Thus do the meanings change. Each such redefinition is a reflection of the ethical, economic and political views of that particular time and place, as seen through a judge darkly.

Thus the history of drunkenness has shown us a good example of the contemporary sociologist's thesis on stratification of the population and isolation of ideas and ways of doing confined to layers or small groups or parts of the larger complex which is called society. The predominant moral idea which originated the statute has been lost, or replaced over the course of time by another notion, namely, that drunkenness is to be punished not because it is immoral but because it is undesirable on account of its social consequences as a public nuisance. The judges and lawyers—who have become a separate group not closely associated with the churchmen and theologians for some hundreds of years—have developed their own ideas and explanations which differ, and may continue to differ, from those of the moralists, in the absence of a universal code of conduct influencing all the people to think alike.

We see, then, that a law may be moral, or it may be amoral, unmoral, or nonmoral, depending on its underlying ethical, economic, or political motivations, the training and background of the judge, the degree to which he reflects the public and the group opinions of his time and place, that is, his concepts of tradition and custom.

PRICE-FIXING STATUTES

The second group or category has been described as price-fixing laws.

It was common to fix commodity prices in early England. They enjoyed a sort of medieval O.P.A. scheme, which did not work very well then either. Here again there was a moral basis. The churchmen preached and the governments imposed what may be described as the "fair price" theory, a notion that every article and every service had a certain fixed intrinsic worth. Thus wages and prices were fixed by law. These statutes, beginning in 1197 or 1202 and growing out of earlier Saxon efforts to establish weights and measures and uniform coinage, were to continue in England and be adopted in the American colonies. As everyone knows they did not survive here. The practice today, except for wartime legislation, is only followed insofar as liquor is concerned in the states which have adopted the state-store system, although the laws of the license states commonly contain provisions which permit control over these matters.

The emphasis today is more on price control than on price fixing. Certain business practices that would be more or less acceptable under a program of free competition are barred in the alcoholic-beverage business. Furthermore, the matter is one that is more interstate than intrastate. Thus the Federal Government, by virtue of its delegated and paramount power over matters of interstate commerce, exercises a more direct control than do the states over these business practices, although state control acts commonly contain similar provisions.

Price wars are controlled by the Miller-Tydings Act of 1937. One of the things this act accomplishes is to legitimize contracts which provide for maintenance of an agreed retail price and prohibit selling at lower prices. Obviously, a price war on distilled spirits is not conducive to keeping the quantity consumed at a minimum level. Many states, by virtue of their control provisions, have power to step in and enforce such a private contract between the manufacturer and the retailer. Labeling of the product, advertising it, preventing adulteration, commercial bribery, the "tied-house" problem, and credit given by wholesaler to retailer, are matters which the Federal Government and the states have legislated about. Great problems of the extent to which the one power is effective over the other, state or Federal, are legal puzzles for which we have no time here, but which are, nevertheless, decisive on the question of local versus national control. I mention these things with two thoughts in mind: First, to indicate the extent to which the original and primitive laws that related to price fixing have grown and multiplied in complexity and ramification to the present day. Here, again, the reading of the control statutes will not, by itself, educate one to an understanding of the alcohol control law. Second, these modern laws are as easily classified under the license heading as under the price-fixing title. And, for purposes of description, it is a difficult matter indeed to separate the two categories, price-fixing and license legislation. There is no separation in the laws and statutes today, and very little at any period of history we might choose to study.

Statutes on Licensing

For our purposes today, perhaps the most significant fact about the old price-fixing legislation is its place in the control pattern, its relation to other parts of the law. Beginning immediately with their original adoption, the price-fixing statutes were difficult to enforce, and continually tightened up by a whole sequence of legislative experiments. That sort of law always is a job to enforce. One quickly gets the impression that it was out of these attempts to tighten up the laws and to make them work that the licensing principle and the great host of license statutes got started.

For example, there was a statute of 1318 which provided that officers of cities or boroughs, to whom was delegated the task of assessing prices, should not, during their terms of office, themselves sell or deal in wines and foodstuffs. In 1353 another statute increased the penalty from a fine to capital punishment upon whosoever should break the assizes, but fortunately this did not last. Here is an early example of the inadequacy of the law alone, when not supported by overwhelming public opinion, to accomplish something admitted by all to be noble in purpose. In 1706 judges who owned breweries or distilleries were forbidden to take part in the selection of licensees who should retail alcoholic beverages. Restrictions such as these are today multiplied in the control acts, and some of them are no more enforceable than they were in the early days. But they fix a standard which is valuable for administrative purposes.

We might have noted, when discussing the first drunkenness statute of 1606, the idea that it was motivated by the difficulties of the enforcement of an earlier license statute, especially that provision which required the tavernkeeper to prevent loitering and disorder in his place of business.

The Puritans have been credited, or debited, depending on your point of view, with initiating these laws. Many of the early control laws were adopted during the reign of King James, when the Puritans were strongly intrenched in Parliament. But, in fact, the roots of the laws we sometimes call the blue laws go back much further, not only to the ecclesiastical promulgations but also to medieval secular ordinances.

For example, there was a statute, in 1325, against persons who haunted taverns, probably inspired by the same motive that had prompted Hammurabi, in 2350 B.C., to order innkeepers to arrest outlaws who came into their places of business. The selling of wool on Sunday was prohibited by a statute in 1354. The holding of fairs and markets on Sunday was curtailed in 1448, and in that law a reason given for its adoption was that Sunday fairs caused drunkenness and strife, and absence from Divine Service. Shoemakers were forbidden to sell shoes on Sunday in 1464. There was a statute aimed at the control of ale selling in a London red-light district in 1433. We have statutes today similar in content, and similar in motivation, to these old examples.

There was a series of statutes against vagrants and sturdy beggars, that is, those able to work, from 1349 to 1562. These also fixed prices and wages. One of them, an act of 1494, contained a provision—seemingly almost an afterthought—which authorized any two justices of the peace in each county or shire to close the alehouses they regarded as unnecessary or undesirable. The power of these justices was almost absolute. No appeal from their decision was provided.

A much earlier act—probably around 1330—had provided that wineshops might be shut up when the price laws were not obeyed by their owners. But that act contains no words of jurisdiction—the job was not delegated to any particular court or officer. In that statute is the Latin word for "license." The final clause reads, "and let not him be permitted to sell wine without the king's license."

Thus was laid the foundation in early statutory law of the idea that selling liquor is a matter of permit from government.

The first true license law was adopted in 1552. From that date onward the justices of the peace were empowered to select persons who in their opinion were to be trusted with the job of operating alehouses, and they were again empowered to suppress undesirable places. The preamble has significance in that it indicates once again that licensing was thought of as a means of controlling prices and the disorderly shops and preventing drunkenness and other more serious offenses. These provisions were extended to innkeepers in 1625, to wineshops in 1660, and to distiller's shops in 1700.

Under this licensing statute, and operating also under the old price-fixing, quality- and quantity-controlling provisions of the longer established statutes of laborers, and the very early assizes of bread, beer and wine, the local justices of the peace and the municipal officers of the chartered towns developed an administrative system which was a very well worked out and very practicable control scheme. English historians and economists have commented favorably on the work of these justices, and described it as truly successful, for its time and place.

The system was directed and manipulated by the king's Privy Council, which we, as children in public-school history courses, once learned was a very bad and undemocratic thing—something which the good people of England had to spend time, blood and tears to overcome. These were the days before the English Revolution, the days of such doctrines as that of the divine right of kings. With the English revolutions this first administrative system came to an end. But under it, while it lasted, licensee selection was well done, a fair degree of control was achieved, drunkenness and disorder were reduced, fees and taxes were efficiently collected. As the licenses were renewable annually, it was open to the justices to impose conditions. And this they did. For example, screens to hide drinking places were eliminated, unclean and inadequate accommodations were improved, closing hours (9 P.M.) were imposed, and music, dancing and other entertainment were abolished. In fact, nearly every feature we now have in our control laws had its counterpart in the English statutes and in the administrative regulations of the justices and of the city ordinances of the period when the American colonies were being founded.

This system was applied in the colonies of Connecticut, Massachusetts, and Virginia, although in New England the overseeing was done by town selectmen rather than by justices of the peace.

A strange result—if it was a result—is reported by one writer. At Harvard University, students' names were listed on the rolls not in alphabetical order but in an order said to represent their relative social standing. And the name of a tavernkeeper's son led that of a minister's son.

The reasons for the success of the system are not far to seek. The powers of the English justices were great, and not subject to court review. These justices were local big-wigs, often representing their localities in Parliament, and working in close harmony with the local churchmen. Remember, also, that the church—the Church of England—was predominant, and of great power. The justices were responsible to the executive, to the king, through his Privy Council, rather than to the legislature, and when something did not work well, it was changed quickly and drastically. Perhaps, also, there was relatively less drinking of hard liquor than there is now. And there were doubtless other reasons.

That system passed away because it rested on the royal supremacy, and has never since returned in quite the same form. With Parliament—and the lower house in particular—achieving supremacy, thereafter the statutory law, rather than that which we now call administrative, was to serve as the definitive expression of the powers of, and over, the licensee. The doors were opened to judicial review and to strict and limiting construction of such powers.

So has the law remained to this day. In the United States especially the law has grown to emphasize a fixed and precise procedure, deviation from which not only will be resisted by the lawyers and judges, but even resented by public opinion, a substantial part of which is strongly pro-court and pro-legislature, and anti-executive, on matters involving law and legal procedure. In the present control laws, no state has gone as far as the English had gone before 1640 in giving power to local officers, or as Connecticut and Massachusetts gave to selectmen in the colonial period. Not only the legislatures, but the courts, are wary of this newfangled thing called administrative law, and jealous of their prerogatives.

I refer to certain doctrines that are typically American in growth and significance: "Everyone is entitled to his day in court"; "there must be a fair hearing." We fear the unfettered administrative tribunal, where the officers are prosecutor, judge, and jury. We call our ideas on this subject Due Process of Law, Equal Protection of the Laws, and so forth. I am not here talking about the Bill of Rights, and such things as the rule against unauthorized searches and seizures, which are also part of the alcohol law. I am concerned at this moment with the peculiarly American doctrine of separation of governmental powers. Our problem—if the administrative tribunal should turn out to be the only efficient way in which the alcohol question can be handled—is one of education, one of learning to respect the new tribunals, of developing a confidence in the system, which will permit extending their powers to the point where the regulations may become effective without injury to basic political freedoms and to the businesses regulated.

Under present statutes, there are some 29 states which follow the so-called "license" plan of liquor control. Of these, only 4 give exclusive selecting power over licensees to a central control board: California, Connecticut, Delaware and South Carolina. At the opposite extreme are Illinois and Wyoming, where local power over selection of licensees is paramount. The remaining 23 states divide the responsibility in greater or lesser degree between local officers and some form or other of central authority. In 18 states, Arizona, Arkansas, Colorado, Florida, Indiana, Kentucky, Louisiana, Massachusetts, Minnesota, Missouri, Nebraska, New Jersey, New Mexico, New York, Rhode Island, South Dakota, Texas and Wisconsin, the state boards have the responsibility, but they must cooperate with local authorities. In some of them the local authority is purely advisory, as in Indiana; in others, local officers take greater parts. In New Jersey, licensing is discretionary, as are revocations, with the local boards. The differences between the states are too numerous to permit crystallization into generalities.

Only 14 of the license states have separate liquor boards. These are: Connecticut, Delaware, Florida, Illinois, Indiana, Massachusetts, Minnesota, Missouri, Nebraska, New Jersey, New Mexico, New York, South Dakota and Texas. In 11 states, Arizona, Arkansas, California, Kentucky, Nevada, Rhode Island, South Carolina (tax boards), Louisiana (state auditor), Maryland (state comptroller), Wisconsin (state treasury department), and Colorado (secretary of state), the great problems of liquor control were dumped into departments that already had full-sized jobs to perform.

Some of the American states rely, as does Denmark, on a system of high license fees to keep irresponsible persons out of the retail business. Others impose only low fees. Some states grant large numbers of permits; others are parsimonious.

I have said that no state has gone as far as the English did in delegating discretion to the administrative tribunals. I have to modify this statement only slightly in order to show that on the matter of appeals a pathway has been opened up whereby the liquor boards may ultimately reach very broad and decisive powers.

Generally, the control acts provide a form of appeal from the decisions of the liquor boards to the courts. Appeal is not mentioned, however, in the control acts of Arizona, Minnesota, North Carolina and Vermont, nor is a statutory appeal provided in Massachusetts, Nebraska, New Jersey and Rhode Island. In Arkansas, Kentucky, Nebraska, Oregon and South Dakota, appeals are limited to cases in which permits are revoked. Delaware and Louisiana, on the other hand, permit an appeal only from a refusal to issue a license. The Illinois statute is a peculiar one, largely because of the pressures brought by local interests in Chicago. Only in Utah and Virginia do the statutes expressly forbid all appeals to the courts.

This picture indicates that a breach with established practice has been made. It is only a very small one. It may be for the best that it is not larger at the moment. The presence or absence of appeal provisions in the statutes will not determine the matter, because if certain constitutional safeguards are thought to be disregarded in any particular case, a court will always be found which will listen to the complainant irrespective of what the statutes may say about it. Even a New Deal Supreme Court, more favorably disposed to the idea of allowing finality to the decisions of administrative tribunals than other courts have been, has carefully kept its hands on one string while ostensibly cutting all the others which once insured judicial review. If it had not been for a national emergency and a world war, even this much might have been denied. Even now, the resistance encountered is such that the success of the liquor license control scheme rests in delicate balance, and its fate is partly bound up with the fate of the whole new administrative fabric from N.R.A. to N.L.R.B. The result is—insofar as the liquor problem is concerned—that the state boards must keep one eye on their local statutes, the other on the courts, while both hands are full of one of the trickiest problems the world has ever produced. One thing can be said: There is a noticeable trend toward cooperation by the courts because of a growing and sympathetic understanding of the immensity and difficulty of the problems involved.

REVENUE ACTS AND TRADE LAWS

The fourth group or category of statutes has to do with the revenue laws.

When it was that governments first discovered the attractive possibilities of revenue from the liquor trade is not now determinable. Excise and customs duties were laid very early. One English historian points out the city of Norwich as perhaps having enforced the assizes in medieval times because of the revenue-producing values involved therein. There is an early record (about A.D. 1000) of an import duty levied on French wines. We are familiar with the practice, during the days of Prohibition, of some rural communities which used their own enforcement machinery as a lucrative source of revenue to finance local improvements.

That the present control laws were motivated as much by the revenue possibility as by the desirability of better control is an inescapable conclusion from reading the statutes, even if we should forget the fact that repeal of the 18th Amendment was urged as a means of fighting the depression of 1929. As pointed out a moment ago, seven states, Arizona, Arkansas, California, Kentucky, Nevada, Rhode Island and South Carolina, use their state taxing departments as control boards.

The same thing is true of the Federal Government. The Federal act is directed toward revenue collecting, and the various controls are primarily intended to protect the revenue rather than to provide a solution of the alcohol problem. The Federal law established, in 1940, an alcohol tax unit in the United States Treasury Department.

Events since 1940 have made this observation a very true one. One of the major purposes of repeal was the hope of eliminating the bootlegger and his illicit product. The present program of very high taxes—however necessary they may be for purposes of financing the war—is nevertheless not conducive to discouraging the bootleggers. While statistics are lacking, it is generally believed that there has been an increase in the flow of black-market liquor in recent months.

Nevertheless, the Federal laws are important, and quite effective, as control provisions. Under the basic permit system, which does not apply to beer, manufacture is well regulated and illicit distilling and interstate shipment made much more difficult than would be the case without Federal laws.

The big question in this field today is that which goes to the matter of cooperation between the state and the Federal authorities. Technically, the Federal jurisdiction is confined by the Constitution to the interstate commerce and taxing powers. The limits of these powers, as applied to intoxicating liquor, are not yet marked out by the United States Supreme Court, although a definite trend is now noticeable in that direction. Actually, these Federal powers are so great and, when exercised, so decisive, that state control could be made to mean very little. No such thing has happened, however. We shall presently see, when we reach the discussion of trade laws, that the contrary may be expected to develop.

The theory of the 21st Amendment is that control over the liquor question is returned to the states, while Congress is empowered to assist the states in maintaining whatever systems of control they adopt. In practical fact there is very little cooperation, as Congress has not utilized its power to any great extent.

If this is the theory, then with control should go the responsibility. Unfortunately, full control and complete protection as a practical matter have not gone to the states. This is a matter about which you will hear more in the lecture on Prohibition, and I shall not discuss it.

One result has occurred, however, which has dangerous implications. I am referring to the tendency to erect trade barriers between the states, under color of the authority conferred (or returned) by the 21st Amendment. In consequence, states have discriminated against each other in favor of their own local interests. This discrimination is accomplished in a variety of ways, of which I shall mention two. First, by means of differential fees and taxes, outstate manufacturers of beer, wine and distilled liquors find their markets narrowed and the field of competition carried over into legislative halls, a place where it should not be, as past history in this country has demonstrated. Here, then, is a situation in which lobbying has come about not because some liquor manufacturer wanted it from a purely selfish point of view, but because of simple and instinctive self-protection of business interests. Second, the discrimination has appeared in the field of transportation. In one state the legislative power was so exercised as to take from a private contract carrier and give to a local common carrier the business of transporting a local alcoholic beverage. In another case, liquor destined ostensibly for North Carolina was stopped in Virginia and confiscated because of violation of a Virginia law which required (1) that vehicles used must follow the most direct route and carry a bill of lading showing the route to be traveled; (2) that the carrier must post a penal bond conditioned on lawful transportation; and (3) that the bill of lading must show the name of the true consignee, who must have a legal right to receive the beverages at the destination stated. I am not objecting to this law. Under the peculiar facts of the second case no one can quarrel with the decision. The United States Supreme Court apparently regarded Virginia's action as justified as a police measure, and perhaps it was. The dangers are, not that states are given too much power by such a decision but that, by virtue of the Court's construction of the 21st Amendment, interstate commerce is no longer primarily a Federal function which permits development of a body of law that is uniform for the country; and that local laws justifiable as police measures will indirectly serve local and pressure-group interests. Let me illustrate. Suppose the Virginia law had required a particular route to be traversed. There is good reason to require such a route, especially for trucks, as they could be more easily watched. But what is to prevent making that route so difficult that a local product is thus given a substantial edge on costs and efficiency of delivery? Here are a few other examples of discrimination: Five states, Iowa, Minnesota, North Dakota, Oregon and Wisconsin, require that beer be manufactured from 66⅔ per cent of barley malt. These states raise most of the barley in the country. Iowa and Washington allow local winemakers to sell directly to licensed retailers, while imported wines can be sold only to the state monopoly which charges a percentage tax. In Utah and Maine, local products are given preference. Ohio requires that wine-blends contain at least 51 per cent of Ohio wine. There are many other such discriminations. They represent retrogression to a period of narrow commercialism and false economic theory, which have been shown time and again to be harmful to national interest. We should not forget that, whatever our attitude toward liquor and our desires to see it made available or strictly controlled or abolished, there are often other values involved of which we must not lose sight.

Time is not available to trace the history of such trade laws. One can be mentioned which will indicate the extent to which a narrow comprehension of national interest was allowed to influence legislation. In a statute of 1605 the English Parliament sought to encourage beer-making and its export, saying in the preamble:

Now for that by the transporting of beer, the custom and poundage that will grow due to the king's majesty for the same beer will be much greater, than when the barley or malt whereof the beer is made is transported, and also that the navy and mariners of this realm will be the more increased, for the one ship or boat load of barley or malt will, if the same be brewed out into beer, make four several ships or boats load of the same burthen of beer to be transported: (4) the tillage likewise of this realm will be cherished and increased, . . . (5) divers port towns will be greatly comforted and relieved, many of his majesty's subjects thereby employed and set on work, and the trades of coopers and brewers will be thereby better enabled to live and maintain themselves, their wives, children and families. Be it therefor enacted . . .

The Parliament thereupon provided a favorable export duty differential on beer as against the higher rate on exported barley. Today, we find our exporters using every means in their power to get greater loads into ever smaller shipping spaces.

One important use of history for our purposes can be made here. In the early days of New England, fishing, and the sale of fish, was the first development beyond simple self-sustaining agriculture. The owners of ships took their catch to the West Indies, where it was sold or traded for rum and molasses. Rum was an effective commodity for the purpose of trading for slaves in Africa. Rum making was a natural business development in this part of New England. The cycle, then, which culminated in the clipper-ship era, was fish, molasses, rum, slaves. When the slave market was affected by failure of supply and reduced demand, much New England money went out of shipping and into local manufactures. Rum became even less productive as its supply increased and its market decreased in competition with whisky from Pennsylvania and Maryland. It did not take, then, much argument to make temperance advocates out of the owners of manufacturing industries when it was shown that alcohol decreases, rather than increases, a worker's efficiency.

This is cited only as a suggestion of the influence economics can have for, as well as against, the moral point of view. It is a historical fact, however, that Henry Ward Beecher, who fought for temperance, found his allies among the industrialists of Connecticut. And it is also true that many of those industrialists got their financial start, or their grandfathers before them, in the fish-molasses-rum-slaves cycle. A study of the Connecticut and Massachusetts laws will disclose a close harmony with the economic interests of the people of that time and place.

DISCRIMINATORY LEGISLATION

The sixth group or category we have designated as discriminatory legislation. We have already described part of that law, which is of significance today, in talking about the statutes which prohibit selling liquor to minors, Indians, intoxicated persons, habitual drunkards, insane people, and so forth.

There are many modern and historical examples of this sort of statute. This is an example: the interdiction laws are of ancient lineage. In the American Colonies the provision that sales should not be made to persons who were paupers and on relief, who had not paid their taxes, or who were habitual drunkards, or as they were then called, "common drunkards," was on all the statute books. These laws are common today. The only problem of any significance here is the one that relates to procedure. Some acts provide that a name may be added to such a list by the selectmen, local judges, or even by request of members of the family of the drunkard. Some require posting of the lists in the taverns—others require no posting, but actual notice to the tavernkeeper in each instance. Obviously, such laws can be enforced only in the small communities.

There was and is much other legislation, most of it not to be found in the control acts. For example, there are the laws against railroad employees and public officers who drink while on duty. In some states, persons injured as a consequence of drinking while on their jobs are denied workmen's compensation benefits. Several states have machinery for the commitment of confirmed inebriates and their affairs to conservators and guardians. Some provide commitment for treatment, as in California and New York. These statutes are older than you think. Most go back to 1854–1867. One, in Virginia, which provided for compulsory treatment, was adopted in 1771, a century before the English reached the same conclusion. The zoning laws, state and municipal, the provisions against granting licenses to permittees within certain distances from schools and churches, and in residential areas, are good examples of this category. Local option legislation might be considered in this category, in that localities are themselves permitted to discriminate application of state laws to themselves, as in one of the Carolinas; and in Maryland, where provision is made for local state stores on popular majorities; or in Maine, where a community can choose between stores and hotel licensees. The legislation which provides for penalties against drunken drivers and for compulsory tests in cases of driving while under the influence of liquor are discriminatory statutes.

When I use the word "discriminatory" I am not using it in the sense of invalid or illegal discrimination. Here, again, there are some technical problems, that of equal protection of the laws, due process, and so forth. Laws are supposed to bear with equal force on all persons throughout the state. But legal history has so developed that classification of cities by size of population, and application of different laws to all members of the same class, is not regarded as "unequal" protection or lack of due process. Thus, a law may work, as in Illinois, when there is only one city in the class marked out by the legislature. New York City is a classic example of this sort of discrimination that is regarded by the law courts as valid discrimination. A good example from the alcohol law is the story of the adoption of the so-called 15-gallon law by up-state New York. The city was known to be against it, so the legislature "seceded" up-state New York.

The new statutory liability of the liquor seller as a party equally liable with the intoxicated person for that intoxicated person's torts and acts of negligence is a situation in point. That law is a valid discrimination, even if grocers are not included under it.

JUDGE-MADE LAW

The seventh group or category has been described as the judge-made law that relates to criminal and civil capacity and responsibility. It should be thought of as those rules of law and equity which relate to the effect of drunkenness in matters of responsibility and mental capacity in crime, contract, deeds, divorce, wills, insurance, torts, workmen's compensation, together with the court rulings on matters of the admissibility of evidence.

There is a great deal of case material on this subject, and to cover it properly would require another lecture. You all know that drunkenness is no defense to a criminal indictment. The Roman law did so consider it, but Anglo-Saxon law has never regarded drunkenness as a defense—not that it could not be so regarded with some reason—but because it would provide too easy an escape for the accused. A distinction is permitted: drunkenness that results in a drunken stupor might be enough to remove any possibility of premeditation, where that element is necessary to constitute the crime charged. But as a practical matter, that depth of drunkenness is sufficient to prevent the accomplishment of any other offense than that of drunkenness itself. On the other hand, it is said that drunkenness is a defense to contract.

This is another half truth. The rule is, that if drink has wholly deprived one of his reason, his contract is invalid unless ratified when he becomes sober. But the condition must be wholly proved. Thus a man may be drunk, but not so drunk as to incapacitate him wholly from understanding his act. If he forms some idea, although an imperfect one, of the meaning of what he is doing, he may be bound, certainly so in the absence of any fraud on the part of the other contracting party. This rule is, of course, necessary to protect the other party, and especially necessary to third parties who must rely on the validity of such instruments as negotiable notes and checks. As a famous English judge, Lord Ellenborough, put it: there must be an "agreeing mind" to make a contract. It seems clear that liquor would have some usefulness for the salesman, under these circumstances. Thus, we will say that a contract entered into while one is not sober is voidable, but not void, and voidable only when the drunkenness has gone far enough to take from the promisor the knowledge that he is making a legally binding promise.

In wills, it is said that drunkenness at the time of the making of the testament must be such as to make the testator a madman, in order that the will should be regarded as absolutely void. In other words, the inebriate must be of unsound mind. Otherwise, mere intoxication will have no effect on the validity of the will. Of course, it is quite possible to show a case of undue influence, with evidence of intoxication induced by one who stood to benefit under a will, signature to which was secured while the testator was in that state. But, in that case, you do not have a question of mental capacity. It is a situation in which the will is valid and subsisting until undue influence is proved.

Obviously, drunkenness, and even much less than drunkenness, as drinking sufficient to affect a man's driving so as to make it unsafe for him to operate an automobile, will render him liable for an injury resulting from the incompetence. In such cases the fact of drinking has some probative force on the question of fact of whether the defendant had been negligent. In practical fact, and you understand I am commenting on the way the law works in a courtroom rather than the way it reads in the textbooks, evidence of drinking is very dangerous evidence from a defendant's point of view in a tort case.

In matters of divorce, drunkenness, if habitual, serves as a ground or justification for divorce if the statute so provides. This subject is entirely determined by the statute law in each state. However, in states which do not provide that habitual drunkenness shall be a ground, it is possible sometimes to base a divorce on evidence of such drunken actions as constitute intolerable cruelty.

I have mentioned the rule relating to workmen's compensation.

Deeds are treated in a similar way to wills. Insurance is somewhat more difficult. Here the matter is not a problem of capacity in a mental sense to contract for insurance, but one of fraudulent conduct in failing to disclose the drinking habit. And the law relating to insurance-company liability under these circumstances is not an uncomplicated subject. Shall we say that if fraud is proved by the company, the policy may be canceled? But it is unsafe for a company to wait until the insured has gone to his Maker to raise this defense.

STATE-STORE AND MONOPOLY ACTS

There remains the final category, which relates to the laws which establish state-store and monopoly systems.

Sixteen states may be said to have adopted the monopoly plan in one form or another. They are Alabama, Idaho, Iowa, Maine, Michigan, Montana, New Hampshire, Ohio, Oregon, Pennsylvania, Utah, Vermont, Virginia, Washington, West Virginia and Wyoming. In addition, North Carolina has a law under which Wet counties under a local option scheme may operate liquor stores. Some counties in Maryland have had the exclusive right to sell spirits and wines while other counties were following the license method. The liquor control acts of Minnesota and Wisconsin also authorize cities to provide city stores if they wish to do so.

Three states, Kansas, Oklahoma and Mississippi, prohibit the manufacture and sale of intoxicating liquor, but they all permit the sale of light wines and beer under certain minimum percentage requirements, 3.2 per cent alcohol by volume, or 4 per cent by weight.

The so-called monopoly plan does not mean monopoly in a full sense. The 17 states named above monopolize by law only the sale of liquor, retail or wholesale, one way or the other. In no state has the government taken over a monopoly of the manufacture of alcoholic beverages. I understand that in Washington and Oregon there is some state bottling and blending, on a small scale. These 17 states contain nearly one-third the population of the country.

Perhaps the most important factor which led the American states to the adoption of the state-store plan was the admiration commonly held for the manner in which such stores were operated in Canada. Notice that of the northern states, all of those that border on Canada have adopted the state-store plan except New York, Wisconsin and Minnesota.

I have made it appear as if there were a sharp difference between the state-store system states and the license states in the manner in which the selling of liquor is controlled. Such is not the fact. In truth, many of the so-called monopoly states also license hotels and restaurants, and in large numbers. So the system is usually a combination of the 2 methods. Furthermore, in Michigan and Ohio, where the state stores retail alcoholic beverages to the general public, there are also a few private dealers who have been named as agents for the state to assist the state in the retailing of liquor by the package. In Iowa, Montana, Utah and West Virginia all alcoholic beverages, including beer, are restricted to state stores. The other 14 states do not sell beer in their stores, but commonly permit its retail by licensees. In Maine, wine may not be sold by private stores, but hotels may sell distilled liquors by the bottle and by the drink to their guests. So also in New Hampshire, at stated times.

The usual practice is to establish a state board which has two duties: (1) to sell, and (2) to govern the liquor traffic in all of its aspects. These boards, like the license boards, are administrative tribunals possessing executive, legislative and judicial powers in some degree. In some instances they have effective powers of enforcement of their control laws, and power to collect the taxes and fees laid down by the statute. They are not in any sense to be compared to private companies or wholesalers. They are state departments, often independent of other departments.

To the same extent as other state boards and departments, they are subject to politics, no more, no less. Generally, the terms of the members are long enough to permit them a high degree of independence, ranging from 3 years in Maine, Michigan and New Hampshire, to 9 years in Washington. The membership consists of from one to five members.

In places where the demand for cocktails and wine is great, as for example in convention cities and resort places, the public monopoly program has been modified to permit licensing of hotels and restaurants to sell by the drink, on condition the liquor be bought from the state monopoly. I quote from Fosdick and Scott, *Toward Liquor Control*, published in 1933:

Established customs cannot be brushed aside at one stroke, and, in some places at least, it may be found necessary to provide for a closely regulated sale of spirituous beverages by the glass for consumption with meals. We return to our two-fold aim in liquor control, which is to leave no legitimate need for the bootlegger to satisfy and, at the same time, to avoid stimulating the demand for liquor. If, for example, there is present an insistent demand for cocktails and liqueurs in a given locality, we may be sure that the bootlegger and the speakeasy will survive to satisfy it. The plain truth is that the legitimate need must be measured in terms of insistence of demand; it cannot be measured by what we might hope would be satisfactory. Thus measured, the legitimate need will be found to vary considerably from state to state and from locality to locality within a single state.

This has been done widely. Eight of the monopoly states, Maine, Michigan, Montana, New Hampshire, Ohio, Pennsylvania, Vermont and Wyoming, with a combined population of nearly 25 million, have legalized private sale of liquor by the drink. Seven states, Idaho, Iowa, Oregon, Utah, Virginia, Washington and West Virginia, will sell only by the package. In the city of Detroit there are 23 state stores where liquor is sold by the bottle; and before the war, there were some 1,500 hotels, restaurants and clubs where it could be bought legitimately by the glass.

DISCUSSION

Chairman (E. M. Jellinek): Not only the total problem of alcoholism is complex but every aspect of it in itself is complex. We have seen this to be so now in the legal aspects of the problem. It is frequently said that lawyers make matters more complicated than necessary, and epigrams to this effect are in abundance. Some of these epigrams are brilliant, but they do not reveal deep insight. The presentation which Dr. Baird has given us has convinced me that the complexity of the liquor legislation does not arise from the lawyer's head, but that the complexity of the law follows the involvements in the life of our extremely complex society.

Helmintoller: In the *Christian Century* of July 5, we are told something about Sweden's liquor control. They say that a hundred years ago the Swedes were the hardest drinking people of Europe but that under their new control they have reduced liquor drinking to 1 gallon per capita per year. Could you tell us more about the Swedish system?

Lecturer: The answer to this question would involve another lecture. I can suggest a book written by Walter Thompson and published in 1935. The new system is not altogether popular in Sweden. There are objectors to it from both the Wet and Dry viewpoints. The Swedish system is not eliminating all drunkenness or crime or bootlegging. However, the Swedish people, who have always been noted for their observance of law and for their careful, sensible enforcement of law, unquestionably are better off now with their system than they were without it. Whether another system would have been better, I cannot answer.

Haralson: If you are prepared to do so, will you please discuss briefly the question as to whether or not the prohibition by Congress of liquor advertising violates the Constitution?

Lecturer: I do not think state legislation would be unconstitutional. Control over liquor has been regarded as a police matter. The police power of the state is that power which has to do with the protection of health, welfare and morals of the people. So any method reasonably designed to accomplish these purposes should be regarded as constitutional. Furthermore, under the theory of the present United States Supreme Court, the reasonableness of such legislation is for the state legislature to decide and not for the Court. There is, however, no Federal police power. Therefore, to give Federal legislation a constitutional validity it is necessary to support it on the basis of the Federal powers over interstate commerce and taxation. I can only say that the definition of what constitutes interstate commerce is a subject of complexity equal to that of the alcohol law. Yet interstate commerce has been held to cover a great variety of things.

Mrs. Grevett: Please elaborate further on the "tied house" problem and what it is.

Lecturer: The problem is one of avoiding those business practices which are commonly exercised and followed in the field of free competition, but which are thought undesirable in the sale of liquor. We permit chain stores, which are a horizontal multiplication of units. We are willing to permit a perpendicular ownership of corporations under holding companies in businesses where the public interest is not disadvantageously affected. Any system of business association which will permit competition to grow in the liquor business increases the social disadvantages of that business. Price wars, control by the manufacturer over the retailer, that "Mister, you haven't been meeting your quota and you've got to get out and sell more of this stuff," is something we will not permit a liquor company to do.

Womer: Dr. Baird, I'm very much interested in the series of questions in the first part of your lecture which dealt with the problem of restating morals. As I understand it, there are three types of approaches to this: the legalistic says that drunkenness is a nuisance, the religionist says that it is a sin, and the scientist says that it is a disease. Maybe they are all right, but if we did restate our position in terms of morals regarding drunkenness, would the acceptance of the new scientific idea of illness involve a loss? Would the fact of viewing it as a public health problem, and not wholly as a moral problem, or simply as a legal problem, have a tendency to increase drinking? Would it have a tendency to encourage us to try to find some way of handling this problem?

Lecturer: That is one of the most difficult questions that might be asked. No man could answer all the problems. Each man must approach the problem from his point of view, affected by his training and his background.

I think it would be well if more could be done along this line and I would say that I don't think this job ought to be imposed only upon the ministers or the sociologists. It's a job that demands contributions from everybody. Suppose you have these various motivations which you say you see behind a certain rule. Now we are going to change the language of that rule, eliminate one or two of the motives. Will we be any better off? We can only be better off in the sense that the language in a rule convinces a larger number of people. That seems to me the only possible way to look at it. If we want, for example, to think of drunkenness as something which is not immoral, do we increase the effectiveness of the rule by calling it public nuisance? I don't think we do. Suppose, however, we call it a disease, do we increase the effectiveness? In other words, will the physician and the psychiatrist be able to convince a larger number of people than the lawyer or the minister? I don't know. It would be harder to answer the physician than it would be the minister, because all you have to do to answer a minister is to show that one's faith is different. But I cannot answer the physician because I might have the disease—I don't know what the disease is—I know so little about it.

In other words, conceivably, selection of the language which describes the things might be made more effective, but whether there can be truth in an abstract sense, that is again a search for a philosophy of the subject.

Chairman: I would like to offer a distinction which is rather important. It was said here that science says that drunkenness is a disease. But no student of alcoholism would contend that getting drunk is a disease. Being drunk, being in acute alcoholic intoxication, and using intoxication as a permanent means of solving one's problems, are entirely different matters. No scientist will tell you that if Joe goes out in order to have a good time and gets drunk, he is diseased. The scientist will look at that event perhaps no differently than the lawyer.

Hoover: There have been instances when radio stations have refused to sell time for temperance programs on the grounds that they contained elements of controversy while at the same time they were accepting liquor ads. Tell us something about the legal aspects of these instances.

Lecturer: I cannot answer that question because I do not know the cases. Furthermore, the problem is an exceedingly difficult one. I pointed out that the Federal Government is empowered with a paramount and perhaps exclusive jurisdiction over interstate commerce. The rule of law in such a situation is that when the Federal Government does act, it usurps the field and thereafter a state legislature can no longer control the matter. That has been done in the radio field. But the wisdom of the Federal statute, and the extent of its application to the question you speak of, are beyond my knowledge.

to accept this view, pointing out that the manufacture and sale of liquor were lawful at common law; that the license system prevailed at the time the constitutions of the states were adopted; and that the status of the liquor business was one to be determined by the legislative branch of the government in the exercise of the police power.

Under our democratic institutions, regulations are enacted by majority vote of the elected representatives, or of the electors themselves. Restrictions, no matter whether in license laws, prohibitory statutes, or constitutional provisions, have shifted constantly, depending upon the prevailing sentiment. License or control laws, supported by a consumer demand fostered by centuries of tradition and custom, promoted by vested interests, and encouraged by the revenue incentive on the part of the state, have not been stable; nor has prohibition, even when reinforced by inclusion in state and national constitutions. The contest between conflicting concepts continues.

Expanding Police Power

State liquor laws are based upon what, in law, is termed the police power. This is incapable of exact definition. The exercise of this power did not come into much use until the latter part of the nineteenth century. Originally, it was likened to the inherent right of social defense, and its exercise was sustained upon the theory of "over-ruling necessity," for example, the right to destroy a building to prevent the spread of a conflagration. It was strenuously denied that it extended beyond this.

Later, the police power was held to include legislation reasonably necessary for the protection of the public safety, peace, health and morals. In recent times the United States Supreme Court has denied that it is thus limited, but holds that the power is inherent in every sovereignty to make such laws as the legislative body shall judge to be for the good of the commonwealth and its citizens. These are constantly changing as new conditions arise.

The history of modern government has been the story of expanding police power. The gradual broadening of prohibitions in liquor laws and the decisions of the courts finally upholding them are no exceptions to this rule in American jurisprudence. Debate upon what constituted the proper delimitations of government has preceded each successive step. Every added restriction has been contested in the courts, and the reported decisions portray the change in public opinion and judicial attitude.

At the outset, the prohibition ideology not only ran counter to the habits and customs of many people, but the proposal that the police power of the state should be invoked to suppress the manufacture and sale of a commodity always lawful, and in which property rights were held to exist, struck squarely athwart the prevailing views of political science.

Early Views on Prohibition

Early temperance agitators had no thought of prohibition as it afterward came to be established. Drinking was then well-nigh universal. Ardent spirits were drunk principally. Malt and vinous liquors were not so extensively manufactured, and the liquor trade had not become so thoroughly organized, nor sales promotion methods so highly developed. At that time the suggestion that the manufacture and sale of liquor could be prohibited by law was so novel as to be absolutely denied by courts and law writers. A well-known author of a law treatise of that period said:

No trade can be prohibited altogether unless the evil is inherent in the character of the trade so that the trade, however conducted, and whatever may be the character of the person engaged in it, must necessarily produce injury upon the public or upon individual third persons. . . . We cannot say, therefore, that the sale of liquor necessarily causes intoxication. On the contrary . . . the cases in which the sale of liquor is followed by intoxication constitute the exception to the rule.

It was in such an attitude respecting the law that the first prohibitory liquor measures were enacted. Their authors, then and later, had to consider not only the evil sought to be remedied, but what it was felt could be done legally in the then existing state of judicial opinion. Therefore, the first prohibitory liquor laws, like the 28-Gallon Law of Massachusetts in 1837, and similar statutes of the period, did not undertake to deny all access to a supply of liquor but only prohibited the retail sale in quantities less than prescribed without a license, although a discretion was allowed as to whether a license should be issued. These restrictions applied only to spirituous liquors.

The validity of such legislation was sustained by the Supreme Court of the United States in the License Cases. With respect to the scope of the state police power, Mr. Chief Justice Taney employed broad language, saying:

And if any State deems the retail and internal traffic in ardent spirits injurious to its citizens, and calculated to produce idleness, vice, or debauchery, I see nothing in the Constitution of the United States to prevent it from regulating and restraining the traffic, or from prohibiting it altogether, if it thinks proper. Of the wisdom of this policy, it is not my province or purpose to speak. Upon that subject each state must decide for itself.

The principles enunciated by the Supreme Court in these cases in 1846 greatly encouraged the advocates of prohibition legislation.

First Prohibition Laws and the Courts

When the series of prohibition or Dow laws of the 1850 period were enacted they were broadened to include the prohibition of the manufacture and sale of spirituous, vinous and malt beverages. The constitutionality of these acts was immediately attacked in the state courts. In Indiana the view was taken that such a prohibition upon a trade recognized as lawful at common law, and with its effect upon property values in liquor, violated rights secured to the citizen by the state constitution.

A somewhat similar opinion was expressed by the Supreme Court of New York in declaring the 1855 prohibition law of that state invalid. It declared that the prohibition of the sale of liquor manufactured before the law was enacted was confiscatory. This case was referred to by the United States Supreme Court in 1874 in a decision upholding the prohibition law of Iowa, where it was said:

The weight of authority is overwhelming that no such immunity has heretofore existed [prior to the Fourteenth Amendment] as would prevent state legislatures from regulating and even prohibiting the traffic in intoxicating drinks, with a solitary exception. That exception is the case of a law operating so rigidly on property in existence at the time of its passage, absolutely prohibiting its sale, as to amount to depriving the owner of his property.

The exception mentioned by the United States Supreme Court furnished a legal reason, in addition to the many practical ones, why it was customary in all prohibitory liquor laws to permit a period of time to elapse between the enactment of the law and the date of its going into effect. The same policy was later followed in the adoption of the Eighteenth Amendment to the Constitution of the United States, which declared that it should take effect 1 year after its ratification.

Many of the state laws of the first prohibition period were invalidated in whole or in part by the decisions of the state courts. There was at this time no provision in the Constitution of the United States which permitted the Supreme Court jurisdiction to review these state decisions. A diversity of ruling arose in different states upon similar questions. The supporters of the prohibition policy were discouraged and peace officers were uncertain about the validity of the law they were called upon to enforce. This confused state of the law and the resulting laxity of enforcement contributed to sentiment for a change of policy in the states where prohibition statutes were still in force and was a factor in their repeal.

Effect of the Fourteenth Amendment

In 1868 the Fourteenth Amendment to the United States Constitution was ratified. It declared:

No State shall make or enforce any law which shall abridge the privileges or immunities of citizens of the United States; nor shall any State deprive any person of life, liberty, or property, without due process of law; nor deny to any person within its jurisdiction the equal protection of the laws.

The Amendment was revolutionary in its effect upon our constitutional system. It constituted a limitation upon the power of the states and vastly broadened the subjects of state action the constitutionality of which was reviewable by the United States Supreme Court.

A fresh series of attacks was now launched upon the prohibition laws of the states, it being alleged that such laws contravened the new Federal Amendment. In 1874 the United States Supreme Court upheld the prohibition statute of Iowa against this contention, declaring: "The right to manufacture and sell liquor is not one of the privileges and immunities of citizenship which the states by the Fourteenth Amendment are forbidden to abridge." This principle was repeatedly reiterated in later cases, and subsequently it was indicated that the subject was closed.

Second Era of State Prohibition and the Courts

During the second era of state-wide prohibition, when the policy of seeking amendments to the state constitutions began, it was insisted that the people of a state could not do this because of the limitations placed on the police power of the states by the Fourteenth Amendment to the Federal Constitution. The argument ran that there was a dual citizenship, that of the state, and that of the United States, and that the right to manufacture and sell liquor was one of the privileges and immunities of a citizen of the United States which the people of a state could not deny since the adoption of the Fourteenth Amendment. In 1887, in the case of Mugler v. Kansas, the Supreme Court answered this argument in these words: "This interpretation of the Fourteenth Amendment is inadmissible. It cannot be supposed that the States intended, by adopting that amendment, to impose restraints upon the exercise of their powers for the protection of the safety, health, or morals of the community." It was further argued that the effect of the Kansas prohibition amendment was to depreciate the value of appellant's property, worth $50,000 for brewing purposes, to less than $5,000 for other purposes, and that this was a denial of due process of law in violation of the Fourteenth Amendment. As to this the Court said:

> A prohibition simply upon the use of property for purposes that are declared, by valid legislation, to be injurious to the health, morals, or safety of the community, cannot, in any just sense, be deemed a taking or an appropriation of property for the public benefit. . . .
> The power which the states have of prohibiting such use by individuals of their property as will be prejudicial to the health, the morals, or the safety of the public, is not—and, consistently with the existence and safety of organized society, cannot be —burdened with the condition that the State must compensate such individual owners for pecuniary losses they may sustain, by reason of their not being permitted, by a noxious use of their property, to inflict injury upon the community. The exercise of the police power by the destruction of property which is itself a public nuisance, or the prohibition of its use in a particular way, whereby its value becomes depreciated, is very different from taking property for public use, or from depriving a person of his property without due process of law. In the one case, a nuisance only is abated; in the other, unoffending property is taken away from an innocent owner.

Regarding the police power the Court declared:

> Government may require "each citizen to so conduct himself, and so use his own property, as not unnecessarily to injure another."
> But by whom, or by what authority, is it to be determined whether the manufacture of particular articles of drink, either for general use or for the personal use of the maker, will injuriously affect the public? Power to determine such questions, so as to bind all, must exist somewhere; else society will be at the mercy of the few, who, regarding only their own appetites or passions, may be willing to imperil the peace and security of the many, provided only they are permitted to do as they please. Under our system that power is lodged with the legislative branch of the government. It belongs to that department to exert what are known as the police powers of the State, and to determine, primarily, what measures are appropriate or needful for the protection of the public morals, the public health, or the public safety.

It was also insisted that the Kansas legislation prohibited the manufacture for export, secured by the Federal Constitution, and that the denial of this right deprived the manufacturers of equal protection of the law. The Court said the record did not raise the issue. Subsequently, it was decided in another case that the commodity did not come under the protection of the Commerce Clause until it had been shipped or entered with a common carrier for transportation without the state; therefore the prohibition upon manufacture was valid, although the effect might be to destroy the right of export.

The decision of the Supreme Court in the Mugler case was a monumental one in the evolution of the prohibition movement, as it settled the following propositions:

1. The states in the exercise of their police power could prohibit the manufacture and sale of liquor.

2. The Fourteenth Amendment did not interfere with the right of a state to adopt prohibition in the exercise of its police power.

3. Compensation for losses incurred by those engaged in the prohibited business was not required by the Fourteenth Amendment.

4. Being a decision of the Supreme Court of the United States, the principles of law decided were binding upon state courts. It settled, on a uniform basis, questions upon which there had formerly been a conflict of rulings in the earlier decisions of state courts.

Another feature of the Mugler decision that had a profound influence upon future developments was the answer given by the Court to the contention that the constitution of Kansas prohibiting the manufacture of intoxicating liquor for beverage purposes was broad enough to deny to an individual the right to manufacture liquor for his own personal use. On this point the Court said:

If, in the judgment of the Legislature, the manufacture of intoxicating liquors for the maker's own use, as a beverage, would tend to cripple, if it did not defeat, the effort to guard the community against the evils attending the excessive use of such liquors, it is not for the courts, upon their views as to what is best and safest for the community, to disregard the legislative determination of that question. So far from such a regulation having no relation to the general end sought to be accomplished, the entire scheme of prohibition, as embodied in the Constitution and laws of Kansas, might fall, if the right of each citizen to manufacture intoxicating liquors for his own use as a beverage were recognized. Such a right does not inhere in citizenship. Nor can it be said that government interferes with or impairs anyone's constitutional rights of liberty or of property, when it determines that the manufacture and sale of intoxicating drinks, for general or individual use, as a beverage, are, or may become, hurtful to society, and constitute, therefore, a business in which no one may lawfully engage. Those rights are best secured, in our government, by the observance, upon the part of all, of such regulations as are established by competent authority to promote the common good. No one may rightfully do that which the law-making power, upon reasonable grounds, declares to be prejudicial to the general welfare.

EARLY VIEWS OF SCOPE OF POLICE POWER

During the early period of prohibition agitation and for a long time afterward the view appears to have been generally taken, by both the friends and foes of the policy, that the state police power could be exerted no further than to prohibit the commercial aspects of the liquor traffic. The position of the temperance advocates was stated as follows:

The opponents of prohibition mistake the case by saying that the state has no right to declare what a man shall eat or drink. The state does not venture to make any such declaration. . . . It is not the private appetite or home customs of the citizen that the state undertakes to manage, but the liquor traffic. . . . If, by abolishing the saloon, the state makes it difficult for men to gratify their private appetites, there is no just reason for complaint. . . . It is therefore significant that the policy of prohibition stops short of dealing with the private act of consumption.

A much quoted work on intoxicating liquor contained the following analysis of the state of the law in the 1890's, based on decided cases:

The keeping of liquors in his possession by a person, whether for himself or for another, unless he does so for the illegal sale of it, or for some other improper purpose, can by no possibility injure or affect the health, morals, or safety of the public, and therefore the statute prohibiting such keeping in possession is not a legitimate exertion of the police power. It is an abridgment of the privileges and immunities of the citizen without any legal justification and therefore void.

It was also held by the courts during this period that a state, through the exercise of its police power, could not prohibit the carrying of liquor into prohibition areas for personal use where no intent to sell was alleged or shown. In North Carolina an act prohibiting the carrying into such an area on any one day of more than half a gallon of spirituous liquor was declared to violate the provisions of the constitution of the State, because among the inalienable rights of men secured by it are life, liberty, the enjoyment of the fruits of their own labor, and the pursuit of happiness. It was there said:

Assuming that the wine or spirits described in the bill of indictment was the defendant's property, the fruits of his labor, he was entitled to carry it with him whithersoever he went, unless, in doing so, he injuriously affected the public morals, health, or safety, or that his doing so was so reasonably related to the sale of intoxicating liquor, which is the thing prohibited in Burke county, as to come within the police power.

Exemptions Made in Prohibitory Laws

Because of these decisions of the courts, as well as to conform to the sentiment of the times, the local option laws of the period related merely to the commerce in liquor. They did not attempt to prohibit the bringing of liquor into no-license areas for personal use, nor could they constitutionally prevent persons residing in such areas from ordering liquor shipped to them in interstate commerce.

Almost all prohibitory laws contained exceptions as to the manufacture of cider and wine for domestic use when made from home-grown fruit. These were no doubt incorporated in part because of uncertainty as to the constitutional power of the state to prohibit transactions not involving a trafficking in liquors. The differences of opinion on the propriety and legality of seeking to extend the police powers of government to include anything other than the commerce in liquor persisted until the movement for a prohibition amendment to the Federal Constitution was well under way.

The Hobson Resolution for national constitutional prohibition, which passed the House of Representatives of the Sixty-Third Congress on December 22,

1914, proposed to prohibit merely the sale, manufacture for sale, and transportation for sale of intoxicating liquors.

Prohibitory laws did not make the purchase of liquor an offense. At a later period, following the adoption of national prohibition, when the concept of the police power had been broadened, two states, Indiana and Texas, did make the purchase of liquor unlawful. Such a provision presented practical difficulties in enforcement. Illicit sales are usually made in secret, when there are no witnesses. To convict the purchaser it would ordinarily be necessary to grant immunity to the seller to obtain his evidence against the purchaser, otherwise he could refuse to testify on the ground of self-incrimination. No reported cases of prosecution for purchase appear in Indiana. In Texas, scores of prosecutions were initiated for the unlawful purchase of liquor. On appeal, such cases were very generally reversed, as the law provided that a defendant could not be convicted upon the uncorroborated testimony of an accomplice, and the purchaser was ruled to be an accomplice of the seller. Under statutes making the possession of liquor, or its possession in prohibited places or situations, an offense, conviction of the purchaser could be more easily secured on evidence of mere unlawful possession.

Possession Made Unlawful

Following the decision in the Mugler case, state prohibitory laws were extended to include possession of liquor for personal use. The constitutionality of such a provision was not passed upon by the Supreme Court of the United States until 1917 in a case involving the Idaho prohibition statute of 1915, which provided: "It shall be unlawful for any person to have in his or its possession . . . any intoxicating liquor . . . within a prohibition district . . . unless the same was possessed under a permit as hereinafter provided." The Court said:

As the state has the power above indicated to prohibit, it may adopt such measures as are reasonably appropriate or needful to render exercise of that power effective. . . .

And, considering the notorious difficulties always attendant upon efforts to suppress traffic in liquors, we are unable to say that the challenged inhibition of their possession was arbitrary and unreasonable or without proper relation to the legitimate legislative purpose. . . .

The right to hold intoxicating liquors for personal use is not one of those fundamental privileges of a citizen of the United States which no state may abridge.

The right of a state to prohibit the possession of liquor acquired between the date of the passage of a prohibition law and the time of its going into effect still remained unanswered. This was determined by the Supreme Court in 1919 in a case involving the prohibition law of Georgia. It was said:

A state having the power to forbid the manufacture, sale, and possession of liquor within its borders may, if it concludes to exercise the power, obviously postpone the date when the prohibition shall become effective, in order that those engaged in the business and others may adjust themselves to the new conditions. Whoever acquires, after the enactment of the statute, property thus declared noxious, takes it with full notice of its infirmity, and that, after a day certain, its possession will, by mere lapse of time, become a crime. It is well settled that the Federal Constitution does not enable one to stay the exercise of a state's police power by entering into a contract under such circumstances. . . . Nor can he do so by acquiring property.

In this case the Court reserved judgment upon whether the law would be constitutional if applied to liquor acquired before its enactment. This point was not finally adjudicated until 1925, when in another case under the Georgia law it was declared that the statute making unlawful the possession of liquor legally obtained before its passage did not deprive the owner of his property without due process of law in violation of the Fourteenth Amendment.

CHANGE IN JUDICIAL ATTITUDE ON PROHIBITION OBJECTIVE

This opinion is also informing on the complete change of attitude of the courts with respect to the aim and purposes of prohibition legislation and the limits of state police power. Mr. Chief Justice Taft, speaking for the Court, said:

The ultimate legislative object of prohibition is to prevent the drinking of intoxicating liquors by anyone because of the demoralizing effect of drunkenness upon society. The state has the power to subject those members of society who might indulge in the use of such liquor without injury to themselves to a deprivation of access to liquor in order to remove temptation from those whom its use would demoralize, and to avoid the abuses which follow in its train. Accordingly, laws have been enacted by the states, and sustained by this court, by which it has been made illegal to manufacture liquor for one's own use or for another's; to transport it, or to sell it, or to give it away to others. The legislature has this power, whether it affects liquor lawfully acquired before the prohibition or not. Without compensation it may thus seek to reduce the drinking of liquor. It is obvious that if men are permitted to maintain liquor in their possession, though only for their own consumption, there is danger of its becoming accessible to others. Legislation making possession unlawful is therefore within the police power of the states as a reasonable mode of reducing the evils of drunkenness, as we have seen in the Crane and Barbour Cases. . . .
For many years, everyone who has made or stored liquor has known that it was a kind of property which, because of its possible vicious uses, might be denied by the state the character and attributes as such; that legislation calculated to suppress its use in the interest of public health and morality was lawful and possible; and this without compensation.

This case was not decided until after the adoption of the Eighteenth Amendment. Undoubtedly one of the legal reasons why the National Prohibition Act permitted the storage of liquor in the home for personal use, when acquired before the passage of the Act, was that the legality of possession under such circumstances had not been decided by the Supreme Court.

The broadening view of the police power of the states is also shown in the decisions upholding the right of the states to include nonintoxicating liquors within the definition of prohibited beverages as a means of lessening law evasion. The Supreme Court, in sustaining the law of Mississippi which prohibited the sale of malt beverages regardless of alcohol content, said:

It was competent for the legislature of Mississippi to recognize the difficulties besetting the administration of laws aimed at the prevention of traffic in intoxicants. It prohibited, among other things, the sale of "malt liquors." In thus dealing with a class of beverages which, in general, are regarded as intoxicating, it was not bound to resort to discrimination with respect to ingredients and processes of manufacture which, in the endeavor to eliminate innocuous beverages from the condemnation, would facilitate subterfuges and frauds and fetter the enforcement of the law. A contrary conclusion, logically pressed, would save the nominal power while preventing its effective exercise. The statute establishes its own category. The question in this court is whether the legislature had power to establish it. The existence of this power, as the authorities we have cited abundantly demonstrate, is not to be denied simply because some innocent articles or transactions may be found within the proscribed class.

The right of the state to regulate or even prohibit entirely the sale of liquor for medicinal purposes was upheld by the courts as a valid exercise of the police power.

Generally speaking, three tests have been applied in determining whether the exercise of the police power is valid. *1.* Does it deal with a threatened evil? *2.* Does it violate any constitutional provision? *3.* Is it reasonable?

Upon the first point the Supreme Court of the United States declared, in upholding a California ordinance:

It is urged that, as the liquors are used as a beverage, and the injury following them, if taken in excess, is voluntarily inflicted and is confined to the party offending, their sale should be without restrictions, the contention being that what a man shall drink, equally with what he shall eat, is not properly matter for legislation.

There is in this position an assumption of a fact which does not exist, that when the liquors are taken in excess the injuries are confined to the party offending. The injury, it is true, first falls upon him in his health, which the habit undermines; in his morals, which it weakens; and in the self-abasement which it creates. But, as it leads to neglect of business and waste of property and general demoralization, it affects those who are immediately connected with and dependent upon him. By the general concurrence of opinion of every civilized and Christian community, there are few sources of crime and misery to society equal to the dram shop where intoxicating liquors, in small quantities, to be drunk at the time, are sold indiscriminately to all parties applying. The statistics of every State show a greater amount of crime and misery attributable to the use of ardent spirits obtained at these retail liquor saloons than to any other source. The sale of such liquors in this way has therefore been, at all times, by the courts of every State, considered as the proper subject of legislative regulation. Not only may a license be exacted from the keeper of the saloon before a glass of his liquors can be thus disposed of, but restrictions may be imposed as to the class of persons to whom they may be sold, and the hours of the day, and the days of the week, on which the saloons may be opened. Their sale in that form may be absolutely prohibited. It is a question of public expediency and public morality, and not of federal law. The police power of the state is fully competent to regulate the business—to mitigate its evils or to suppress it entirely.

The decisions cited established that state prohibitory laws do not violate rights secured by state constitutions or by any provision of the Federal Constitution; that it is for the legislative branch of the government to determine whether the prohibition is in the public interest; and that such laws meet the requirement of reasonableness, and are valid. From the early narrow interpretation of the police power over intoxicating liquors to the present view of its plenary extent marks a radical departure.

This changed judicial attitude was not reached suddenly, but only after a long period of litigation and as public sentiment on the liquor question changed. This suggests the query: Why, if the states finally attained such comprehensive power to deal with the liquor problem, was a prohibition amendment to the Federal Constitution adopted? There were strong and compelling legal reasons that contributed to this end, in addition to the moral, social and economic reasons usually advanced. These grew out of the inability of the prohibition states to deal effectively with liquor introduced therein in interstate commerce. This came about as a result of a series of decisions beginning in 1888, in which the Supreme Court reversed its construction of the Commerce Clause that had obtained since the inception of the Government.

IMPORTS AND INTERSTATE COMMERCE

The Constitution, by Article I, Sec. 8, vests in Congress the power to "regulate commerce with foreign nations and among the several states and with the Indian tribes." By Article VI, the Constitution and laws of the United States are made supreme, so that where there is a conflict with state legislation, the latter must yield.

The law with regard to liquor imported from foreign countries was established in 1827. A Maryland statute required importers to obtain a license and pay a fee of $50 for the privilege of importing liquors and other goods. The Supreme Court held the state imposition conflicted with the exclusive right granted Congress to regulate foreign commerce, and also that provision of the Federal Constitution which declares: "No state shall, without the consent of Congress, lay any impost or duty on imports or exports, except what may be absolutely necessary for executing its inspection laws." It was further ruled that the state law could not apply to imported liquors so long as they remained in the hands of the importer or his agent in the original package. This decision was predicated on the fact that Congress had laid an import duty on the goods in question.

In the first case to come before the Supreme Court involving the transportation of liquors in interstate commerce, a different rule was applied. In 1846, in the License Cases, one of the issues was the validity of the New Hampshire statute prohibiting the importation of liquor without a license, as applied to a barrel of American gin purchased in Boston and shipped coastwise to New Hampshire and there sold by the importer in the original barrel. It was insisted that the requirement of the state law imposed a restraint upon goods in interstate commerce and was unconstitutional. Mr. Chief Justice Taney said:

> Upon the whole, therefore, the law of New Hampshire is, in my judgment, a valid one. For, although the gin was an import from another State, and Congress has clearly the power to regulate such importations, under the grant of power to regulate commerce among the several States, yet, as Congress has made no regulation on the subject, the traffic in the article may be lawfully regulated by the State as soon as it is landed in its territory, and a tax imposed upon it, or a license required, or the sale altogether prohibited, according to the policy which the State may suppose to be its interest or duty to pursue.

As this decision was construed, it was held to allow the states, in the exercise of their police power, to impose reasonable regulations upon goods shipped in interstate commerce so long as Congress had not acted.

In 1888, following the adoption of the prohibition law in Iowa, a suit was brought by dealers in malt liquors against a railroad company to compel it to accept shipments of beer into Iowa, which it had declined to do on the ground that the sale of beer was against the law of that State, which forbade any common carrier bringing any intoxicating liquor into the State unless a certificate was first obtained from a county auditor establishing the legality of the transaction. It was insisted that this imposed an unconstitutional burden on interstate commerce.

By a divided court the state law was held invalid and the carrier was required to accept the shipment. The majority opinion declared that the purpose of conferring on Congress the power to regulate commerce was to secure the free movement of goods and to insure against state interference except such incidental local regulations as were long recognized, such as quarantine and similar restrictions; but that since liquor was a recognized commodity in commerce the state law must yield.

There was a strong dissenting opinion in which three justices concurred, pointing out that this view was in conflict with the unanimous decision in the License Cases, the principle of which had been accepted and acted upon by the people for nearly 50 years, and that Congress had not declared any different rule. They said:

If, therefore, as the Court now decides, the Constitution gives the right to transport intoxicating liquors into Iowa from another state, and if that right carries with it, as one of its essential ingredients, authority in the consignee to sell or exchange such articles after they are brought in, and while in his possession, in the original packages, it is manifest that the regulation forbidding sales of intoxicating liquors within the state, for other than medicinal, mechanical, culinary or sacramental purposes, will be of little practical value. In this view, anyone—even a citizen of Iowa designing to sell intoxicating liquors in that state, need only to arrange to have them delivered to him from some point in another state, in packages of varying size, as may suit his customers. Or he may erect his manufacturing establishment or a warehouse just across the Iowa line, in some state having a different public policy, and thence with wagons, transport liquor into Iowa in original packages. If the State arraigns him for a violation of her laws, he may claim—and, under the principles of the present decision, it may become difficult to dispute the claim—that, although such laws were enacted solely to protect the health and morals of the people, and to promote peace and good order among them, and although they are fairly adapted to accomplish these objects, yet the Constitution of the United States without any action upon the part of Congress, secures to him the right to bring or receive from other states intoxicating liquors in original packages, and to sell them while held by him in such packages, to all choosing to buy them. Thus the mere silence of Congress upon the subject of trade among the states in intoxicating liquors is made to operate as a license to a person doing business in one state to jeopardize the health, morals and good order of another state by flooding the latter with intoxicating liquors against the expressed will of her people.

The Court reserved judgment in this case upon whether the right of transportation of an article of commerce from one state to another included by necessary implication the right of the consignee to sell it in unbroken packages where the transportation terminated. This question was answered 2 years later, on April 28, 1890, and the position of liquor as a commodity in interstate commerce was further strengthened by a judgment holding that state peace officers of Iowa were powerless to seize liquor imported for sale in original packages and stored in a dealer's warehouse in the state. Again there was a strong dissent by Mr. Justice Gray, concurred in by Justices Harlan and Brewer. In this case the majority of the Court declared: "The authority of Pierce v. New Hampshire, in so far as it rests on the view that the law of New Hampshire was valid because Congress had made no regulation on the subject, must be regarded as having been overthrown by the numerous cases hereafter referred to."

The effect of these rulings was revolutionary. They gave to liquor in interstate commerce a status never before possessed. The liquor trade was quick to take advantage of its new immunity. All manner of frauds were perpetrated against the policy of prohibition states. Carriers were required to accept shipments of liquors to consignees they knew to be fictitious, and in spite of knowing that the shipment was intended for sale in violation of state law. The solicitation of C.O.D. orders became a regular business, until these practices were penalized by amendments to the Federal penal code in 1909. Original package saloons were conducted in many places. Distillers and brewers established depots and warehouses in prohibition states and systematically solicited business by mail. In some instances express agents were employed to send in names of residents who might be induced to buy.

THE WILSON ACT

Within 4 months after the Original Package decision was announced, Congress passed the Wilson Act of August 8, 1890, which provided as follows:

That all fermented, distilled, or other intoxicating liquors or liquids transported into any State or Territory or remaining therein for use, consumption, sale, or storage therein shall, upon arrival in such State or Territory, be subject to the operation and effect of the laws of such State or Territory enacted in the exercise of its police powers to the same extent and in the same manner as though such liquors or liquids had been produced in such State or Territory, and shall not be exempt therefrom by reason of being introduced therein in original packages or otherwise.

This Act was immediately challenged on the ground that it was an unconstitutional attempt on the part of Congress to delegate to the states the regulation of commerce among the states. It was also insisted that after the passage of the Wilson Act it was necessary for the states to reenact their laws to claim its benefits. The constitutionality of the Wilson Act was upheld in 1892. The Court declared that the effect of the Act was to remove the impediment to state action that formerly obtained, and that it was not necessary that state laws be reenacted.

The question next arose as to the meaning of the words "arrival in the state" as used in the Act. The events leading up to the action by Congress would suggest that what was intended was a return to the interpretation of the law that had existed under the decision in the License Cases.

The majority of the Court said that "arrival" meant delivery of the liquor at its destination to the consignee in the original package. There was again a strong dissent by Justices Gray, Harlan and Brown, who insisted that the language and history of the legislation showed that arrival within the territorial limits and jurisdiction of the state was meant. The limitation placed on the Wilson Act by the majority of the Court so restricted its application as largely to destroy its effectiveness as a means of removing the impediment to the operation of the state law. Thus, where a defendant purchased liquor in North Carolina for his own use, loaded it in his buggy and started home, and as soon as he crossed the state line and before his arrival at home, he was arrested, it was held that he had not "arrived" at his destination, and that the liquor was not subject to seizure, nor he amenable to the state law.

Many questions also arose as to the meaning of "original packages." In a case from South Carolina it was held that the right of persons to import liquor for personal use was derived from the Constitution of the United States and could not be prevented by state law, notwithstanding the Wilson Act.

Following the decisions of the Supreme Court in this case, the belief seems to have become current that the courts might uphold reasonable regulations by the state upon the introduction of liquors in interstate commerce for personal use, while they would not uphold a complete prohibition. In some of the state prohibition laws of the period exceptions were made permitting a citizen to have shipped to him a limited quantity of liquor for personal use. These were sometimes referred to as "quart a month" laws. There were, therefore, supposed legal reasons why such exceptions were adopted, as well as a possible concession to the public opinion of the state.

The effect of the altered view taken by the Supreme Court was to make the right to transport liquor in interstate commerce paramount to the police regulations of the state enacted for the public peace, health and welfare, even after Congress had indicated by the Wilson Act its intention to remove any impediment to the effectiveness of state enactments with respect to liquor. Much of what happened afterward is due to the reversal of the position of the United States Supreme Court in its interpretation of the Commerce Clause of the Constitution.

THE WEBB-KENYON ACT

The clash between state and Federal interests became acute, and lasted until 1917, when the Supreme Court of the United States finally upheld the validity of the Webb-Kenyon Act of March 1, 1913, which removed the interstate commerce protection from liquors when shipped into a state in violation of state law and intended by any person interested therein to be received, possessed, or used in violation of state law. This Act carried no penalty enforceable in a Federal court but simply allowed state laws to attach to liquors upon arrival at state lines when intended for use in the state. The Webb-Kenyon Act was vetoed by President Taft on the advice of Attorney General Wickersham, who declared it to be unconstitutional. It was passed by Congress over the veto. The question of its validity was twice argued before the Supreme Court. As to the basis for sustaining the Act, Chief Justice White declared:

The fact that regulations of liquor have been upheld in numberless instances which would have been repugnant to the great guarantees of the Constitution but for the enlarged right possessed by government to regulate liquor has never, that we are aware of, been taken as affording the basis for the thought that government might exert an enlarged power as to subjects to which, under the constitutional guarantees, such enlarged power could not be applied. In other words, the exceptional nature of the subject here regulated is the basis upon which the exceptional power exerted must rest, and affords no ground for any fear that such power may be constitutionally extended to things which it may not, consistently with the guarantees of the Constitution, embrace.

THE REED BONE-DRY PROVISION

During this period, immediately preceding the adoption of national prohibition, two additional measures were enacted by Congress which somewhat changed its previous policy and extended more active aid to the prohibition states. The first of these was the Reed Bone-Dry Amendment of March 3, 1917, which provided:

Whoever shall order, purchase, or cause intoxicating liquors to be transported in interstate commerce, except for scientific, sacramental, medicinal, and mechanical purposes, into any State or Territory the laws of which State or Territory prohibit the manufacture or sale therein of intoxicating liquors for beverage purposes shall be punished as aforesaid, Provided, That nothing herein shall authorize the shipment of liquor into any State contrary to the laws of such State.

This was a new departure in that a penalty was provided enforceable in the Federal courts by which the National Government for the first time undertook actively to aid the prohibition states.

An anomalous situation grew out of this legislation. A defendant, while transporting a quart of whisky on his person in a trolley car from the state of Kentucky into the state of West Virginia, was arrested for violation of the Federal Act. He defended on the ground that the Federal law was intended as an aid to the state policy, and that while the state law made unlawful the manufacture and sale of liquor, it did not prohibit transportation of the quantity involved for personal use. The majority of the Court held, however, that Congress by the Reed Amendment had declared its own policy, that the Reed Amendment was a valid regulation of commerce by Congress, and sustained the conviction. There was a dissenting opinion in which Mr. Justice McReynolds said: "The Reed Amendment as now construed is a congressional fiat imposing more complete prohibition wherever the state has assumed to prevent manufacture or sale of intoxicants." Later it was held that the transportation of intoxicating liquors for personal use by the owner in his own automobile into a prohibition state was unlawful under the Reed Amendment.

ANTIADVERTISING PROVISION

The Act of March 3, 1917, known as the Jones-Randall Anti-Advertising Amendment, withdrew the mail privilege from periodicals containing liquor advertising, and prevented their circulation by mail, in any state in which at the time it was unlawful to advertise or solicit orders for such liquors.

State Police Power and Federal Taxing Power

The internal revenue laws of the United States have for many years levied special occupational taxes upon manufacturers, retailers, wholesalers, and so forth, of liquors. The question arose as to the right of the Federal Government to collect such taxes in states where such occupations were prohibited by law; also whether the taxes, if paid to the Federal Government, conferred any right to carry on the business in violation of local policy. It was held that "These licenses give no authority. They are mere receipts for taxes." And, "Congress cannot authorize a trade or business within a state in order to tax it."

In 1864 the internal revenue laws were specifically amended to provide that such a license should not be construed to authorize any business prohibited within any state or territory by the laws thereof, or to prevent the taxation of the same business by the state. The Supreme Court said:

There is nothing hostile or contradictory, therefore, in the Acts of Congress with the legislation of the state. What the latter prohibits, the former, if the business is found existing notwithstanding the prohibition, discourages by taxation. The two lines of legislation proceed in the same direction, and tend to the same result. It would be a judicial anomaly, as singular as indefensible, if we should hold a violation of the laws of the state to be a justification for the violation of the laws of the Union.

The present internal revenue code, T. 26, Sec. 3275, provides that prosecutors in states may obtain from the collector of internal revenue lists of persons paying these special taxes. In some prohibition states a provision is included in their codes that the possession of such an internal revenue tax receipt shall constitute prima facie evidence of violation of the state law. Where such a provision exists, the Federal tax laws may operate as an aid for the more effective enforcement of the prohibitions of the state statute.

Other questions have arisen with respect to the right of the Federal Government to exact taxes from a state which conducts the liquor business as a state monopoly. It was ruled many years ago that the conduct of the liquor business was not a governmental function and that the state was subject to the taxes. The same principle was reiterated by the Court after repeal. It has also been held that profits from bootlegging operations are taxable under the income tax law.

The Eighteenth Amendment

The rapidly changing public sentiment of the country was manifested by the increased number of states adopting state prohibition, the extension of no-license areas under local option, and the enactment of special legislation in other states. The mounting prohibition majority in Congress was evidenced by the vote for war restrictions, war prohibition, and a series of prohibitory acts applying to the District of Columbia, and Federal territories, such as Hawaii, Puerto Rico and Alaska. The impatience over the long delay in securing satisfactory adjustment and judicial settlement of the conflict of state-Federal control over liquors in interstate commerce contributed to the demand for national constitutional prohibition.

The Hobson Amendment for this purpose had been passed by the House of Representatives by a majority vote of 197 to 189 on December 22, 1914, but failed to secure the required two-thirds vote.

The effort was renewed on December 18, 1917, when the Sixty-Fifth Congress submitted to the legislatures of the states a resolution proposing the Eighteenth Amendment to the Constitution of the United States. This provided:

Section 1. After one year from the ratification of this article the manufacture, sale, or transportation of intoxicating liquors within, the importation thereof into, or the exportation thereof from the United States and all territory subject to the jurisdiction thereof for beverage purposes is hereby prohibited.

Section 2. The Congress and the several States shall have concurrent power to enforce this article by appropriate legislation.

Section 3. This article shall be inoperative unless it shall have been ratified as an amendment to the Constitution by the legislatures of the several states, as provided in the Constitution, within seven years from the date of the submission hereof to the States by the Congress.

The Amendment was ratified by the last of the necessary three-fourths of the states on January 16, 1919, and its prohibitions became effective 1 year later, on January 16, 1920. It was subsequently ratified by the legislatures of 10 additional states, or 46 of the 48 states of the Union.

With the incorporation of the prohibition amendment into the Constitution substantially all of the legal objections which had been urged to state prohibition were renewed with respect to national prohibition, together with new ones growing out of our dual form of government. In original actions brought on behalf of the states of Rhode Island and New Jersey, national constitutional prohibition was attacked on the ground that neither the people nor the states had power to adopt such an amendment, since it was not, in effect, an amendment or addition to the Constitution, but an alteration of the form of government because of the authority and duty conferred upon the National Government to enforce prohibition which, it was alleged, was destructive of the police power of the states.

The validity of the amendment was sustained in conclusions announced by the Supreme Court in the National Prohibition Cases. It was held that the subject was within the amending power under Article V of the Constitution; that the amendment was validly submitted by a two-thirds vote of Congress, which meant two-thirds of a quorum present and voting, and not two-thirds of all the members elected; that the referendum provisions of state constitutions had no application to amendments to the Federal Constitution; that it was binding throughout the entire territorial limits of the United States, bound all legislative bodies, courts and public officers within those limits, and of its own force invalidated every legislative act of Congress, state legislatures or territorial assemblies which authorized or sanctioned what the amendment prohibited.

In a later case, in 1930, it was contended that there were differences in types of amendments to the Constitution; that it was the intention of the framers of the Constitution that consequential amendments might be submitted to the legislatures for ratification, but that amendments like the Eighteenth, which, it was alleged, affected the liberties of the people, must be submitted to conventions for ratification. This proposition was denied by the Supreme Court, which held that under the alternative plan of ratifying amendments provided by Article V, the Congress was the judge of the method to be followed; that all amendments to the Constitution up to that time had been ratified by that method; and that the Eighteenth Amendment was legally adopted.

CONCURRENT POWERS

A number of questions were raised regarding the meaning of the term "concurrent power to enforce" used in the amendment. Concerning this the Court declared it did not mean joint power; nor require that legislation thereunder by Congress, to be effective, should be sanctioned by the states; nor that power to enforce was divided between Congress and the several states along lines which separate foreign or interstate from intrastate affairs; and that the prohibitions of the amendment might be exerted against the disposal for beverage purposes of liquor manufactured before the amendment became effective, just as against that subsequently manufactured for beverage purposes.

The meaning of concurrent power was later more thoroughly analyzed. Mr. Chief Justice Taft, speaking for the Court, said:

We have here two sovereignties, deriving power from different sources, capable of dealing with the same subject-matter within the same territory. Each may, without interference by the other, enact laws to secure prohibition, with the limitation that no legislation can give validity to acts prohibited by the Amendment. Each government, in determining what shall be an offense against its peace and dignity, is exercising its own sovereignty, not that of the other.

It follows that an act denounced as a crime by both national and state sovereignties is an offense against the peace and dignity of both, and may be punished by each.

From this interpretation of the amendment it followed that the Federal law did not supersede state prohibition laws or municipal ordinances, or prevent future enactments which did not authorize what the amendment prohibited; that such legislation did not have to be identical with the Federal act, but might vary in many particulars, as, for example, in the definition of intoxicating liquors, the penalties provided for infraction, the regulations as to nonbeverage use, or for the forfeiture of property used for illegal purposes.

There was a conflict of ruling upon whether a state legislature could adopt the Federal statute by reference, but where such a state law undertook to adopt not only the existing Federal law but future changes, this was held to be an unconstitutional delegation of power by the legislature.

The amendment did not repeal the Webb-Kenyon law, and a West Virginia statute requiring a permit to import intoxicating liquors was upheld as applied to flavoring extracts, when such an alcoholic preparation came within the definition of liquor under the state law, notwithstanding that the seller had a permit issued under the Federal law authorizing the transaction and insisted that the product was not intended for beverage use and that it was entitled to immunity as a commodity in interstate commerce. The Court held that under the Webb-

Kenyon law, removing the interstate protection from liquor imported into a state when intended by any person interested therein to be received, possessed, or used in violation of state law, the state was entitled to fix the conditions of importation and to define the term "intoxicating liquors," of which right it had not been deprived by the Eighteenth Amendment or the National Prohibition Act.

Other questions relating to the validity of the amendment itself involved the requirement of ratification within 7 years. This was the first amendment in which such a limitation had been imposed. The Supreme Court said: "Of the power of Congress, keeping within reasonable limits, to fix a definite period for ratification, we entertain no doubt." This case also settled that it was the date of action by the last of the necessary three-fourths of the states, and not the date of proclamation issued by the Secretary of State, which determined when the amendment became a part of the Constitution, although by its terms its prohibitions were not to take effect until a year after ratification.

The amendment and its enforcing statute were held to abrogate a treaty entered into between the United States and Great Britain on May 8, 1871, which gave to British subjects the right to transship merchandise under customs bond through the United States from one British possession to another. Subsequently, by a series of new treaties entered into with a large number of foreign countries, the status of liquors as sea stores on foreign ships entering American waters was adjusted, and the right of search of vessels suspected of smuggling liquor was extended to 1 hour's sailing distance from the coast.

The Eighteenth Amendment was held to apply to the Philippine Islands but the enforcing statutes did not, owing to the terms of the Philippine Organic Act.

The National Prohibition Act

On October 28, 1919, Congress enacted the National Prohibition Act, Title II of which was to enforce national constitutional prohibition. The objection was made that since the prohibition amendment did not become effective until January 16, 1920, the enactment of the statute in advance of that date invalidated it. The Supreme Court held, however, that the amendment became a part of the Constitution upon ratification on January 16, 1919, and conferred authority upon Congress to pass the enforcing statute, although by its terms the prohibitions were not to become effective until a year later.

Without exception, the enforcement features incorporated by Congress in the National Prohibition Act to give effect to constitutional prohibition had their counterpart in some state prohibition law. These provisions had stood the test of the courts as valid exercises of the police power. The argument was made that since the Federal Government is one of granted powers, and as the National Government does not have the inherent and broad police power possessed by the states, Congress, in enacting legislation for the enforcement of the Federal amendment, was limited by the exact language of the grant. Thus, it was claimed that as the prohibitions laid and the power conferred related to the manufacture and sale of intoxicating liquors, Congress was without authority to adopt the definition of liquors contained in the National Prohibition Act, which prohibited liquors containing over ½ of 1 per cent of alcohol by volume, since the inclusion of beverages clearly not intoxicating exceeded the grant conferred by the Constitution. The Court denied this contention in the eleventh paragraph of its conclusions in the National Prohibition Cases, saying:

Congress did not exceed its powers, under U.S. Const., 18th Amend., to enforce the prohibition therein declared against the manufacture, sale, or transportation of intoxicating liquors for beverage purposes, by enacting the provisions of the Volstead Act of October 28, 1919, wherein liquors containing as much as ½ of 1 per cent of alcohol by volume, and fit for use for beverage purposes, are treated as within that power.

A like argument was made that since the prohibitions of the amendment referred to beverage use only, Congress was without power to adopt the provisions of the National Prohibition Act and its supplement prohibiting the prescribing of malt liquors entirely, and limiting the frequency and quantity of spirituous liquors that might be prescribed for medicinal purposes.

The provisions of the act regulating the use of alcohol for industrial purposes were likewise attacked on similar grounds.

These objections were held to be without merit, since a similar view was taken with respect to the power conferred upon the Federal Government by the Eighteenth Amendment to that which had been taken with respect to the enactment of prohibition under its war powers, namely, that where power had been expressly conferred upon the National Government for a particular object, it carried with it by necessary implication full power to adopt such regulations or prohibitions as were necessary in the legislative judgment to give it effect, and that such legislation might have incidents and characteristics similar to the exercise of the police power of the states.

During the period of national prohibition the joint power of the state and Federal Governments was sought for the first time to be used in the enforcement of a police measure; and not only through the use of the ordinary criminal processes of each jurisdiction, but the taxing power of the Federal Government was also invoked, as well as that of some of the states, to accomplish the same end. In addition, jurisdiction was conferred upon Federal and state courts to use their equity powers to prevent recurring violations by issuing injunctions for the abatement of nuisances declared by statute to grow out of the manufacture and sale of liquor.

The National Prohibition Act provided that upon evidence of illegal manufacture and sale a tax should be assessed and collected upon the person responsible at double the regular rate, with an additional penalty of $500 on retailers and $1,000 on manufacturers. The payment of the tax conferred no right to engage in the manufacture or sale of liquor, nor did it relieve from any criminal or civil liability.

At first these exactions were assessed as ordinary taxes and collected by distraint. Later, the Supreme Court approved the granting of an injunction to restrain the collection on the ground that the imposition was a penalty for law violation and not a tax, despite the Government's contention that the revenue laws denied the taxpayer the right to enjoin the collection of a tax. The majority of the Court held that the exaction lacked the characteristics of a tax. A similar view was taken in a later case, where it was held that such an imposition could not be assessed without opportunity for notice and hearing. Subsequently, the regulations were amended to provide for the collection of such exactions by civil suit.

In 1931 the Court ruled that where a defendant had been convicted of the offense of selling liquor, the Government could not thereafter maintain a civil action for the recovery of these exactions applicable to the same sales, since the impositions were in effect penalties imposed for crime.

In 1935, after the repeal of national prohibition, the Court held that a special excise tax penalty of $1,000 imposed by the Revenue Act of 1926, Sec. 701 (first contained in the Revenue Act of 1918), upon all liquor dealers carrying on business contrary to the law of the state, could not be collected. The Court declared that the purpose of the act was to punish and not to tax, and that with repeal the Federal Government had no power to punish in aid of prohibition, and therefore the imposition was illegal. Such penalties were exacted, however, during the period of national prohibition, in addition to the tax penalties provided in the National Prohibition Act. It is well settled, however, that a business may be taxed, notwithstanding that it is prohibited and punished. Many violators of the National Prohibition Act were proceeded against for tax evasion.

Soon after the enactment of the National Prohibition Act it was held that the penal provisions of the internal revenue laws were repealed where substantially the same act was punishable under the National Prohibition Act. In 1923 the Court held that Congress by the passage of the Supplemental Prohibition Act of November 23, 1921, had revived the penal provisions of the internal revenue laws as of that date, although a prosecution under one statute was a bar to a prosecution under the other, where the same transaction was involved. Thenceforth, during the period of prohibition, the two systems of legislation continued in effect except as the revenue laws sanctioned the carrying on of the liquor business for beverage purposes. In a great many cases prosecutions were brought under the revenue laws rather than under the National Prohibition Act, because the penalties of the latter were less severe until the passage of the Jones-Stalker Act of March 2, 1929, and also because in many jurisdictions it was easier to secure convictions for the evasion of taxes than for offenses against the prohibition law. For the same reason the conspiracy statute was widely employed.

The National Prohibition Act declared that any premises where liquor was manufactured, sold, kept, or bartered in violation of its terms were a common nuisance, and their keeping a misdemeanor. In addition, both Federal and state courts having equity jurisdiction were empowered by the Federal Act to issue injunctions, both temporary and final, for the abatement of such nuisances by ordering the premises closed for 1 year. Under the statute it was held that notice of intention to seek a temporary injunction was not required. The act further provided that such proceedings could be brought by the attorney general, United States attorneys, the commissioner of prohibition or his assistants, or by the prosecuting attorneys of any state or its subdivisions. Proceedings of this character were also authorized to be brought in state courts in the name of the United States.

If the owner of premises knowingly permitted them to be used for the illegal manufacture and sale of liquor, the property became subject to a lien for the payment of the fines and costs against the person illegally using them. A proceeding for the forfeiture of a lease of premises used for law violation was held to be one arising under a law of the United States, and it was held that diversity of citizenship was not required to give the district court jurisdiction.

Acquittal on a criminal charge of maintaining a nuisance was declared not to be a bar to the granting of an injunction against maintaining a nuisance because of difference in degree of proof required, since one related to past acts and the other operated prospectively.

The act provided for the forfeiture of liquors and property used in violation of its terms, which were not so drastic as those contained in the internal revenue laws for tax evasion. Under the former act the right of innocent lien holders was exempted from forfeiture, while under the revenue acts an absolute forfeiture of all rights was authorized.

As most cases of illegal transportation under the prohibition law also involved nontaxpaid liquor, it was held that the government could invoke the severe forfeiture provisions of the revenue acts where tax evasion was involved.

Where fraud upon the revenue was practiced, conviction of the owner of property of the criminal offense was not a bar to proceedings to forfeit the distillery, since in revenue cases the action is one in rem against the offending property.

Under the National Prohibition Act it was held that conviction for the sale of liquor barred a civil proceeding to collect the tax penalty imposed for the sale by the prohibition statute. But the arrest and prosecution of an offender under the National Prohibition Act did not bar forfeiture of the property under the revenue laws where tax evasion was involved.

SEARCH AND SEIZURE

Few phases of prohibition and its enforcement provoked more antagonism and litigation than the search for and seizure of liquor held in violation of the law. This was true of both Federal and state legislation. The constitutions of most states, as well as the Federal Constitution, guarantee against unreasonable searches and seizures, and the Fifth Amendment to the Constitution of the United States provides that no person shall be "compelled in any criminal case to be a witness against himself." The National Prohibition Act provided: "No search warrant shall issue to search any private dwelling occupied as such unless it is being used for the unlawful sale of liquor, or unless it is in part used for some business purpose, such as a store, shop, saloon, restaurant, hotel, or boarding house." Warrants were required to be issued under the limitations of the Espionage Act of June 15, 1917, which outlined the procedure to be followed. The Supplemental Prohibition Act of November 23, 1921, provided a penalty against any officer "who shall search any private dwelling without a warrant or who shall maliciously and without reasonable cause search any other property without a warrant."

Many cases involving the sufficiency of search warrants were presented to the courts, both as to the sufficiency of the evidence upon which a warrant was issued, and also the adequacy of the description. An affidavit of belief of violation of the law was held insufficient, and the evidence obtained upon such a defective warrant was inadmissible and the liquor ordered returned.

The act of officers in executing a search warrant and illegally destroying liquor found on the premises without a court order was held not to render a sample retained as evidence inadmissible in a criminal prosecution.

The Fourth and Fifth Amendments to the Constitution of the United States are limitations upon Federal agencies only, but in a state having no state enforcement law it was held that liquor seized by state troopers without a search warrant, while acting in aid of the enforcement of the Federal law, was inadmissible.

Where officers executing an arrest warrant charging conspiracy searched the premises without a search warrant, the seizure of liquor found was illegal and the evidence inadmissible where no offense was committed in their presence.

Prohibition agents who in the nighttime smelled the odor of mash coming from a garage and searched it, without a warrant, were held to have acted illegally. The seizure was unlawful and the evidence inadmissible.

It was held that the Fourth Amendment did not prevent the search of an automobile by Federal agents without a warrant where the officers had probable cause to believe that liquor was being illegally transported.

The act also gave a right of civil action against any person selling or procuring liquor for another, the consumption of which produced intoxication and injured anyone in person, property or estate. Such action was maintainable in Federal and state courts and survived against the estate in the event of the death of either party.

Smuggling

The question arose concerning the application of the Eighteenth Amendment and its enforcing statutes to liquors on board foreign ships when entering the territorial waters of the United States, and as to domestic ships when on the high seas. The Court held that the legislation denied the right to foreign vessels to have liquor on board as sea stores, and that the amendment did not apply to American ships outside of territorial waters.

Following this a series of treaties were negotiated with the United States and the principal foreign maritime nations whereby such nations were granted the right to bring liquor into American waters and ports as sea stores under seal in exchange for the right of an extension of the distance within which vessels suspected of smuggling might be searched. The measure of distance provided by these treaties was 1 hour's sailing distance from the coast, determined by the speed of the vessel. Under the provisions of the customs laws known as the Hovering Acts, search of vessels suspected of smuggling was permitted when within 4 leagues of the coast.

The Court declared that the effect of the treaty with Great Britain concluded May 22, 1924, was to limit the distance of search to 1 hour's sailing time, and to modify the earlier Hovering Acts as far as they applied to countries with which the United States had similar treaties. It was held that under the terms of the treaty, persons outside of the territorial waters of the United States engaged in a conspiracy to import might be prosecuted for such conspiracy when apprehended within the jurisdiction of the United States.

Modification of Definition of Intoxicating Liquor

On March 22, 1933, while ratification of the amendment to repeal the Eighteenth Amendment was pending, Congress passed an act entitled, "An Act to provide revenue by the taxation of certain nonintoxicating liquor, and for other purposes." The effect of this was to withdraw the penalties of the National Prohibition Act from the manufacture and sale of malt and vinous liquors containing ½ of 1 per cent or more of alcohol by volume and not more than 3.2 per cent of alcohol by weight. It authorized the issuance of permits to engage in such manufacture. The effect was to withdraw from the Federal courts jurisdiction in prosecutions for the manufacture and sale of beverages of that alcoholic strength.

As state laws defining intoxicating liquors were based upon their police power, it was held that the act did not have the effect of legalizing such beverages in the states where such liquors came within the terms of the prohibition law. Shortly thereafter the legislatures of all the states modified their state definitions of prohibited liquors to permit the sale of malt beverages of this alcoholic strength.

The question arose whether the 3.2 per cent beverage act contravened the Eighteenth Amendment to the Constitution by legalizing liquors actually intoxicating. Some of the lower courts declared it valid.

In Kentucky, where an injunction was sought against a railroad company to require it to accept shipments of such malt beverages, and the railroad company declined on the ground that to do so would contravene the Eighteenth Amendment and the state law, the Court of Appeals held that the question whether such beverages were intoxicating under the statute of the state was one of fact. The constitutionality of the legislation was not passed upon by any case reaching the Supreme Court of the United States.

The Twenty-First Amendment

On February 20, 1933, the Seventy-Second Congress adopted a joint resolution proposing an amendment to the Constitution of the United States, as follows:

Section 1. The eighteenth article of amendment to the Constitution of the United States is hereby repealed.

Section 2. The transportation or importation into any State, Territory, or possession of the United States for delivery or use therein of intoxicating liquors, in violation of the laws thereof, is hereby prohibited.

Section 3. This article shall be inoperative unless it shall have been ratified as an amendment to the Constitution by conventions in the several States, as provided in the Constitution, within seven years from the date of the submission hereof to the States by the Congress.

On the date of the submission of this amendment, 14 states were without enforcement codes to carry into effect the policy represented by the national prohibition amendment. These were: Arizona, California, Colorado, Illinois, Indiana, Maryland, Massachusetts, Montana, Nevada, New Jersey, New York, Oregon, Washington, and Wisconsin.

On December 5, 1933, the proposed amendment was ratified by the last of the required three-fourths of the states. One additional state subsequently ratified. An innovation was introduced in the submission of this amendment, as it was submitted to conventions to be called in the states to act upon it. This was the first amendment to be submitted to the states under the alternative plan of ratification provided for amendment of the Constitution. It provided the nearest method possible under the Constitution to allow a direct vote of the people, as in practically every state the delegates to the conventions were elected in a state-wide vote on the basis of their stand for or against ratification. Only 33 per cent of the qualified voters participated in the election of delegates to the conventions in the states to consider ratification of the Twenty-First Amendment. Of these, 27.3 per cent voted for candidates against ratification and 72.7 per cent for delegates favoring repeal.

A number of suits were filed in state courts to test the validity of the laws providing for the election of delegates to the ratifying conventions.

The Supreme Court took judicial notice of the ratification of the Twenty-First Amendment and declared that it had the effect of striking down the National Prohibition Act, which depended upon the Eighteenth Amendment for its validity, and immediately deprived the Federal courts of jurisdiction over prosecutions under the act, even though such crime was committed before repeal.

Prohibitions of the Twenty-First Amendment

The second section of the Twenty-First Amendment has been construed as freeing the states from the limitations formerly imposed upon the police power by the Commerce Clause of the Constitution, so far as it relates to the importation of liquor for use in the state. Thus, a state law denying the right to import except upon payment of an import fee was held valid.

The states may now pass laws discriminating against liquor from other states, and the Fourteenth Amendment does not prevent this, even as to liquors on hand, or they may now pass retaliatory laws against the importation of liquor from other states which discriminate against their own product.

Under its police power a state may limit transportation of liquor to common carriers only and deny this right to contract carriers, although the latter hold a license from the Federal Government.

None of these things could have been done before national prohibition. It has also been held recently that, independent of the Twenty-First Amendment, the state may require a permit for the transportation of liquor through its confines when destined for another state, and also that the regulations of a state requiring through transporters to use the shortest route, requiring a bond against diversion, and the presence of a bill of lading showing destination, are valid.

The amendment did not deprive the Federal Government of power to regulate imports from foreign countries.

Under the amendment, regulatory provisions of state liquor laws were declared inapplicable to land within a state ceded to the Federal Government as a national park, although the state tax laws on liquor did apply there.

Police officers of a prohibition state were without authority to seize liquor in transit to a military reservation within the state over which it had ceded exclusive jurisdiction to the Federal Government, as the second section of the Twenty-First Amendment did not apply. Under the Assimilative Crimes Act—by which Congress had made it a Federal offense punishable in a Federal court to do any act made illegal by state law—where there was no corresponding Federal statute, such transportation, if punishable under that Act, was the responsibility of Federal officials.

Summary of Legal Effect of the Twenty-First Amendment

1. It leaves to the states the responsibility for determining the type of liquor legislation to be adopted.

2. It frees the states from the limitations formerly imposed upon their police power, as applied to liquor imported in interstate commerce.

3. It guarantees this freedom by constitutional provision, which cannot be repealed or modified by a majority vote of Congress.

4. It places liquor in interstate commerce in a different category from other merchandise.

5. It imposes upon Congress the duty to carry into effect the intent and purpose of the amendment by aiding in preventing the importation of liquors in violation of state policy, no matter what the state law may be—regulation, state monopoly, or prohibition.

6. Congress has already recognized this obligation by the passage of the act of June 25, 1936, entitled, "An Act to enforce the Twenty-First Amendment." It provides a penalty enforceable in the Federal courts for introducing liquor into any state if it is not accompanied by such permit or license as may now or hereafter be required by the law of such state; or if all importation or transportation of intoxicating liquor is prohibited in such state by the laws thereof. This provides a limited measure of cooperation which can be enlarged as the public sentiment in the states demands.

7. It has once more reunited within the state full power to deal with both interstate and intrastate phases of the liquor problem which may affect its domestic and social policies.

8. It has removed the rigidity of the policy fixed by the Eighteenth Amendment, to make state laws responsive to public sentiment without the need for changing the entire structure of government.

9. It has restored to state and Federal Governments the discharge of their natural and traditional functions.

Conclusion

The evolution of the provisions of the Constitution of the United States as they relate to intoxicating liquors has been the result of experience and the logic of events. Had it not been for the change of attitude of the Supreme Court which began in 1888, and the long delay of 27 years that ensued until the validity of the Webb-Kenyon Law was finally established, it is questionable whether there would ever have been either an Eighteenth or Twenty-First Amendment to the Federal Constitution.

The importance of liquor as a social problem is suggested by the fact that it is the only subject which has twice caused the American people to change the structure of their government.

From the legal standpoint, past efforts have not been in vain. Out of them have come developments of great portent in future dealings with problems arising from alcoholic beverages, both as to the state police power and as to the relationship of the National Government to them.

Out of the turmoil and litigation the liquor traffic has emerged with no constitutional sanction but faces a very much broader concept of the scope of the police power of the states.

It is now established that the manufacture and sale of liquor is a privilege and not a right. The privilege exists by sufferance only and can be withdrawn at any time by the state without compensating those affected for losses suffered. The police power can be exerted not only against the traffic in liquors but also against their possession for personal use.

The Twenty-First Amendment has reallocated state-Federal responsibility for liquor legislation and offers a new approach to the entire problem.

History also records a tendency toward the use of a more democratic method of deciding public policies with respect to liquor. This is shown by the invoking of local option; by the use of the initiative and referendum; by the resort to advisory votes and by the action of Congress in submitting the question of the repeal of national prohibition to conventions in the states for ratification, the delegates to which were elected upon the specific issue of whether they were "for" or "against" the change.

Under the Constitution, and before the law as interpreted by the courts, the liquor question stands to be adjudged by the people through democratic processes. The wisdom or folly of legislative procedures will depend upon popular understanding of the subject in all of its moral, social, economic, scientific and political aspects. This offers a challenge to such a student body as this. You can do much toward influencing sound individual and social attitudes.

DISCUSSION

Chairman (E. M. Jellinek): Mrs. Colvin has asked for the floor to offer some comment.

Mrs. Colvin: I suggested to the chairman that while we have had a very wonderful presentation of the history of the legal aspects of prohibition and I know of no one in the country who could have done a better job than Mr. Dunford, there are other things that I hoped might be said here on prohibition. He said, "Would you like to say a few words?" I said, "Yes, and I hope mine will be just as objective as the others." I would like to say just a few words about why prohibition was repealed, and I am going to suggest that the Wets and the Drys are equally responsible.

There are two lines of political thought among the Drys: the pressure method or nonpartisan method, and the political method which is direct action. Each side is just as sincere as the other, but in getting legislation, we all know that it can be secured in a nonpartisan way through pressure methods. All the Drys of the country united in an effort to secure national constitutional prohibition. The law was submitted and passed through public pressure created by election of public officials, both Democrats and Republicans, who were committed to it. Then, as far as law was concerned, it was all done. Next it came to the state legislatures and again the same thing happened. Drys were elected and they were in an overwhelming majority in the states, and the ratification of the law was secured.

When it comes to the enforcement of a law, that cannot be done by the pressure method except in unusual circumstances. For instance, if a mayor of a city lets things get too bad, the pressure of public opinion can exercise some influence. He will enforce the law as long as public pressure, public attention, is called to it. However, ordinarily he enforces the law 365 days a year, but he is one person. He is not made up of men from each political party; he is elected by a political party and that party decides how he shall act. If the party itself is not committed to any particular legislation, then the man does not enforce the law. The law was passed, the Eighteenth Amendment was written into the Constitution, but the political organization which enforced the law was not committed to it. The law was violated.

There was an attempt at enforcement in 1920 when William Jennings Bryan was chairman of the National Democratic Committee and the Committee was in the hands of the Drys. He said he thought the next step, which was within the Constitution and no longer a political partisan question, was that it should be written into the platforms of each of the parties. It would have been a nonpartisan issue then, if both parties had declared for the enforcement of part of the Constitution. But there were groups who did not believe in its being done that way, and while Mr. Bryan went to the convention in San Francisco in 1920 and asked for Dry planks in the political platform, there were other groups there who were just as sincere, but who said, "No, we don't want it in a political party platform, we don't want it dragged into politics—it's a great moral issue." And so because there were Wets as well as Drys in the party they didn't want to divide the issue and it wasn't written in. The same thing happened at the Republican convention that year in Cleveland.

After the Eighteenth Amendment had been passed, a group of prominent people in this country met in Washington and organized a movement for the express purpose of seeing that it never should become operative. They went to newspapers and said, "You'll get a lot of money from advertising; it will mean a lot in your exchequer if you'll come along and help." They went to multimillionaires. The Congress of the United States passed the N.I.R.A. It was approved in June of that year and there were some extra taxes: A tax of 1½ cents on benzol gasoline, a tax on dividends, a tax on corporations, a tax on excess profits. Then these men said that the Congress should demand that the budget of the United States be balanced or the Eighteenth Amendment to the Constitution be repealed; this extra tax on gasoline should be repealed, taxes should be lowered, and the excess profits tax and the corporation tax decreased; these will be taken off in the event the people vote for the repeal of the Eighteenth Amendment. They then went all over the country and suggested that everyone who owned an automobile had a stake in the repeal of the Eighteenth Amendment and would save taxes on their gasoline if it were repealed. Everybody who owned a big corporation would save on the corporation tax and everybody who paid an income tax would save money.

Then they began to read all the Dry literature and they took all of the epithets and all of the things that had been said against liquor and its influence and turned them against prohibition. Prohibition was the thing that made men drunk, prohibition was the thing that caused all the trouble in this country. And I believe that a good deal of the opposition, of the disregard of the Constitution itself and of the nine old men in the Supreme Court, can be laid at the door of the Wet propaganda. Students from Harvard came into my office one day. They wanted to discuss this, and they talked about the Constitution, and they said, "What do we care about the Constitution; it's a scrap of paper; when we don't like it we change it." Then I began to talk about the Supreme Court, which, as Mr. Dunford has said, upheld every single item of Dry legislation that had been passed, and they said, "What do we care? They are just nine old men." So that disregard of the Constitution, the disregard of the respect that we had always had for our Supreme Court, came through that Wet propaganda during that time.

I wanted to say these things because there are a lot of people who have believed, because of the Wet propaganda which is going on today, that prohibition was a terrible failure. May I say this one word more? Out in Ohio Wesleyan University, the last year of the repeal campaign, there was a class that was financed by Will Bigelow, who is the editor of *Good Housekeeping* magazine and an alumnus of the school. In that class a most unusual procedure was carried out. He suggested that the teachers should be those who believed in the Eighteenth Amendment and those who did not. They had all the prominent Wets of the country go out there to say everything they could against prohibition. They had an equal number of Drys go there. The students would listen to one side one day, then the next day to the other side. There were 47 who took the course, and when they began, about half of them said they believed in prohibition, half of them said they did not. After they had listened to both sides, one after the other, they knew how to question both sides. That kept on for one semester, and at the close of the semester every one of them said that they believed in the Eighteenth Amendment. I've always said that the people who knew the facts would take the right side, and I think one of the reasons that people so glibly say "I don't believe in prohibition" is because they don't know what they're talking about. They just believe what the Wets tell them, that prohibition is a curse and the cause of everything that's bad, and don't see in the law what it can do and what it did do.

May I say what happened on the last day of that class? The reason I know about this is because I was asked to speak. At the last, there were so many students interested in it that they had Friday night and Saturday for a public presentation of both sides at the same time. We had two statisticians; one who represented the Wet organization and the other, not from a Dry organization but from the United States Government Department of Prohibition. The Wet statistician said this: "Prohibition has failed because it has only succeeded in reducing consumption of liquor 35 per cent." But did you get the word "succeeded"? He said it failed, because it only succeeded in reducing it 35 per cent. While the Government official said, "Prohibition has reduced consumption 65 per cent." There was only 35 per cent as much drinking. While taking even the Wet figures, prohibition reduced consumption more than any other method that has ever been tried. I felt that I wanted this chance to say this because there are a lot of people who still do not believe it.

Chairman: I think, Mrs. Colvin, that we are all very grateful for your presentation. Naturally, there are sentiments and beliefs involved in it, but I think you have given an example that beliefs can be presented with great self-restraint. I would not be the least bit afraid of discussion from all sides so long as it were done with the same moderation as you have shown.

I now suggest that the questions, for the time being, should be directed to Dr. Dunford and pertain to the legal material which he has presented, and should not try to prove but to clarify issues.

Mrs. Phillips: Does the Federal Government receive revenue from the sale of liquor?

Lecturer: Oh, yes, that has been the policy of the Government. In the beginning, liquor revenue was derived from two sources. One was customs duties, which were proposed by almost the first Congress. The other source included a form of internal revenue taxes. Prior to the Civil War, except during war periods like that of 1812, liquor was no important source of internal revenue to the Government. From 1864 on it has become an important part of the budget of the Federal Government through the levying of excise taxes and also occupational taxes on persons engaged in retail sale, brewers, manufacturers and others.

Robinson: What will be the effect of the Oklahoma decision regarding shipment of alcoholic beverages interstate? I refer to the liquor shipped to military personnel.

Lecturer: I do not think that that decision is correctly understood. The Twenty-First Amendment prohibits the transportation or importation of intoxicating liquors into a state for delivery or use in violation of its law. Fort Sill Military Reservation, it is true, is in the State of Oklahoma. But it is an area acquired by the Federal Government under the terms of the Constitution for military purposes. In the Act of Cession the state had granted exclusive jurisdiction to the Federal Government so that it is exclusively a Federal area. The question arose in this way: Police officers of Oklahoma seized a shipment of liquor consigned to the Fort Sill Reservation. There was some question about the legality of the seizure, since they did not have a warrant. The case did not turn on that point primarily; it was also a question whether the state officer had the right to make the seizure under what is known as the Assimilative Crimes Act. That is an act of Congress that provided that if ever a transaction is made unlawful by the law of the state, or the omission to do an act is made unlawful by the law of the state, and there is no corresponding Federal statute on the subject, then the state law should be adopted as a Federal law. The question was, whether the state officers could seize and prosecute under the circumstances in the state court. The Supreme Court of the United States held, first, that the provision of the Twenty-First Amendment did not apply, since the liquor was not intended for delivery or use within the area in which the state had retained jurisdiction. Second, that the state officers had no authority to act under the Assimilative Crimes Act since it was a Federal act and to be applicable at all could be enforced only by a Federal agent. The court did not decide the question of whether the transportation was punishable under the Assimilative Crime Act. I think the implication of the majority opinion is that it was and is the obligation of the Federal Government to proceed under that act. That question has not been decided, but the extent of the decision of that case was simply that the Twenty-First Amendment did not apply because the state had ceded its jurisdiction.

Question: We have a practice here, in the State of Connecticut, whereby anyone who wishes to sell liquor in the state can go to the Federal authorities in Hartford and secure, for $25, a stamp which he can put on liquor, which can then be sold in any way he sees fit without reference to the state laws. That is one of the things which has been very difficult for the Liquor Control Commission to handle. There are relatively small amounts of liquor that are seeping out into all parts of the state under Federal permits. I wonder whether this is really legal or whether there have been any decisions or any actions covering that situation.

Lecturer: Shortly after the passage of the Internal Revenue Law in the Civil War, this very question arose in the License Tax Cases, in which the question was whether, since the Federal Government had required retail liquor dealers and others to obtain a license from the Federal Government, that conferred the right to carry on a business in violation of the law of the state. The Supreme Court of the United States declared that it did not; that Congress had no right to legalize a business in order to tax it in violation of state powers. The license was simply evidence of the payment of the tax, and by recent acts, in the Internal Revenue Code, there is a provision which expressly declares that the payment of the tax shall confer no right to conduct a business in violation of the law of the state. It further provides that the state prosecutor can apply to the Collector of Internal Revenue for the lists of persons who pay the Federal tax, and that Federal list can be used as evidence in a proceeding under the state law for prosecution for carrying on the business. Now in many of the state prohibition laws, formerly, there was included a statement that the possession of Federal revenue tax receipts should be prima facie evidence that the business was carried on in violation of the prohibition laws of the state. That furnished one of the strongest measures possible of aiding the state in enforcing its laws. The state prosecutor, if he was diligent, simply got the evidence, produced it in the state court, and he had a prima facie case. Of course, with the changes that have come about, with the recodification of the laws in a great many of the prohibition states, that provision was omitted; when prohibition became a part of the Federal Constitution it didn't seem necessary to retain it.

Matthew: I have this question, that is still unanswered in my mind, as to the legality in connection with military premises. I understand that General Marshall has issued an order stating that all hard liquor should be removed from military premises. We have some of those military premises in the state of Kansas. There is constant transportation into military premises of hard liquor. We have no protection in the matter; we have no alternative. What I want to ask here is, Who is the violator? Is it the officer that gives the order, the company that sells, or the man who transports the liquor? Somebody is violating a Federal act and getting away with it. It is an indictment, I think, against our Federal Government.

Lecturer: I would say that the answer to this question would depend entirely on the facts in the given case. The difficulty there is not primarily a lack of law, but a failure of those responsible for executing it. If it is an area over which the Federal Government has exclusive jurisdiction, it is primarily the responsibility of the Federal Government, the War Department, the Department of Justice. That is a matter for political action by appealing to your representatives to get action if the law is actually violated; your congressman, your governor, your senator, whoever is responsible for the condition if it affects Kansas. If it is a matter beyond the jurisdiction of the state, then they, of course, have no jurisdiction. If it is an area that is exclusively Federal, then I think the state officers would not have any right to act; that is, by actual seizure. They could bring pressure by way of public opinion to demand that the Federal Government execute its obligations, if the law applies.

There are several things that might be involved. There was passed, in 1901, the Anti-Canteen Act that made it illegal to sell intoxicating liquors in any military reservation. That law has been in force since 1901 and was the law that General Marshall called to the attention of the officers under him. There has since become involved the question of the Twenty-First Amendment prohibiting the introduction of intoxicating liquors into the state in violation of state law. If an area in the state is made into Federal territory there can be no state law violated therein. If there is a violation of a Federal statute it is subject to the jurisdiction of Federal officers. The question of getting them to act is a matter of the ordinary procedure of getting any officer to act about any violation.

Smoot: What recourse has a Dry state when those statutes or regulations of the Twenty-First Amendment which concern the transporting of liquor into its borders are violated?

Lecturer: There are two effects of the Twenty-First Amendment on that situation. Formerly, before the Webb-Kenyon law, if a man went into a Wet state or a license state and bought liquor, carried it to his car and transported it into a Dry state, the Courts held that state police forces of the prohibition state could not touch him at all —that he was immune. The state law did not apply until his destination was reached. Now the effect of the Twenty-First Amendment is to make it possible for state police officers to act immediately if a man crosses the line with liquor in his possession. The state has full authority to deal with the matter. Coupled with that is also the obligation of the Federal Government to enact proper regulations to police liquor across state lines so that neighboring states shall not be used to violate the laws of other states, no matter whether they are prohibition, license, or monopoly states. That is a purpose of the Amendment.

The distilling industry now has to get a permit, and if there is evidence of a conspiracy with people in prohibition states to introduce liquor in violation of the state laws, the basic permit to do business can be revoked by the Federal Government. It is a most complete and full authority and permits the states full power of action, coupled with the obligation of Federal officers to aid them. Each jurisdiction performs a function, and the problem then is one of stimulating public opinion. Of course, if you don't get the law to operate, it's the old question of enforcing prohibition or enforcing regulations which license liquor. I don't see that there is any particular difference between this situation and any other, so far as the liquor laws are concerned.

Hoover: Under our present laws, how effective may be the enforcement of local option in small political units? Does local option lead inevitably to state prohibition and then to national prohibition?

Lecturer: As to the effectiveness of local option, I would say that the question of how far the prohibitions of the Twenty-First Amendment apply to local option has not come to the attention of the Supreme Court. I cannot answer what they would hold. My personal view as a lawyer is that when it does come there, they will say that the amendment meant what it said; that if a local option law is in force, prohibiting receipt or possession of liquor, and a man tries to introduce liquor from an adjacent state into that no-license area, it is an attempt at delivery for use in the state in violation of its law; therefore, it is against the policy and the language of the amendment. But as I say, that question has not yet been passed on by the Court. As to what is the effect of continued extension of local option on prohibition, I would not venture an opinion.

Mrs. Lewis: There are many suggestions concerning the use of liquor taxes for hospitalization and rehabilitation of alcoholics. Would such allocation of revenue be brought about by the pressure of public opinion on state legislatures or on the Federal legislative bodies?

Lecturer: Where taxes are allocated depends on the nature of the tax and who levies it. If it is a state tax, it is subject to allocation by the state authorities. If it is a Federal tax, it is appropriated by Congress or allocated by Congress. They can make allocations if it is a subject upon which the Federal Government wants to cooperate. Now there has been in the past a policy of the Federal Government to aid the states in certain matters like road-building. The Federal Government makes grants in aid to the states for any number of things if they appeal to the legislative discretion of Congress. To that extent the Federal Government, in connection with some such project, might make an allocation.

Analysis of Wet and Dry Propaganda

Dwight Anderson

THIS is to be an hour of informal running comment based upon an examination of Wet and Dry propaganda which has appeared in the course of the year last past. Before coming upon this platform I obeyed the injunction which appears in theater programs—"Choose your exit now." I am to have an hour in which to put you on the spot. Then you are to have an hour to put *me* on the spot. "He who goes gunning for others finds that others go gunning for him."

It is always a question whether one can make himself utterly understood to another person. Oliver Wendell Holmes said that when two people are talking, there are in reality six persons involved. First, you, as I think you are; and I, as you think I am; then there is you, as you think you are, and I, as I think I am; and then there are two more—each of us as we really are; which makes six in all.

The propagandist uses words to conjure with. It is a form of magic. Sometimes the effects are so subtle as to defy analysis. Use of the scalpel of intelligence shears away excrescences of language which pass for thought. Nothing remains of some of our most treasured phrases. You remember the story, perhaps, of the fish seller in Philadelphia who had the sign in his window—FRESH FISH SOLD HERE. A customer came in and said, "Why the 'here'?—Just, FRESH FISH SOLD." So he put up a sign with the "here" off. The next customer who came in said, "Why 'fresh'?" He thought that over and then put up a new sign—FISH SOLD. And the next customer said, "Why the 'sold'?" And that sounded reasonable to him, so he put up a sign that said just FISH. The next customer came in and said, "Why do you put that sign up there? You can smell this place for five blocks!"

In preparation for this address I collected over a period of 6 months all the Wet and Dry propaganda I could find. I subscribed to a number of Wet and Dry magazines and read many books. I piled these all on a table until, really, I was soaked with Wet propaganda and parched with Dry. And when I came about two weeks ago to look it all over, the task seemed too prodigious. It was necessary, before I even began on the accumulated pile, to get down to fundamentals and, before I started, find out what an analysis of anything is.

Consulting Webster, I learned that analysis is to arrange in order or grouping either thoughts or objects. So I put the Wet stuff in one pile and the Dry stuff in another pile and put the neutral in a third pile, and I found it all very confusing. I expect to become even more confused as I tell you about what was in all this propaganda, but the subject itself is confused, as we shall see.

If you read the *Wine and Liquor Retailer*, or the *Beverage Retailer Weekly*, the *Tavern News, Tap and Tavern*, or the *Brewery Worker*, the *Allied News Bulletin*, or *Frankly Speaking*, and then read *The Foundation Says*, the *Voice*, the *National Prohibitionist*, the *Scientific Temperance Journal*, the *International Student*, *Forward*, *Temperance Education Journal*, the *White Ribbon Bulletin*, the *Arkansas White Ribboner*, *Southern California White*, *Temperance Education Bulletin*, the *National Voice*, you can hardly keep yourself from being on both sides of the controversial subject at the same time. If you read *The Rape of Temperance*, *Responsible Drinking*, or Herbert Asbury's *Carrie Nation*, you will certainly oppose prohibition; but if you read *The Amazing Story of Repeal*, *The Wrecking of the Eighteenth Amendment*, *The Passing of the Saloon* (in 1908), or *King Alcohol Dethroned*, you will certainly be strong against liquor and all its works. Every statement made on one side of this keen controversy is matched by a contrary statement made on the other side.

MEANING OF PROPAGANDA

Let us decide, then, what we mean by propaganda. We know something about analysis. We have put the Wet and Dry material in two different categories. We have found that there are affirmations and denials on both sides. Alfred M. Lee of Wayne University has defined propaganda as

The use of words, symbols, ideas, events, personalities, and the like with the intention of building up or destroying an interest, cause, project, institution, or person in the eyes and minds of a public. Differently stated, propaganda is the point of view overtly stated or covertly applied for the purpose of influencing the thought and action of others.

That definition will serve our purpose as well as any. Now of course what both sides of this controversy mean to do, or at least mean to appear to do, is to be seeking the truth. And of course *there* is a word which, so far as I am concerned, I will not try to define. It is defined in the dictionary but it has many meanings and many facets. In *The Education of the Will*, Jules Payot says that the chief use to which we put our love of truth is to persuade ourselves that what we love is true. The Japanese have a saying that the truth is that which under the given conditions is best calculated to be believed.

We are told, on the one hand, that liquor caused the Pearl Harbor debacle; on the other, that such a statement is an infamous accusation of our troops. We are told that liquor retards the war effort, that it promotes the war effort; that there is a shortage of liquor, that there is not a shortage of liquor; that Prohibition was put over while our soldiers were away, that Prohibition was not put over while the soldiers were away; that the liquor people are promoting the Bond campaign because they wish to help the war effort, and that the Bond-campaign promotion is merely dust thrown in the eyes of the public to hide the nefarious nature of the trade; that juvenile delinquency is caused by liquor, that juvenile delinquency is not caused by liquor; and so on down the entire list of possibilities. The condition is comparable to that described in *Only Yesterday*, by Frederick Lewis Allen, regarding Prohibition days. He said:

Whatever the contributions of the Prohibition regime to temperance, at least it produced intemperate propaganda and counter-propaganda. Almost any Dry could tell you that Prohibition was the basis of American prosperity as attested by the volume of savings bank deposits or that Prohibition had reduced the deaths from alcoholism, emptied the jails, diverted the workman's dollars to the purchase of automobiles, radios, and homes. Almost any Wet could tell you that Prohibition had nothing to do with prosperity but it caused the crime wave, the increase of immorality, the divorce rate, disrespect for all law which entailed the very foundations of free government. The Wets said the Drys fostered Bolshevism by their fanatical zeal for laws which were inevitably faulty. The Drys said the Wets fostered Bolshevism by their cynical law-breaking. Even in matters of supposed fact, you could find, if you only read and listened, any sort of ammunition that you wanted—one never saw drunkards in the streets any more, one saw more drunkards than ever; drinking in the colleges was hardly a problem now, drinking in the colleges was at its worst; there was a still in every other home in the mining districts of Pennsylvania, drinking in the mining districts of Pennsylvania was a thing of the past; cases of poverty as a result of drunkenness were only a fraction of what they used to be, the menace of drinking in the slums was three times as great as in pre-Volstead days.

EFFECT OF PROPAGANDA

Now, may I make clear at the outset that, in the discussion which follows, my effort is to appraise the effect of the propaganda which I shall examine upon the people who receive it. So far as I am concerned in this respect, it makes no difference whether alcohol is an anesthetic or a narcotic. The fact interests me not at all. The effect of the dissemination of the fact upon people who hear it interests me very much indeed. So if that is to be the course of our thinking now, it will be well for us to understand something about how the people of the country may be grouped numerically with reference to their natural intention. I am indebted to Dr. Jellinek for the figure that there are in the United States 100 million people of drinking age, assuming that to be 15 and over. I am indebted to him also for the statement that 50 million of these people use liquor; and that it is estimated that of the 50 million abstinent, 17 million are abstinent through conviction. I will extemporize a fact now and make a guess that of the 50 million who drink, there are also 17 million who believe in abstinence for the other fellow. They take a drink once in awhile but they want to see liquor controlled, and perhaps by means of prohibition if other methods fail. They recognize the evils of liquor and they think the only way to minimize these is to control the liquor traffic; so you might say that those 17 million think and talk Dry but act Wet. We would thus have 34 million people who, you might say, have a predilection for the Dry side and 66 million who are, as we might say, "sitting in the bleachers." They are neutral, on the whole; about half of them drink, and the rest do not, but have no strong convictions on the subject.

Now we are going to go through the Wet propaganda and say this is effective and this is not effective, and then go through the Dry propaganda the same way and say this is effective and this not effective. But not just to be a common scold. We are not going to get anywhere in doing that. It is easy to criticize. It is difficult to be creative and helpful. We are interested merely in measuring what this propaganda is doing to people in the bleachers, and our test of effectiveness is to be just that.

Now the people in the bleachers hear these statements pro and con, and pro and con, and pro and con. And the people in the bleachers are prone to think they are watching players on the Dry side who are mostly talking to their own team, and on the Wet side largely talking to their own team. These people are the ones who must be reached if any change in sentiment and opinion is to be brought about. Now we do not need any opinion surveys or expensive "sampling" technique to be successful in doing this. All we have to do is to be a common everyday average person ourselves for a moment and test the statements on how we react to them ourselves. We only need to bring to a discussion such as this what Eddie Guest said he possessed, "a first-rate mediocre mind." I think we all, probably, possess that. It resolves itself pretty largely into a sympathy with the ordinary man, a sufficient gregariousness to associate with all kinds and sorts of people upon a basis where they open up and one gets an opportunity to see inside them.

LIQUOR ADVERTISING

First, I want to take up the liquor advertising very briefly. I am indebted to Mr. Squires for the statement that 28½ million dollars was spent on liquor advertising in 1942. So, we accumulated a lot of liquor ads, stacks of them. And we classified them into categories. We found Four Roses, Three Feathers, Seagram's, Calvert's, Schenley's, Mt. Vernon, Haig and Haig, M and M, Park and Tilford. I have four pages of these ads here that were gone over and classified, and I do not think it necessary to read this list but I do wish to tell you the classifications that they were put into and show you some samples.

It seemed to me that this advertising fell into three different categories: "competitive," "convivial," and "prestige." I am groping for a better word than "convivial." But certainly nobody can be mistaken about those which are "prestige" advertisements. They associate drinking with estimable things and estimable people. Then, other advertisements are merely competitive and are easily recognized; they associate liquor with nothing. They show a picture of the bottle and aim to popularize the name so that when one is picking his whisky he will select the name that has been made most familiar to him. Then there is what I call the convivial or gregarious, which associates the particular brand advertised with hospitality, conviviality, Christmas, holidays, old scenes of a romantic symbolism—ships, taverns, colonial days. These advertisements suggest periods or moods of relaxation, and other ideas and psychological situations which usually accompany drinking. They bring tradition in for the purpose of stimulating a prestige association. Here is an Old Grandad advertisement. The very name is prestige-building. This advertisement is competitive, too, for we have the bottle shown to associate it with the colonial scene and "Old Grandad" himself. It imparts an idea that this whisky has prestige—is something desirable. Here is an advertisement of Four Roses which is prestige-building and also competitive because the picture of the bottle is identified in our minds with this particular brand. Here is copy, prepared in a running series of advertisements called "Metropolitan Moments," which consists of cartoons of a distinguished-looking old gentleman who is always complaining because he can't get his "whisky sours" and "old fashioneds" made with Calvert Reserve. That is prestige copy. Peter Arno's cartoons associate that particular whisky with a distinguished-looking person or a person who looks as if he might be one of the so-called "best people." This prestige-building advertising is effectual. That is to say, a favorable opinion of the particular brand of liquor is gained with people in the bleachers. But sometimes the advertiser goes altogether too far (and I am, of course, only expressing my opinion as an average reader who is trying to view these things as the people in the bleachers are viewing them). When we come, as Calvert does, to picture in these large full-page ads, which you have doubtless seen, distinguished-looking people with a glass of liquor in their hands, carrying captions such as FOR MEN OF DECISION and FOR MEN OF WISDOM, FOR MEN OF VISION, FOR MEN OF ACHIEVEMENT, FOR MEN OF PERSPECTIVE, FOR MEN OF DISTINCTION, we are going a little too far with the prestige idea. There is something about the extreme to which this goes that makes it doubtful in my mind whether or not it does not produce quite the opposite effect. It is too patent, direct. Calvert should "relax." There is a saying in Alcoholics Anonymous, "Easy does it." I think the gentleman in the dress suit whom we see wailing disconsolately for Calvert in "Metropolitan Moments" is much too genuine an old soak to be associated with the pompous phony aristocrats who blatantly declare they are men of distinction, as if Calvert made them so. In fact, I think the old gentleman would want his "old fashioned" mixed with something besides that kind of advertising to be as palatable to him as Calvert's Reserve must have seemed to get him in such a state about it.

Some advertising is exclusively competitive. Here we have Old Taylor with just the bottle. Here we have Haig and Haig with just the bottle. That is purely competitive—so that you will pick Haig and Haig rather than Black and White or whatever the names of the rest of them are.

Practically all Old Taylor and Old Forrester advertising is competitive copy, although there is a tie-up here with a picture of a ship which carries an aura of tradition and prestige, romance and pleasant thoughts of that character. Here is Schenley. There is considerable prestige here; while the bottle is so large they are really selling the whisky and not ideas about the whisky, still they bring the associations in because they say, "What every woman wants to know about a man is whether or not he picks good whisky," and then, "What every man wants to know about a woman is that she appreciates the care with which he chooses flowers for her and whisky for himself." Now that is very cleverly done. It registers in the bleachers. Here we have some of the convivial sort of advertising—a grandson has arrived, and the old boys are opening something up and going to have a drink. This is true to life and warms the cockles of the hearts of the people in the grandstand. Then here is "To the spirit of Christmas that's yet to come." It simply shows gentlemen who are offering a toast to Christmas that's yet to come. This registers. Any of our Dry friends who think alcohol is not commonly associated with Christmas need only to open their eyes to learn differently. Here is a festive convivial scene—"America's Christmas toast for 1942." That kind of advertising is more in keeping with what alcohol does to many people, most people, perhaps, than some of the other. And it seems to me that the man in the bleachers will be more moved by advertising which sticks to the goods that are being purveyed. However, I think that the Dry forces are very much overestimating the effect which this advertising has upon the public.

People think for themselves. The cumulative effect over a period of time doubtless is to make whisky to some extent more acceptable as a social custom, but you do not create customs through advertising, you do not create customs through propaganda. I will not say that it has no effect, but I do think that the principal effect of liquor advertising is competitive. I think that it sells one brand rather than another, and increases total consumption but little.

ADVERTISING AND CONTROL

A man out in Spokane, Washington, years ago ran four saloons which he called stores. His name was Jimmie Durkin. On almost every rock outside Spokane that was big enough to have his name in white paint, it was there. And if the rock were large enough to contain a little more, it was something like this —"Durkin says, Don't Buy Booze if Your Children Need Shoes." He ran full-page advertising in the daily papers. One of these ads said, "Don't come into one of my stores and try to buy a drink for one of my bartenders because he doesn't drink on duty or he wouldn't be working for me. Do you go into a grocery store and buy a sack of flour and ask the clerk to have a sack of flour on you? Then don't come into one of my stores and ask one of my clerks to drink while he's on duty. He is paid to sell my goods, not to drink them." It was sensational and phenomenal advertising. It might be possible that liquor advertisers could take a cue from some of this effectual advertising that Durkin did, to the advantage of his customers and to the advantage of the people as a whole.

Working in the Wet field are several organizations. The Allied Liquor Industry issues a news letter principally devoted to the trade, informing people what the Drys are doing. They have a woman's section which is endeavoring to mobilize the women in the industry to oppose local option and prohibition tendencies. Also, an effort is made by this organization to induce women to bring their influence to bear upon the men to remedy or control certain conditions within the industry which are inimicable to its existence.

Another organization, the Conference of Alcoholic Beverage Industries, devotes most of its propaganda to self-regulation. They emphasize this phase of the work even more perhaps than the Allied Liquor Industry does. I have here a pamphlet gotten up by the Allied in which they state their purpose is, "cooperation with military and civil authorities, preventing sales to minors, self-regulation of industry, efforts in connection with absenteeism, preventing sales to intoxicated people." It is entitled "By Our Deeds."

I quote a sentence from some of the Conference of Alcoholic Beverage Industries' publicity to its people. "Remember it is your store or tavern in which the public meets the industry. Your part in the public relations program is a mighty important one. In the final analysis, public opinion depends largely upon you."

They issue mats for publication in newspapers under such captions as, "Self-Regulation at Work," "Ministers and Tavern Men Prove Cooperation Mutually Beneficial," "It Can Be Done, Minneapolis Taverns Prove It," "Bureau to Check on Minors' Ages Declared Successful."

Mr. Lawrence McCracken of that organization gets out releases which are published widely in the Wet press. He has one on drunken driving, another one on alcoholism, another one entitled, "Five Per Cent of Patrons Seen a Menace to the Industry," another one, "Drunken Drivers Seen a Big Threat to Tavern Business."

This is effectual with the trade to some extent, at least, and it is acceptable to the people in the bleachers. However, we notice that the same organization, Conference of Alcoholic Beverage Industries, publishes a community recreation bulletin and endeavors to get tavernkeepers to engage in civic enterprises for recreational places for boys and girls. In estimating the effect of this propaganda on the people in the bleachers it is extremely doubtful whether or not it is a natural tie-up. Now the tavernkeeper as an individual might very well go into a thing of that sort, but for a group of tavernkeepers to be advocating recreational facilities for youth—well, about the next thing we would expect to see would be to have them advocate a social worker in every bar. At any rate, they are not the most likely people from whom the men in the bleachers would expect such a movement to spring.

Now, let us examine some headlines, rushing over them rapidly, in *Tap and Tavern* and some of these other publications: ENFORCEMENT'S UP TO YOU, GELDER TELLS LICENSEES; BEER INDUSTRY GAINS FAVOR, SAYS JURIST; TAVERN MEN TO HAVE ROLE IN NEW PROGRAM; WHISKY BOOTLEGGING TO THRIVE IF CERTAIN RESTRICTIONS ARE LIFTED; BIG SIX-FOOTER MUTE EVIDENCE FOR DEALER (that's the person who was 6 feet tall and got a drink, but in fact he was a minor, and the tavernkeeper went to jail and they played that up).

In summing up the attitude and the propaganda of the Wet forces, we come to the inevitable conclusion that it is defensive. They are threatening the industry with prohibition and local option. It strikes a balance of tones from hope-for-victory to fear-of-defeat. The same thing is true, however, of the Dry people. The identical technique of propaganda is used by both sides. The attitude of the Wets at the present time is defensive, but it is of a type that is acceptable and not repulsive to the 66 million people in the bleachers.

The Accessible Audience

A great deal of money is spent on Wet propaganda. But I do not think that this accounts for its success. It is more likely that it succeeds because of the constituent composition of the audience. The audience is already 66 per cent accessible. On the other side—the Dry side—only 34 per cent are readily accessible. It simply resolves itself into the fact that it is good business for the liquor industry to spend enormous sums for the purpose of keeping 66 per cent convinced of what they already are inclined to believe. The Drys have a task that cannot be achieved by the expenditure of money alone. If they would lower their sights and compromise on moderation instead of all-out total abstinence, their propaganda would immediately be more acceptable to the 66 per cent and they would compete with the Wets on a more equal footing. Please remember, I am not advocating this, or in fact anything else. I am simply telling you what I think would happen if they did a certain thing. I might add, too, that they will never get to first base with the grandstand until they do so.

I have heard the statement made many times (and I want to remark upon that) that this Wet advertising influences the editorial attitude of newspapers. It may do so with a few newspapers, very small papers, but it's difficult to believe that it influences the large newspapers. The large newspapers are responsive to the sentiments of the 66 per cent who, while neutral, are more accessible to the Wet propaganda than they are to the Dry. The *History of Prohibition* is a document published by the *Brooklyn Daily Eagle*. It contains some 600 editorials printed between 1914 and 1933. It is very well worth examining as a reflection of the average attitude of the urban, metropolitan public. Curious to know just how much liquor advertising the *Brooklyn Daily Eagle* published, I wrote the publisher and received a letter from him in which he said that less than 1 per cent of their advertising is liquor advertising. I have sat in the editorial chair of a newspaper myself and have also been concerned with the business department of various periodicals, and I am acquainted with a large number of publishers and editors. I cannot be convinced that 1 per cent of the advertising is going to influence any publication. I believe that the *Brooklyn Daily Eagle's* attitude is reflective of that of its editors and readers and that it is honest and above suspicion.

DRY PROPAGANDA

Now if we turn to the Dry propaganda we find a different situation. I don't want to be too critical, but here are headlines from a publication called the *American Issue*, the subtitle of which is, "An Advocate of Christian Patriotism." Well, frankly, the *American Issue* is an advocate of total abstinence and I wish they would say so; because were they to say so, it would be more acceptable to these people in the bleachers when they learn that prohibition, and not patriotism, is in fact the principal purpose of this publication. If they will excuse me for saying so, it is misleading and therefore not quite honest. They have headlines: THE GREATEST OF HOMEWRECKERS; WHEN JOHN BARLEYCORN CARRIES THE PISTOL. Now the men in the bleachers are going to regard such headlines as not typical. They are going to be unmoved, unconvinced. I am quoting now from the *Gospel of Temperance Work*, issued by the American Temperance Society in Washington, just a sentence, "Among the victims of want and sin are found those who were once in possession of wealth . . ." and the old story of the descent into poverty and woe caused by alcohol. This is no doubt true in many instances. The men in the bleachers look at that and then take a squint at the 50 million people who use alcohol in this country. They neither have a pistol in their hands—all of them—nor are they all clothed in rags, these 50 million users of alcohol. The picture will in large part be rejected. The men in the bleachers may remember the story of the two men who were looking up at a tall building in New York. One of them said to the other, "Do you admire that building?"—"Yes, I do."—"By the way, I notice that you smoke." "Yes, I smoke."—"How many cigars do you smoke a day?"—"I smoke 10 cigars a day."—"What's it cost you?"—"Cost me 25 cents apiece."

—"Well, now, that's about $900 a year, and I think maybe you take a drink, don't you?"—"Yes, I take about 10 drinks a day."—"What do they cost you?"—"About 25 cents apiece."—"I think you chew tobacco, too, don't you?"—"Yes." He added it all up and he said, "Now, you're spending about $2,000 a year. In 20 years that $2,000 at compound interest, together with the additional money that you would have made if you had been abstemious in all these things, would have totaled enough so you might own that building over there."—And the man turned to him and he said, "Do you smoke?"—"No." —"Do you drink?"—"No."—"Do you own that building?"—"No."— "Well," said the other man, "I *do!*"

I am quoting from the *A.T.A. Bulletin* in Alabama. "Famous total abstainers—Abraham Lincoln, Robert E. Lee, William Jennings Bryan, John J. Pershing, Sergeant Alvin York, Josephus Daniels, Cordell Hull, Douglas MacArthur, Colin Kelly," and a lot more. And of course the author should have gone on and said that among the others who were totally abstinent were Al Capone, Mayor Hague, Mohammed, Adolph Hitler and Benito Mussolini. Check! Counter-check. For each argument on one side, there is a good one on the other.

I must hurry through these examples that I have culled. Here is the *Union Signal;* the subtitle is "A Journal of Social Welfare." Well, again, we must think that this subtitle might be more acceptable to the people in the grandstand if it said what it frankly is, or said frankly what it really is, a journal advocating total abstinence. I will not quibble with the word "Temperance" in the name of the Woman's Christian Temperance Union. It has been there too long. Webster does give "abstinence" as one of the subordinated meanings of the word "temperance," but "temperance" in its primary meaning means moderation, not abstinence. And the Woman's Christian Temperance Union is not for moderation. But established names cannot be changed easily, and the word "temperance" has been so identified with the idea of total abstinence in the name of the W.C.T.U. that changing it should not even be suggested. Headlines like these show their attitude: STAMPEDE FOR HOLIDAY LIQUOR; LIQUOR STILL HIDDEN IN CHURCH BELFRY; NURSE SHOOTS PATIENT AFTER DRINKING; DRINK TURNS PATROLMAN INTO MURDERER; PARALYTIC STRUCK BY DRUNK DRIVER; LIQUOR AND BAD COMPANY LEAD TO JAIL; DRUNKEN BOYS LED TO JAIL. These headlines are not addressed to people in the bleachers. They are addressed to people in their own group, the players on their side. It is difficult, in fact, to find anything in the *Union Signal* which is addressed to anybody but the members of the Woman's Christian Temperance Union. And that is all right. I am not critical of that in the sense that there is anything wrong about it. I am simply appraising the situation and indicating that these attitudes are not doing anything to the people in the bleachers who, *I* think, are the ones that we must do something about before we can make any progress in this subject. The Wets reach them. Why should not the Drys make the attempt? One excellent pamphlet of the W.C.T.U. is *Learning to Choose*. It is about sobriety and good citizenship. *Learning to Choose*—that is casual, that is objective. We do not find here an intensity of zeal or excess of emotional, purposeful, resistance-creating aggression. The trouble with aggressiveness is that it creates a reaction of opposition and that, in turn, results in frustration which breeds more aggression. As I shall try to show shortly, my concept of a program for propaganda on the subject of alcohol is an indirect one—one that is not aggressive, and one that could be acceptable to the 66 million people in the grandstand.

Another excellent article in the *Union Signal* is "Carriers of Alcoholism." Now that is suggestive—"Carriers of Alcoholism." The cover of the January 8, 1943, issue carried an excellent statement which gets over to the people in the bleachers—KEEP SOBER WAS SAFETY WARNING—with a quotation from the Greater Chicago Safety Council: "First, if you drink, don't drive, or vice versa. Second, if you ride with someone else, be sure the driver of the car is on the wagon." That is acceptable to the people in the bleachers. They reproduce a graph here, of absenteeism, credited to the *West Virginia Issue*, showing a Monday peak. That is very significant, and that is effective with the 66 million people in the bleachers. The presentation, so far as this publication is concerned, shows that most of its content is directed to people within the group. They are talking principally to each other.

The Art of Appeal

I am not going to take up the education courses of the W.C.T.U., because I am not competent to judge them, and inasmuch as they are largely addressed to youth they fall into a realm which is outside my province. I can, however, point out a rather interesting thing. In the Syllabus of the W.C.T.U. we have a statement that "a poison is anything which, absorbed into the blood, interferes with the proper operation of any of the organs of the body." (P. 17, 7th edition, Syllabus.) The last paragraph states: "The nature of a poison is not changed by the (small or large) amount taken, nor is the action changed in kind. The difference is only in degree." That, I think, has been corrected because I note in the *Union Signal* of January 1, 1944, an editorial entitled, "Caution in the Use of Scientific Terms." It says:

Not infrequently one sees alcoholic beverages referred to as a poison and so they are once it is understood that the word poison is given several definitions by the dictionary but that it is particularly necessary to guard one's speech when referring to alcohol in conversation with children. At home and at school they are taught that poison must be left entirely alone on penalty of immediate illness or even death. If they hear alcoholic beverages referred to as poison, and yet see people use them without apparent harm, the children may come to disregard the word "poison" when it is applied to other substances whose effects are more immediate.

That is excellent!

This type of propaganda, shown by the picture on the front page of a pamphlet, *The Shadow of the Bottle*, is wholly ineffectual with the 66 per cent in the bleachers. The calling of alcohol a poison is ineffectual with them. They will not accept it; they reject it because they drink and see people drinking without poisonous effects.

I did not mention some of the advertising of the Conference of Alcoholic Beverage Industries—the Old Judge cartoons, "The Old Judge Says." The

American Businessmen's Research Foundation is countering with other cartoons in the same style, which are good. They are very well done, casual, and objective. I understand that they have sent out 4,000 of these mats to 400 different newspapers to counteract the effects of the "Old Judge" series, which is widely distributed.

In an analysis of the publication *The Foundation Says,* we can apply the same judgment. In large part it seems to be devoted to its own group, and with the exception of these cartoons and some other occasional content it is addressed to its own followers.

Here is a leaflet: "Who, Me?" If I were going to give a prize for propaganda, the most effective piece of propaganda that has come to my attention, "Who, Me?" issued by the Oregon Liquor Control Commission, would win it.

Are you all familiar with it? I need not read from it? "Yes, drinking is a part of social life that has existed during the whole period of recorded history." Do you hear the bleachers saying, "Yes, yes" to that? "There are people who have been moderate drinkers all their lives and have neither become drunkards nor apparently ever suffered any ill effects." The bleachers say, "Yes, yes," to that. "But every person who drinks should keep in mind that moderate drinkers may turn into excessive drinkers and that no one begins by being a drunkard but drifts into it gradually." Your man in the bleachers says, "Yes, yes," to that also. Now we are getting under his skin just a little. We get him accepting, accepting, accepting, and finally he is led to the point where he reads, "Then watch out! Do not fool yourself by thinking that no matter what the case may be with other people, you can always stop drinking whenever you want to." I won't read the rest because you can imagine what it is. Very effective!

Then we have this document, written by Dr. Strecker of the University of Pennsylvania, a psychiatrist, published by the Pennsylvania Liquor Control Board, "Are You a Social Drinker?" And this "Word of Warning" by the Michigan Liquor Control Commission at Lansing. The same type of objective, casual approach. It registers in the bleachers.

Now, I can imagine a man going to some of these people and saying, "Am I going to become an alcoholic? Is there any danger of my drinking too much?" I am told that here at the Yale Plan Clinics men come in who are moderate drinkers and say, "Is there any danger of my becoming an alcoholic?" Alcoholics Anonymous finds that a number of people come to them and say, "Any danger of my becoming an alcoholic?" I cannot imagine anyone going to the president of the local W.C.T.U. and saying, "Any danger of my becoming an alcoholic?" I point this out only to show that they really are talking only to their own group, that they have no contact with the crowd. They are taking in each other's washing. These other people are really being listened to by the 66 million people in the bleachers. They are having some effect upon them— upon their thinking and acting.

Now, you know we are told it is a manly thing to drink. The saying is, "Drink like a gentleman." Swagger around and all that, and that is part of drinking. Well, you are not going to overcome the mores by a direct attack like this pamphlet in my hand, "It's the Drinker Who's a Sissy." That just "ain't so"! Can you imagine what the bleachers would do to that if you passed it around? Talk about mobbing an umpire! And, incidentally, does it make a person a sissy or not a sissy if he drinks or doesn't drink? Why attack a fiction with another fiction? And did not our good friends, the Methodist Board of Temperance, fall into a trap when they came back and answered that? Did they not admit the cogency of the argument? Bad stuff for the bleachers, because it created a "horse-laugh" even here in this audience. And this is not the 66-million group. This is not the bleachers I am talking to. I feel I am definitely talking to two grandstands here, each of opposing convictions. There is the Yale grandstand and the Harvard, and you can pick which is Yale and which is Harvard; I would not dare do that. But even you laughed at the thought of the drinker being a sissy.

SANCTION OF THE COMMUNITY

Now to sum up the Wet and Dry propaganda. I am told by leading spirits in the Dry forces that they recognize that they cannot bring about prohibition. Their object is to castigate the industry so that it will clean up as much as possible and ameliorate some of the bad effects of alcohol. Well, now, I think almost any of us will agree that it has something of that effect. The Wet people are clever. The smartest thing they ever did was when Prohibition expired. The *New York Times* came out with a headline that Prohibition had been repealed at 2:15 p.m., and Roosevelt said, "The American public must never let the saloon return." And it didn't. The liquor people changed the name of the saloon to "tavern" right away. So the saloon has not come back and Roosevelt has kept his promise. That was the smartest thing they ever did because the intentions and connotations surrounding the "saloon" are gone, and now we have something else. You were told this morning about tavernkeeping way, way back in the year 1400 or something, and the business is now tied up with a brand new set of connotations, with history, continental discovery, the "good old days" that are so estimable and traditional.

I am not going into the mores and the customs surrounding drinking. That has been done here as a part of this course by men who are sociologists and who can present those things in a scholarly way, which I would not know how to begin to attempt to do. But in the behavior of people in the bleachers the customs and sanctions of the community are seen as matters of fact which our Dry friends do not take enough into account.

We had something happen last year in the field of thinking about alcohol when the Yale School of Alcohol Studies started. A propagandist, in testing anything, takes little symptoms of attitudes more than he relies on calculated polls. When *Time* came out and announced the Yale School of Alcohol Studies, saying at the top of the story, "Here's to good old Yale, Drink her down, Drink her down—" and when the Harvard *Crimson* said, "It is understood that Yale is starting a School of Alcohol Studies . . . significant," we have a keen reflection of the mores, of the popular attitude. Those two publications would not have spoken in this tone if it had not been acceptable to a large proportion of their readers. And the readers think this whole business of alcohol is just a row between two teams of players, two opposing teams, and they just cannot accept the possibility that into this maelstrom of crimination and recrimination has come an objective approach. But it has come, and we will find more and more, as a result of this School, an objective attitude by the public. Newspapers are reporting events which are made to happen from this objective attitude here, gradually wearing down the resistance to the thought that it must be a prohibition thing or it must be a liquor thing. The idea will gradually increase so that there can be a scientific approach disabused of any predilection on either side.

Alcoholics Anonymous has indirectly conveyed to people the idea that alcoholism is an ailment, and removed some of the moral implications, taking the subject a little way out of the praise-and-blame category so that it can be discussed with some of the stigma removed.

A FOUR-POINT PROGRAM

I am going to offer some suggestions for a program formulated in four points which I presented here last year. At present the public is quick to suspect that any education on the subject of alcohol is either Wet or Dry. They believe, the average man thinks, that there is nothing that can be done about a boozer who is perverse and refuses to listen to reason. This work at Yale and the work of Alcoholics Anonymous is breaking that thought down.

If we make our approach more indirect to the people in the bleachers by talking about the *alcoholic*, not meaning you, necessarily (saying that to the man in the bleachers), we shall not get into a head-on collision with the mores or the free intention of these people.

Here are four postulates, four objectives for such a program: First, that the problem drinker is a sick man, exceptionally reactive to alcohol; second, that he can be helped; third, that he is worth helping; fourth, that the problem is therefore the responsibility of the healing profession, as well as the established health authorities, and the public generally.

Now when the time comes that everybody in the United States has accepted the thought that the alcoholic is a sick man, that he can be helped and that he is worth helping, what's the next thing that's going to happen to all these people, of their own volition—not because some Dry organization tells them about the evils of alcohol but because they come to the conclusion themselves? Next thing they're going to think of is, Am I drinking too much? Is this friend of mine drinking too much? My lady who is giving her cocktail party on Park Avenue will *not* insist on the second or third cocktail when someone declines. She won't insist on someone taking a drink who declines in the first place, as she is likely to do now, because she will not be sure that this person isn't one who should never drink alcohol at all because he is possessed of an idiosyncrasy for it. (I leave it to Doctors Haggard and Jellinek to put that in scientific terms, but they tell us that there are certain men in whom alcohol produces an excessive reaction.) They will become a little disturbed on their own part. It will tend to make drinking less socially acceptable when it comes to be known that sickness can result. Everyone examines himself, Am I in danger? And it is effective with the grandstand because it is *not* aimed directly at them.

There is an organization being formed, not allied with any Wet or Dry organization in any way, for the purpose of education on the subject of alcohol-*ism*. It is to be called, The National Committee for Education on Alcoholism. It will have an office in the Academy of Medicine Building in New York City. Mrs. Marty Mann, who is a student here with you, is to be Executive Director. I think we are all very glad to know about this. We should all of us lay aside our differences and unite on the problem of alcohol*ism*. Through that we can open doors and move faster to greater moderation by a larger proportion of the people in the grandstand who are at last brought to accept these postulates.

We know these facts. They are simple. We do not have to worry about any-one quibbling or anyone coming back and countering them. Mr. McCracken, in one of his articles that I thought was splendid, advocated that the tavern-keeper get acquainted with Alcoholics Anonymous. When he saw a man in his place that he felt was drinking too much, to suggest that he contact Alcoholics Anonymous. That is splendid propaganda.

Everyone can agree on the need for helping the alcoholic, although not all of you may go with me as to what the effects of the acceptance by everyone of these four concepts would be.

Mark Twain said once to a group of newspaper men: Get your facts right. Be sure you have them correct. Then you can put them in whatever order you want to to make them mean anything you wish.

THE SUMMING UP

To sum up. A survey of Wet and Dry propaganda indicates that the Wet forces are doing more effectual work than the Drys. For every argument ad-vanced by one side there is a counter-assertion from the other. Both publish their statements with what appears to the bystander to be adequate evidence. This leaves the impression with the neutral person that he is witnessing a fight between two antagonists. He is confused and in large part unmoved. The superior effectiveness of Wet propaganda is not so much because more money is spent by the Wets as because they direct their propaganda at the bleachers whereas the Drys are talking to their own team. It is not my purpose to verify or to refute statements of these antagonists but to attempt to appraise their ef-fects regardless of whether they are true or false. For this reason it is necessary to understand something about how the population of the country seems to be arrayed and that, as we saw, was 50 per cent personally drinkers and 50 per cent personally abstinent. There are 34 million persons who are arrayed on the Dry side as a matter of principle, and who are accessible to Dry propaganda, leaving 66 million who are Wet or neutral as a matter of principle, and who are sitting in the bleachers. The 66 million people who are sitting in the bleachers are inaccessible to much of the Dry propaganda primarily because it makes of this question a moral issue. They are, however, accessible to Wet propaganda, which is less aggressive and therefore encounters less resistance. We know that aggression breeds resistance and results in frustration which again breeds aggres-sion. The organized Dry groups are extremely aggressive and they meet with great antagonism.

Those people sitting in the bleachers would be accessible if the approach for abstinence were made indirectly and presented not as an ostensible objective but in such a way as to cause the man in the bleachers to come to the conclusion that abstinence is desirable of his voluntary and spontaneous intention.

When the public has fully accepted the four postulates which I mentioned, what would follow would be an interest in knowing whether they or their friends might be on the way to becoming alcoholics. With the stigma of alcoholism removed by acknowledging that it is a disease, the whole subject can be brought out in the open and discussed. The door would be open wide to a new approach toward changing the mores, certainly in favor of moderation in the use of alcohol among those who wish to use it, and to total abstinence among those who do not wish to use it, not because it is wicked or harmful to them personally, or unlawful to drink, but because it is their voluntary way of life.

DISCUSSION

Chairman (E. M. Jellinek): When the curriculum was drawn up it was thought advisable to include an analysis of Wet and Dry propaganda, but there was some doubt whether such a job could be done objectively. Mr. Anderson has solved this problem perfectly. He has found an objective basis of presentation through reference to the reaction of the bleachers. He has accomplished more than objective presentation, he has also made a constructive analysis valuable to both sides.

In last year's summer session I said that the greatest fault with the alcohol propaganda literature was that the propagandists were writing for each other. The Wets and the Drys want to win new adherents through their propaganda, but they write largely for those who are already in their folds. There is a good reason for this. Neither the Wets nor the Drys present here take any exception to my colleagues and myself talking about these matters as we do. But none of the Wets and Drys would adopt our way of discussing these matters, because of the fear that they might be branded as heretics by their own groups. But there might be a way of overcoming that danger by showing their friends how the bleachers react to their propaganda, just as Mr. Anderson has shown you. Mr. Anderson, representatives of the W.C.T.U. said that your presentation gave the impression that "The Battle of the Bottle" was a W.C.T.U. production. They disclaim authorship of this leaflet.

Lecturer: It was published by the Review and Herald Publishing Co. of Takoma Park, Washington, D.C. However, that type of thing prevails in the W.C.T.U.'s *Union Signal.* I also neglected to call to your attention the objective pamphlets written by Harry S. Warner. They are splendid. In my opinion, it is the best material on the whole that is appearing on the Dry side. It is fully acceptable to the people in the bleachers.

Mrs. Sherbine: I would like to make just a comment. You mentioned the pamphlet "A Syllabus of Alcohol Education" by Bertha Rachel Palmer. That pamphlet is designed especially for teachers and would not reach the students in the classroom. Therefore, it seems to me that the comment which you made on the statement relative to poison would not be applicable for the reason that it is especially for teachers and would not be used directly by the students.

Lecturer: Well, are the teachers expected to keep it confidential?

Mrs. Colvin: No, but may I answer that? That admonition about the word and the definition is given especially so that the teacher may properly interpret the word to the student and that there shall be no confusion on the part of the student in his thinking.

Davies: The state of Oregon has attempted to ban certain types of liquor advertising having to do with home, church, religious holidays and certain prestige factors such as coats of arms. Do you advise that such a law be put into effect in the states as much as possible? Would it do more harm than good?

Chairman: Please, do not ask Mr. Anderson whether he would advise this or that. But you may ask him what effect he would expect from such legislation.

Lecturer: Well, after all, we come at last in all public relations work to a very simple formula. That is common honesty. Now, there are evils in the liquor traffic. There are statements about liquor which are not true and if the liquor people are not smart enough *not* to make them, somebody had better come along and help them, because the man in the bleachers is an unerring discerner of honesty. The public will know whether the statements made in liquor advertising are compatible with the facts as everybody concededly knows them to be; if they violate these too much, they themselves will be the principal sufferers. The people in the grandstand will reject them. No law except the law of common sense is needed here. I think that covers your point, as well as *I* can, anyway.

Mrs. Colvin: I would like to call attention to the fact that in the leaflet which we all cheered, "Who, Me?" by the Oregon Board, the picture on the back was taken from a poster which the Methodist Temperance Board has used for several years.

Kilgore: You did not mention the role the motion picture industry seems to be playing in Wet propaganda. Are uncalled-for drinking scenes in movies part of any organized effort of the liquor industry? In your opinion, what is the effectiveness of such propaganda, if it is propaganda, or even if it is unconscious propaganda and not deliberate?

Lecturer: I have no knowledge whatever as to whether or not the motion picture people are receiving any perquisite from the liquor industry. I believe that the industry would be foolish to pay for what it can get for nothing. Motion pictures reproduce a certain stratum of American life today, and in that stratum, drinking is as much a part of the mores as eating dinner. A cocktail is taken before dinner in countless homes of perfectly respectable people in the larger communities, and a motion picture which didn't have drinking scenes in it would not reflect life as it is today. He who says differently walls himself off from life and goes with his own kind and talks with nobody but those who agree with him. He is not likely to be helpful in any solution of this problem because liquor is here and is used everywhere one goes. Like it or not, the fact remains that the motion pictures reflect conditions as they are.

Mrs. Sherbine: Mr. Anderson, you said you were not an educator and yet you wanted to evaluate an educational book.

Lecturer: I didn't evaluate the "Syllabus" of the W.C.T.U. I picked out two things there and made statements regarding their effects upon the bleachers, and practically asked the ladies of the W.C.T.U. that they make up their minds regarding the poison statement, because in the Syllabus they say one thing and in the editorial in the *Union Signal* they say something else.

Chairman: Both the statement from the Syllabus and that of the editorial emanated from the W.C.T.U. and they are not in agreement.

Lecturer: That's right. Now the men in the bleachers would want you to make up your mind on that and I don't think they will accept a statement of such common knowledge as to say of carbolic acid that an ounce of a solution containing one part in five million of carbolic acid is poisonous. I don't believe that they will accept it. I believe that they will accept the other statement, more probably, and I'm simply analyzing that and what its effect will be as appearing to be true or false. As I said before, I'm not interested in the absolute truth or falsity of it but only in what the reaction of people to its apparent truth or falsity would be. The statement that alcohol is a poison is not acceptable to the people in the bleachers. They won't believe it. The statement is acceptable only to the W.C.T.U. group and others of like opinion and sentiment.

Vredevoe: Are there any age limits to those in the bleachers?
Lecturer: Over 15. They're over 15 years, they're all of drinking age.

Hawes: If the Dry team wishes to reach the bleachers' 66 million, will they not have to use newspaper and magazine advertising instead of their own group publications?
Lecturer: No. I don't think so. I think the greatest publicity force in the world is word-of-mouth—get people talking. Change in attitude of the Dry forces is the thing that is needed and then that will be disseminated and permeate all the Dry activities and will ultimately reach the bleachers.

McCracken: For the record, I would like to make a minor correction. Apparently, I failed to make myself clear to Mr. Anderson about one part of the work of the Conference of Alcoholic Beverage Industries. We do publish a community recreation bulletin but this bulletin is not circulated among tavernkeepers and we do not urge tavernkeepers to take the lead in establishing recreation centers. In fact, we definitely urge them not to take the lead but to offer their assistance where their assistance is asked. The reason we publish this bulletin is that our field studies and the field studies of the Michigan Liquor Control Commission established a definite relationship between drinking by minors and adequate recreation facilities. As a result of those studies we visited the Federal Recreation Commission and some of the state recreation commissions and asked them if there was any way in which we could help. They advised that we publish this bulletin. I just want to offer this by way of explanation. I appreciate the fine remarks that Mr. Anderson has made about other parts of our work.
Chairman: At a meeting of a group of ministers where I spoke about the alcohol problem, a minister showed the bulletin which you mentioned, Mr. McCracken, and read paragraphs from it. He said, "On what grounds does the C.A.B.I. claim to be an advisor to communities on recreational matters?" But then he added, "But if we ministers don't do anything about them, then we'll just have to see the advice coming from the alcoholic beverage industry."

Hoover: The liquor interests are using the radio. In your opinion, Mr. Anderson, what will be the cumulative effect on the children's or young people's (part of the bleachers) attitude toward alcohol, especially when it says, "Taste the delightful, delicious, refreshing goodness of Blank's beer"?
Lecturer: I think we often overlook one thing in thinking about propaganda. First, the propaganda may make an emotional impression on you if you disagree with it, but it may make little if you are not interested one way or the other. Second, everybody doesn't believe everything they read and hear. Some people do their own thinking. We teach, let us say, total abstinence to our children. As a means of getting them "fixed" against liquor we teach them, perhaps, that people worthy to be emulated do not drink. Then they get out in the community and they find something different. They get in with the Jones boys around the corner and they go home with them and find that the refrigerator has beer in it, and Johnny says to Bill, "You've got poison in your refrigerator!" So Bill says to his Mamma, "Johnny says we've got poison in our refrigerator." And then the parents don't speak to each other. Now, early in life, we come in contact with our environment and I think it's wise to make only such statements as will bear

scrutiny when the child grows old enough to come out from our protection and make up its mind for itself. The same thing goes the other way around. You hear over the radio certain statements about a certain beer. Parents also make statements; friends make statements; the child observes what goes on about it. All of these forces exert an influence. The statement made over the radio is only one of many influences. Consequently the statement on the radio does not have, on impressionable but unbiased minds which are supposed to believe every word that is said, anywhere near the effect that it is supposed to have by those to whom the statement is a challenge to establish belief. I can't help but think that any of us is inclined to overestimate the efficacy of the propaganda of our antagonists. This propaganda has some effect, yes; but a decisive effect, no. All the influences brought to bear are going to build up to the final belief that the child has one way or the other on this or any other subject.

Lecture 24

Penal Handling of Inebriates

A Panel Discussion

Hon. William M. Maltbie, Ralph S. Banay and Selden D. Bacon

Maltbie: I do not propose to try to tell you today what I think the courts should do in dealing with the alcoholic. I shall use a matter-of-fact approach in an effort to describe what the attitude of the law and the courts is today toward drunkenness, and if I comment on some of its weaknesses, I am sure that I shall strike a responsive note in the hearts of at least some of you. I want to say this, though, at the very beginning: One of the most dangerous things about which to generalize is the administration of criminal law. A thing which may be true of one state, even true of most states, may be wholly untrue as regards the particular state with which you are concerned. Each state, as you know, has its own laws, its own methods, and its own institutions. Therefore, any attempt to state generally the attitudes and the methods of the courts toward any crime is fraught with danger. So please remember that caution. When I generalize, I do it in full consciousness that what I say may be wholly inapplicable to any particular state.

Crime is a rather variable standard. What is a crime in one age may be a virtue in another. Perhaps we have gone rather the other way—what may have been a virtue in one age may have become a crime in another. I think it is well, in considering drunkenness from the standpoint of the courts dealing with it, to see just wherein it constitutes a crime.

Speaking very generally, you can define a crime as some act, or omission, which is so fraught with danger to the well-being of society, that society itself, in the form of the state, assumes to attempt to curb it by inflicting punishment. There are a great many civil wrongs, as you know, for which the only curb applied by society is the right granted to the individual who is wronged to take into his own hands the matter of securing recompense. But a crime is of such moment to the well-being of the state that the state itself assumes to punish it.

A very high authority says that drunkenness, as such, was not a crime under the old common law, that is, under that law which never took the form of statutes but which was the thoughts and feelings of sober-minded citizens finally pronounced in some judicial decision. However, as early as 1606, in the time of James I, in the England of the Puritans, Parliament enacted a general law concerning drunkenness. And I think it is of sufficient interest so that I might read a part of it to you:

Whereas the loathsome and odious Sin of Drunkenness is of late grown into common Use within this Realm, being the Root and Foundation of many other enormous Sins, as Bloodshed, Stabbing, Murder, Swearing, Fornication, Adultery, and such like, to the great Dishonour of God, and of our Nation, the Overthrow of many good Arts and manual Trades, the Disabling of Divers Workmen, and the general Impoverishing of many good Subjects, abusively wasting the good Creatures of God. . . .

It then continues by enacting that anyone convicted of being drunk should be fined 5 shillings, and if the fine was not paid and could not be collected from his goods, then the offender was committed to the stocks for a period of 6 hours. Blackstone comments, and it has its point today, that the period of 6 hours was that which presumably would be necessary to restore the drunken man to his proper senses.

With that statute in effect in England in 1606, of course, it was not remarkable that the Puritans who settled in Massachusetts Bay should bring over a like notion. And as early as 1645, in an act which regulated inns, they provided that any person who might be found drunk, either in the inn or elsewhere, should be fined, and they provided additional heavier penalties according as the offenses became more numerous, including whipping, the stocks, and imprisonment. In preparing the code of 1650 in Connecticut, Roger Ludlow borrowed very largely from the statutes of Massachusetts. It is not surprising, therefore, that it became the law of Connecticut that any person found drunk should be subject to punishment. But Roger Ludlow was a very able lawyer and he foresaw that the courts would have difficulty, as they have had ever since, in attempting to determine just what constitutes drunkenness. So, in his law, he said that a drunken man was one "who shall be bereaved, or disabled, in the use of his understanding, appearing in speech or gesture." Now, you might expect laws of that nature in Puritan New England. But I was rather interested, in turning to the early laws of Virginia, as exemplifying colonists of another type, to find that as early as 1632 Virginia had a law which provided that every person "who shall be drunk shall be punished by a fine of five shillings to be paid to the church wardens." That was quite a common provision in those early laws—the fine went to the church wardens. Ever since then, and today in this country as a whole, either by statute or by ordinance, there are penalties for those who get drunk. I believe it can be said, however, that in most instances they are incurred only for drunkenness in public, drunkenness in public places, or drunkenness accompanied by acts of a disorderly nature. Mere drunkenness, as such, is penalized only in a few states, and even where the law is capable of that broad extension, as a practical matter it is not enforced against one who keeps his drunkenness private.

Generally speaking, I think it may be said that throughout this country, by law or ordinance, a person who shows himself to be intoxicated in a public place, particularly if in addition to that there is disorder, is subject to arrest and presentation in court for punishment. We can start, then, with the fact that practically everywhere in this country drunkenness of that character is a crime and is subject to punishment. And, after all, when you come to think about it, it is a perfectly rational position for the state to take. It is perfectly true, as those old parliamentarians back in the time of James I said, that drunkenness is the source of a great many other evils. Not only that, but our legislatures can very well say that the mere sight of a drunken man staggering down the street is an offense to decency and good order. There is a very rational basis, then, for approaching intoxication, at least where it is in public, as a crime, and for dealing with it as a crime.

Having gotten that far, the next question is: Drunkenness being a crime, how do the courts attempt to deal with it? Let me again go back to fundamentals. Throughout the ages various rationalizations have been placed back of the infliction of punishment for crime by the state, but I think that today, at least, we have reached a basis of straight thinking where we admit that there are only three reasons for the attempt of the state to punish any crime: 1. Deterrence—deterring the man from committing further offenses and deterring others from committing like offenses. 2. Segregation, that is, the placing of a man apart from his fellows so that he cannot, if he would, further impair their well-being. 3. Reformation, that is, producing a change in the individual so that his outlook on life, his sense of responsibility to his fellows, his regard for his own place in society, takes on a different aspect, and instead of being an Ishmael he becomes again a valuable and useful member of society. All attempts to deal with crime, no matter how serious it is, in the courts must be tested by the application of the questions: Is it justified in view of the deterrence which it may bring about? Is it justified in view of segregating an individual from his fellows? Is it justified in that it holds out some hope of rehabilitation or reformation?

To serve those purposes, the laws in the courts have really but four tools. They can impose fines. They can inflict a sentence of imprisonment—confinement. They can use either one of two modern methods which have grown up within the last few years—probation or parole. There is another method, which has been somewhat approved in other countries and which has its counterpart in very recent Massachusetts law, but which is extralegal for most of the country. This is the process by which a man who is found intoxicated in the street is brought into a place of confinement and held until he is sober, and then let go without ever being presented in the court. That is a practical way of dealing with intoxication which works on some occasions but which is really extralegal, and I do not propose to dwell on it except as I may mention it in connection with the Massachusetts law.

Now let us take up those various methods of dealing with crime with relation to this particular offense of intoxication and test them a little by the recognized objects of the infliction of punishment. Let us take the fine. I do not think any of us, if we stop to think of it, would very seriously consider that the imposition of a fine of $5, $10, or $15, and it rarely goes above that, upon a man who is found intoxicated, accomplishes any purpose whatsoever. As is usually the case a sentence of imprisonment exists as an alternative to the payment of the fine. Sometimes a man is put on probation to give him a chance to pay the fine. This probation perhaps keeps him from offending for a short time and so there may be some slight gain. But the difficulty with the fine is that it is, shall I say, so undemocratic. As applied to the well-to-do man it means practically nothing. As applied to the poor fellow who is without means, at best it probably means hardship to him and to those who are dependent on him, and, at worst, it will culminate only in imprisonment. I do not think there is today any defense or defenders of the infliction of fines upon persons who are intoxicated as a practical method of attempting to arrive at any curbing of the evil.

Theoretically, confinement or imprisonment is capable of serving all the legitimate ends of punishment: Deterrence, in depriving a man of his liberty; segregation, in putting him apart from his fellows and under close confinement and supervision; and rehabilitation or reformation or both. I think that if the question of whether a sentence of imprisonment does really act as a deterrent were put to almost anyone having practical experience in dealing with intoxication in the courts, he might truly answer, "No." There are many reasons for that. One is that the offense, from the standpoint of moral character or immoral character, does not deserve a long period of confinement and consequently the periods are short—5, 10, 20 or 60 days—rarely more than that, and this does not greatly deter the type of man who is presented in court for intoxication. Another and deeper reason is that the motivating causes of drunkenness, as a rule, are such that the psychological influence of imprisonment does not accomplish very much in the way of deterrence.

Since the punishment inflicted on the common drunkard, if it is not a fine, is a very short term of imprisonment, this necessarily means that he will be held in the county jail, the city jail, or the lock-up. That is the only provision made in most states for the detention of persons who have committed an offense of this nature. Therefore, in considering imprisonment and its effect upon drunkenness, it is necessary to evaluate the jail as a means for the reformation of the offender. Segregation does not play any part in this case because the man is not kept in prison long enough to be considered segregated in any way. So I am not paying any attention to that. But from the standpoint of reformation or rehabilitation, which after all is the goal toward which, in the administration of criminal law, we are more and more rightfully tending, and in an evaluation of imprisonment for the drunkard as a means of rehabilitation or reformation, you have to look at the jail and see what kind of an institution it is.

I refer to the report of the National Commission on Law Observance and Enforcement. Some of you may remember that commission under the chairmanship of that very able and distinguished lawyer, George W. Wickersham. I have taken one of its reports, made in 1931, and I quote from it the description of the jails of this country as they were seen by a foreign observer. He said:

There are no words to describe the almost-medieval conditions in the county jails. Usually no distinction is made between those who have been sentenced and those who are awaiting trial and who perhaps are innocent of any offense. There is no provision for giving the prisoners adequate work or exercise in the open air. In matters of light and air, sanitary and hygienic conditions, the cells can, without exaggeration, be compared to stalls for animals and at that to the neglected stalls that might have been found in country districts at least half a century ago. Furthermore, in many cities the jails are as a regular thing obliged to receive double and triple the number of inmates that they were built to accommodate.

Is that a place of reformation for the offender? That was in 1931. I presume that since then the conditions of the jails have somewhat improved; I hope they have the country over. But I venture to say that today in this country, by and large, that description is accurate. You will recall that I said in the beginning that one cannot generalize about this, and here I want to enter a caveat as regards the jails of the State of Connecticut. We do still have our medieval institutions. The buildings are mostly a hundred years old or more. But there has been a very definite improvement in the jail conditions since 1931, an improvement—and I commend this to your consideration—which has been almost wholly due to the fact that the men who are now in charge of them have taken a different attitude toward those who are placed in their care. They really are interested in their welfare, in doing what they can for them, and in bettering the conditions under which they are confined. But I venture to say that, the country over, there are not many places of which that can be said.

Now, of course, there are the other two means about which I have spoken— probation and parole. Because some of you may not be familiar with these two methods, may I take just a moment to tell you what they are and to distinguish between them, for I think we tend to bulk them together. Probation is an instrument of the court. A man comes into court, sometimes while he is awaiting trial, and instead of sending him to prison he is placed in the charge of a probation officer under such conditions as the court sees fit to impose regarding the way in which he shall conduct himself. The sanction back of that lies in the fact that, should he violate those conditions, he can then be brought into court and the sentence of imprisonment imposed. It is a means by which a man is permitted to go at large among his fellows, yet with the strong arm of the law always over him, ready to bring him back if he misbehaves.

Parole, on the other hand, is an instrument of the administration of the prison. Of course, in some instances it is administered by a separate board, but it only applies where a man has served a part of his sentence, and he is then permitted to go at large under the supervision of a parole officer for the balance of the term.

Probation is an instrument of the administration of law in the courts; parole is an instrument of the administration of the penal institution.

In the case of drunkenness, parole plays practically no part because very few states, if any, have laws permitting parole of those who are convicted of intoxication and very few states, if any, have parole systems connected with their jails. Probation, however, does afford a very fine instrument for dealing with certain aspects of the problem of the intoxicated person in court. It is extremely flexible in that the court may place the man under such conditions as it sees fit when it gives him over into the charge of the probation officer. To take an instance: Suppose a man is brought in for intoxication and the court thinks he ought to go to the Yale Plan Clinic for observation and treatment. The court can impose a sentence of 30 days in jail, suspended on condition that he go to the Clinic for observation and that he take any treatment which they prescribe. Also, probation renders a very useful and increasing service in that cases may be referred to the probation officer for investigation before sentence. Probation is a very fine means of dealing with the intoxicated person, but it labors, this country over, under the very great handicap of the fact that most of the courts in our country do not have adequate staffs of competent probation officers to perform the type of work which they could and would like to do. That is one of the problems confronting the social worker today this country over—the building up of a better probation staff in connection with our police courts.

I should like to call your attention to the statutes in two states because they represent about the farthest that legislation has gone in attempting to deal, in the courts, with intoxication as a crime—the laws of Massachusetts and New York. I do this because I think they show the possibilities of the use of judicial machinery as an aid to any method of dealing with intoxicated persons.

First, take Massachusetts. I want to say that the Massachusetts statutes are not crystal clear, and I would have been much happier if I could have checked what I have to say with a person familiar with their practical operation. So I speak subject to correction. This is the gist of the statutes. Any person who is found in a state of intoxication in a public place, or found in any place committing a breach of the peace or disturbing others by noise, may be arrested by any police officer and held in custody, in a suitable place (not, you see, in jail), until he has recovered from his intoxication. That is the first step. When he gets there and is sobered up, the officer in charge must inform him that he has the right to make a written statement of his name, his address, his means of employment, the persons who are dependent upon him, if any, and his record of convictions for intoxication over the past year. If there is a probation officer connected with the court, that statement would go to him and it is then his duty to investigate. If not, then the man in charge of the place of detention is supposed to investigate and report. Next morning, or as soon as the court is in session, report is made of the case. I should have said that after the man has made this statement he is ordinarily permitted to go at large, provided the person in charge of the place of detention feels that he will respond if summoned into court; or, if there is a probation officer, upon direction to him. At the next session of the court a report of the case is made. If the magistrate is satisfied that everything that can be done has been done simply by holding this man until he sobered up, nothing is done except that a record is made of the case. If, however, the man has been convicted at least four times within the preceding 12 months, he must appear in court. If the magistrate feels that something should be done besides making a record of the case, or if the man has been convicted at least four times within the last 12 months, he is summoned into court. Then the court has several alternatives. It may send him to jail for not more than 1 year. Or, it may commit him to any place provided by law for common drunkards. If the offender is a man, it may send him to the Massachusetts Reformatory; or if a woman, to the Reformatory for Women. Or the court may impose a fine of not more than $15, or it may place the prisoner on probation and prescribe the terms thereof.

You see the great flexibility of that provision. The court can do almost anything it thinks wise with a prisoner, from letting him go to sending him to the Reformatory.

In New York the Inferior Criminal Courts Act contains some rather elaborate provisions concerning the offense of public intoxication. If the offender is a woman, the court may commit her to any one of a number of semiprivate institutions—for instance, the House of the Good Shepherd; or it may send her to the State Farm for Women. A male offender may be sent to the Men's Reformatory. Whether male or female, they may be committed to a workhouse or jail for a definite time of not more than 6 months. A fine may be imposed. In connection with that, there is provision for letting the offender go at liberty under probation so that he need not be confined if he has not the cash in his pocket at the immediate time. There is a very interesting additional provision which represents about the furthest the courts have gone in the attempt to deal with drunkenness if it is an offense. The law provides that upon the appointment of a board of inebriety in New York City, and upon its certificate that its hospital and industrial colony is ready to receive inmates, the complaint against the offender, as in Massachusetts, may be dismissed, and the court may place him in charge of an agent of the board upon such conditions as it may see fit to impose, violation of which would mean that he would be subject to one of the other penalties. You see, he is even taken out of the charge of the ordinary probation officer and placed in charge of an agent whose special function it is to deal with this particular social evil. He may be fined, with a provision, as in Massachusetts, whereby he may be permitted to go at liberty to obtain the money to pay the fine. A second offender may be committed on an indeterminate sentence of 6 months to 3 years. And, finally, he may be sent to a workhouse for a period of not less than 1 and not more than 3 years.

The point of my calling particular attention to those laws is this: There really is nothing in the mechanics of the judicial administration dealing with drunkenness as a crime which does not permit flexibility, so that almost any disposition can be made of the man for which the society, the state, will afford means. What is *not* necessary, is reform of the courts, or the judicial administration. What *is* necessary is that the existing machinery should be equipped with the tools to accomplish its purpose. In other words, what you need to have, if the courts are to approach this problem measurably is not reform of the judiciary machinery but the establishment of some methods of treatment, some method of diagnosis like the Yale Plan Clinics, or some institutions particularly adapted to the care of the inebriate. You have the machinery. What you lack is the tools.

Banay: Medicine and law have many common points of contact, inasmuch as the subject, the aim and the function of both professions are the conduct and behavior of human beings. It is a privilege for a physician to listen to the presentation of a distinguished scholar and authority on the subject of the law because the law is the crystallized expression of the attitude of the man on the street— the expression of the thought and feeling of society toward the offender. And the legalistic viewpoint up to these days still holds that drunkenness is a crime. It is a defensive reaction on the part of society. As Chief Justice Maltbie explained, drunkenness is a very great risk and a very great hazard to the property and the individual well-being of the members of the social group.

In order to lessen the risk, we devise methods of controlling this offense. The aim of medicine is exactly the same, but we study the methods of the law with these thoughts in mind. Are they sufficiently strong and sufficiently efficient, and do they really fulfill the aims of the community for which the laws were devised and are enforced?

As you know, the legal aim is primarily a correctional one and starts out with the viewpoint that the individual is completely responsible for his act or for his behavior. The question is: Is this attitude nowadays, in view of certain advancements in the natural sciences and medicine, still adequate? Can we still function defensively on a level of rational behavior, or do we commit an injustice to the individual when we suppose that his act was a responsible act, a premeditated act, or an act over which he has complete control?

I had the opportunity a few days ago to present here the medical concept that a large proportion of problem drinkers are sick men. I do not mean to imply that all drunkards are sick, but the real problem drinkers are individuals with serious personality deviations, serious mental problems, and a serious degree of compulsion over which they have very little control. Suppose the alcoholic is mentally deficient. Suppose he is the subject of a compulsion as much as any other neurotic who is, however, more fortunate because his symptom does not conflict with social regulations—for instance, turning the doorknob five times upon leaving his apartment. The neurotic realizes that it is unreasonable, silly, ridiculous, and still he has to proceed in this manner each time he leaves his apartment. It is a compulsive act—a primitive compulsive act. In many alcoholics we discover similar compulsions, similar obsessions which drive them to the act of drinking. In that state, when an alcoholic is drunk as the result of his compulsion, he is really no different from the individual who experiences a delirium caused by fever, a contagious disease, a physical trauma, an emotional shock, or an accident. In the latter case the individual is absolved or granted a mitigation of the full force of the law. In the case of the alcoholic, however, there is still the inclination to preserve, to a great extent, the full effect, the full severity, the full sadistic drive of the law or the machinery of legal enforcement.

Is this attitude constructive? Does this attitude bring the result we are aiming at? Apparently not. Take the common drunkard, a man who breaks the peace, who is a nuisance on the street, is picked up by the police, arrested, placed in jail for a few days until he sobers up. We find that within a few hours, sometimes within 1 hour of his release, he is returned to the jail in a glorious state of drunkenness. If we scan the police records we find that a very large number of men have been arrested from 30 to 200 times for drunkenness, and some of them once or twice also for some petty offense. That is, we have a large group of people who do not commit crimes but who behave offensively. Arrest is apparently not an effective treatment in the adjustment of this individual.

Jailing is intended to be a treatment of the inebriate habit. It is a treatment in which time alone is supposed to do the trick, and a very short time at that. It is not within reason to expect that a habit, or a disease, or a neurosis, so deeply rooted, should be adjusted by the passage of a few hours or days of isolation without any constructive element entering into the procedure. So much for the common drunkard who populates the jails. And now let us look at the prisons, inhabited by criminal offenders who may be confined there for many years. And many of these criminals are alcoholics. These criminal offenders are segregated from the rest of society. They are not a menace at the moment; but 98 per cent of all offenders will eventually regain their freedom. Let us reexamine at what stage of hazard the individual will be at the time of his release from a state prison.

We all realize that there have been considerable improvements in hygiene, in administration, in the physical set up and in the quality of food in the prison system. But this, in itself, is still based on the utmost restriction of individual free-dom; not just the freedom of movement, but the freedom of privacy and the freedom of expression. All these things constitute a very serious deprivation to the individual which will activate an extremely hostile and undesirable attitude in the man at the time of his release from prison. I know of criminal inebriates who were confined to state institutions for as long as 30 years and who, upon release from prison, were in a state of profound intoxication within a few hours. If time itself would effect a cure, or a lessening of the inebriate inclination, this sort of case would not occur.

Segregation itself cannot, of course, be effective unless it is a selected segrega-tion. If we place first offenders together with habitual repeaters, the most con-firmed offenders, who are so distorted mentally that there is no possibility of expecting any correction, the final result will be that the latter will not be influ-enced by the first offenders but the reverse. The first offenders will contemplate how and where to commit their next felonious offense after leaving the prison.

In order to establish reformation or correction in a state prison, one would have to streamline the system. This would involve discarding the subtle form of sadism which is practised in prisons. I am not referring here to corporal punish-ment but to the attitude and humiliating influence of many of the forces attached to correctional institutions. To some extent the employees are themselves serving sentences—the difference between them and the prisoners is that they carry the keys—and to a great extent they are confined and resent this. In order to relieve this form of frustration they become very subtle and sadistic. It is the common experience of prison physicians, who to some extent receive the confidences of the prisoners, that the guards day after day remind their charges that it is of no use to plan what they will do on parole, for "You will be back before a week or 10 days." This and many other forms of subtle sadism hurt these individuals because they are vulnerable, because their egos are so enormous as to have led them into this predicament. Their egos will become even greater and much more likely to be bruised if you restrict their possibilities for expression and expose them to a situation where they cannot express at least adequate hostility toward the environment.

You will find that alcoholic offenders are recognized as such only when they get into conflict with their environment. The alcoholic who drinks just as much as the one who has been arrested will not be publicly stamped and stigmatized as long as he indulges at home, but as soon as he shows a degree of so-called "social incontinence" then he is regarded as a criminal.

What do we do for the people within the walls of the institutions? We have institutions which can boast of progressive methods. You will find schools, librar-ies, social workers, assignment wards, industries of all kinds to train these indi-viduals, during the time of confinement, for a decent social attitude, for self-supporting responsibility, and for the insight necessary to gain better control over their instinctual habits. These things are all very impressive on paper but when the man enters a prison his assignment will be determined primarily by what he can offer to the institution for the common welfare and not by what the institu-tion can give him for the larger good of society when he is released. Conse-quently, you will find that men who, through training, could mature emotionally and intellectually, will be assigned to subservient tasks because they are usually the short-timers. It will take anywhere from 1½ to 2 years to train a man for an occupation or trade. The foreman of the shop is aiming for production. He wants to have men who most likely will stay with him after they obtain adequate training. Consequently, you will find that most of the shops which were devised to train for social and economic competency will be filled with long-timers, if not lifers, men who have the least chance to effect a gain and to express it in their social organization outside the prison. This is just one indication of the incongruities in planning and effecting correction.

You also find that most of these advanced workshops are planned for production so as to be self-supporting. Consequently, they will stress production first and ignore the possibility of the effect of this sort of work-integration on the individual. And they will emphasize a narrow aspect of training instead of giving a broad and general training in a field which will raise the efficiency and market value of the individual upon his release. Again, you will find on a competitive scale that prisoners are poorly compensated for what they produce, perhaps a few cents a day or a few cents an hour. The individual in prison is suppressed, his emotions become frustrated, his plans are crushed; he is thrown into too close competition in a social atmosphere which is most conducive to an unhealthy pattern of living. After 2 or 3 years this individual is a complete waste to society. And if he is, in addition to his criminal trend, an alcoholic (28 per cent of them are) the waste is extremely great and the efforts of society to redeem such individuals are practically reduced to nullity. Generalizations are dangerous, but one can say that at least as far as inebriety is concerned there has been little insight into the handling of human material in many of these institutions.

I do not want to indulge in daydreams of what should be done to establish a more efficient plan of action for the redemption of alcoholic offenders, because the action starts right here. If the law is the crystallized expression of the opinion of the man on the street, then apparently we should not alter the law first, but we should first attempt to change public opinion so that it may be crystallized into more efficient, more up-to-date laws and methods of law enforcement.

In order to effect this change, one would require a tremendous amount of wisdom, a tremendous amount of benevolence, and very great fortitude, not just to overcome certain very strongly established patterns of administration and thinking but to produce profound changes in those who are responsible for the administrative staffs.

Bacon: The point I would like to bring out is directed more at the jail than at the prison. There may be many people who drink excessively, whether you would call them alcoholics or not is perhaps a fine point, who are held in the prisons; but for the problem of drunkenness, certainly the jail is very important.

What happens when the man comes into the jail? You might imagine a nice Board seated around a mahogany table saying, "What shall we do for George?" And one of the men speaks up and says, "Well, I haven't got enough men down here." The Board says, "All right we'll send him there." That may happen in a state prison, but not in the jail. There when a man comes in he is given a number and "get on your way." They may have him take a bath. From that point on, although that man may be asked to help in the kitchen, the chances are he will not do anything; and when I say not do anything, I mean almost exactly that. He may stay in his cell from breakfast until lunchtime; then he will have lunch. After that he may have an hour or an hour and a half of wandering around in the jail—that means up and down one corridor—until suppertime; then he will go back into his cell. On some days the men may get out for 2 hours, but there are no shops or work. Some of them do not get outdoors at all. There is no particular reason why they should get outdoors. That would require another guard, and where are you going to get the other guard? Well, the community is going to pay for the other guard; but just try to sell that idea to the community.

I agree with Judge Maltbie that the function of deterrence in the jail is very, very weak. One of the characteristics, which we have seen already, of the typical arrested alcoholic is that he is socially a very disintegrated person. He is an aggressive, isolated, scared, dreamy, nonfunctioning individual. In other words, he is a "bum." And what are you going to do about it? What can you hope to do about it? You can hope for social rehabilitation. But where are you going to put him for social rehabilitation? I can think of three things: You can put him in a vacuum; or you can put him in a jail; or you can put him in a social situation. He is not going to learn how to be a socialized person in a vacuum or in a jail. In a vacuum, he presumably would not learn anything. In a jail, he is going to learn, if that is possible, how to be more unsocialized than he already is.

I will just emphasize a few of the things that Dr. Banay has mentioned. First, no responsibility. This is the chronic alcoholic's, or generally drunken person's, usual state anyway. He is an irresponsible person, and in jail he can be as irresponsible as he wishes. He is a person who has very poor work habits. The jail is just perfect for him, because there is no work, and so there are no habits. He is a person who usually cannot carry his end of any social relationship; he lacks reciprocity, he lacks give and take. In the jail he does not have to do anything of this sort. He sits in his cell all day long. How is placement in this sort of environment for 10, 20, or 30 days going to teach this person how to get along with his wife, with his landlord, with his neighbor, and so on? The answer is clear; it is not going to do it at all.

One other point. It is very easy to criticize the jails, but just consider the position in which the sheriff, jailers, turnkeys, and the others are put. It is all very well for us to be humorous or to be sad about the jails. It is always easy to blame. But what are those in charge of the jail going to do? I do not know what they can do. If I were asked to take on their responsibilities, and live up to some ideal or some minimum code, I would have to give up, because I could not do it. With the facilities and funds available to them, with public opinion what it is, with people there for a short time, the only thing I could think of would be to get a good sum of money, and hire a crew of people to give the place the most scientific cleaning possible. I have been told that even that would not get rid of the bedbugs and various other insects; that it would be impossible—"you'd have to burn the place down." Nothing else would do. I could not think of much else to do. I do not see that it would do much good to put brand new equipment, brand new personnel, and so forth, into the jail. I think that it would be a waste of the equipment, and would leave a very frustrated group of people who had tried to do something that they could not carry out. Although we may be very critical of the jails let us not generalize by saying that it is all the fault of the jailers, the sheriffs, and the turnkeys. If they were the most kindhearted and brilliant people in the world, it is doubtful whether they could do much with the enormous population which keeps shuffling in and out and over which they have been given control.

DISCUSSION

Chairman (E. M. Jellinek): Before the discussion begins, Dr. Bacon would like to make a remark.

Bacon: I'll take a little advice. I should have taken it before from Judge Maltbie, when he said that one should not generalize. My remarks were based on the few jails that I happen to know. Those are Connecticut jails. I have been corrected to the effect that in New York, and, I dare say, in some other states, although not too many, there is a segregation policy as far as minor offenders and alcoholics are concerned, and that there are regular work programs. It just so happens that the State of Connecticut, in some ways, is not so lucky as it might be.

Haralson: It was mentioned that in New York State inebriates may be sent to a special institution under the new law there. Will you please tell us, at least in a general way, what course of treatment you would expect to find in an institution of that kind?

Banay: In all probability, that institution would not satisfy our concept of treatment. The first requirement of such an institution should be a very careful study of the individual, of his physical and mental health, social background, his needs and demands, and the best ways in which he might satisfy them in socially approved ways. Of course, the institution in New York is still in a nebular state, but I doubt that it will comply with this basic requirement.

Watson: I have two questions. First, has any definite attempt ever been made by either the states or the Federal Government to curb the liquor problem through educational processes, and if not, why not?

Maltbie: I suppose you might say that a very rudimentary attempt is being made in the requirement by all states that the public schools, in connection with instruction in health and related subjects, shall give instruction as to the effects of alcohol on the human system. I suppose that takes on more or less of an aspect of dealing with its social implications, also. Aside from that I know of no attempt that has been made. The why, of course, is a very broad question, and I think it goes back to the thing which I have tried to emphasize—the way in which the social consciousness has refused to recognize the problem of intoxication for what it is, refused to recognize its implications in economic, social and moral loss to the community as a whole. If we can once get people to recognize that, I am sure that the path toward these other goals will be much easier.

Watson: My second question is more specific. Is any provision made by the state to care for the family of a man who is sent to prison for a long time for drunkenness?

Maltbie: There is not. There is no provision whatsoever for the care of the dependents. Of course, sometimes they come under laws which provide for the dispensation of charity by the state. But as such, there is no provision, and there is none for any compensation to the man who is sometimes—not often, but sometimes it happens—wrongly incarcerated, and finally is able to satisfy the authorities of that fact.

Bancroft: In Rochester the jail is scrupulously clean, because cleaning is the only work the men have to do, but I must admit that the men come out much worse than they go in. What are we going to do with these men?

Bacon: If the question refers specifically to what those in charge of jails are going to do with the men, it is a different question than if you ask, "What are we, meaning everybody, going to do?" In reference to court and jail, I think the first step is a belief and a feeling, an understanding on the part of judges and prosecutors that this is a complex problem. That is an absolute essential. Once they have that in mind, I think that certain steps will follow. First, there are various sorts and types of people who come into this situation of drunkenness, and have come into it for different reasons. Therefore, it is impossible to believe that exactly the same treatment—if you can call going to jail treatment—is going to affect all of them in the same way. It is not. It follows that it will be necessary to discriminate between the different types and to supply better tools. As Judge Maltbie pointed out, the existing machinery is sufficient, but more tools are needed. And as far as the jail itself is concerned, unless the whole character of the jail changes considerably, unless it is equipped with people who can diagnose, unless it is equipped with the personnel and material necessary for therapeutic purposes, all they can do is try to maintain certain standards of cleanliness, nutrition, and so on. I don't think you can put the responsibility for therapy on the sheriffs. They haven't the equipment or the personnel or the money or the time. I realize that this is a very negative answer, or perhaps a very pessimistic one.

Maltbie: May I intervene? In the first place, Dr. Bacon is too young to remember the jails as they were of old. I want to reassure him to this extent—they are much better than they used to be, and for the reason which I stated, because the men who are in the jails, as we have an illustration right here, really are thinking about the problem as they never used to think about it. The other thing is this matter of employment in the jails. You know, that is influenced by an act of Congress, known as the Hawes-Cooper Law, which prevents, absolutely prohibits, the interstate shipping of prison-made goods. Consequently, all our penal institutions are put to it to find anything on which they can employ the men. It might be better if they could go back to the old system of contract clothing manufacture and that kind of thing, which had its faults, to be sure, but did afford a method of employing the men. But coming to this specific question, I think that here in Connecticut there is a relatively simple solution, and that is, as small a state as we are, to establish a single institution to which men of this type can be sent, an institution staffed with the proper personnel for individual diagnosis and for determination of what treatment should be given. I don't know how this applies in other states, but here in Connecticut this procedure seems advisable. Now that isn't necessarily an expensive proposition at all, because we have state buildings—for instance, the reformatory at Cheshire—that are vacant, and plenty of land that could be used for this kind of an institution, provided you could build up the proper equipment and the staff to have charge of it. That is not a dream; it is a very practical solution, which would go a long ways toward meeting the problem, because the system of diagnosis, which you said is basic to all treatment, could be put into operation, and the Board could be given power to deal with the individual inebriate as they think best.

Chairman: I should like to add a few words out of the experience of our Yale Plan Clinics. We have found here the greatest understanding on the part of the judiciary, the prosecuting attorneys, and personnel of prisons and jails. They have shown the greatest willingness to avail themselves of the advice which the Clinics can offer. Very often the probation officers have brought men and women over to us for diagnosis, and sometimes for treatment.

Lecture 25

Medical Treatment of the Inebriate

Robert Fleming

BEFORE discussing the treatment of alcoholism it would be well to explain my own concept of the term. To this end I have a diagram, shown here, which I always keep in mind when dealing with a patient. It has been of great practical usefulness to me in spite of the fact that it is oversimple and rigid. But perhaps its clarity may compensate to some extent for these faults. When actually treating patients, clarity is greatly needed, and especially so in dealing with a subject as complicated and with as many ramifications and contradictions as that of alcoholism.

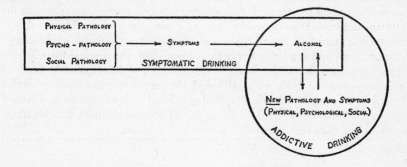

As indicated in this diagram, the chronic drinking of excessive amounts of alcoholic beverages seems to be of two general types or stages—symptomatic drinking and true addictive drinking.* In symptomatic drinking the individual takes alcohol in an attempt to obtain relief from the symptoms of some underlying condition which, as indicated, may be physical, psychological, or social, or any combination of these. Alcohol, as a drug, is very effective in providing quick temporary relief from many painful and chronic physical disturbances. Similar relief may be obtained from distressing psychological conditions. "Social drinking" is a special and currently common type of symptomatic drinking in which the etiological determinants are to be found mainly in the social usages and customs of the community and in the individual's attitudes and social relationships generally. The treatment of symptomatic drinking is simply the treatment of the underlying pathological condition—physical, psychological or social. If the underlying condition can be removed or relieved by nonalcoholic means, as is often the case, then the individual will stop drinking.

It is possible for some individuals to drink moderately *upon a symptomatic*

*The terminology used here does not agree with that in some other lectures. For clarification of terminology see subsequent discussion, p. 398.

basis for many years without the appearance of serious difficulties. The intervals of time involved are long—often a matter of decades. However, if any individual (no matter how healthy or how well organized he may be) drinks heavily enough and long enough there will inevitably appear, sooner or later, *new* pathology and *new* symptoms *as a result of his drinking*. The new pathology may lead to symptoms of a physical, psychological or social nature from which, in time, the individual will eventually learn to seek relief by recourse to more alcohol. It is a curious and essential fact that many symptoms, which originally owed their existence to the chronic action of alcohol, may be temporarily relieved or forgotten by taking more alcohol.

When the vicious circle of "drinking to relieve symptoms which have been caused by previous drinking" has been established, then the condition is that of true addictive drinking [see diagram]. When, for example, an individual drinks to assuage feelings of inferiority and remorse arising out of previous alcoholic excess, or to relieve indigestion or decreased appetite due to alcoholic gastritis, or as a result of the social dislocation attendant upon loss of job or wife because of drinking, then that individual has become caught in the addictive vicious circle. The problem of his treatment is then enormously complicated, compared to the treatment of simple symptomatic drinking. Treatment of true addictive drinking involves, first of all, the disruption of the vicious circle that is at the center of the problem, and after this has been accomplished, the original basis for the early symptomatic drinking—often heavily overlaid and encrusted by years of dissipation—must be dealt with. Although the psychiatrist has many powerful weapons in his armamentarium (psychological and occupational tools, aversion therapy, pharmacological agents, and so forth) there is no more difficult treatment problem than that presented by the alcohol addict.

SYMPTOMATIC DRINKING

Now let me cite some examples to illustrate what I have been saying. The first is that of drinking based on a physical condition. The patient I have in mind is a woman who, when I saw her several years ago, was 55 or 56 years old. Some 20 years before she had been widowed and left with two small boys and no money. She was very capable and resourceful; she went to work and did a fine job raising those boys. She put them through college; they married and made their own homes. She was free and well-to-do. She built herself a large house and planned to settle down and spend her declining years in comfort. She had developed the habit of going to bed right after dinner; lying in bed, she could read until she was sleepy, then turn out the light and go to sleep. Her life went along smoothly, but after a time she began to notice that it was difficult for her to sleep. She had a pain in the back of her neck and it was hard to get her neck comfortable on the pillow. The pain became increasingly more severe until finally the problem of sleep, largely because of this discomfort in her neck, grew serious. A friend suggested that she try a little brandy at bedtime; she did, and, to her surprise and gratification, the pain was relieved. She went to sleep and slept comfortably all night. If a little brandy was a good thing, more brandy was better. The result was that in time she was taking about a quart of brandy every night in order to sleep. That is fairly heavy drinking. The physical disturbance that gave rise to the pain which caused the insomnia that led to her drinking was arthritis of the cervical spine.

The treatment of symptomatic drinking is, in theory at least, simple. It is the removal of the underlying condition. In the case of this woman it was possible to relieve the pain of the arthritis of her cervical spine by nonalcoholic means. She has had no difficulty with drinking since that time, which was 4 or 5 years ago.

For symptomatic drinking based on a psychological disturbance, I suppose that the commonest single cause is what we call the anxiety neurosis or, at any rate, an anxiety state, because alcohol is so helpful in relieving anxiety and other tensions. This situation is illustrated by a patient I had, a man in his early twenties who, one day, was sitting in the barber's chair having his hair cut. Without any warning, without any apparent cause, he suddenly became panic-stricken. Nothing had happened; he was just overcome by apprehension. He dashed out of the barber shop with his hair half cut and could not be persuaded to go near a barber for about 3 months. Then he learned that if he took a drink it would get him through a haircut. It relieved that anxiety and apprehension which had been associated in some way with a barber shop. That sort of situation is not at all uncommon. It is often possible for the psychiatrist to relieve, or satisfactorily deal with, an anxiety neurosis—or other psychological situation—which leads to symptomatic drinking, and thus to relieve, simultaneously, the drinking problem.

Social drinking needs little comment for it is common, widespread, and familiar to everyone. The problem here is what to do about the individual's attitude toward social drinking—and it is often a difficult problem.

Now let us turn to the possible eventual consequences of excessive drinking which starts out on a symptomatic basis—physical, psychological or social. At first, nothing of serious consequence may develop, and whatever is to come may not develop for a very long time. But if an individual keeps on drinking excessively long enough, a new pathology, a new disease process, will arise. The nature of this new pathology may be physical or psychological or social, or any combination of these. The possibilities are large. Physically, I think, perhaps the gastrointestinal tract first, and the central nervous system second, suffer the most. As might be expected, the stomach and the upper gastrointestinal tract bear the brunt of chronic alcoholism. It is unusual for any individual who has been doing much drinking over any period of time to be free from some degree of alcoholic gastritis, inflammation of the lining of the stomach. Loss of appetite is a common symptom of alcoholic gastritis.

Psychologically, all sorts of conditions and situations may develop. The individual who has done much drinking over any period of time is certain to get into trouble. As his drinking increases he gets into more and more difficulty. Everybody, so to speak, has a whack at him: his parents, his wife, his friends, even his children (if he has older children), the local vicar, his employer, his neighbors and the police. It is not at all surprising that as this situation continues the drinker develops certain rather definite psychological changes. It is a rare alcoholic who does not ultimately develop feelings of inferiority and inadequacy. These are perhaps the most striking psychological changes, especially the feelings of inferiority.

It is difficult, and perhaps artificial, to separate psychological and social consequences. But certain of them we can classify as social. The individual will have trouble with his job. He will come in late or not show up at all. He may lose his job and get another. He will have trouble at home with his wife; he may lose his wife. These symptoms have arisen as a result of his drinking, as the result of the action, direct or indirect, of alcohol. The discouraging and central fact is this—that although alcohol has caused all this, it is not long before the individual finds that his troubles will be relieved, or mitigated to some extent, or he thinks they will be, by more alcohol. Thus, if he comes home of an evening tired, his stomach upset because of the drinking of the night before or during the day, he has no appetite for dinner; the sight of food may actually be a little upsetting. But if he has a couple of cocktails he can sit down and eat well. If he lies awake at night, nervous, tense, worried about this, that, or the other situation, some personal relationship perhaps, wondering what in the world he is going to do about it, the whole night may slip by. But if he has a couple of highballs, he can sleep well. As the result of his drinking, the night before, he lit a cigarette, let us say, and dropped it, setting fire to the upholstery on a chair of which his wife is particularly fond. In the morning he will sneak out rather guiltily. He knows what sort of reception he is going to get when he comes home that night. It is the most natural thing in the world for him to stop on the way home and fortify himself for that reception.

ADDICTIVE DRINKING

Thus it is that a vicious circle becomes established—a circle of drinking to relieve symptoms, or to relieve pathology, which has been caused by previous drinking or by some other condition. From this vicious circle there develops what I have called true addictive drinking. When this circle has been established the problem of treatment becomes enormously complicated. Treatment of the original underlying situation does not now stop the drinking because a new situation has been superimposed upon the original one. Again, if we break the vicious circle, we still have the original situation to deal with. I shall exemplify these matters later. For the moment, bear in mind that I am, for the sake of clarity, presenting the interplay of forces in the development of addiction in an oversimplified way. The actual situation and its relations may be enormously complex. The diagrammatic approach which I have discussed here serves as a guide, a map, to basic relations and, to that end, it is useful.

What one tries to do in treating true addictive drinking is, as I have said, to break up the vicious circle that has been established and then deal with the original situation as best one can. And there are certain generalizations I should like to emphasize at this point. The first is, I think, the more important because of its theoretical implications. It is this: Anybody can become involved in this circle. Any normal human being, I do not care how well organized he may be physically or psychologically, if he drinks enough and over a long enough period of time so that symptoms arise from his drinking, may attempt to relieve them by more drinking—addictive drinking. Some individuals are much more vulnerable than others to this entanglement. Some individuals are much more susceptible to the action of alcohol than others; but any normal human being can get caught if he drinks enough and long enough. I heard recently of a man who died at the age of 93, having drunk a quart of Scotch whisky every day for the last 60 years of his life. During this time he successfully managed an important business. I do not think he was an addictive drinker, but I do think he would have become one if he had lived another 10 years. His grandson, who was a patient of mine, tried to emulate the old gentleman and only got to the age of 37; he did not have the old man's constitution. He did not have the stamina and the good sense that his grandfather had.

The second generalization, which is extremely important from the standpoint of treatment, is one that is universally accepted. It is this: The only objective of treatment which stands any chance of success is total abstinence. I do not know with certainty why an individual once caught in this vicious circle can never successfully be a moderate drinker again. But it is true; there is absolutely no doubt about it. Everybody who has had any experience is agreed about this. The individual who has become a problem drinker is faced with the choice of going on as a problem drinker or being totally abstinent. If you have total abstinence as your therapeutic objective the chances of success are not too poor. I should place them at, say, three out of five. If you try to make a moderate drinker out of your patient, your chances are nil. It is not possible to make a moderate drinker out of an addictive drinker.

Steps in Treatment

With these generalizations in mind we may now discuss some of the tools that the doctor, or psychiatrist, or therapist uses in dealing with this addictive vicious circle. Theoretically what one tries to do is to relieve all of the symptoms, thereby relieving the cause for drinking. The physical aspects are often easier to deal with, and it is highly important that the physical condition of the patient should come under consideration early, perhaps as the first feature in any treatment program. By means of a physical examination an evaluation is made of the patient's condition and then steps are taken to correct any physical disturbance. You have, I am sure, already covered in previous discussions some of the effects of drinking on the body, so I shall not need to go into that.

It is frequently desirable to hospitalize the patient. In the normal, nonpsychotic, uncomplicated alcoholic I have found that a period of perhaps a week or 10 days, sometimes shorter, sometimes longer, in the general hospital is often a useful start. The problems of sleep and of nutrition are frequently the most urgent ones. Their solution requires good nursing care which, in the average community, can be obtained only in a hospital. One encounters, not infrequently, a fair amount of prejudice against alcoholics in general hospitals, but with education it is possible to bring the hospital staff to see the role which the hospital can play and to change this attitude. In Boston, at the Peter Bent Brigham Hospital, the staff is much more cordial to my alcoholic patients than they were 7 or 8 years ago. At present there are difficulties because of the war; the hospitals are crowded and are, for that reason, reluctant to accept alcoholics. I am sure that after the present emergency is over the situation will be much better than it was a decade ago. Naturally one has to exercise care in the selection of patients to be sent to the general hospital. Ten years ago I had the feeling that most alcoholics should be institutionalized, that is, sent to mental hospitals. But I have changed my mind on that and now feel that a mental hospital should be kept as the last resort.

Many alcoholics who have been drinking over a long period of time have a curious feeling of fatigue; they are all tired out. I am not sure what the basis for this feeling is; it may be, to some extent, psychological, but not entirely so. This feeling may be relieved by a drink. I had, as a patient, a woman in her late thirties who was a school teacher. She had been quite a social drinker over a period of a decade or so but in the last 2 or 3 years had become more or less of a problem drinker. Her major complaint, when she came to me for treatment, was a terrible lethargy which developed about 2 or 3 o'clock in the afternoon and which was relieved by a drink. This drink would start her off on the day's drinking. In a case like this—and this type of symptom is found in a fairly large number of alcoholics—benzedrine sulfate may be helpful. It worked well with her and actually gave her more relief than a drink. She was able to teach and go about her life acceptably without recourse to the alcohol which she did not want to use. That was on January 16, 1937; I remember the date because she said that was the day of her last drink and she has sent me a telegram every year on that anniversary. She continued to take benzedrine all through the spring and summer. I saw her in September and asked her about benzedrine and she said, "Oh, I haven't been taking that for about a month or 6 weeks. I find it doesn't work any more. But I don't have that tired feeling any more. I don't need to take either a drink or benzedrine." That has been my experience with benzedrine in a situation in which it is of the most benefit. The tired feeling which is so characteristic of a certain group of alcoholics will tend to clear up with the benzedrine treatment, but sometimes it will take quite a long time. When it does clear up, the individual no longer gets much reaction from benzedrine, and I have never seen it become an addiction problem in itself.

Various sedatives are used in the treatment of the insomnia which is often very disturbing to the alcoholic. After an acute binge there may be a period of a few days or a week when the problem of sleep is an urgent one. There is no wholly satisfactory sedative. The barbiturates and other sedatives are widely used, but I think they are rather dangerous. I have known a number of individuals who became addicted to barbiturates. Chloral hydrate, I think, is a little better, but I have seen one or two instances of addiction to that. Paraldehyde is by far the safest sedative; it is also unpleasant to take at first, but an alcoholic will get used to it and even get to like it. It is of interest that at the Church of England Temperance Society Hall for the treatment of alcoholism they succeeded in substituting addiction to paraldehyde for addiction to alcohol before they realized the danger. The Director was able to write a paper on 40 cases of paraldehyde addiction.

Insulin and intravenous administration of glucose solution is often helpful in getting through the first few days. I believe that it is best, if one can, not to prolong the withdrawal period with sedatives, but it is often very difficult to do so. The administration of alcohol should be stopped abruptly. There is no point whatever in tapering off; it just prolongs the agony. Nothing is gained and there is no danger whatever of getting a psychosis, such as delirium tremens, by abrupt withdrawal.

Even at this early stage in the care of the alcoholic a great deal can be accomplished by a general psychological approach. What I usually do, when it is possible, is to draw the diagram I have employed here and use it in explaining to the patient about his condition. It helps to gain the patient's confidence at the outset by giving him the idea of how you look upon him as a problem. The chances are that by utilizing such a diagram as this, he will interpret the relation in the light of his own experiences. He will become interested. He may say, "Well, I started out this way as a social drinker." He will fit himself into this framework, and that is a good psychological attitude for him to have as he starts out on a program of treatment.

The feeling of inadequacy and inferiority, which I think is often a secondary result rather than an original cause of drinking, is something that the doctor can attack at the very beginning of treatment. Many alcoholics are brought to me almost literally by the scruff of the neck. They come with the idea—"Well, my folks think I'm crazy. This fellow is going to put me away. This is the last straw." It is reassuring to a patient to have you point out how these feelings of inadequacy and inferiority have come about as a result of the way he has been handled. He vaguely realizes that his drinking is not all his fault, and that in some way which he cannot understand he has been caught in an entangling situation. But he has not a single defense. His friends, his wife, or his parents will point at him and say, "He did this or that." And it is true that he did and he cannot justify his behavior. After years and years of being absolutely defenseless in this situation, he is finally brought in contact with somebody who explains the situation in a way that shows it is not wholly his fault. When he understands that his feeling of being always in the wrong is really something that his associates have produced in him, although they haven't meant to do so, it cheers him up. He thinks, "Here, at last, is somebody who understands me." So, as I say, I like to start off with what you might call the psychotherapy of alcoholism, by talking about the feelings of inferiority and inadequacy that I know the patient has. One can gain his confidence in that way.

RESOURCES IN THE COMMUNITY

The physician can count on a number of resources in the community that are often useful in handling the individual patient. I am thinking particularly of such organizations as Alcoholics Anonymous and the Salvation Army, and various church groups which may be very useful. One of the difficulties at present in an urban community is for the individual patient to find and carry on some sort of a healthy, interesting and not boring social life apart from alcohol. It is difficult to find a totally abstinent community. Dr. Gabriel of Vienna, who has been especially active in the problem of treating the alcoholic, was much concerned over the sort of community to which the patient goes back after treatment. He developed a very good system. He had an institution that would hold about 80 men and 12 or 15 women. On the first Saturday or Sunday after a patient's admission, he would get the patient's relatives to come in and have a conference with him. He continued to have contact with the families of the patients and after a patient had been in the institution several months he had managed to work the various patients' families into an acquaintanceship, some sort of common social life. By the time the patients were ready to leave the hospital they found ready for their social life a whole new set of friends who had been through this same experience. They had in common the knowledge of the necessity for total abstinence. Actually in Vienna there was a community of "graduates" of the Alcoholic Division of the hospital and their families. It was a good situation and well worth the effort to obtain it. Alcoholics Anonymous may serve in much the same social way. It makes the treatment of the individual patient simpler.

In respect to therapy itself, some patients are not suitable for Alcoholics Anonymous while others find immediate help. I recall a patient, a woman in her thirties, who had been a severe alcoholic for 14 or 15 years. She had been treated by any number of psychiatrists and nothing seemed to work. Finally, in desperation, in the middle of the night (I shall never forget this experience), we decided to take her to a mental hospital. It was her first contact with such an institution, and I do not know of a more difficult situation. I look back upon that night with horror. She did not want to go, and she was not going to go. It became a problem of taking her against her will. Her husband was afraid of her and so was I, but I managed to get her to drink some liquor with chloral hydrate in it. She drank this and nothing happened. We waited around and finally I gave her some more, and she got a little sleepy. Then I gave her an injection of morphine and she immediately became unconscious. Her heart rate was irregular and feeble and I thought, "Is this woman going to die?" In my anxiety, I gave her some caffein and she woke up. There we were, just where we started. Finally, by main force, we got her into an ambulance and off to the mental hospital. The next day she escaped and came home drunk. I had to go through that whole affair again and again, and she was in and out of that place over a period of a year and a half. In addition, she had various other forms of treatment. Everything was tried. Finally, after she had spent 5 or 6 months in the institution, she came home with good resolutions. But within a week she was drinking again. Her husband came to me (I can still see him sitting there in that chair); he was beside himself and said, "What are we going to do now? We've tried everything." He had had a discussion with a lawyer regarding the possibility of getting a divorce; that would at least settle the problem as far as he was concerned, but she would still have her problem, and he had feelings of loyalty. As we were sitting there, one of the members of the Alcoholics Anonymous group in Boston called me up about another patient. I asked him to see this woman. He said he would and, to make a long story short, her husband went down there that afternoon and figured out a way of getting her in contact with the group so that it would not appear that he had conspired against her. She has not had a drink since. It has been a year and a half, and it has been a marvelous relief for the whole family.

One reason why I go into this story in such detail is that there is a point in it which I think is important in the treatment of alcoholism in general: There is such a thing as a "ripe" alcoholic, and there is such a thing as trying to do too much too quickly. I think that Alcoholics Anonymous was able to be so strikingly successful in that case because of all that had gone before. The woman herself was looking for an excuse to stop drinking at that time. I think that if we had put her in touch with Alcoholics Anonymous 5 years previously, it might not have worked so well.

Patience is, perhaps, the most important single attribute that the therapist must have in treating the alcoholic. There are no miracles in this therapy. He should be prepared to spend days, months, and years. I am suspicious of a quick cure, for it often turns out to be just a disillusioning experience after a few weeks of abstinence.

Alcoholics Anonymous is, as I say, an important and useful group in this country. In England, Scandinavia and New Zealand, the Salvation Army has been a very effective therapeutic agency. Here it is effective also, but usually at an economic and social level which does not make it generally useful for the private patient. In Sweden and in New Zealand there are islands which are quite isolated where there are colonies for the treatment of alcoholics. The objective of treatment there is religious conversion. The Salvation Army, which is particularly active there, feels that if an individual is converted he then is cured. It is surprising how often it works out that way, and I think there is merit in the idea. The objective is to substitute something for alcohol rather than to deal with any particular underlying cause. It seems to me that an organization like the Salvation Army, striking in its social manifestations—its music, its singing, its conversions, and so forth—offers, in some cases, a pretty effective substitute for drinking.

Psychotherapeutic Approach

Psychoanalysis has been rather disappointing as a means of treating the ordinary alcoholic. A certain amount of symptomatic drinking is, of course, on a neurotic basis, but I should hesitate to make an estimate of the extent. In cases where an original, pre-existing, underlying neurosis has been the cause of the individual's symptomatic drinking, the psychotherapeutic approach, including psychoanalysis, may be successful, or at least it is the rational approach. But psychoanalysis as a specific therapeutic approach has not turned out to be wholly satisfactory.

I had a patient, a man of about 43 or 44, whom I want to mention here because his case illustrates drinking on a neurotic basis. He had been drinking about a quart of whisky a day for 22 or 23 years. Nothing much happened during most of that time, but in the last year or two he had become fairly disorganized and rather severe symptoms began to develop. Ordinarily he would start off in the morning with an occasional drink; he would consume about a pint during the day and then he would bring another pint home with him, which he drank in the course of the evening. He never became severely drunk until the last year. I put him into a general hospital and stopped his drinking. He was a little shaky and had some trouble sleeping for a week or so; his stomach was upset; but in the course of a week or 10 days he felt fine and was discharged from the hospital. I saw him about once a week to follow the situation and deal with whatever developed. After about 6 weeks he called me on the telephone and said he must see me right away. He was panic-stricken. He drove a laundry truck and one of his duties was to deliver laundry packages to apartment buildings; he used the back stairs and these were not well guarded along the edges. He had the feeling that he was about to fall off. The higher he climbed, the stronger this feeling became. Finally, he got to the point where he was not able to deliver his packages—the very thought of doing so frightened him. He said, "You know, when I was a young man, along in my late teens and early twenties, I used to have these feelings, especially with regard to height, but also with subways and streetcars as well, and I found that if I'd take a drink, it would relieve these feelings. In the past week it has been with the greatest difficulty that I have kept from drinking, not because I craved the drink, I didn't, but simply because of the relief I know alcohol will give me for these symptoms." What had undoubtedly happened in this man's case was that originally, as a youth of 19 or 20, he had had an anxiety neurosis, with these symptoms of anxiety and panic associated with specific situations. Over a period of time he had learned to deal with that neurosis by means of alcohol, and then for 20 years or more that neurosis was literally "pickled" in alcohol. Then the vicious circle was established and the secondary symptoms and secondary pathology arose and he became a typical addictive drinker. I was able to remove the secondary symptoms and get him off the alcohol. Then, after 6 weeks, there appeared the old neurosis which had been there all that time. This case illustrates some of the difficulties that are encountered in treatment. It illustrates another point: There is no specific craving for alcohol. After an individual, who is an addict, has been drinking to great excess, he may develop nervous symptoms which he knows alcohol will relieve, as aspirin will relieve a headache. But once he is over these symptoms, there is no craving whatever for alcohol. The problem in the case of this laundry truck driver, after having got rid of the alcohol, was still the original one for which alcohol had been taken in the first place. It had to be dealt with, but it was no longer a specific alcohol problem. It was a problem in the field of psychiatry, a highly technical problem but one which this individual had attempted to solve with alcohol.

CONDITIONED-REFLEX TREATMENT

One of the important tools in the treatment of alcoholism is the so-called conditioned-reflex or aversion treatment which has, I believe, been discussed in some of the seminar sessions. I have had some experience with it and found it useful. The basic idea is an old one; it is to build up an aversion to alcoholic beverages so that the alcoholic will become nauseated at the sight, taste, or smell of them. A famous physician of the second century, in Rome, used this method in principle; he put live eels in wine and then made the alcoholic drink the wine. The eel was supposed to cause disgust. That, of course, is not the method in modern practice. Some years ago Dr. John Y. Dent, in England, developed a procedure which I have used in 30 or 35 cases. The drug apomorphine is employed; this drug stimulates the vomiting center in the brain. When a dose is given by hypodermic injection, the individual receiving it vomits in 2 or 3 minutes and is very ill for about 10 minutes. The original treatment was drastic. The patient is first given hospital care in preparation for the treatment and then, in the actual procedure, he is given an injection of apomorphine. About 2 minutes later, just when he is going to be nauseated, he is made to drink a full glass of whisky or some other alcoholic beverage. The patient drinks it and then, to his surprise, he vomits it right up again. Some 4 hours later the procedure is repeated; and again at 4 hours. The patient is not allowed to have anything to eat or drink except the beverage, which he vomits up. The average individual can stand this rough treatment only for a day and a half or 2 days; an occasional patient may continue for 2½ days. By the end of this time he is in a very sorry condition indeed. He is then bathed and dressed, given a glass of milk and a sandwich, or a small amount of any attractive food. He finds that the food has a wonderful taste and he is greatly relieved not to have to drink whisky, or gin, or whatever beverage he has been using. Among my patients about 25 per cent were cured of their drinking by this treatment.

The technique of this treatment has been considerably improved at the Shadel Sanitariums and they obtain better results. Dr. Voegtlin developed the procedure that is employed there. Emetine is used instead of apomorphine; the effects of this drug last longer. The patient is first sobered up and got into good shape. No sedatives are given. Then he is taken to a treatment room which may be arranged in a rather special way. There is a bar, spotlighted; the room is more or less soundproof and dark. The patient sits before this bar with a bucket in front of his legs, and the therapist sits to one side. On the bar are bottles, glasses and ice, arranged as attractively as possible. There is a good deal of suggestion involved in the whole procedure. Then the patient is given an injection of the emetine. Time is watched very carefully and just before he is going to become nauseated the therapist gives him a drink. He drinks and vomits; he drinks again, and vomits again. The drinking is stopped just before the point at which the nausea will wear off. It is very important that the patient does not retain any of the beverage, that is, that he does not get drunk, because this would tend to prevent the building up of the aversion. After the treatment he is put to bed and in 2 or 3 hours he is feeling all right again. Under the Shadel method the patient is given a treatment each day to a total of 6 to 9 days. Then 1 month, 2 months, 6 months and 1 year later he comes back for a single "reinforcement" treatment. Sometimes benzedrine is given 2 hours before the treatment to make the pain and the unpleasantness of the whole experience more keen. Dr. Voegtlin has reported a high rate of success. His criterion of cure is a 4-year period of total abstinence, and on this basis he and his associates have reported as high as 65 per cent recoveries. This is by far the highest percentage of cures that has been reported. Our average in Boston at the Washingtonian Hospital with this method is not so high; it is between 45 and 50 per cent. I think the average would be higher if the cases could be selected. All who have employed this method agree that the young drinker is much more difficult to treat than the older one, and this is true of all other methods as far as I know. I think Dr. Voegtlin said in his original paper that he had not successfully cured any alcoholic who was under 28 years of age, and that has also been my experience.

DISCUSSION

Chairman (*E. M. Jellinek*): It is most gratifying to us, Dr. Fleming, that many features of your views on the nature of the alcoholic and the development of alcoholism coincide with our own views. Your experience, as well as ours, has shown that while a certain segment of the inebriate population comes to its addiction through some initial pathology of the personality or of the physical make-up of the individual, many inebriates start without any psychological or physiological handicap but become addicted through events which occur in the course of their excessive drinking. But you, as well as we, have found that even those who start as normal personalities show pathological changes in their personality reactions. In brief, we agree that ultimately all addicts, or let us call them compulsive drinkers, are inflicted with an ailment as real as are those conditions which are generally recognized as diseases.

Our ideas do not conflict at any major point, but our terminology hardly seems to meet anywhere. We have been using the term "symptomatic drinking" to denote excessive drinking as one of the modes of expression, as one of the symptoms incidental to—but not causative of—a psychosis. I must concede that one may talk, if it serves his purpose, of social drinking as symptomatic of a culture. After all, terminology is only a matter of convenience. But I think that one loses some of the facility of discussion in applying the term symptomatic to a large variety of forms which need to be distinguished from one another. Perhaps one day all of us interested in these matters will arrive at a common terminology.

I would like to clarify one point. You said that anyone who "drinks enough, and long enough" can become an addict. These, I suppose, are individual matters; you would not have a certain limit of what is enough to cause addiction, but rather what is enough for Mr. A. and not for Mr. B. On the other hand, I would assume that you do not mean that anybody drinking moderately for any long period may become an alcoholic. Surely in spite of individual variation there must be a lower limit below which nobody would become an addict irrespective of the length of time.

Lecturer: That is right. There is such a lower limit.

Gross: Mr. Shadel told us the other day in our seminar that they used no psychiatric treatment in connection with the aversion treatment at the present time, and they continue to have excellent success. I am a psychiatrist; perhaps we emphasize too much the role of psychiatry in the treatment of alcoholism. To the best of my knowledge, the recoveries under psychiatric treatment are about 30 per cent; but here is a treatment outside of psychiatry which seems to give 60 per cent success. I wonder whether the results would be even better if this treatment were combined with psychiatry?

Lecturer: That is a good question and it raises many puzzling issues. I have the impression that almost any form of treatment will produce about 35 per cent recoveries. Some years ago I made a survey of the situation in Europe. In England, where the treatment of alcoholism at that time was very rudimentary, they had about 30 per cent cures. They did all the things they shouldn't do according to our present views. In Sweden, there was a highly complex, highly organized state system, a beautiful system for the treatment of chronic alcoholism. There were special hospitals out in the country and many occupational opportunities. But they had only about 35 per cent cures. In Switzerland, where they have a somewhat similar system but highly organized along the line of private control, they still had only about 35 per cent cures. If one wanted to experiment, it would be interesting to do something ridiculous in the way of therapy; and if it were done, I believe that 35 per cent of the patients would stop drinking. There is something curious about that 30 to 35 per cent of cures.

I am skeptical of the mental hospital and the psychiatry involved in such an institution. I think it often does more harm than good unless it is used very carefully and as a last resort. I have seen many individuals who have been problem drinkers and who became worse after they had spent a period in a mental hospital. Their relatives thought they were crazy, so they put them in mental hospitals; in the hospitals they came in contact with the mentally ill; and when they got out they just had another and challenging reason for drinking. I think that specific psychiatric techniques can be useful in dealing with the feeling of inferiority which is almost universal in alcoholics who have been alcoholics for any length of time.

I am rather suspicious of what you might call "confessional psychotherapy" in connection with the treatment of alcoholism. That is why psychoanalysis has not turned out to be successful with alcoholics. If you were to walk out on the streets and select the first man that you saw, bring him into the office and treat him as a psychiatric patient, you would soon dig up all sorts of suggestive psychiatric data. You would find he had a mother and a certain relationship to her. As a psychiatrist you might become greatly absorbed in this or some other aspect of his life, and before long you might well believe that you had happened to pick a psychiatric patient. I think that is what happens with some alcoholics. The general practitioner and the internist do not want to have anything to do with them. So they get relegated to the psychiatrist, who is eager to help and who brings to bear upon the specific problem all that he has been taught about the neuroses, the unconscious, and the early experiences of childhood. He goes to work on the alcoholic patient and succeeds in finding all sorts of psychiatric matters which probably have little bearing on the alcoholism. It is, I think, along the lines of counteracting the feelings of inferiority which have developed that psychiatric techniques are apt to be more useful in treatment.

Ertel: To what extent is hypnosis being used to cure alcoholism, and is it effective?

Lecturer: I don't know. I have had no personal experience with hypnosis myself, but I have had one or two indirect contacts with patients who have been treated with hypnosis. One of these was hypnotized in connection with the conditioned-reflex treatment some 8 months ago, and he has done very well, but I cannot speak from personal experience.

Chairman: I wonder, Dr. Fleming, whether you think that one may take exception to hypnosis on the grounds that in the hypnotic treatment the patient always remains dependent upon the therapist; he is never put back on his own feet.

Lecturer: That sounds very sensible.

Vredevoe: Have any studies been made on the effects of smoking, coffee drinking, and so on, in checking the excessive use of alcohol? Is there any curtailment of excessiveness, or a transfer?

Lecturer: I don't know of any typical objective work along those lines that I could cite. We have had experiences which would suggest that something else has been substituted for alcohol. It is not at all difficult to substitute certain drugs for alcohol. I had a patient once, a man in his late twenties, who was a very heavy drinker; he was also a heavy worker and in robust physical condition, and I applied the conditioned-reflex treatment vigorously. When we were through, he ate ravenously and felt fine. He said, "Doctor, what I would rather have than anything else would be a double chocolate ice cream soda." For the next few months he used to drink quantities of sweets, and I have the feeling that he took sweets as a substitute for alcohol. I do not know of any critical studies on this subject.

Hendricks: Will you please state what your opinion would be of establishing a state institution to be devoted exclusively to the treatment of alcoholics?

Lecturer: I would be in favor of that. I think it is a public health problem, and one of the great difficulties has been the mixing up of the problems of alcoholism and of mental diseases. While they have points of contact, I think by and large it would be much better for alcoholism to be kept quite separate from the problems of "insanity." It is a public health problem of sufficient severity to justify special state institutions for the treatment of alcohol addiction.

Chairman: The only misgivings I would have about that would be that in such an institution there would be a tendency to treat all alcoholics on the same scheme. If one could be sure that there would be differential treatment on the basis of diagnosis, I would have much more confidence in it. I would be afraid that everybody would either get "conditioned reflex" or everybody would be exposed exclusively to psychotherapy.

Lecturer: It would depend on the personnel.

Miss Faulconer: It is understood that an addict can be cured only by total abstinence. Is there such a thing as a tapering-off process?

Lecturer: I am greatly opposed to a tapering-off process for several reasons. In the first place, it is actually much more difficult. You prolong the individual's withdrawal symptoms, and, theoretically, I think it is never good for a physician who is treating the problem of alcohol to prescribe alcohol.

Mrs. Sloan: Would the vicious-circle approach, such as you have described, be a good one to use with the person who is not yet an excessive drinker but who is well on the way to becoming one?

Lecturer: I think so. It is simple and easily understood. On the other hand, it raises an interesting issue. I have never personally seen anyone cured of alcoholism by frightening him. I have placed alcoholic patients in the violent wards of mental hospitals, and they have come out and said, "Oh, I'll never drink again Doctor, after what I've seen and been through." But it doesn't work for long. I have heard of people who, while under the influence of alcohol, have killed someone in an automobile accident, and then stopped drinking. I suppose such cases do exist, but I am careful never to threaten, never to expand on the horrors that face an individual if he keeps on drinking. It is all right to explain in clearcut, simple terms, without any coloring of threat, what is going to happen if he keeps on drinking.

Question: In using the aversion treatment, what effect does knowledge of the methods have on the patient? If he knew that an emetic was purposely being associated with drinking, would it have less effect than if he did not?

Lecturer: The feeling at one time was that one must be cagey about explanations and only tell the patient that you were giving him medicine to help withstand the effects of the drinking. Now, the curious thing is, it doesn't seem to make any difference whether you tell the full truth or not. I do not evade. The patient does not blame the injection, but says it makes the liquor taste differently. I make quite a show of opening the bottles in his presence so that he will see there is nothing in there. We do not "dope" the liquor. But I don't think it matters whether he knows he is getting an emetic or not. It works just the same.

Mrs. Clark: Are there any figures that would tell us how the percentage of cures, which you gave as 35 per cent, would compare with cures of psychiatric patients where alcohol is not involved?

Lecturer: That is a good question, but I don't know whether I can answer it. There are many different types of psychiatric cases and of treatments. The first that comes to my mind is the use of the electric-shock treatment in depressions. By and large about 80 per cent are cured. The treatment of general paresis by malaria yields about 30 per cent cured and 30 per cent improved. I don't know that there are any good figures on schizophrenia.

Chairman: The rate of cure for schizophrenia is 25 to 30 per cent, and that rate is reported for nearly every cure that has ever been tried. I suppose that coincides very well with spontaneous remissions in schizophrenia. But I don't think that in the case of alcoholism 35 per cent would cover spontaneous remissions. I think there would be a very low percentage only. To what would spontaneous remissions of alcoholics amount to, in your experience, Doctor?

Lecturer: I have very little to base it on—I don't see spontaneous remissions in alcoholics. Every once in a while, of course, you do hear of some alcoholic in the community who spontaneously stops drinking.

The Role of Religious Bodies in the Treatment of Inebriety in the United States

Rev. Francis W. McPeek

THERE have been millions of inebriates in this world and perhaps not more than a few hundred thousand have been brought back to sobriety. Yet a few hundred thousand is a great multitude. And of those inebriates who came back, tens of thousands were led by the counsel of religious friends to the consolation of religion. Even in these days of psychiatric counseling many psychiatrists feel that those whom they counsel, those men and women torn by conflicts and doubts, those who stand on insecure, makeshift foundations, may find the peace they are seeking through a view into the world of God.

Psychologists say the inebriate has a poorly integrated personality, and sociologists say that he is not integrated into society. We may safely accept these views; they mean that the inebriate has not found his relation to God and thus, also, not to his fellow men.

The inebriate creates for himself a world of which he occupies the center. He is not willing to give up the power that he wielded as an infant, the power to make everyone dance to the tune of his cries. Man wields that power completely but once in his life. As he progresses in the use of his hands and feet and brain he must give up more and more of his power over his social environment and increasingly comply instead of being complied with. Those who, for some reason, have not the ability to see this, or have not been helped to see it, have not been "brought up" properly, get into those grave conflicts which they tend to solve through neurotic behavior or through intoxication.

What is it in religion that can relieve these men and women from this artificial adjustment, and to what extent have religious bodies in the United States recognized an obligation to afford the aid of religion to inebriates?

I shall cite some aspects of religion that apply to the egocentric alcoholic in the words of great religious writers. A selection from the records of some religious bodies will serve to illustrate the historical development of the religious therapy of inebriety in the United States.

William James wrote, with keen insight:

There is a state of mind known to religious men, but to no others, in which the will to assert ourselves and hold our own has been displaced by a willingness to close our mouths and be as nothing in the floods and waterspouts of God. In this state of mind, what we most dreaded has become the habitation of our safety, and the hour of our moral death has turned into our spiritual birthday. The time for tension in our soul is over, and that of happy relaxation, of calm breathing, of an eternal present, with no discordant future to be anxious about, has arrived. Fear is not held in abeyance as it is by mere morality, it is positively expunged and washed away.

Essentially, as James observed, this state of mind is the fruit of faith, a faith so great and powerful that fears and doubts and conflicting desires are swept away before it. Life takes on a strange, beautiful newness. The sight and sound of fellow beings create feelings of childlike wonder. Even the sensations of taste and smell may be heightened. But above all, those who have come into the experience are left with a deep assurance. "One thing I know," said the blind man healed by Christ, "that, whereas I was blind, now I see." Before this secure awareness of God all perplexities of both an intellectual and a moral nature are resolved. Those who have been hotly troubled and fatigued with the strain of moral effort find, in place of their accustomed conflicts, a simplicity in decision, a quietness of movement, a certainty of direction, and an abiding joy in life. They can testify with St. John: "And this is life eternal, that they might know thee the only true God, and Jesus Christ, whom thou hast sent." They live in the "eternal present."

Through the ages the Church has attempted to cultivate this experience and state of mind in the lives of her faithful. Contemplative or meditative prayer, as it has long been called among the mystics, has been chief among many methods. If you will open the writings of almost any Christian soul, you will see that kind of prayer, and all it means, touched upon. Augustine, Meister Eckart, Jacob Boehme, John Tauler, Thomas à Kempis—these and hundreds of other names familiar to students of religion give the same advice.

It is, moreover, the insistence of historical Christianity that no man can live fully without a knowledge of and dependence upon God. Incomplete, with fragmentary powers, with unrequited human hopes, with a sense of inadequacy and moral unworth, he must find his health and strength as much without as within, as much beyond as here. No one is exempt.

The gospel of Christianity is always preached as an immediacy; not as something that happened a long time ago, or as something which is to come, but as something which is. "If any man will repent and turn from his sins," says Meister Eckart, "God will in the twinkling of an eye forgive them, and they will be as though they had never been." If some psychiatrists are right in their judgment that the problem of guilt is often uppermost in mental and emotional illness, it will be no new thing to the Christian religion. There is a standing requirement for most of us, and that is that we be forgiven and that we be able to accept forgiveness. And I mean, too, that we shall be able to forgive ourselves. It is the haunting sense of guilt, of estrangement from those we most love, and of being less than conscience tells us we ought to be, that provokes gross disturbances of spirit and often of flesh. When a man can accept forgiveness and see with humility the even flowing of the spirit of God in his life, he is a well man and fit for anything.

Very few religious experiences occur in a social vacuum. To begin with, the man who undergoes a conversion experience, whether it be instantaneous or over a long period, usually does so in part because he already knows something of religion. The memories of childhood regarding prayer and other devotions, the scraps and bits of religious knowledge that may long have been unused, the recollections of friends whose lives were touched by the love of God—all these things are operative. Faust, as you will remember, resolved to commit suicide because he had not managed to learn the whole truth of man to which he had devoted his entire years. He was arrested in the act by the sound of children's voices outside raised in the singing of their Easter hymns. By such incidents, old bits of our life stuff—associated with a sense of long-lost security—are revitalized and take on new importance. Intuitively, one knows that the life of trust and confidence, often represented by a childlike faith, is the only one possible. Only a thing such as this can hold us together meaningfully against the swift shocks and threats of the times in which we live.

The deep-running desires for a faith which unites and heals the soul and directs the will, and the bits of emotionally tinged knowledge of God from earlier times, are refreshed or activated in many ways. Sometimes they are strengthened by chance words heard or read—a phrase overheard from conversation in a public place, a radio sermon, a service of public worship, a quotation from the Scriptures in an unexpected place. Augustine was converted by reading a single passage; St. Anthony by a single word. In these and other instances, the conflict of the soul had been so heightened that the tension was unendurable. As easily and readily as a small key throws the tumblers of a complicated lock, so the casual word or event may precipitate a resolution of a complicated illness of the soul. In one moment there is self-reproach and pride and hopelessness; in the next there is release from self-condemnation, and humility and steadfast conviction of personal worth.

But even more effectual than the chance or the casual in stimulating both the longings and the fears which precede new birth of soul is often the sudden awareness of a long-standing human sympathy and friendship. It is as though God used the understanding acceptance of a friend to make clear His own acceptance and pardon. Only when we no longer fear censure from a fellow being can we be sure of His perfect love for us. Only when we know that the friend, too, has been, or is, as involved in sin as we, do we no longer need to fear censure. Monica, the beloved mother of St. Augustine, was forced into total abstinence as a small girl by virtue of the fact that a crotchety old serving maid caught her in the act of tippling and scolded her. In his confessions, Augustine gives thanks: "Thou, O Lord, Governor of all in heaven and earth, who turnest to Thy purposes the deepest currents, and the turbulence of the tide of times, didst by the very unhealthiness in one soul heal another. . . ." And Augustine adds this: "Lest any, when he observes this [i.e., the reformation], should ascribe it to his own power, even when another, whom he wished to be reformed, is reformed through words of his."

It is true that the very unhealthiness in one soul may heal another. There are many abstinent or temperate sons of drunken fathers. But by all odds the most of those who find their way back to sobriety after years of indulgence find it because they first find a friend with whom there is no necessity of pretense. The scold, the crank, the moralizer, the contemptuous—these serve usually only to widen the abyss, already so great, that separates the inebriate from those to whom he most truly wishes to belong. The hallmark of the good friend is his stability and freedom from censoriousness; the hallmark of a religious friend is not only these things, but also a humility tempered with unshaken faith.

To these religious elements we add one other—the moving power of mass example. In history it is plainly to be seen that men have been caught up time and again in some great process. Not realizing and not caring what was working in them or how, they have performed prodigious feats. Wars have swept them along to heights of heroism; disasters have made out of selfish individuals communities of heroes. This factor occurs again and again in religious history. Purifying movements have flooded through the church, engulfing and carrying along thousands who felt they had no religious vocation. Left in their wake have been new religions, new sects, new orders. Looking backward, subsequent generations have wondered how these people found the spirit and strength to do what they did, for what they did often shifted the center of gravity of whole civilizations, gave them new and better orientations. Banded together they could accomplish, and did, vastly more than was possible to them individually. Such phenomena as these have to be remembered if we are fully to assess the value of religion in the treatment of inebriety. By secular historians they are sometimes dismissed with such terms as "mass hypnosis" or "group suggestion," or the like. By these and other terms it is intended to dismiss the phenomena as improper or irrelevant human data, in fact, as something shameful. But the occurrence of conversion is well established in history and in everyday life.

Now let us consider together some of these realities in the last century of American life.

EARLY RELIGIOUS TEMPERANCE SOCIETY

One hundred and twenty years ago Lyman Beecher sat by the bedside of a dying parishioner. The man was young, but already a chronic alcoholic. His father, also a drunkard, Beecher had been able to help; not so the son. "I indulge the hope," Beecher was to say later, "that God saw it was a constitutional infirmity, like any other disease."

That inebriety should be regarded as a disease was not the only shrewd insight gained from this and other tragic pastoral experiences by this remarkable clergyman. What he observed and learned about alcohol he crammed into six sermons on intemperance and preached them in the same year the young man died. They were so well done that they literally anticipated every strategic and tactical device used by temperance workers in the century following. These generations of temperance enthusiasts very often neglected several things, however, that distinguished Lyman Beecher and enabled him to see the problem so clearly—his humility and his refusal to condemn. Beecher remarked:

Nothing should be said by way of crimination for the past; for verily we all have been guilty in this thing. . . . All language of impatient censure against those who embarked in the traffic of ardent spirits while it was deemed a lawful calling should therefore be forborne. It would only serve to irritate, and arouse prejudice, and pervert investigation, and concentrate a deaf and deadly opposition against the work of reformation. . . . Let us all rather confess the sins which are past, and leave the things which are behind, and press forward in an harmonious attempt to reform the land, and perpetuate our invaluable blessings.

Beecher's desire was to acquaint the people with the facts and this became at once his greatest hope and chosen method. Other means might be used, but it was upon education he chose to place most reliance. Employers would remove liquor from their establishments as soon as they knew its economic loss. People would not drink when they learned it was unnecessary to their health. Christians would unite in opposition against it when they understood its violent effect on their spiritual lives. A society of some kind was required if these facts were to be brought to public attention as they deserved, and in 1827 the American Temperance Society was organized.

The nine annual reports of this society, ending with 1836, deal heavily with the economic and moral costs of inebriety. They revile the grogshop keeper. They appeal to medical opinion. They solicit the condemnation of the church. But of immediate interest to us is the fact that for the first time in American history sympathetic, religious effort was extended toward the rehabilitation of the common drunkard. Not often stated as one of the cardinal aims—for the cardinal aim was to prevent drinking—but always implied, was that of rescuing the alcoholic. In the seventh annual report, for example, there are listed 38 persons from one New York village who had been restored to sobriety by the temperance workers. Almost invariably these little case histories wind up with the statement that the subject had returned to the church and to a religious framework of life.

These restorations not only did something to those who experienced them, but also to those who helped bring them about. Says the author of the document:

Those of my neighbors, who have undertaken, in reliance upon God, the work of reforming drunkards, do not feel and act toward these wretched beings as they once did. They have learned highly prized lessons on this subject in the great school of Temperance Reform. Formerly, they despised the drunkard. Now they feel, that no class of men are entitled to draw so largely on their compassion, as drunkards are; and especially do they feel this, when they consider how much they have themselves done to make drunkards. For who of us can in truth say, that he has done nothing towards continuing the rum drinking custom in our country?

Continuing with his report, the same writer makes some further observations as to the reasons of therapeutic success:

The drunkard's self-despair arises, in great measure, from the conviction, that he is an outcast from public respect and sympathy. Of this we have been aware in our efforts to reform him; and we have sought to show him, that, as to ourselves at least, this conviction shall henceforth be groundless. We have taken great pains to persuade him that we are his friends, and that every improvement in his habits, however slight, would proportionally and promptly elevate him in our esteem. We have also cheerfully consented to the practice of self-denial, by which we could gain his confidence; for in no way can you surely win men's hearts to you as by submitting to obvious self-denial for their sakes. . . . Whilst inculcating the doctrine, that the drunkard, to be thoroughly reformed, must relinquish wine, cider, and malt liquors, as well as ardent spirit, we have seen and submitted to the necessity of giving up these drinks ourselves. . . . But should we, whilst insisting upon his disuse of these drinks, indulge in them ourselves, he would despise our inconsistency and selfishness; and we would only make the matter worse, by attempting to justify ourselves in saying to him: "These drinks are safe for us who are sober; but you, who have lost your self-control, are not to be trusted with them."

As to the extent of this reclamation, not too much is said. The annual report of 1833 states that in 5 years of existence the society had managed to sober up 5,000 known drunkards. The emphasis, in statistical reports at least, was placed on membership in the societies—which in this year was claimed to be above one million—and on the reduction of distilleries and other similar gains. In 1836 the American Temperance Society became the American Temperance Union, and its pledge was broadened to include abstinence from all alcoholic beverages. Within 3 years, 350,000 persons had signed this pledge, but the efforts to reclaim the drunkard seem to have dropped from sight.

The Washingtonian Movement

Perhaps the most famous of all religious movements for the reform of the drunkard was the Washington Temperance Society, organized in April, 1840, in Baltimore. Let me quote the very interesting account of its origin:

Six individuals, who were in the habit of associating together, were seated, as usual, on Friday evening, the second of April, 1840, in Chase's Tavern, in Liberty Street, Baltimore, where they were accustomed to meet almost every evening for the purpose of enjoying mutually the benefits which the establishment and the society of each other could possibly afford. There were, William K. Mitchell, tailor; John H. Hose, carpenter; David Anderson, blacksmith; George Steers, blacksmith; James McCurley, coachmaker; and Archibald Campbell, silver plater. A clergyman, who was preaching in the city at the time, had given public notice that on that evening he would deliver a discourse upon the subject of temperance. Upon this lecture the conversation of our six heroes presently turned; whereupon it was determined that four of them should go and hear it and report accordingly. After the sermon they returned, and discoursed on its merits for sometime; when one of the company remarked that, "After all temperance is a good thing." "Oh," said the host, "they're all a parcel of hypocrites." "Oh, yes," replied McCurley, "I'll be bound for you; it's your interest to cry them down, anyhow." "Tell you what, boys," says Steers, "let's form a society and make Bill Mitchell president." "Agreed," cried they. The idea seemed to take wonderfully; and the more they laughed and talked over it, the more they were pleased with it.

After parting that night they did not all meet again until Sunday, when they took a stroll, and, between walking and treating, they managed to arrange the matter to their entire satisfaction. It was agreed that one of them should draw up a pledge, and that the whole party should sign it the next day. Accordingly, on Monday morning, William K. Mitchell wrote the following pledge:

"We, whose names are annexed, desirous of forming a society for our mutual benefit, and to guard against a pernicious practice which is injurious to our health, standing, and families, do pledge ourselves as gentlemen that we will not drink any spirituous or malt liquor, wine, or cider."

He went with it about nine o'clock to Anderson's house, and found him still in bed, sick from the effects of his Sunday adventure. He arose, however, dressed himself, and, after hearing the pledge read, went down to his shop with his friend for pen and ink, and there did himself the honor of being the first man who signed the Washington pledge.

All the rest signed the pledge, of course, and they continued at first to meet in their old rendezvous on Liberty Street. At their second meeting they had two new members, and the subsequent meetings became so large that they were soon compelled to find other quarters. By Christmas time they had enrolled thousands of new members. Their historian says:

The peculiar characteristics were: First, a total abstinence pledge. The idea of a partial pledge seems never to have entered the minds of these honest fellows. Second, the telling to others what they had known by experience of the evils of intemperance and of the good which they felt from entire abstinence. They knew of but one way to rid the world of the evil, and that was to strike directly at its root. They knew, too, if others could know as they did of the suffering which resulted from the custom of drinking, they would renounce forever this destructive habit.

The Society was filled with evangelical zeal. Within a short time they descended upon New York City, there holding many meetings with the double aim of getting temperance pledges signed and of sobering up the inebriates. Nor was their influence channeled through their own Society alone. Numerous other groups sprang up under their direct stimulation. The Sons of Temperance, the Temple of Honor, the Order of Good Templars, the Cadets of Temperance, and the Bands of Hope, were a few of those owing their origin to the efforts of the Washingtonians. The missionaries chosen were invariably former inebriates.

The explanation given for their success was a simple one. In the first quarterly report, in 1841, we read:

The man takes a pledge, and from his bottle companions obtains a number of signers, who likewise become sober men. Positively, these are facts. Now, can any human agency alone do this? All will answer, No; for we have invariably the testimony of vast numbers of reformed men, who have spoken in public and declared they have broken off a number of times, but have as often relapsed again: and the reason they give for doing this is, that they wholly rely on the strength of their resolution without looking any higher, but now they feel the need of God's assistance, which having obtained, their reform is genuine. The question is often asked, and with a great deal of propriety, too, Do they all hold out who sign the pledge? We answer, No. Some—and be assured, the number is very small—go back to drinking again; but as soon as it is known to any of the society that this is the case, the backslider is waited upon by some friend, who seldom fails to induce him to sign the pledge again and commence anew, and then the fact of his having violated the pledge fills him with shame and repentance and is the means of his adhering more rigidly to it.

The work of the Society did not end even here. When the inebriate had signed his pledge, they reported, his first business was to get rid of his filthy rags, and his second to take care of his family,

which he can very soon accomplish by applying to our committee for relief, who immediately looks into their wants and renders them all aid in their power. . . . We have furnished a large amount of clothing to those who have been entirely destitute of everything but what they stood in, and that so filthy that it was necessary, before they could put on anything clean, to go and strip themselves and thoroughly wash their bodies; and the next thing to look to was the family—if a group of half-starved beings could be called a family. . . .

This practical kindness was incumbent, then as now, for there were no resources available. The society of the day, the members noted with melancholy, might pull a drunkard out of the street to keep the horses from running over him, but that was all. They asserted:

The community should be made acquainted with the fact that the reformation of one drunkard is of more value to them than they probably appreciate at present. In the first place, a public nuisance is abated; for surely such is a drunkard. Next, a family is provided for, by him on whom the duty should devolve. An acquisition is made to society. You have the skill and product of the industry of the reformed man; and instead of having him to support, he assists to support those who are really objects of charity; he is zealously engaged in reforming his fellow-inebriates; he becomes a useful member of society in whatever sphere he may move. . . .

Eventually, as the movement gained strength, the idea of an institution for treatment purposes rose in favor. Known as the "Home for the Fallen," it was opened on September 5, 1858, under the superintendency of Albert Day. Medical and religious interests alike had combined in support of the venture, and it was looked upon as a permanent step forward in the treatment of inebriety, which had so long been a principal interest of the Society.

Habitual drunkenness was considered to be a physical as well as a mental and moral disease, and medical care was therefore to be made available, but stress was laid on moral treatment. Members of the staff were to treat their patients as "members of a well regulated family." Attendance at prayer and other religious services was entirely voluntary, and coercion in any other matter was strictly forbidden.

One of the leading features of the Home Government [was] the entire absence of any compulsory restraint upon the movements of the inmates, they being allowed to go and come at pleasure, walking the city, and going and coming at will, under the sacred parole of honor that they will strictly observe the very mild and salutary laws of the institution of which they are inmates and members.

These unusual liberties were possibly granted in part as a revolt against the confinement of the inebriate in prisons and mental institutions then common. For the rest, they represented the studied belief of the Washingtonians that reformation was a possibility only when the patient found the strength he needed in his own person and in his God. Their philosophy of treatment and their practical methods were plainly stated in a lecture entitled "A Plea for the Intemperate," delivered in 1841 by Dr. David M. Reese of the Albany Medical College. He asked:

Can it be that in a Christian nation there are more drunkards than Christians? . . . The treatment of the victim of intemperance can [not] be expected, until the public estimate of such shall be revolutionized, and the idea of their hopelessness no longer finds a place in the public creed. They are shunned and avoided as though, like the sufferers by the ancient leprosy, or the more modern plague, their presence was contagion, and their very touch death. . . . But we plead in their behalf, that they are men; fallen men, it is true, degraded men, physically and morally diseased, but not invariably so. . . .

When the inebriate is in a sober moment, said Dr. Reese, let someone gain his confidence by unequivocal proofs of affection for him as a fellow being, and by similar proofs of a sincere desire to be his friend. Reason with him at such intervals and you will find him accessible, especially if you convince him that amidst the wreck of friends, which he has consciously suffered, there is one who still survives, whose heart throbs with emotions of human sympathy, and who still cares for his soul. . . . Having secured his confidence, you may now tell him, in all faithfulness, but still in tones of kindness, that he is destroying his health, blasting his character. . . . Now he will put in his plea of extenuation, and allege that he cannot help it; that he has made the effort again and again; that he has sincerely, honestly, and faithfully tried to abandon his destructive habit, but he cannot help it . . . it is true that "he cannot help it"; and if unaided by human instrumentality, he must perish. . . . You may remind him that when there is help nowhere else, there is help in God, and that "earth knows no sorrows that Heaven cannot heal"; and by these and like means you may prepare him to give you some proof of his sincerity to forever abandon the inebriating cup. This can be done by inducing him to become a member of the Order of the Sons of Temperance, or some other association of that kind, pledged to the principles of total abstinence, and thereby surrounding him with individuals and associations that are constantly bringing before his eyes the miseries of the past and anticipations of the future. . . . The past must be buried in everlasting forgetfulness, no allusion being made to it by word or deed. Let him be treated precisely as though he had never fallen, and soon your reclaimed neighbor will feel that he is himself again, and show you that he is a man. . . . We are prepared here to record our deliberate persuasion that there is good ground for hope for every drunkard in the land, if each of them can have one friend who is willing to admit our plea and act accordingly. . . .

Writing nearly 50 years later, William Henry Blair, then United States Senator from New Hampshire and a prohibitionist, was not disposed to admit that the Washingtonian movement had been of any very discernible use to the nation. He said of the early members:

They kept the pledge, became apostles of its principles, and the movement spread all over the land. In a few years six hundred thousand drunkards had been reformed, of whom, however, all but one hundred and fifty thousand returned to their cups. The moral of this movement is that we must save the boy if we would be sure of the man. On the whole, it may be doubted whether the Washingtonian excitement was a blessing or a curse; because, unfortunately, many of its most zealous and active promoters discouraged all resort to the enactment and enforcement of laws against the traffic. The result was that when the nervous exaltation of the communities had passed away, and the extra momentum of moral forces was exhausted, public sentiment not being crystallized into the enduring forms of law, the enemy came in again like a flood and prevailed mightily once more. To be sure, one hundred and fifty thousand reformed men had adhered to their pledges and were saved; but what are one hundred and fifty thousand among so many?

Whether the good Senator was right in his final summation is debatable, but surely to the credit of the Washingtonian movement must be placed this fact: More than any other group they drew public attention to the inebriate as a sick man, in need of kindness and wholesome medical and spiritual care. They laid the groundwork upon which all similar movements of later date have built their structures and their programs.

ACHIEVEMENTS OF FATHER MATHEW

To be an Irishman during the nineteenth century, according to some observers who have been somewhat prejudiced in the matter, was to be a drunkard. That Ireland had been converted once was commonly known, and a bit disapproved of in the best American circles. The Irish were a bit too much on the Roman Catholic side to suit unyielding gentlemen of Calvinistic persuasion. Consequently, America—and the rest of the world to boot—was startled when it learned that Ireland had been converted a second time. This was the conversion from riotous and carefree drinking to absolute sobriety. The man who accomplished this feat in several short years, according to enthusiastic biographers of his own day, was a plump priest of medium height and a good fund of humor. His name was Theobald Mathew, and the Society of Friends got him into the temperance business. He was bearded one day in Cork by what the biographer called a "respectable protestant," and the task of temperance reform laid upon him. "Mr. Mathew," the old man said, "you have got the mission, do not reject it."

For a year and a half thereafter—it was in 1838 that Father Mathew began his work—things moved along quietly and not at all spectacularly. Gradually, however, the fame of the society that was meeting regularly in a place called the "Horse Bazaar" traveled along the banks of the Shannon. Men came from Kilrush, from Kerry, and Limerick. At first they came by the dozens and hundreds, and then they demanded that Father Mathew come to them. Day after day he traveled the length and breadth of Ireland, making temperance talks, taking pledges, and blessing those who gave their word to abstain in the future.

Of the Irish people, the biographer further observes, it may be said that they are "of quick, of intuitive perception; they see promptly, and see correctly what is good or evil. They are a people of ardour and impulse, and what they do, they do at once. Their quickest acts are generally their best; and he that would get them to do great things must go with the rapid current of their thoughts and feelings." Father Mathew was obviously capable of matching their stride. He took pledges in the early morning hours, or at sunrise; he received them while he was at lunch or on horseback; he took them singly when he could persuade an individual, and he took them eight or ten thousand at a time. One report says:

It is no exaggeration to state that between Galway, Lihghrea, and the road to Portumna, there were from 180,000 to 200,000 persons who took the pledge, and received the benediction of this extraordinary man. Wherever Mr. Mathew administered the pledge, he admonished the people on the nature of the promise they were about to make, and the inviolability with which it should be observed. He said to them that when casting off the yoke of intemperance, they should also abandon every other vice, such as rioting, faction, fighting, private combinations, illegal taking of firearms, serving threatening notices, and so on. He exhorted them to forget religious animosities, to live in peace with all, to observe the laws of God and man, and to respect the powers that be, not from fear, but for conscience's sake. He spoke with great ease and fluency, and his addresses were remarkable for their variety and appropriateness.

Of the exact numbers who entered upon the abstinent life at Father Mathew's instance, history cannot tell. Observers estimated that millions fell under his influence, and claims were made that within the period of one year Ireland's consumption of ardent spirits was almost halved. In any event he worked notably for a period of about 10 years and won for himself a name that stands out not only in Ireland, but also in the United States, which he visited in 1849.

Again he enjoyed remarkable success. The Irish population of the eastern cities heard him with interest and enthusiasm, and he left in his path dozens of "Father Mathew Total Abstinence Societies." One history of the temperance movement, entitled *Battling with the Demon*, records that perhaps 7 out of 10 of those who took their temperance medals from him relapsed into their old habits. But he had added a great impetus to the temperance movement here, and among a people who had previously been untouched by it. Following him the Paulists, Passionists and Jesuits especially concerned themselves with education among the people to whom they ministered, and Father Mathew's groups became the basis of the Roman Catholic Total Abstinence Union of a few years later.

By some of his contemporaries the good Father was regarded more as an enthusiastic reformer than an organizer, but, as far as I can learn his effectiveness silenced even the critics among the respectable Protestants who claimed the honor of having started him off. More than that, he may well have been an important influence in shaping the attitudes of the Right Reverend John Ireland, to whom Pope Leo XIII addressed a communication on temperance in 1887, and of James, Cardinal Gibbons, a powerful advocate of temperance and abstinence among the Catholic population of their days.

Religious Sponsorship of Treatment of Inebriety

The revival of interest in reclaiming the inebriate and in helping him to a new way of life was not confined to the Washingtonian movement. Parallel with it were the programs and efforts of many lesser known individuals and groups. Each of these aided in the creation of positive sentiment toward the alcoholic, but most of the efforts were short-lived.

An almost unrivaled record of persistence was established by Dr. J. Edward Turner. While still a student in medical school he became interested in inebriety, became convinced that it was a disease in the narrow sense of the word, and decided to devote his full interest to it. For 16 years following this, according to his own claims, he labored to bring about the erection of the institution that was finally to be known as the New York State Inebriate Asylum.

During this time, he stated, he made over 70,000 calls on potential subscribers to the work, innumerable visits to physicians and clergy, distributed 20,000 pieces of educational literature on the subject, and took 4 transatlantic trips to study European methods of treatment.

Whatever may have been the truth of later charges that he mishandled institutional funds, respect must be paid to Dr. Turner for the tremendous educational job accomplished. He met with opposition in the New York Legislature, which could not see the point of appropriating tax funds for the care of the alcoholic, or even passing legislation of a character enabling treatment. He met with point-blank refusals from persons he solicited. Said one farmer: "I cannot believe the disease theory of drunkenness. My Bible teaches that the drunkard is a criminal in the sight of God, and he is forever debarred from heaven." Another gentleman, a college professor, "refused his signature on the ground that the enterprise of building asylums for the drunkard would encourage drinking. The moderate drinker would imagine that if he became a drunkard he would go to an asylum and be cured, and hence the fear of becoming such would be entirely removed."

That all persons of moral conviction did not share these sentiments was evidenced by the fact that the Rev. Henry Bellows of Union Theological Seminary, in New York, as well as many other clergymen, actively assisted in the work. At the laying of the cornerstone of the institution on September 24, 1858, Dr. Bellows made some remarks that are as true today as when he made them:

I remark that it can never weaken the sense of moral responsibility, anywhere, privately or publicly, to acknowledge anything that is true; and that there is not the least reason to fear, that to make provision for the rescue of the miserable victims of an hereditary or abnormal appetite for drink will diminish in the least, in those conscious of the power and obligations of self-control, the disposition of the conscience to exercise them.

We might as well expect public schools for the indigent to weaken the standard of private education among the wealthy; or asylums for the deaf and blind, to make possessors of perfect eyes and ears careless of their safety, and indifferent to their preservation; or humanity towards the aged and the suffering to promote idleness and improvidence among the young and healthy; or forcible restraint for the violent, to destroy the habits of self-control among the peaceable, as to imagine that asylums for inebriates will promote and increase drunkenness. . . .

We have indeed, never a right to ask the blasphemous question, what the effect upon society is to be, of human and just measures. We may trust that the effect of such measures will be good, and only good, from the nature of things.

By 1868, even though he had been ousted from the institution and was busily at work attempting to establish another, it was plain that Dr. Turner's ideas, assisted by expositions of Dr. Bellows and other religious leaders, had begun to take hold of the public. In the *Atlantic Monthly* of that year an article by Parton declared:

Inebriate asylums, rationally conducted, cannot fail to be worth their cost. They are probably destined to become as generally recognized a necessity of our diseased modern life as asylums for lunatics and hospitals for the sick. . . . It is possible that the cure of inebriates may become a speciality of the medical practice, to which men, gifted with requisite talent, will devote their lives. . . .

A few other institutions dedicated to the care of the inebriate were sponsored by religious groups in the late nineteenth century. Among these was the New York Home for Intemperate Men founded in 1877 as a result of Moody and Sankey gospel meetings. This institution is still in existence, known as Chester Crest, but apparently it never aspired to anything but the most elementary medical care. Others of lesser reputation flourished for a brief time and passed away. Much work was done in city missions and particularly by the Salvation Army. The Army, however, has focused its efforts on the conversion experience and has made use of its own general facilities and of other community resources when these were needed in aftercare. Those who wish to read a portrayal of the Salvation Army's methods and approach may consult Hall's biography of Henry F. Milans (*Out of the Depth*).

Generally speaking, the Salvationists have capitalized on the same techniques that have made other reform programs work: (*1*) Insistence on total abstinence; (*2*) reliance upon God; (*3*) the provision of new friendships among those who understand; (*4*) the opportunity to work with those who suffer from the same difficulty; and (*5*) unruffled patience and consistent faith in the ability of the individual and in the power of God to accomplish the desired ends.

After Milans' conversion, says Hall, he sat out in the open in New York City and "the consciousness of an Almighty Presence, imminent and interested, gave his spirit great calm. There, in the solitudes of the great city, on a park bench, the Presence seemed to whisper to him lovingly: 'Fear not, I will help thee; I will sustain thee, for I have redeemed thee. Thou art mine!' And strength came to him."

The Emmanuel Clinic

Illustrative of a later development in the use of religious elements in the treatment of inebriety is the work of the Rev. Dr. Elwood Worcester and Samuel McComb, together with that of the physician, Isador H. Coriat, at Emmanuel Church in Boston. Begun shortly after the turn of the century, the so-called Emmanuel movement had a lively impact on the thinking of churchmen and church workers in this country.

The center of the work was the clinic operated under the auspices of the church. The philosophy was that both medicine and religion have essential places in the treatment of any disease, but most particularly in the treatment of the functional illnesses. In the first book published by these three men, *Religion and Medicine*, they strive to inform the public on what they are attempting:

We believe in the power of the mind over the body, and we believe also in medicine, in good habits, and in a wholesome, well regulated life. In the treatment of functional nervous disorders we make free use of moral and psychical agencies, but we do not believe in overtaxing these valuable aids by expecting the mind to attain results which can be effected more easily through physical instrumentalities.

Scientific procedures were employed in diagnosis and case records were kept. The use of specialists was frequent. When physical medicine was indicated, it was given, but it was accompanied by skilled religious counseling. The then current knowledge and opinions on the nature of the unconscious mind were freely drawn upon by specialists. Suggestion and autosuggestion were frankly employed.

In connection with inebriety, many of the viewpoints expressed by these workers have been subsequently rejected. They accepted the theory of reproductive germ damage; they held that children of drunkards suffer to an almost incredible extent from various forms of mental and nervous diseases; that these children will inherit enfeebled or defective physical constitutions because of their parents' constant tippling, and so on. The only differential diagnosis was between the chronic alcoholic and the dipsomaniac, by which they distinguished between the steady drinker and the periodic. The principal form of treatment, when abstinence was agreed to, was hypnosis and suggestion. All this was in 1908. By 1931, Worcester and McComb, again writing jointly, their book this time called *Body, Mind, Spirit,* had seen, and had liberally used, many advances in the field of medical psychology. The older doctrines of Charcot and Coué had given way before those of Freud, and much was taken from the latter. But the firm belief in the instrumentality of religion remained unshaken, and the equally firm belief that religion and medicine must go hand in hand:

From the beginning we have associated ourselves with competent medical men and surgeons. Indeed, had such cooperation been refused, I should not have dreamed of assuming responsibility for the sick in mind and body. For many years most of our patients have been sent to us by physicians, and in all cases which involved more than the need of moral and spiritual advice we have left no stone unturned to procure the best diagnosis and medical care obtainable.

In dealing with the inebriate, three conditions are laid down. The alcoholic must wish to stop of his own volition and not simply because his wife or someone else requires him to submit to treatment. Only those who seriously propose total abstinence for the rest of their lives are accepted for treatment. And no discussions are held with persons who are in a state of intoxication.

The treatment process, after these conditions have been satisfied, is partially in the field of therapeutic analysis of the patient's problems, the use of suggestion, and sometimes hypnosis. Suggestion is used only when the patient has been relaxed and is in condition to respond to it. Specifically, something like this is said:

You have determined to break this habit, and you have already gone . . . days without a drink. The desire is fading out of your mind, and the habit is losing its power over you. You need not be afraid that you will suffer, for you will not suffer at all. In a short time liquor in any form will have no attraction for you. It will be associated in your mind with weakness and sorrow and sickness and failure. . . .

The patient is built up physically by the use of nourishing food, exercise, outdoor living, and so on. There is a search for new occupations and interests. "On the whole, our successes have been far more frequent than our failures," the authors report.

Out of the Emmanuel movement has grown a very definite interest in the alcoholic. Mr. Courtenay Baylor, whose name is familiar to students of the treatment of inebriety, was long associated with Drs. Worcester and McComb. Those who wish to know more about his views and methods may read Dwight Anderson's article "The place of the lay therapist in the treatment of alcoholics" in the QUARTERLY JOURNAL OF STUDIES ON ALCOHOL (Sept. 1944). The principal elements in the treatment are catharsis, surrender, and relaxation— and these are carried out or induced through the use of religion.

Conclusion

This has been a brief and highly selective survey of a century's efforts among religious people to bring the healing power of God into the lives of those who suffer from inebriety. Certain things may be held as conclusive. Towering above them all is this indisputable fact: It is faith in the living God which has accounted for more recoveries from the disease than all the other therapeutic agencies put together. How men will explain this—how they will deal with the realities of changed lives—remains with their reason, their judgment, and their conscience. But the realities are there. There have been those moments in the lives of millions when the tension in their souls was over, when they felt a happy relaxation, when they could breathe calmly again, when they did not need to be afraid any more, when they knew, indeed, the secret of James' "eternal present," which, after all, is better put as the "eternal presence."

Quite in the same way we have seen that the means by which these redemptions have been achieved have almost invariably been the same. There have been present good, kind friends, who understood so much they did not have to be told, who could listen without condemnation to any recital of human misery, who could tell their own stories of defeat and victory over failure, who could keep on believing in their drunken friends no matter what happened. They could believe so much, that their faith was contagious; and eventually it passed into the lives of those they wanted to help. Regardless of their gifts of background, their intellectual and other endowments, the thing that has chiefly characterized all of these friends has been their humility in the face of the weakness of themselves and others, and their unquestioning reliance upon the wisdom and grace of God. Highbrows and bums, rich men and poor, judges and carpenters, prisoners and clergymen—they have all been successful as long as they have said with the Psalmist: "God is our refuge and our strength."

We have also seen something of the long battle put up by spirited, self-sacrificing men to gain public acceptance of the knowledge that inebriety is a disease, and that the alcoholic suffers as acutely and as tragically as anyone afflicted with any other of the wide range of human ills. It has come as a shock to some of us to know that what we have recently heard about as the problem of convincing the public that the inebriate is a sick man is a problem recognized for many decades, and by practically all those who have honestly tried to help since the beginning of the nineteenth century. The most sensitive students saw the matter clearly then, as the most sensitive see it now. Yet, rather than be discouraged because of the slow advances in public opinion, we must all accept it as a challenge. We are not a lesser breed. We know more, and we believe as much.

Let me close with a quotation from the Rev. Dr. Roswell D. Hitchcock, an associate of Dr. Bellows, this time from a speech made before a small audience in New York in 1855. He was pleading for the establishment of a decent place to house and treat the inebriates of his own day. As we pick up his address, we note that he has just said that the creation of an institution is not a question of ethics or of speculation, but a work in which we may all engage without surrendering the other ways in which we think the alcohol problem may be solved. He continues as follows:

Daily there reel in our streets intoxicated men, boisterous and violent, endangering the peace of society in public places, carrying a curse to dependent families; daily the grip of the law tightens upon them and drags them to answer for their evil deeds. What shall be done with these men? As things now are we have nothing for them but our prisons. The man who has been guilty of only one glass too much, goes in with felons, and takes the chance of coming out again a felon himself. In any case, we must foot his bills, providing him with food and clothing. Is it not immeasurably better, both for him, for his family, and for ourselves, to give him an asylum rather than a cell? Which is better—I put it to Christian feeling, nay, I put it to common sense—which is better, the iron wristlets or the silken cord?

There is room for much in the solution of our alcohol problem—for interest and earnestness and zeal—but none for condemnation and rancor and bitter reviling. It is understanding which intelligent churchmanship must seek, not a scapegoat. In point of fact, it is well for us to begin just where Lyman Beecher did—with an honest confession of complicity in the sin of the kind of a world which can produce alcoholics.

Social Case Work with Inebriates

Sybil M. Baker

URING the past month you have thought of the inebriate as a sick person. You have studied his body from a physiological standpoint, you have examined his personality to learn the effects of alcohol and for help in understanding his reactions. You have been told of the sociological implications. The alcoholic has been revealed not only as an individual who needs help, but as a member of society whose behavior influences and is influenced by all sorts of other people and situations. The laws that have been drawn up to protect and punish him have been described to you. You have now reached the point where you are thinking of the solution of the alcohol problem through education, control and treatment of the alcoholic individual by psychiatry, medicine, religion, social case work, and group activities that provide substitution and conversion.

BACKGROUND OF SOCIAL CASE WORK

Because you represent all professional fields there will be considerable variance in your previous knowledge and understanding of my subject. Some of you who are social workers will bear with me if I tell you much that you already know. Probably there is no profession about which there is more confusion. When one talks of a doctor of medicine, everyone knows there has been certain specialized training resulting in an ability to pass examinations to obtain state licenses. The same is true of the lawyer or the nurse. Most people know what a minister, an architect, or an engineer is. In all of these professions there are people with the same training and experience, but in social work there is a traditional use of the title for almost all who help other people, especially those who are poor or in trouble. Social work really began at the time of St. Vincent de Paul. Through the years the emphasis has changed from work for or with the poor or unfortunate to assistance to anyone who is unable to lead a productive and satisfying life with his own resources. The art or skill of helping is considered as important as the help itself, for without the skill the intended help may really hinder.

Training is now standardized in a 2-year uniform program following 4 years of college. Many of our best older social workers have not completed such a curriculum but, instead, have served a full apprenticeship in a reputable agency. If they have continued to study and read and to take special courses, they probably have acquired the same basic knowledge as the school graduates. It is difficult now, however, for anyone to obtain recognition as a professional social worker without the academic training. Particularly is this true of social case work. I go into all this detail because I want you to know what you have the right to expect of the social case worker.

The student in the graduate school spends about half of his time in the classroom. There he is given a brief picture of physiology and disease, not how to diagnose a condition but how to become aware of certain symptoms and their significance and to obtain knowledge of the etiologies and possible means of prevention. He also gains a knowledge of psychology, psychiatry, sociology, community organization, and government. The law curriculum includes law relating to the family, to housing, indebtedness and social protection. Household management and nutrition are also studied. In all of these the emphasis is on the social significance and on developing an awareness of the problem and of the resources available for its treatment.

What are the norms and acceptable variations? Case work is the tool or skill with which a social worker endeavors to assist families and individuals in developing both capacity and the opportunity to lead personally satisfying and socially useful lives. Most of this skill is developed and utilized through interviewing—a process whereby the client is encouraged to talk of his experiences, his anxieties and his aspirations, helped to seek for and verbalize what he feels to be the cause of his difficulty, and to understand his experiences and his reactions to them. He is encouraged to recognize and develop his strength and resources, to seek treatment for his weaknesses or to accept them as untreatable. The social case worker acquires part of this skill in the classroom by a study of techniques and an analysis of the practices of other workers. But the other half of the graduate school experience is spent as an apprentice in the field of social work under supervision. There the student is taught how to establish contacts, how to strengthen the relationship, inspire confidence, and control interviews. The last may sound authoritative but it really is not. Some clients wander in talking, evade certain points; others reveal emotional problems which only the most skillful can handle. The case worker must not only learn how to stimulate the client's desire to give essential data but also her own limitations, so that the client will not bring out emotional problems beyond the case worker's skill and capacity to treat. She must have warmth, yet not identify herself emotionally with the client. As she is often working with more than one person in the family or the community, she must maintain impartiality in her case work. Otherwise, the client is not free to help himself. Of all the professions, social case work is undoubtedly the most conscious of its dependence on others, and their interdependence. It draws on all the professions for diagnosis and treatment, as its goal is well-rounded, satisfying and productive living. It is conscious of gaps in the community pattern resulting in voids or situations inimical to social welfare. And it is one of the functions of social work to make sure of the facts, demonstrate the need, and attempt to arouse the interest of those best qualified to remedy the situation.

You come from all over the country; you know many social workers. As I go on to the presentation of case material I want you to try to evaluate the depth of the case work involved and the skills utilized so that you can determine what those social workers whom you know can perform at the different levels of treatment. In your own experience try to think of the contributions of other professional people, recognize the limitations imposed on you by reason of education, personality, time and experience. Consult the others and draw them into your planning. Your own work will be enriched thereby and those you wish to help will likewise benefit.

There is no one answer to the problem of inebriety, probably no one solution to any single problem. You perhaps know the story of the rural judge who wanted to impress his court with his learning. He bought a fancy book cover, but the sheets in it seemed so thin that he substituted a Sears-Roebuck catalogue. One day a man was brought before him for misdemeanor. The judge opened his book, perused it carefully, and said, "I fine you $3.99." The arrested man protested. Quickly the clerk stopped him and whispered, "You can just be thankful he's looking at pants and not pianos." We can be thankful that there are any cured alcoholics, for their treatment has been just as haphazard. Fortunately, some reached the one kind of treatment that could help them most. Now, with the introduction of the diagnostic clinic to try to determine the type of alcoholic and the type of treatment to which he is most likely to respond, we can hope for better results. This utilization of all resources is the basic philosophy of social case work.

We have another basic philosophy, one of the most widely accepted in our field, and I quote from Florence Hollis: "The client must be in control of the guiding of his own life, making for himself the choices that are necessary, in fitting his individual desires into the social fabric. The case worker may help him to see more clearly the nature of the world in which he lives, may help him to use his own powers more effectively, and may at times soften the impact of external reality. But the final choice of the pattern the client wants his life to take, in matters large and small, is his and not the worker's to make." Perhaps there are some diseases that affect the individual alone. If you break a leg, it is your leg and you cannot walk, but immediately someone else has to feed, bathe and care for you. Perhaps you broke it by accident, or through carelessness; you feel guilty about it and angry about having this broken leg imposed upon you. Maybe someone has to take your place in business to support the family. Inebriety almost invariably affects others as well as the alcoholic; it produces innumerable emotional reactions so that the behavior of others close to him, the marital partner, for example, is altered or aggravated. Many people say that we ought not to study the alcoholic but the person the alcoholic married. A vicious circle is created and even if the alcoholic ceases drinking, the social situation may be fraught with danger and block the accomplishments that we really seek. Therefore, the social case worker seldom sees the alcoholic as an isolated person but rather as an integral part of the world he lives in. Others in that world must gain insight into his problem and their reaction to it in order to help him become a well-adjusted person like themselves.

EXCERPTS FROM CASE RECORDS

Case 1

Mrs. M., for example, was an executive, a capable person, better educated than her husband. She could earn more on very satisfying jobs. She was jealous of their only child, who favored the father. She knew all the facts of inebriety and asked help in meeting them. Mr. M. had worked irregularly and drank almost constantly except during brief periods of abstinence. Her need was to have him drink to reveal himself as her inferior. She took him for medical and psychiatric treatment and then removed him against advice. She pushed him toward undesirable jobs, always rationalizing that they were desirable. A separation might be necessary to release Mr. M. to work out his own solution. In the meantime, she was the one who needed case-work therapy. She sought the worker's advice and must learn to understand herself and find a satisfying outlet for her emotional drive. Otherwise three lives will be wrecked. I am not implying that she is responsible for his drinking, but she is one of the reasons why he continues.

Case 2

In contrast, Mr. A., 40 years old, was a skilled but irregular worker. He began drinking and getting into difficulty at 17. When examined by the physician he was found to have a congenital deformity of the sexual organs, easily corrected by operation. More than 2 years earlier he had obtained medical advice, but shame and fear prevented the operation from being performed, although he once started for the Mayo Clinic, and once even for Europe to have it done. Each time funds were drunk up en route. The psychiatrist was able to help the patient verbalize his fears and to interpret his emotional behavior. The social worker obtained the history from the mother, interpreted the situation to her, and arranged with a surgeon to perform the operation on credit. The money for hospitalization was obtained by loan. He had good potential earning power, so it seemed best to have him meet the cost of getting well himself. After his recovery, the social worker helped him plan for his idle hours. He enjoys bowling and he joined the State Guard. He worked steadily and all bills were paid within a year. Never before secure enough to marry, he did so about 2 years later. There was a brief drinking episode soon after his marriage but his wife was helped to understand and there was no recurrence. This man's inebriety was symptomatic of his great anxiety. Even had the primary cause been removed, the habit of drinking was very strong. It is doubtful whether he could have remained abstinent if substitute activities had not been planned and if members of his family had remained critical and suspicious. In Mr. A.'s case, the social worker did not deal with his emotional problems at all, but her work was in utilization of family and community resources to relieve the emotional strain. Although the skill of interviewing was utilized with the mother it was for interpretive purposes and did not attempt to draw out or treat her own emotional reactions.

Case 3

I now want to read to you excerpts from a record covering 2½ years of close relationship between a social case worker and a family where the husband and father was an alcoholic. I have tried to show the interviewing processes, the use of material furnished, the evaluation of significant data and reactions, to make intensive work seem justified in a seemingly hopeless situation. Here the treatment of the wife was of equal importance to that of the husband. Throughout, the social worker controlled the situation so that other external forces would not interfere with and retard the process. Let us call them the H. family. The father, aged 40, was born in England; the mother, 38, was born in the United States. There were five children when we first knew them; they are now Betty, aged 15, Robert 13, Doris 12, Peter 10, Mary 9; and a 1-year-old baby, Leonard. They first became known to a family agency in October 1940 and had brief contacts until July 1941, the usual requests being for relief; these were met. On October 10, 1941, Mr. H. came to our office to apply for clothing for the children; he had been drinking. Please remember that I am only selecting brief excerpts from the record, as is true of all the excerpts; there are large gaps. After discussing the clothing needs, I talked with him about his drinking. He said he takes a glass of liquor once in a while but does not get intoxicated and has not for a long time. Although this did not seem likely, I dropped the matter and discussed the work situation and job possibilities with him. In going over the clothing needs I pointed out that the family was always being referred for clothing or coming in during emergencies; and that I did not feel we should continue meeting these emergency requests. It would seem that there are reasons in the home that produce emergency situations and that these can be avoided. In this contact, my first with this man, it was necessary to establish a good rapport and not give him an opportunity to create defenses. That was why the subject of drinking was not pursued further. We discussed mainly the problem he was talking about but reverted to a basic cause of the difficulty rather than just the acute need as presented.

In the next few days there were several contacts with the wife. My impression was that Mrs. H. was aggressive, tense, and nervous. An indication of this was that she was worried about her bills and the attachment of her salary. I mentioned that finance companies had a division of personal relations, and that we might contact them. Almost immediately we heard that she had dug out the name of the person in a department of a finance company that we had talked about, and had contacted him, saying we had referred her to the company. About 3 weeks after the first application, Mrs. H. came to the office saying she was very discouraged with Mr. H. "He won't cooperate; his work history is poor." When I asked about his drinking she denied that this was excessive or interfered with his work; she seemed protective of him. She described as one of his difficulties that he was very stubborn, insisting on having his own way even though the whole family suffered as a result. She thought our agency might help him in getting work, but that he did not seem concerned enough to come to our office for an interview. Her whole report was quite superficial. Previously, he had worked in a store as a meat cutter; later, the store was given a liquor license. The employer drank a lot with no harmful effects but Mr. H. got quarrelsome and walked out on the job. Then Mrs. H. began to work; she said there was no alternative. She then said, "He's not an alcoholic and drinking is not a problem with him now." She thought her working did make him feel more inadequate, but there was nothing else she could do. She obviously needed to assert her own independence.

Twelve days later Mrs. H. telephoned for an appointment. She was upset because Mr. H. was drinking very heavily and asked that the worker call. This was done. It was hard to find a place in the living room to sit down. The springs of all the chairs and the couch were broken and resting on the floor, so that one had to sit on the framework of the furniture. There was a small oil burner, but it smoked and the oil leaked onto the floor. Mrs. H. was no longer protective of her husband. He was now drinking heavily and not eating—going to pieces. She thought him a fine person when not drinking. He had always supported the family well until 5 years before. She would hate to get a separation from him because the children were fond of him. She desired help for him. I mentioned the fact that there is a hospital where alcoholics can go for care. We said we would like to see Mr. H. before any decision was made for him to go there. This time the suggestion of a plan was made. That was on a Saturday morning. On Monday morning the worker received a telephone call from the hospital that Mrs. H. had taken her husband there on Saturday afternoon, stating that the social agency would be responsible for all arrangements. When she took him there, his clothing was dirty and ragged. She carried out the same pattern as with the finance company. Four days later Mr. H. left the hospital, against advice, with a diagnosis of hypertension, enlarged liver, high blood pressure and vitamin deficiency. His condition had been quite serious on admission but there had been considerable improvement, although he was still on the verge of delirium tremens. He insisted that he had to go to work as a truck driver. I think that is important; it shows the physical condition that often exists and also emphasizes the fact, which many of us who treat alcoholics feel, that except for the treatment of a physical condition, which is important, not much is accomplished in the sense of long-time treatment unless the patient himself desires it.

That same day Mr. H. came to the office; he was in bad physical condition, rather frightened by his experience. He said he must get hold of himself or there was no hope; that he needed guidance toward finding the right place to work. I told him that we have a vocational guidance department but that he should think it over for a week or more and discuss it later; that he was recovering from an illness and the test results would not be accurate. He accepted that and an appointment was made for the next week. The postponement was to avoid a rash plan to step immediately into something which he had not thought through and into which, at the moment, he might be projecting all the need of his drinking, and the associated problems. If he could get vocational testing just then, the work would be fitted right into that pattern and none of the underlying causes would have been touched at all. A week later he came to the office. He was sober and composed; said he was eating well. This time, vocational guidance was discussed at greater length and it was decided to refer him to the vocational guidance department at the hospital, rather than to the one connected with the agency, so that there would be more chance of getting the out-patient department to care for him later. During this interview he gave considerable family background and employment history. He did not want to return to the trade of meat-cutting; he wanted to learn to be a welder. He had once had a brief experience in a mill, working on machines. As recreational interests he reported bowling and fishing. He commented on his own appearance as that of "a bum." He was offered help in getting a suit. He said Mrs. H.'s earnings did not allow for much in the way of clothing. He talked of her work, saying that he had felt like more of a failure since she had gone to work but now he had made up his mind to do something so that he could support the family and she could stop. The emphasis on the relief, I think, is interesting. We had seen his appearance during all this time, but now it was as if he was trying to do something to get himself out of it, to do something so that his appearance would really make him conspicuous. It was evident that his chances of getting ahead and developing vocationally would be better if he were better dressed, so the suit was purchased for him.

At this time the whole family was brought to the attention of the community. The school, in particular, was making complaints that the children were absent and tardy, probably due to oversleeping; they seemed exhausted in the school, were poorly dressed and neglected, and their heads were infested with lice. We explained to the school what we were doing and said we would try to remedy the situation; that we were thinking of getting a housekeeper for the family. The next day Mrs. H. said she was very happy about the improvement in Mr. H., and this time she was sure he would not drink again. He was more helpful around the house and she has tried to compliment him. There had been no demonstrated affection, but as he was trying, so was she. I pointed out that it was helpful for him to feel important and wanted; without this, there was likely to be more drinking. I expressed my belief that she was too optimistic in saying he would never drink again, because he probably would. If she made up her mind that he would not, she would be disappointed and make the situation worse. She agreed that this might be true, but really thought I might be wrong; rather typical, I think, of a wife. With the permission of Mr. and Mrs. H. I interviewed Mr. H.'s employer. He said that Mr. H. had been a good worker, that drinking had not interfered until the past 5 years; that Mrs. H. was a very aggressive, domineering person, a poor housekeeper and manager, and always had been. She never had liked working at home; preferred working outside. It was interesting that the problem of Mrs. H. was similar to that of Mr. H. They had the same emotional drives, but she resorted to overactivity in employment outside the home, while he resorted to drinking. Because of this, because we were not handling her problem alone at the moment but were trying to work on the relationship between the two, it seemed best for her to continue her work, with the housekeeper going in daily, for we could not take care of her in the house.

The psychologists in the vocational therapy department tested Mr. H., found that he did seem to have promise of success as a welder, and arranged for him to go back on W.P.A. (which was then active), from which he could be transferred to a training project after he had served a certain period. Just before Christmas Mr. H. began drinking again and became very discouraged about his lack of will power; his wife was also downhearted. The house was still in fairly poor condition; the bedding was inadequate. Money for second-hand mattresses was provided, primarily with the hope that the children would get more rest and be adequately warm. During January things continued to get worse. Mrs.

H. thought Mr. H. had no will power left at all, that although his intentions were good he could not rouse himself enough to take any action. She thought she was getting the same way, and that there was nothing she could do to set things right. I asked her where she thought they would end and she said she had been too weary even to think about it. I told Mrs. H. I did not feel their present home conditions could go on as they were. If there were only Mr. and Mrs. H. to consider, that would be one matter, but with five children being neglected, someone must take action. She was probably right in thinking Mr. H. unable to do anything for himself at the present time; perhaps she would have to be the one to arouse him. I told her that the alternative to planned action on her part was the Society for the Prevention of Cruelty to Children. At this point we felt that Mrs. H., at least, had to recognize the reality of the situation, that either she would have to take care of the family or there must be a housekeeper, for there are certain standards below which the children could not be allowed to go. She talked about Mr. H.'s behavior when drinking and his attitude toward the children. This brought out that Mrs. H. thought the children more fond of Mr. H. than of her. He was more demonstrative with them.

In the middle of January Mr. H. asked for hospitalization. It had all been discussed in the previous situation; we felt that he was seeking help and we encouraged him to be admitted. Then we arranged for a housekeeper to come to the home at noon to get the children's lunch and to clean. We commented that the oil burner still leaked, that Mrs. H. had always planned to get things attended to but somehow never carried these plans through to completion. The school was still worried about the children. During the period when Mr. H. was in the hospital the plans for the housekeeper worked out unusually well. The home was clean, the children's attendance became better and the very minimum supply of dishes and things of that sort were furnished. Very soon after his admission, two of the girls were hospitalized; Doris for pediculosis—head lice to such a serious extent that her head was completely shaved; and Mary, with acute appendicitis. The latter was found to be extremely malnourished and while convalescing from the appendicitis, a rheumatic fever set in which showed that we had to plan on a long hospitalization. The school nurse and the physician at the hospital both felt that the condition of the children on admission to the hospital was so serious that they would have to be referred to the Society for the Prevention of Cruelty to Children. That Society, fortunately, agreed to take no action because of the interest and activities of the family agency. That, I think, was a triumph for the case worker, because the intervention of another agency at this point would have disrupted a program to save a family. The S.P.C.C. recognized that and did not intervene.

Mr. H. remained in the hospital for about 2 months, worked part of the time and came home on visits. The family was very anxious to move because they had inadequate and dark rooms. Mr. H. told his wife that after staying in the hospital where everything was kept clean he could not bear to return to a place as dirty as his home. Early in March he had one episode of getting some beer and was very hostile to the hospital and everyone else who was trying to help him. But conditions generally were progressing. The housekeeper was still there, and was getting along fairly well. In April Mr. H. drank a little more. Mrs. H.

threatened a separation. He agreed to accept the conditioned-reflex treatment which was being given at that hospital. But he was very fearful of dying. He sensed that the causes of his inebriety would still be there. Mrs. H. seemed to react to this as though she were an onlooker and not concerned with it at all. He wanted her to stay at home with the children while he was in the hospital, fearing her contact with men at her place of employment. After she had agreed, to please him, we guaranteed aid for the 2 weeks that he would be in the hospital so that Mrs. H. could stay home with the children.

The family then moved to another flat where there was more room and more sun. Mrs. H. shopped for second-hand furniture successfully, having money enough of her own. During this period Mrs. H. had a recurrence of stomach and abdominal pain which the doctor said was "just nerves." A discussion disclosed that she always had the pain when she was home running the house. She felt that she must work; she could not be happy doing housework, yet never again could she leave the family alone. She thought the children needed the housekeeper, who had more control over them than Mrs. H. Mr. H. undertook the conditioned-reflex treatment, then thought he would like to go back to his church and did so; he also took some interest in Alcoholics Anonymous.

In May 1942 Mr. H. was transferred to a training project on the W.P.A. In making plans for Mary's further hospitalization, Mr. H. refused to accept a foster home. The doctors thought they should go ahead without considering him, because he was an alcoholic. But we were able to interpret his needs to be an important part of the plan and the doctors did not insist on acting contrary to his wishes. In interviews with Mrs. H. I tried to give her some understanding of her husband's difficulty and of his need to feel that he was the man of the house and had an important place there; that she was such a smart and capable person that she tended to make him feel unimportant, even though she did not intend to do this. We talked a good deal of women of great importance who had made a great success of their homes because they played themselves down and played their husbands up. We discussed her aggressiveness and its effect on Mr. H. Since Mrs. H. was quite articulate, she was very likely to interrupt him and his tendency was to let her do so and withdraw from the conversation completely. Mrs. H. agreed to try to overcome this and remarked that she had not realized it before. Mrs. H. knew that she could go to work; the housekeeper was available. She was more contented now because she was under no real pressure and did not feel she had to put up with something indefinitely. She did apply for one job but was not hired because the employment manager told her she did not look as though she could take orders. She came to discuss this with me and seemed rather overcome at his telling her this. We discussed her mannerisms and the threats they offered.

In September 1942 Mr. H. had finished his training and was employed at the shipyards as a welder. There had been many intervening complications, difficulties and delays, but during all that period there was no temptation to drink. At this time Mr. H.'s income was quite adequate, and we worked with both him and Mrs. H. in planning the budget and the family expenditures so that they would participate equally in that part of the home arrangements. Between June and November 1942 most of the interviews were with Mrs. H. It seemed necessary to keep in close contact with her, otherwise she might undo some of the work already done with Mr. H. who, in the meantime, was seeing the psychologist and the psychiatrist at the hospital. She did not return to work, although she considered it, and did some typing at home. She occasionally had some abdominal pain. By way of compensation she was encouraged to participate in outside activities, and she attended some cooking classes. It was observed that she was carrying over some of the techniques discussed with her to the training of the children. Christmas 1942 Mrs. H. described as the best Christmas for several years. For one brief moment on Christmas day she had thought of what it had been like a year ago, but immediately forgot, because it was like a nightmare in comparison with the present. In January 1943 Mr. H. was seriously ill with influenza and drank. This seemed much worse to Mrs. H. because her hopes were so high and things had been going so well. She threatened a separation. I said that of course she could do what she felt was best, but if we had become discouraged about Mr. H. as quickly as she did, we would not have thought him worth the investment of our help in the first place. I encouraged her to think of herself as one of those most responsible for his successful treatment.

In May 1943 the family, who had really been constantly seeking to raise the level of their living, were able to obtain an apartment in a housing project. I should report that it, and their home before that, were always immaculately clean and the children were really beautifully cared for. It became evident that along with his job in the shipyard Mr. H. had to have some more outlets. He immediately, of his own accord, applied for a position with the Coast Guard Reserve. After telling the story of his past difficulties, he was accepted and given a uniform. He said that it was amusing that one of the things he had to watch out for was whether men going onto the pier to work had been drinking.

It was not all roses even after that. There has been one drinking episode since, but he did not lose his job because of it. He explained it on the ground that he was "such a pig-headed person." He regretted his English ancestry; he felt it a handicap that he was so stubborn, but said he was trying to learn that others were at least 50 per cent right. He recognizes that certain characteristics the children have are identified with his behavior. When he started to drink again, the little girl had a slight recurrence of rheumatic fever and one of the little boys began to be truant from school. He said, "It's my fault that they are doing this, I realize that when I slump the children slump."

This record is illustrative of the close interplay of emotional situations resulting in a completely disorganized family unit and it emphasizes the perseverance necessary in applying case work treatment. Satisfactions equivalent to work were found for Mrs. H. and both she and her family benefited. Actually, her emotional drives and conflicts were similar to Mr. H.'s, as I said before. He escaped into inebriety; she into employment to the neglect of her home and children. There is an old Chinese proverb, "A trip of a thousand miles starts with a single step." Donald Laird adds, "and you can build self-confidence by following the same plan." We do not really know the single step that made Mr. and Mrs. H. so disturbed but we have, step by step, been building up confidence. My job with this family probably will not be completed for another 2½ years.

Case 4

The J.'s are only recent acquaintances. Mr. J. was in the hospital with delirium tremens when the family was referred for financial assistance and guidance. Mrs. J. had had a successful major operation 5 years before; they had two adolescent sons, brilliant lads, and a baby boy. Mrs. J. was a slave to Mr. J. and completely subordinated her desires and will to his. Fearful of arousing his anger, although he was not an "ugly" alcoholic, and believing she should give him every nonalcoholic drink that he desired, she carried soup and similar things to him to the hospital for 3 days, scarcely touching food herself. At the time of her operation the boys had learned of her fears, and the older boy became overly shy and introverted. The psychiatrist who saw him then commented on the successful results, due largely to the mother's effort to understand the part she played in the boy's anxiety. She reverted, however, and the boys were now torn between their concern for their mother and the emotional shock of seeing the father in delirium tremens. They felt some resentment because so much of her attention was paid to the father. He recovered from the acute delirium and is now back at work and having weekly interviews with the psychiatrist. Mrs. J. has been seeing the case worker twice a week. At first entirely protective of Mr. J., she is now more frank about the real story and more analytical of the effect of her oversolicitude and maternalism on him and on her. She speaks of Mr. J.'s early home life as unhappy and deprived. When she married him, she resolved to make life easy for him. She now recognizes the potential danger in the boys' question, "Why shouldn't we have ice cream or ginger ale when he does?" With Mrs. J., one has to be constantly alert to the dangers of telling her what to say or do. Although normally an independent person financially, receiving relief has created new fears. "Will it stop? Can I buy this?" Then she swings over to the opposite course and buys things they have needed for months but that are no more necessary now than 3 months ago. One cannot be too critical in this period for she is utterly confused and her feeling of guilt is very strong. We do not know the underlying causes of this. The boys were so involved in the emotional confusion at home that we have sent them away for a 4-week vacation. By the time they return, Mrs. J.'s home may be more stabilized. At the moment, Mr. J. says he saw too much of the hospital ever to drink again, and Mrs. J. says that he has learned his lesson. You all know how long a treatment road has to be traveled from there.

Case 5

Mr. F. was referred to us by the court where he had gone because of Mrs. F.'s drinking. We had previously known them for about 3 years. Mrs. F. had been seriously ill with a chronic kidney disease that resulted in several miscarriages. Their only child was premature, sickly and malnourished. Mrs. F. was drinking excessively but received no treatment for it. Mr. F. did not come to us for 6 weeks after being referred. He was especially afraid of alcoholism because his father had died of an alcoholic psychosis in a state hospital. Mrs. F. was strict with the 12-year-old son, while he was lenient. She was jealous of their comradeship. He said that although he went to the court, he did not feel that jail or institutionalization would help. She was sick at the present time and had no desire to change, and he doubted that she would come to the office. She always felt too tired but insisted on her home being immaculately clean. She would not see the court worker again, feeling that the latter sided with Mr. F. She resented the efforts to encourage her to join a club or to help the Red Cross. This resentment is rather common with alcoholics and indicates a hostility aroused when well-meaning people make suggestions of what to do before finding out how the client feels about it and what he wants to do. Mrs. F. came to see us 2 days later about a possible vacation plan for George, the son. She did not know Mr. F. had been in. She described George as a very nervous child who talked incessantly with small talk and had a queer manner of walking. She said he needed a disciplined routine and separation from Mr. F., who was spoiling him. She knew definitely that Mr. F. was setting George against her, and feared he was getting to be a "smoothie" like his father. Here we see how a child can become a pawn between his parents and exhibit physical and emotional symptoms due to the resulting strain. This is one of the common situations in which husband and wife accuse each other of the same characteristics. Mr. F. wondered why everything had to be "so high class" for his wife, as she was not a wealthy girl. Mrs. F. said that when they were married she thought he earned $35 a week; actually, he earned $100 a month, but he allowed her to take a $50-a-month apartment. He had no sense at all; always tried to be a good fellow, to build himself up to be a very important person. Yet later she said she had done so much to bring the family level up that she thought her husband should be very grateful to her, but he was not. He would live in a cellar were he allowed to. She blamed Mr. F. for her drinking; he was thoughtless of her. George really enjoyed her drinking, for then his father indulged him more.

At the end of her first visit to the office I made note of the fact that she was glad she came in; she had found it good to talk things over and was eager to come again and talk and plan. I explained that it would be helpful if she could talk things over with her husband since cooperation between the two is always helpful. She decided to come again in a week. I then remarked that Mr. F. apparently recognized the same difficulties in their situation, for he had been in a few days ago desiring to relieve it. She was a little surprised that he was sufficiently interested to come in and said it might help in the plan to send George to a camp if I could talk it over with him, too. I suggested that perhaps there was more to the situation than just a plan to send George away; that there were probably a great many more reasons for her fatigue than her physical condition; that it might help to talk things over and decide why she felt and acted as she did. In conclusion, she said that she would talk things over a little with her husband.

Two days later she telephoned. He had been amazed at her coming to a social agency after she had refused to continue at the court. She had then told him that she had a right to go where she wanted to and where she felt she could get the best help. She told him this yesterday, and this morning he had really said a good word to her, that perhaps she was wiser in coming to the agency, as he had come before he really thought she was concerned enough about herself to go for help. When Mr. F. came back by appointment he immediately asked what his wife had said about him. He had asked her, but she merely said, "Just wait and see." Mrs. F.'s behavior, even when sober, came under discussion. If he asked her to go some place, she said she was too tired; on the other hand, she complained that he did not want to take her. If he worked, he was neglecting her, and if he did not work, he was lazy, so he really did not know quite where he stood. I expressed understanding of this. It might be somewhat difficult for him, but had he tried to relieve the situation by noticing the little extra things that she did and mentioning them to her? He smiled; after so many years of marriage he was beginning to take her for granted, and he must begin to notice her extra good cooking and the little things that she did about the house. I explained, too, that Mrs. F. was likely to have disguised feelings of guilt about her drinking, which were disturbing to her. He said that this seemed very true to him as she was more likely to drink liquor at home, away from people, than out in the open, although on occasions she had gone to a tavern when he had thrown her out of the house. The fact that she could admit her drinking was seen as good, although she was still not ready to admit that it was a problem to her, or to realize that drinking was not a solution but, as a matter of fact, something that caused more difficulty afterward. When she was in a drunken stupor, Mr. F. reported, he would say nothing to her. Later, however, he was likely to be furious and call her a slave to the bottle. They would argue and she would become more disturbed and drink again. Rather than take the blame herself, she would yell at him as being at fault. I explained to him the mechanism of projection, the ease with which one can blame someone else rather than oneself; and also the fact that people who drink compulsively often need a kind of warmth and understanding, rather like all of us. He admitted, finally, that perhaps some of it was his fault and said he would try to be different so that no matter what he did, good or bad, she could find no fault with it. I emphasized the real need of each to participate in any change they both wanted and to work together toward it.

Was it difficult for him and his wife to have the same case worker? Did he feel that his wife might be talking about him and turning the worker against him? They were both free to have another worker, or different workers. Mr. F. said he felt it was best this way, as social case work had been explained to him, and the part the social worker plays as an objective outsider, not taking sides, seeing the good and bad in both parties and pointing out and recommending what changes might be possible. In this part of the interview I was dealing with the element of jealousy which can enter into any situation. Mrs. F. separately expressed the same desire to continue with one case worker. It was necessary to see George about his camp plan and Mrs. F. suggested that we ask him anything we liked about both parents. She was assured that this was not our purpose or desire. Later, George told us in leaving that he would be glad to come in again with either parent. He knew that I was seeing them both, and it is possible that there was an attempt to make George align himself with one parent or the other.

In interpreting to Mrs. F. her husband's reaction to her drinking, I identified this with his association with his father, suggesting that some of his concern about her might be indicative of his love and devotion and his desire to have her respect him. Her relationship to George was discussed, and her neglect of Mr. F.

when George was a baby. Throughout this situation so much material had come out that I could watch for the most pertinent facts and, when possible, note something that each had brought up which could later be developed constructively. A little later Mr. F. said he had thought a lot about what the worker said and tried to see the reasons for things. He guessed the worker was right in having said there is a reason for all human behavior and he imagined that he himself did some of the crazy things that he accused his wife of doing. I emphasized that he was an important factor in the treatment of his wife and tried to prepare him for another spree, suggesting that he try to consider now how he would react to her next episode.

Ten days later Mrs. F. drank, but not a great deal. She rationalized it as usual. A picnic had been called off; every 2 months you ought to wash all the poisons out of your system; it washes the pus out of your diseased lungs, etc. It seemed safe now to ask Mrs. F. whether she really believed all this. Her face lighted up, she laughed and said she guessed she was "not kidding" either herself or me. After this she became a bit argumentative, said she was not sure she liked coming into the office but realized the agency liked to make camp follow-ups and she might let George come in alone. I commented that we would see whether she might not feel differently later; there was no need to decide now. Then, showing that Mr. F. was really thinking about his behavior, she commented on one big change that had come about: Her husband was acting so differently that she might not need to drink again for a long time. In no way whatsoever had he tried to antagonize her.

No one can predict the final outcome of this situation, but with both parents releasing some of their pent-up feelings to the case worker, George is less likely to be the pawn. In each interview the case worker endeavors to do a very little interpretation and to find some one thing each marital partner can do to help the other. It is very much like working with children; not exactly like offering a bribe, yet something of the philosophy which recognizes the real emotional immaturity of both husband and wife and endeavors to help them develop maturity in planning and living.

Case 6

There are times in social case work when the worker does psychotherapy. Here she is on thin ice and must be conscious of the fact, and watch extremely carefully not to go into the unconscious; but she may work with deep emotional problems that are on a conscious level. I am going to describe a situation to illustrate this.

Mr. C.'s mother died shortly after his birth and due to an accident he was nearly blind. His father remarried when C. was 5 and his stepmother had no children. She became very fond and protective of C., teaching him at home and helping him prepare for business. He became an efficient clerk but early was drinking quite heavily. Following his marriage he immediately returned to his mother's home where she was definitely "first" with him and with the first child, a son. Mr. C.'s drinking increased, and his wife finally left home, taking her second child. Mr. C., with the older boy, remained with his mother, and his excessive drinking continued. He could no longer hold a job, and at this time a social worker was consulted. Some interpretation was attempted with the couple but the man was hostile and little was accomplished with him. Fortunately at this time he became ill and hospitalization was necessary for many months. This gave the social worker an opportunity to help the wife plan for the future. She had been a poor manager and housekeeper and had justly warranted some of Mr. C.'s mother's criticism. She therefore studied food and money planning and the home was ready for Mr. C. when he was discharged from the hospital. Then the case worker planned to wean him from his mother. Gradually friendship formed and reliance on the worker increased. The wife was helped to be more maternal, thus assuming some of the mother characteristics, yet at the same time deferring to her husband as head of the family. After many months Mr. C. learned to depend more and more on his wife and less on the case worker. During this period he became able to work again and assume responsibility for the home. In the meantime the mother was not forgotten although she was slower to share in the plan. Mr. C.'s drinking, which had been resumed upon his discharge from the hospital, practically stopped, but the case worker did not feel that final success had been achieved until several years later when the young couple finally moved to another part of the city quite distant from the mother's home.

A real transference situation was handled in this situation, and that can be very dangerous. Many of us get involved in transferences in our daily living but usually normal events help to control them. In psychotherapy, however, the psychiatrist or other therapist must be certain he can handle the counter-transference and eventually withdraw from the situation with the client more maturely able to handle his own problems.

If one thinks of the profession of social case work as one in which an attempt is made to understand each individual in the light of his background, intelligence, interests, and emotions, and to help him live more happily, satisfactorily and productively in his world, it will be seen that there is no special technique for the inebriate. It only requires greater thoughtfulness, more careful analysis of behavior patterns and one's own reaction to them. It demands intense patience and kindliness, and a sincere prayer for wisdom to meet each crisis. With probably no other group of clients must there be greater consciousness of the usefulness of other individual and community resources and an awareness of when and how to use them.

DISCUSSION

Question: Does your experience show any cases where the reaction from the children growing up in the alcoholic home had been particularly the concern of the case worker? And, especially in large families, have you found that it is the oldest child in the family who shows signs of nervous tension or of reaction? You did mention, in one of the case histories, the prompt reaction of the oldest child, whose father recognized the fact that his own behavior had much to do with the child's change in behavior. I wonder if that is a point that has been brought out to any extent in the work with families.

Lecturer: I do think in practically every instance the child is quite seriously involved in the emotional strains, and it is interesting that often the actual affection is for the alcoholic parent. I think this is partly because when he is not intoxicated, as undoubtedly the other lecturers have told you, he is usually a pretty good fellow and above the average in sociability and companionship, while the nonalcoholic parent is likely to be more on edge, more irritable and more rejecting toward the child. Right there you have a rather abnormal set-up. I think that as far as actual case work with them is concerned, we are less likely to do the case work with the child, although we do try to give him the normal encouragement, the normal outside activity, probably to a greater extent even than children in other situations. But I think the treatment often has to be carried out with both parents and a case worker can't spread herself too thin in treating a family. It might even arouse more jealousy if she took on the intensive work of dealing with the child. I think we have felt that we had to relieve the emotional strains at home, and if we did relieve them, the child had a normal chance of adjusting. If you found that he was showing abnormal symptoms afterward, you might then deal with him individually. We have that in the case where the child is talking incessantly. He actually has developed very serious emotional habits. A habit clinic probably wouldn't treat him at the moment, because the situation at home is too bad, but as soon as we can get that situation relieved, either we will accept him for case-work treatment or seek psychiatric treatment for him as part of the problem. But the child's problem often has to be subordinated to the primary situation.

Graham: How do you get in touch with a case in the beginning? How is it brought to you in such a way that you are free to work with it?

Lecturer: That is a very common question asked of the social worker. Except for the protective agencies, no good social case-work agency goes into a situation without the family wanting them to. That is why I said that the fundamental idea is the client's own right to choose. Social workers have attempted to go into too many situations to accomplish something, but unless the family wants them to, they cannot work successfully. On the other hand, one can sometimes do a good job of interpreting his services to the person he wants to reach. I have sometimes worked for several months with someone in the community who wanted a certain family to come to us, telling him what to say to the family to get them ready to come to the agency. Now, the actual referrals come from clients themselves, who have heard of us from some written material or some other source. And they also come through other clients who have been working with us; they come from hospitals and from other social agencies. I would say that people can come from any source, but they must have some idea of wanting to come in the first place. And if we want to treat them, it is up to us to be good salesmen of our wares. I am not a believer in the tenet that some social workers held several years ago, that you tell a client the first time he is there what you have to offer and then, if he doesn't come back, it means that he doesn't want service from you. I think we have to realize that we are dealing, in almost all social work, with unhappy, maladjusted people; it doesn't matter whether they are wealthy or poor or whether it is something serious or trifling about which they come. They don't know you and they don't know whether they are going to trust you, so how should they know whether they want to tell you their gravest troubles? I say that it is up to us to be good salesmen, or we don't deserve to have them come.

Mrs. Phillips: Do you have situations when the case worker works with Alcoholics Anonymous in her treatment?

Lecturer: Yes, I think quite frequently. My alcoholic woman has been in A.A., and Mr. H. went to A.A. for quite a long time and has been really helped by the personal relationship with one A.A. worker. However, he has such a keen sense of inferiority that he has the idea all the A.A.'s are rather high-hat in dealing with him, that they are much more professional people than he is—he considers himself of the laboring group. I don't think he is right, but it is his rationalization for it and he has not continued going. I, personally, am more inclined to use Alcoholics Anonymous for women than for men. I don't know of any special reason for that, except that I think the women have been more seriously lacking in social outlets which, I think, the A.A. has furnished extremely well. I believe in A.A. very much. I don't think it is the only answer, but I think it is one of six or eight and has tremendous importance in this field.

Davies: In any of the case studies, was the local church or minister used in any way for rehabilitation of those studied?

Lecturer: In the particular cases I mentioned here, the church was not consulted by the case worker as a primary resource. Mr. H. went back to his church during the treatment and has been closely in touch with it, and the case worker has worked with the priest (he was Roman Catholic) since Mr. H. received treatment under the family rehabilitation plan. In the J. family, the case of the man who was in the hospital with delirium tremens, the church played a very important part with both him and the family. The minister's attitude there, however, is rather a moralistic one. We have met with that situation frequently and have sometimes found it inexpedient to go to the parish in connection with some of the alcoholics. Leaving out these cases, we feel that the church has a very important part to play but unless we know that the particular minister or priest we can contact has some knowledge of alcoholism, or is receptive to new ideas, we do not consult him.

Miss Cox: Many of your case histories show recurrent drinking in spite of treatment of individual difficulties. When future difficulties arise, will these people be able to make any permanent adjustment instead of resorting to alcohol?

Lecturer: I am sorry if I did not show in the excerpts from these records that we thought there was improvement. I, personally, would be very dubious about any treatment where the person stopped drinking immediately, because I'd just think we hadn't met the crisis. I feel more confident when a client has recurrent drinking episodes, for that is how one learns to deal with the situation. The lapses demonstrate the need of getting at the underlying problems. I think that that is where the case worker's strength goes—to get the person to understand himself and his escape into inebriety so that gradually he builds up reserve and does not have to resort to intoxication. But it is a slow process. In the family where the transference was carried out from the mother to the case worker and then to the wife, the resolution of that situation took nearly 8 years. In the H. family, with which we have been working $2\frac{1}{2}$ years, we had a man who had not worked for more than about a week at a time for a year; a home that was in as poor a condition as you can find in any part of the country in the very worst slums; children who were as neglected as any. And yet these were rather intelligent people. Now we have a good home, a devoted family and loyalties, and a man who has only slipped once in 18 months. I consider that pretty successful treatment. You may remember that I remarked, at the end of that case, that it would take another $2\frac{1}{2}$ years to have the foundation built up. I don't think you can change patterns that have been forming themselves a very long time, often from earliest childhood, in a very short time.

Pastoral Counseling of Inebriates

Rev. Otis R. Rice

IT is almost an effrontery for a hospital chaplain and a parish priest to come and speak before a group like yours which now, for some weeks, has been listening to experts in this very important field. I want you to know that I understand fully my own limitations in presenting this subject this morning, but that I also feel that any minister of the gospel, priest or rabbi, has a right to say something about the problem of counseling the inebriate. Every one of us meets the problem in one way or another. Sometimes the alcoholic comes to us directly and asks for help; sometimes, in an almost literal sense, we stumble upon him; and we find the problem in the interest groups in our parishes. Then there are indirect ways by which the minister comes across the problem. The family comes to us and says, "What can we do? This member of our family is having a bout with alcohol; it is one of many such experiences that he has had. What shall we do? Can you help us in this tragic situation?" And, finally, the intelligent and alert pastor is always aware, through community attitudes and community action, that within his reach there are problems connected with the misuse of alcohol.

All of us who are pastors or priests or rabbis must sooner or later face the problem of what we are to do personally about the alcoholic. At the present time we have various approaches and, of course, quite varied attitudes toward the problem of alcohol. Some of my colleagues say, "We are frankly afraid of the problem and we run from it whenever we can. We are too busy with other things to bother about the alcoholic and so we get out from under. Usually we say to him, 'When you're sober, come back and talk with me.' If we are dealing with a family, we say, 'I am not an expert in this field, therefore, go somewhere else.'" Some of the clergy are particularly stringent in the judgments which they make of alcoholics, and take advantage of their acquaintance to give him a lecture on the sinfulness of his condition, his lack of will power, and the other degradations into which he has fallen. Some of my colleagues say that they have a different technique. One of them says, "I pray with the alcoholic and then I kick him out, but sometimes I am so mad that I do not have time to pray." Still another approach is that of the religious leader who says, "I have a prayer group and we will pray for you, or I personally will pray for you, and I want you to go home, get down on your knees and ask God's help."

Still another approach is that of the wise parish priest, rabbi or minister who attempts at once to refer an alcoholic for professional assistance to the psychiatrist, to Alcoholics Anonymous, or to the clinic. But, finally, there is a group of us who feel that under certain circumstances, and in the case of certain types of alcoholics, we have a responsibility as ministers of the gospel to deal directly with their problem. To some extent what I have to say this morning will be about this actual counseling of the inebriate.

Before we approach this subject, however, I want to point out that the minister has unique limitations and dangers as well as certain unique advantages and resources in dealing with the problem of the alcoholic. I believe that these dangers and limitations, resources and advantages, accrue to the minister also in many other types of parish problems, but I want to point them out particularly in reference to the alcoholic.

DANGERS AND LIMITATIONS

First of all, one of our limitations is that traditionally we are thought of by people as having a "holier than thou" attitude. An alcoholic said to me once, after we had worked together for about a year, "You know, before I came to you, I thought I'd rather be found dead than talking to a parson." And back of that expression was the idea that clergy are overly critical, that they make quick judgments, that they believe themselves to be better than other folk, and therefore are constantly being critical of other people's actions and attitudes. We have that distinct liability, when it comes to making our services available to the alcoholic. He is afraid of us because of this reading of our attitude, whether he is correct or not.

The second limitation is an obvious one. Most of us are not trained for this work. We are handicapped because of our limited knowledge of the subject and because of our limited experience. Many of us fear to deal with other people's lives because we do not know the facts, because we do not have the skill, because we have not had the training.

Another drawback for the clergyman is that the counseling of alcoholics, and that also is true of the counseling of any parishioner, takes a great deal of time. Ordinarily one must see an alcoholic three or four times a week for the first few weeks, and then a couple of times a week for a month or two more, and then once a week for a considerable length of time. With our responsibilities to our parishioners, with our responsibility for the administration of the parish, with the time which we should spend on the preparation of sermons and of our services of worship, we may not have the right to give much opportunity to alcoholics to consult with us.

There is an even greater danger, and that is, that we may become emotionally involved with the people whom we counsel. It is certainly a fact when an alcoholic comes to us and pours out the innermost secrets of his heart, confesses his own feelings of degradation and of weakness, that something dynamic happens between us. If we are understanding, if we are helpful to him, then a rather dangerous emotional involvement is set up which we may find it difficult to break. Furthermore, this involvement, or the potentialities of involvement, sometimes gets us into difficulty with our parish. The congregation is critical of the minister, priest or rabbi who gives a great deal of time to any particular individual or group of individuals.

I know a young minister on the staff of a large church in New York City who, a number of years ago, started out counseling alcoholics. He did an exceptionally fine job but eventually the vestry told him he had better find another parish, because a number of people had reported that men with liquor on their breath were coming into that church, and this would never do. (Think of it, the Christian Church is no place for a person in trouble, for one who has liquor on his breath!) So this clergyman had to go elsewhere, and I must say that he found greater freedom in a detached position than when he was actually a member of the staff of this large city church.

Another of our limitations is that some of us are so completely divorced from any medical or psychiatric assistance that we have no one who can guide us in our work. You know very well that frequently there are medical problems along with the psychological and religious problems of the alcoholic. Those of us who are so situated that we cannot have medical assistance sometimes find that we are particularly handicapped in dealing with the alcoholic in the first stages of our counseling procedure.

Finally, there is the very obvious danger of being guilty of malpractice on human souls; that we shall become so involved with an individual that our interpretations will be erroneous—that we shall do more harm to this man's soul than we do good. And I, for one, believe very sincerely that malpractice on human souls is infinitely more reprehensible than malpractice on human bodies. We are in danger, all of us of the clergy, of being guilty of this malpractice because, as I said before, we may have no aptitude for this work, we may not know the facts, or our training may have been faulty.

Resources and Advantages

When all these dangers and limitations have been catalogued there is still a good list of our opportunities, resources and advantages. I want to run briefly over them. And in so doing, may I stress the fact that the minister has an amazing opportunity of remote preparation for the counseling of alcoholics. By remote preparation I mean that by his very life among his people the minister makes himself a part of their thinking and a part of their group. Therefore, the alcoholic and other individuals with other difficulties can find their way to the parson simply because in the past they have known and trusted him. Observe the way in which the average parish priest keeps his contacts with his people over a long period of time. Perhaps the individual priest himself may not continue, but his clericate does continue. When a child is born, he visits the family or the hospital as a matter of course and arranges about the baptism of the child; the child is baptized in the parish church and many of the parishioners attend the service. He is especially concerned with the father and mother of this growing child for the first 3 or 4 years of the child's developmental life—a tremendously important period, as you all know, in relation to the later emotional and religious maturity of the individual. The church school is usually the first school to which the child goes, for, in many instances, the Sunday School or the parochial school begins a year or so earlier than does the public school. Therefore, this may be the first opportunity that the child has to meet with other children growing up under other family disciplines, an important nodal point in any child's life. There, the parish priest, or the pastor, or the minister has an opportunity to touch the life of the child and particularly to prepare the teachers who are responsible for the emotional and religious development of that child in what those teachers should know about problems of emotion and problems of religion.

Then, in the normal course of events, the minister or the priest has an opportunity to prepare the child for confirmation or for coming into the full citizenship of the church by joining the church. In the preadolescent or adolescent period the minister, or the priest, or the rabbi has an unusual entree into the life of the individual in this very critical period. You see, all the way from birth through the first years, the early school period and the adolescent period, there has been this normal touch of the parson upon the life of the growing child. Then the child goes away to school or college, goes away to work, and the pastor follows with interest the life of this parishioner. When he is contemplating marriage, it is to the priest, or the rabbi, or the minister that he goes for his premarital counseling. Again the impact of the pastoral relationship upon the growing individual comes at a nodal, critical point of his life.

I hardly need point out that when a person is ill, when a person is in a joyful crisis, and also in a depressing crisis, or at the point of death, he is attended by his spiritual advisor if he is connected with some religious organization. Therefore, you see, there has been this long period of preparation in which the minister, priest or rabbi finds his way into the heart and meaningful life of the individual whom he is to serve. I hardly need point out that preaching, the religious education program of a parish, the interest groups, the parent study groups and the like are other opportunities for the intelligent minister to prepare the way for later pastoral contacts.

If an individual has heard his minister preach; that is, if he has heard sincere preaching; if he has been well attended by his minister, then it is the most natural thing in the world for him to seek out that sacred minister when he is in difficulty and lay before him his problem. This is what I mean when I say that we have a distinct advantage because of our remote preparation for each of our pastoral acts, whether it be the counseling of the alcoholic or something else. You see also the implications of this remote preparation for our dealing with the family of the alcoholic, which is such an important part of our task.

In the second place, the clergyman has a privileged relationship with his parishioners. I say privileged in both the traditional and the legal sense. Is it not interesting that in the Army and Navy of the United States the chaplain is now the only officer whose communication with men is privileged? This is some earnest of the importance of that relationship in civilian life. When I say privileged relationship, I mean that legally the priest, rabbi or minister cannot be forced to divulge confidential communications. And therefore, down through the ages, people have gone to their sacred minister because he could be trusted to maintain the seal of confidence, because in that privileged relationship the person felt safe. It goes almost without saying, that the sacred minister, whether he be Protestant, Catholic or Jewish, is a father image. He represents something, God help us, that is to the parishioner or to the client above the everyday life of the individual. We are not worthy of it—don't misunderstand me—but in the mind of the penitent, or the parishioner, or the member of the congregation, this representation is real, and in that privileged relationship, in that almost idealistic symbolizing situation of a sacred minister, much can be accomplished.

A third point, and this is another of our advantages, is that in one sense we are not tainted by the touch of professionalism. We have no financial axe to grind in the transaction. The question of the $20-an-hour analytical interview does not come up in the case of the sacred minister. Sometimes we wish there were a little more financial economic return to our parish, at least for the hours and hours we have spent with our parishioners. Sometimes it is probably true that if one pays for the services of a professional counselor one can then command his time and can be more frank in questioning the interpretation of that counselor. Be that as it may, I think for some people it is a boon that we are not professional in the usual sense of the term. Granted that there are many people who would go to a doctor or a psychiatrist about the problem of alcohol but would never go near their minister, or their parish priest, or their rabbi, the fact remains that there is a large number of folk who, because of their attitude toward the sacred ministry, will go to the parson and would not go to some professional counselor. We can also take to ourselves this advantage, that under certain circumstances we can enter situations uninvited. The physician, the psychiatrist, the lawyer, the teacher, and the professional consultant with alcoholics, usually has to be called in to the situation. The sacred minister does not have to be called in; it is our sacred duty when a death occurs in our parish to be the first to call, if we have not been at the bedside of the dying where we ought to be. We are the first to call when a baby is born into a family. We are the first to join the family in expressions of joy at some happy event, or to express our sympathy at bereavement, so that we have the natural entree. We are there, in a sense, "as of right, and not by grace." We have the right to go into the homes of our people. This may sometimes be a disadvantage, obviously, but at least many times it becomes a distinct advantage in dealing with the alcoholic.

Let me speak also of some of our social resources. Most of us in parish life have interest groups, religious-worship groups, parent study groups, or the like, which form a smaller social entity into which the alcoholic can, at some point, be introduced. And usually the interests of these groups are so varied that we can meet the social interests and needs of the alcoholic in this way. Again, this sometimes may be a drawback because it may frighten off certain isolated alcoholics; on the other hand, it is a distinct advantage for us to have these social resources. We also have a good many professional contacts within our congregation itself. Most of us know good lawyers, good social workers, good teachers, good physicians, who are members of our congregation. Therefore, we are able frequently to consult with them, about problems that come to us, outside of the professional setting of the clinic or any official set-up which might be disadvantageous in our dealing with the alcoholic.

Finally, we have certain unique religious resources, I even go so far as to call them tools and treasures, which we can use in dealing with the alcoholic. If you will bear with me a moment I will speak of these at another point in our discussion, but I want to say here that among the great advantages of the sacred minister, as he works with the alcoholic, are his unique religious tools and treasures. May I now say that it seems to me that the sacred minister approaches the problem of alcohol in four different departments of his work with people.

EDUCATIONAL OPPORTUNITY

There is, first of all, his educational opportunity. I have already spoken of remote preparation for the counseling of the inebriate. Just think what it means to have each Sunday, or each Sabbath day, a platform from which one can give out facts, from which one can give real instruction. I do not mean for a moment that the ordinary parish priest should spend many Sundays a year talking about the facts regarding alcohol, but certainly he ought to speak about it at times during the church year. Moreover, in his informal talks with groups, certainly in relation to his church school and to his whole program of religious education, he should include some mention of the problems of alcohol and the facts about alcohol as he knows them. That is why some of you come to this School, so that you will have the actual facts regarding alcohol which you can use in your talks with your people and in the instruction of your groups. This is the preventive aspect—is it not?—the comprehensive educational opportunity of the sacred ministry, and we should not neglect it. I do not know enough about what you have been collaborating on in this School to know whether or not you will agree that in many instances we know that inebriety goes hand in hand with poor emotional adjustment; and that, therefore, religiously as well as socially, we are concerned with seeing to it that sound religious education goes hand in hand with sound emotional education. Therefore, our responsibility for the smooth developmental life of the child and the young man and woman is most important. Here again is a preventive opportunity, open to the sacred ministry, of so teaching, of so directing the lives of individuals, that eventually more and more children will grow up well adjusted so that there will be no neurotic misuse of alcohol on their part.

The first general area in which all of us work is the educational or preventive. The second area in which we come into contact with alcoholism and its problems is in our relations with the family and the associates of the inebriate. Many of us first approach the problems through the families, or the associates, or the employer, or the employee of the alcoholic. Here again our understanding of the problem, our scientific knowledge, and our familiarity with the literature, will help us in explaining the facts to families of inebriates, freeing them from many misapprehensions and allowing them to become more and more objective about the problem, remembering always that the objectivity of the family and of the associates is one of the most important single factors in the cure of the alcoholic. There will be practical suggestions which we can give; there will be practical information about professional resources which we can give to the family, even if we never see the alcoholic himself. We should know where the nearest clinics are; we should know who the best psychiatrists are; we should know how to get in touch with Alcoholics Anonymous; we should know what lay folk in our community have been particularly successful in the counseling of alcoholics. These data we can pass on, with the proper suggestions, to families and associates.

The third general area with which we are concerned in this problem is that of the preparation of the alcoholic himself for receiving assistance. This is by no means a small part of our work. A task has been very well done indeed if the sacred minister has, by his understanding attitude, his counsel, his friendship, and his advice, made it possible for an alcoholic, of his own free will, to go to some specialist in the field and say, "I am ready for help." This is, I think, a most important function of the minister, whether he undertakes direct counseling of the alcoholic or not—the preparation of the inebriate for referral or for help. It is a ticklish job, a job that requires a great deal of understanding and is, I submit, itself a part of the counseling process. No minister need feel ashamed that he himself was unable to tackle the problem of an alcoholic if he has helped that individual to seek professional assistance elsewhere. Indeed, the minister can take a good deal of credit to himself as he sees that alcoholic improve and finally reach the cured stage because he has set him on the way. Of course, and this is an important point, the minister never relinquishes his pastoral responsibility simply because the alcoholic has been turned over to someone else. Just as a minister follows his parishioner to the hospital, the jail, or elsewhere, even though other chaplains are provided, so in relation to the alcoholic he continues his pastoral ministration even though the conduct of the case itself is not in his hands. (And we parsons had better be careful about the use of the word case; these are souls and not cases.) The pastor finds it important to follow the situation and give whatever of religious ministry is necessary during the healing process.

DIRECT COUNSELING

And, finally, we come to the fourth area, which is that of direct counseling of the inebriate, and that occupies most of our time and thought this morning. May I say that the sacred minister, as a counselor of the inebriate, has the same role and the same responsibilities, the same resources, which are to be his in the counseling of any parochial problem. The counseling of the alcoholic does not differ basically and fundamentally from the counseling of any soul who comes to the pastor. There are certain special observations that have to be made about the technique used in counseling the alcoholic. The pastoral counselor requires certain special data in counseling the alcoholic but his basic principles and approaches are the same. These approaches are, first, as an intelligent, understanding friend; second, as official representative of a religious community; and third, as the official and authorized custodian of the treasures of that religious community.

When I say intelligent friend, I mean that every minister who counsels alcoholics ought to know at least as much as any intelligent layman about the problem of alcohol, and probably more. That again is why you are here at this School, so that you can be intelligent friends. You have learned that there are certain things you do not do for the alcoholic. You probably realize some of the dangers of the misuse of religion and friendship at this point. You do not minimize the sin, or the problem, or the illness of the alcoholic, but you are, nevertheless, his friend. He is in difficulty and you are well aware that it is a serious matter. The trouble with some of the clergy is that because they are afraid of the problem, in a sense they try to "laugh it off," to minimize it. I shall never forget, as long as I live, going to the bedside of a dying sea captain in a city hospital just a few days after my ordination and I, like the fool that I was, said, "Well, Captain I hope we can arrange things so that you'll get a fine new ship in just a few days and sail out into the harbor." And he said, "You damn fool, I'm dying, and I sent for a priest, not a fool." Think of what that meant to me then and has meant to me all through the years of my ministry. It was a salutary lesson, but it was pretty horrible that I had to be taught it by a dying man who needed my ministration.

The alcoholic must find in the sacred minister the intelligent, understanding friend who is willing to stand by, even though there has been sinning and degradation together with the illness and emotional inefficiency involved in his situation. The intelligent friend must sometimes provide medical care. The intelligent friend of the alcoholic must sometimes provide shelter while he sobers up. The intelligent friend must sometimes go at once and deal with the family or the employer of the alcoholic in order that he may have time in his other role to counsel creatively with this parishioner of his. So I stress again that one must be an intelligent, understanding friend, even if one is a sacred minister. There are some men in the ministry who think somehow that their ordination is enough and that they no longer have to use their intelligence. Our ordination does not ordain us to the abandonment of the use of our intelligence, but instead places upon us a most stringent responsibility that we shall be intelligent friends of the people whom God has entrusted to our pastoral care. That is our first role and it is, incidentally, our first resource. If the alcoholic finds in his pastor someone who, though reserving his own judgment, nevertheless is understanding and willing to stand by, then a good part of the battle has been won.

The second role of the sacred minister is always that of the representative of the religious fellowship. It is fascinating to see in the chaplaincy of the armed forces the interchange of fellowship. A Jewish rabbi kneels by a dying Protestant and the Protestant can accept from that rabbi religious consolation and his prayerful help, not alone because the rabbi is set apart in his own congregation and church but because he represents the religious fellowship to which the Protestant belongs as well. One sees that so often in hospital work. I am frankly an Anglican priest, yet I go to the bedsides of Protestants of all denominations. I go to the bedsides of Roman Catholics, the bedsides of Jewish patients, and there is a certain rapport set up because I am a sacred minister. Of course my technical job, the job which I want to do as soon as possible, is to get this patient's own spiritual adviser to him, but already there is an opportunity to help and to do something simply because I, like his own minister, have been set apart by the fellowship. I remember that the alcoholic is always lonely, the alcoholic always feels a sense of isolation, and there is usually a great deal of the element of guilt and hostility in his situation. Now it is within the fellowship of a religious group that many of these emotional problems are solved. The sense of belonging, the sense of "I am not alone," is tremendously important to the alcoholic and to any other person in his difficulty.

I cannot think of a good illustration from the province of the alcoholic, but I can think of the time when I took some flowers from the altar on a Sunday morning to a little old lady who was dying in a large city hospital. It happened that I was third or fourth curate on the staff of a large city church, and when I brought these flowers to her bedside I said, "Mrs. Blank, the rector wanted me to bring these flowers which were on the altar when we prayed for you this morning." She looked up at me with tears in her eyes and said, "You mean that all those people prayed for me?" In a moment she was caught up into the worshiping congregation before her altar, and she was no longer alone. Almost every familiar religious act which the sacred minister performs is in relation to the religious community to which he and his parishioner belong. Why do we usually have our baptisms and our marriages and our funerals in the church? Because by that fact we have had the interests and concern of the Christian fellowship to which the individual belongs. They are there again as of right, and not by grace. The whole church is concerned with the developmental life of the little babe that is being baptized, of the couple who are pledging their vows together, of the soul of the departed when the shell of that soul is brought into the church in Christian burial. I am speaking from the point of view of the parish church, and am only expressing my own ideas, but I do believe this holds true for ministers of any faith; that these ministers represent the fellowship of a community. Symbols of this are, as I said before, the social, the worship, and interest groups within the fellowship, into which the isolated individual can be quite easily and naturally introduced.

So we have first, the sacred minister as the intelligent, understanding friend; second, we have the sacred minister as the official representative of a religious fellowship; and third, the role which is probably more nearly unique. The sacred minister is ordained, authorized, and set apart to do certain things that no layman can do. Now we will differ among ourselves a good deal as to what these acts are, what the treasures are that are vouchsafed to the sacred ministry, but let me run through some that came to my mind because they bear on our work with alcoholics.

TREASURES OF THE MINISTRY

First of all, there is the sacred minister as a custodian of the word of God. Again we would differ as to our interpretation of the authority of the word of God, but the use of the word of God with alcoholics is important. I do not mean reading passages of terrible condemnation or promise of the wrath of God. Nor do I necessarily mean the reading of proof texts. I do mean that the word of God in its revelation of Divine concern for the individual can often bring the alcoholic back into a feeling that his life is worth while even though he has lost his self-belief and those around him have lost their belief in him. The word of God is of tremendous importance in our ministry to human souls. It must be used intelligently and well. The other day, as I left the bedside of a man who was on the critical list and came down the corridor of our hospital, I saw a parson striding down the hall, and I said, "I've just come from Mr. So-and-so. I suppose you're the Rev. Dr. So-and-so that I just sent for?" He said, "Yes," and I looked at him in horror for he had a pulpit Bible under his arm and he was going up to minister to this dying man from a pulpit Bible. He looked at me, a stranger to him and a professional chaplain in a church hospital, and he said, "Padre, what shall I read to him?" His own parishioner! This man, who had been a minister of the gospel for 20 years, asked me, a stranger, what to read to his own parishioner who was dying. There, you see, was a lack of understanding of the use of his tools. Many times one does not read long passages from Holy Writ. The other day a young man was going up to the operating room for a serious operation, and he said, "I'm not much of a religionist and I haven't been in church in many years; can you give me something to say as I go up for the operation?" I said, "Say, 'Underneath are the Everlasting Arms.'" A little later I saw him in the anesthesia room before he had received his anesthesia, and I could see his lips moving, "Underneath are the Everlasting Arms." He was on the operating table something like 4 hours. I was at his bedside as he came out, and these were his words: "Our Father who art in heaven." Through that period of unconsciousness something had been happening as a result of the words I had given him. Before he left the hospital that youth was reconciled with his own church and was again receiving the sacraments of his church.

There, I think, was an example of the use of Holy Writ to help a person through a crisis, and often we need to do that with the alcoholic. So one of the treasures of the sacred ministry is the word of God.

A second treasure of the sacred ministry is (and I dislike to use the word because it is discounted so in these days) a sound theology. If you wish to call it by another name, it is the lore of the fellowship to which the individual group belongs. I can speak only of my own theology, which I hope is a workable one and in keeping with that "once delivered to the Saints." There are two aspects of theology that are tremendously important in dealing with the alcoholic. One is a sound doctrine of man and the other is a sound doctrine of God. In the sound doctrine of man, we must avoid the dangerous theology that is rife in the world today. One of these dangerous doctrines is the doctrine of "sweetness and light." One of my Bishops once called it, "The doctrine that all the world is lovely and I am lovely too." Now anyone who knows anything about life, anyone who knows anything about alcoholics, knows that all the world is not lovely and he himself is not lovely too. The sound doctrine of man rests upon the assumption that man is a miserable sinner. You know, in my church they tried to take that phrase out of the prayer book some years ago. Think of voting yourself not a miserable sinner! There have been no attempts in the last few years.

We are miserable sinners. We begin from that point. We have fallen far short of what God would have us be. We have gone far astray from our close relationship with God, and by our sinfulness have departed from our close union with God. Let us begin at that point. It is a pretty good place to begin with the alcoholic. We in the church are not a company of saints but we are a company of sinners, and the sooner the alcoholic can realize this the better it is for him. But that is only half the doctrine of man.

The other half of the doctrine of man is that we are potential sons of God. It is from the fact that one is a miserable sinner, and the acceptance of the fact that by God's promise one can become His son, that cures are made and that lives are made worth while. Again I am speaking only of my own doctrine and my own attitude toward theology. In dealing with alcoholics this sound doctrine of man, as I call it and believe it to be, is tremendously important religiously and emotionally.

Then, in the second place, there is the doctrine of God. One of our dangers in religion is to portray God only as a wrathy, neurotic old man. And some religions do just that. I once came upon our internes in the hospital discussing a psychiatric case. They looked at me very shamefacedly when I came in and tried to change the subject, but I knew them pretty well and finally they said, "We were discussing your God. We think he's a neurotic old man." Why? Because they were completely misinformed as to what intelligent religious folk think about God. They had probably been subjected to two or three very unfortunate sermons; they had had no background in theological thinking at all; and they saw nothing of the creative, loving relentlessness in our doctrine of God which urges all of life on to perfection, the element in our doctrine of God which tells us that when we are truly sorry there are means by which we can accept God's forgiveness. I have spent quite a bit of time talking about theology, but I think it is tremendously important for the minister as he deals with the problem of alcohol. So we have the word of God, we have theology, and then we have the art of prayer.

Prayer can be used and misused in the treatment of the alcoholic, but certainly prayer, properly taught and properly used, is one of the greatest adjuncts in our work with alcoholics. I shall say more about this later on, but I only suggest here that while we are supposed to be teachers of the art of prayer, most of us are not on our knees enough and therefore we cannot teach other people. If the alcoholic has got to be on his knees 10 minutes before he seeks the help of the parson, the parson ought to be on his knees 20 minutes before he attempts to counsel the alcoholic. You understand, I am sure, that the worst thing for some alcoholics would be to have the parson say, "Now, my son, we will kneel down and tell God about your horrible sin." Most alcoholics are already guilt-ridden enough. Prayer will come later in the counseling procedure; or, perhaps, actually verbalized, it will not come at all.

Now we come to a point on which we will differ very greatly. That point is the rites, the ordinances, and the sacraments and their value to the alcoholic. Again I speak only from my own limited experience and from my own particular tradition. But the sacraments and the rites of the church—again I mention that we differ as to their use—can be tremendously meaningful to the alcoholic. Take, for example, the sacrament of the Lord's Supper! I don't see why more Protestant churches do not use the Lord's Supper more frequently and more effectively in dealing with the alcoholic. Here is a strengthening spiritual food. Here is the ordinance, or sacrament, as you will, by which one comes close to God. There is also the use of the sacrament of confirmation, of the rite of joining the church. Then there is the matter of the laying on of hands, the anointing of a sick person. I know that we differ among ourselves about these things, but remember this, that the rite or the sacrament, whatever your doctrine of it may be, is something objective that is done; and in the symbolizing faculty of the alcoholic this is of tremendous psychological importance, regardless of what you may believe about its immediate spiritual significance.

Finally, we should be teachers in the art of following a rule of life. The alcoholic needs very drastically a framework in which to live his life, not only during his treatment and during his reeducation but afterward. The sacred minister should be a spiritual director of souls, so that he may arrive at a sensible rule of life for the alcoholic. This will take time, and will involve such things as meditation, intellectual reading, spiritual reading, exercise, proper care of the body, prayer and corporate worship. Now, of course, I am talking about parishioners in churches where these things are matters of course; I am also talking about the alcoholic who comes to the minister because the minister is supposedly a man of God. I will not compromise. I am first, last, and always a minister of the Gospel, and I am primarily interested in the religious and spiritual life of the individual. Incidentally, I want to be a good counselor and psychologist, but I cannot pull any punches about the fact that my main job in life is to be a minister; therefore I have to give to the alcoholic the best that I possess. And one of the best things for me is my rule of life and the way that I follow that rule of life.

Here, then, are three of the roles of the sacred minister as he counsels with the alcoholic. The intelligent, understanding friend; the official representative of a fellowship, a religious fellowship; and finally, the authorized custodian and ordained dispenser of the treasures of the religious fellowship. You see that the religious minister, as he counsels the inebriate, is not without resources. He has the three approaches, the three roles, as he deals with the alcoholic.

ATTITUDES OF THE ALCOHOLIC

I think there is time for me to mention one other matter, and that is the way in which the alcoholic comes to the sacred minister. He may seek help himself, and happy is the minister who has inspired the confidence and the trust of his parishioners so that an alcoholic can come to him directly. Instead of being annoyed and disturbed by this fact, the sacred minister ought to be very proud and ought to thank God that He has given him this opportunity.

The inebriate may come to the minister in a disguised approach. He may come to damn his sermon of last Sunday, he may come to discuss matters of theology with him and never mention his problem of alcohol. He is usually sounding out his pastor to see whether he is a counselor before whom he can open his heart.

The inebriate may be sent by family, by associates, by friends, by his employer, or he may come voluntarily. Or, and this is a rather unfortunate approach, the inebriate may come because a judge has ordered him to, or his wife has forced him to consult with the sacred minister. This is an obvious handicap in facing the situation. And, finally, the minister may seek out the inebriate.

As I said in the early part of the hour, because of the remote preparation of the minister, because of his ordination, because of his sense of responsibility, he may have to enter a situation uninvited. Now, there is a great deal of difference between mixing into people's lives because of idle curiosity and going to the person who is in trouble with a sense of duty and a sense of responsibility, in great humility and without passing judgment.

You probably recall the story of the absent-minded preacher who dreamed that he was preaching and woke up to find that he was. There are some in my profession who avow that they never do any counseling and that, therefore, they are not interested in the procedures of counseling. The truth of the matter is that every impact of life upon life, whether from the pulpit, or in intimate conversation, or in pastoral life, is a form of counseling. Whether we like it or not, whether we are fully aware of it or not, every one of us is day by day counseling someone else, so that every contact with the alcoholic is an opportunity for counseling and it is, in fact, counseling in one form or another. It is obvious that the strongest position is that in which the individual himself comes directly to the pastor and asks for help. The most creative attitude of the alcoholic, as far as his possible rehabilitation is concerned, is when he says frankly, "I am in trouble; here is a situation in which I can no longer handle myself and I need someone's help."

Unfortunately most pastoral counselors are forced at times to sit on the sidelines and see an alcoholic go down, down and down; to see a family become more and more disturbed, to see the emotional upsets in the lives of the children, and to see the beginning of an almost complete disintegration of the family situation, before the alcoholic gets to the point where he is willing to receive help. Curiously enough, we must sometimes wait until the alcoholic gets worse before we can begin to help him get better. This is a tragic truth; it probably reflects poor technique on our part and a lack of understanding. We shall hope and pray that in the future we will be able to enter the situation earlier and therefore give better pastoral service both to the inebriate and to his family. When the minister finds it necessary to enter an alcoholic situation uninvited, I must say very frankly that his results are not nearly so satisfactory as when he is directly sought out by the alcoholic or by his associates. I would say, however, that it is not an impossible situation, and if the pastoral work has been properly done, the minister will frequently find that the alcoholic can accept the suggestion that he needs help, or at least that the alcoholic will accept the fact that the minister is ready to help when the alcoholic is ready to be helped. That is a difficult situation to have to face. While the pastor is waiting for the alcoholic to come to him, there is much that he can do with the alcoholic's family. It is not necessary to remind you that the alcoholic in his family situation is a very pathetic individual indeed, nor must we lose sight of the fact that the family of the alcoholic is in a real situation of tragedy. The amount of hostility, the amount of antagonism, the amount of sympathy and pity, the amount of sheer lostness that one finds in the family of an alcoholic must be taken into account as we minister to the general situation.

First of all, may I suggest again that one of our tasks is educational. That is, we must explain to the family of the alcoholic something of the meaning of alcoholism, something about the prognosis and cure of the disorder. In some instances, if we place the right literature in the hands of the family they will better understand the situation, some of the antagonisms and hostilities will be allayed, and it may be easier for them to assist the alcoholic in seeking help. In any case, the family of the alcoholic definitely needs our aid and assistance and our pastoral concern. Actually, we know that the attitudes and cooperation of the family are of tremendous importance as we counsel with the alcoholic.

Techniques of the Counselor

Now may I presume upon your time and patience to run through, briefly, what we pastors think of as our technique. You will be rather amused that we dignify our procedure by such a word as technique, but I think it is important for us always to be aware of what we are trying to do and the steps we are trying to take. May I say again that the pastoral counseling of inebriates is not essentially different from the counseling of an individual who has a religious, spiritual or emotional problem. The steps, very simply, are these: The first and most important one is securing the rapport. There is nothing esoteric, there is nothing mystical, about this thing which we call rapport, although it is very difficult to describe. Rapport is the dynamic relation that exists between two people when one is sharing with the other his innermost difficulties, and where the other is understanding, with all the intelligence and empathy he can muster, of the problem which is brought to him. It is probably true that for many an alcoholic who comes to consult the pastor, it may be the first time he has been able to talk freely and without reserve about anything that comes to his mind. He may have had a father who was sympathetic to a point, sympathetic in certain areas, but quite unsympathetic beyond certain points or in other areas. He may have had a mother who was perhaps oversentimental, and he knew that he could not bring the reality of his situation to her. But for the first time he meets someone who understands—his pastor. And in the simple catharsis, in the simple pouring out of his sins, his degradations, his difficulties and his anxieties, something happens that creates an atmosphere in which much more can happen and much more of a creative nature will happen. Now the attitude on the part of the counselor is tremendously important, and this is especially so in building up the rapport with the alcoholic.

Everything in us seems to reach out toward judgments, toward condemning this person who comes to us, what he has done to himself, what he has done to his relationship with God, what he has done to his family, what he has done to his vocation. These are things that are deplorable, and there almost seems to be a straining within us to make a judgment, to offer punishment for what has occurred. Yet it is precisely in the objectivity of the counselor, and the willingness to hold his judgment in abeyance, that the great secret of his effectiveness lies. Mind you, the pastoral counselor is not condoning sin but he is learning to love the sinner, he is learning to love the person who is ill, he is learning to love the person who is in conflict, and through his love for him he is allowing him to grow and to begin to solve his own problems. Now when I say love, I do not mean that we want to become too involved with our parishioners. The objective attitude is the one which we try to create. It must be midway between being so sleepy and so dull in the situation that we can hardly attend to what our parishioner is saying, and, on the other hand, being on the edge of our chair saying to ourselves, "Oh boy, oh boy, oh boy!" The pastoral counselor who is bored by a situation and finds himself going to sleep, the counselor who is too eager to hear all the terrible recital, either one of these extremes vitiates the building up of the rapport. The counselor must be shockproof, he must be disgust-proof, and, as far as possible, he must hold his judgments in abeyance. He is not condoning whatever of sinfulness there is in the situation, but he is listening in order that he may build up the rapport and secure the data which he needs in order to make his own estimate of the seriousness of the situation that comes to him. Therefore, attitude is tremendously important in securing the rapport.

In counseling, the little details are often important. We cer.... consult with our people where we will not be interrupted. We r.... certain that our conversations with our people are held in strictest.... One of the dangers is that we will use the material that we hear in our.... sessions for sermons on Sunday. Last year, after coming to this Scho.... into the country and there attended a service at a small parish churc.... iny horror the preacher got up and started his sermon with these words: "During the past week one of our most attractive young widows came to me and said . . ." Before he got five words beyond the "attractive young widow" all of us were looking through that small congregation to find her. There was not an attractive young widow in the crowd, but she might have been there and I just wonder what she would have thought. It turned out that her question was a pretty good one to have asked the pastor, and yet that man had no business retailing that conversation in that form to that particular congregation.

The amount of time we have available is important. Usually in dealing with alcoholics our first interview ought to be long enough so that he can really tell his story and so that we can begin the rapport. Remember that the alcoholic slips away from the rapport very easily, and he may go on a spree immediately after our first conversation with him because the rapport has not been established. Therefore we vary our procedure with alcoholics by spending perhaps a little more time with them than we do with other folk who come to us with their problems. If possible we try to see the alcoholic each day, perhaps even twice a day for the first few days, until the rapport is built up. The first and most important step in counseling is building up the rapport and handling it intelligently.

One of the things we certainly should not do is try to collect spiritual scalps. There are many clergy whom you see practically dangling them from their belts. They enjoy having people dependent upon them, they enjoy having people hang on their every word because of the overimportance of the rapport. When a minister begins to feel that he is enjoying the counseling situation too much and enjoying the parishioner's dependency, then he would better stop counseling.

Now the second step, a perfectly natural one, is the securing of the data necessary to understand the situation. The pastoral counseling of the alcoholic is primarily a matter of trained listening—listening and helping the individual to talk himself out until he understands his problem and his own resources for solving it. The best counseling is done when the pastor has said next to nothing. One of my colleagues says that the pastoral counselor usually ought to limit his conversation to encouraging grunts. It is the hardest thing in the world for a preacher to do this. We are taught to preach at the drop of a hat, and that is one of the things we may be guilty of doing in our counseling.

If I may digress for a moment, I want to tell you about a great preacher in New York City who decided that he would become a pastoral counselor. He sat down by himself and discovered, through careful thought, that there were only 47 different types of human problems. He therefore got 47 cards and headed each of them with a human problem. Then he went through his sermon barrel and picked out all the pertinent passages from each of his sermons that would apply to each of these 47 different problems. He filed these in a case behind his desk. When the poor parishioner came in to consult him about his trou-

...es he was allowed to speak just a few sentences and then the pastor said, "Aha, that's Number 16." He pulled out card 16 and read him the sermon passages and the prayers appropriate for problem Number 16. He was very surprised to find that after the first week no one came back to consult him. We can understand why. The pastoral counselor must listen and he must listen in order to get the data on which to base his own interpretation of the situation and on which the parishioner may base his interpretation. Everything is grist for the counselor's mill. He should watch how the parishioner behaves, how he uses time, and the response which he makes to the counselor's interpretation. The alert pastoral counselor is listening always for the things that the parishioner does not say but which are important and inherent in the situation. One of the questions which the counselor is constantly asking himself is, "How did it happen that this parishioner came to me at this time; why is alcohol a special problem for him now, at this point?" That, you see, is getting a cross-section picture of the situation; finding out the relationship of the alcohol problem to other problems in the milieu of the parishioner at that time. The pastoral counselor listens always for resources of the parishioner, his family, his social setting, his strong loyalties, the things that he has done in the past which were creative, and the things he has done which he considers to be his worst sins and failings. These are all important data for the pastoral counseling. The first step, which continues through the whole procedure, is that of securing the rapport and maintaining it at the right level. The second is securing data. Every single day, hour after hour, the pastoral counselor is listening and is storing away in his own mind these important disclosures of his parishioner as they affect the parishioner's future, his present and his past.

The third step, a rather dangerous but important one, is the interpretation. I should qualify that by saying that the tentative interpretation of the data is arrived at, if possible, with the help of the parishioner, and always held in abeyance until the parishioner can accept the interpretation.

You know how dangerous it would be if the pastor in the first hour, even if he suspects it, were to say, "It seems to me your trouble is you are using your alcoholism as a means of punishing your wife for being such a puritan." If he loves his wife he can hardly accept that interpretation at that point, and his wife would be just as mad as he, if you offered her that interpretation. And yet you may see, almost from the first hour, that there is something of sadism in his misuse of alcohol. It is his way of punishing either his wife or his family, or punishing his father-image for being such a dominating, domineering and authoritarian kind of person. So there are the first three steps: securing the rapport, gaining the data, and making in one's own mind a tentative interpretation of the facts. I suppose a doctor or psychiatrist would call this diagnosis, but we had better not use that word.

The fourth step ought to appear as we go along; it should be a concomitant of the third step. It is this: A tentative solution or plan worked out, if possible, by the parishioner and not by the pastoral counselor. The inebriate says, "I begin to see why I started to drink at that point. I think I understand now how I'm using my alcoholism against my environment. Can it be that I'm trying to punish my family?" The pastoral counselor does not say, "Oh yes, aren't you keen and wonderful? That, of course, is the thing. I've known that for weeks." He says, "Well, it might possibly be so. Tell me more reasons why you think this to be so. Suppose you go home and test it out and see. How would that work?" The parishioner says, "Well, I think I'll try that out." There is a simple plan and a simple solution, or the beginning of a solution. The parishioner says, "I'll see if my interpretation of my alcoholism is right." He goes home and tries it out. He comes back in a few days and says, "No, I don't think that's true at all because of this, and this, and this." The provisional plan or solution is usually never the final one. One moves on with the parishioner, helps him to express himself more and more, gaining more data, and stands by him as he tests out his various solutions.

The final stage in our counseling, the fifth, is that of resolution of the rapport, or the referral of the individual to some other agency or authority. Many times what we do in our counseling is to get enough of the data and enough of the interpretation of the situation to see that we are unable to handle it. Therefore, we move on to the stage of referring the parishioner to someone else. That is good counseling. Certainly one of the adjuncts of good counseling is the ability to understand that we cannot handle the situation, that we do not have the objectivity, or we do not have the knowledge to deal with it, and our task then is to refer. The religious counselor has an entirely different kind of referral to make. He may, in fact, refer the individual to a psychiatrist, to Alcoholics Anonymous, a social agency, or to a clinic. But he also has a duty to perform with regard to the rapport, which may involve the parishioner's dependency. The intelligent pastoral counselor knows it is dangerous for him to continue in such close rapport with the parishioner that he will keep coming back, being dependent upon him, asking for his advice. And the sacred minister as counselor always has the further responsibility of referring—if I may use the word, and I do not use it in an impious way—of referring the individual to God. In other words, the only dependency which the pastoral counselor wants to achieve is the dependence of the individual on God, upon his church and the use of the sacraments of that church. Thus there is, in a sense, a referral which the pastoral counselor always makes. It is sometimes difficult for him, because he enjoys being depended upon, he enjoys being an oracle for this person who comes to him. It is so easy for him to rationalize that position and say, "He still needs me, therefore, I will hang on to him." But the intelligent, consecrated pastoral counselor wants, as soon as possible, to make this individual self-dependent on the one hand, and dependent upon his religious traditions on the other. Now you and I might disagree about the importance of that stage, but I think it is obvious that it is necessary for the religious counselor.

These, then, are the very simple stages that we try to go through in our counseling: First, securing a rapport which is strong enough so that in the dynamic of it something will happen. Second, getting enough of the data through our listening process so that we shall begin to understand. Third, achieving with our parishioner a tentative interpretation of his difficulty in relation to the rest of his life. Fourth, evolving some tentative solution or plan which the parishioner then seeks to work out. Fifth, the resolution of the rapport; and, in a religious sense, referral of dependency to some religious center; in some instances, where it seems advisable, referring the parishioner to some other authority. These form our simple technique, covering months and months sometimes, involving also some use of what psychiatrists might call active therapy, in that we refer to some social agency or to some expert in the field.

RELATION OF COUNSELOR AND ALCOHOLIC

Now, finally, a practical word or two about the pastoral counselor and the alcoholic. The alcoholic needs to have his time carefully planned for him at the beginning, and therefore the discussion of a rule of life is, of course, important; but many pastoral counselors have to find activities for the alcoholic. There comes into play the relationship of the pastor with members of his parish who perhaps might temporarily employ this alcoholic while he is being counseled by the pastor. It may be that the pastor has certain monetary resources which would allow him to look out for the creature comforts of the alcoholic while he is going through the process of counseling. The pastoral counselor must expect bad lapses on the part of the alcoholic although these are not always necessary. Many times the alcoholic goes back to his inebriate habit almost as if there were autonomous urgency to do so but the pastoral counselor must be ready to face this fact. He may spend a good deal of money outfitting the alcoholic with new clothes and a new overcoat only to have him come back after a spree a week later having sold the overcoat and the clothes. Those are things that the pastoral counselor has to face. Now there are many social factors in the parish, in the community to which the pastoral counselor has entree. I have spoken of a number of activity groups, interest groups, and worship groups within the parish. There are also groups of various kinds in the community where the alcoholic can work but, remember this, the alcoholic must be given a job or a place that is a real one. Anything in the nature of a job created so that he can be busy will not be helpful. The alcoholic is very keen in understanding when you ask him to do something that has no value to the community, or to anyone else. Therefore, the task to be assigned or set must be a real one. It must not be too difficult, for the alcoholic is usually driven by perfectionism. It must be within the scope of his own innate ability.

One must stay very close to the alcoholic's ego.

The alcoholic is more suspicious and more sensitive to implied criticisms or to implied censure than almost any other subject of pastoral counseling. As one counsels with the alcoholic, one uses the actual word "we." "Now what do we find in the situation?" one asks. "What could we do with this problem that you have brought?" Just such simple technique as using the word *we* helps. The alcoholic must always feel that we are close to him, and that we are on his side, even when he is bound in some instances to go through two or three sprees or lapses. One must be very intelligent in the use of hostility in the counseling situation. I wish there were time to say a great deal about that. The alcoholic is usually eaten out with guilt and he is also beset by much hostility and by much hatred—hatred for himself, hatred for his father-image, hatred for his family, hatred for his church. Much of it is unconscious but nevertheless present. The pastoral counselor must not be self-righteous if the alcoholic begins criticisms of him. Yesterday morning at about a quarter past four, I had a long distance call from California. It was a former parishioner who had gone alcoholic. He had called up from California to tell me what he thought of me, my sermons, my handling of the church work, and my parents, if any. He was quite uninhibited in what he said to me. I have no doubt that what he said about my sermons was fairly true; there were some important criticisms which I am going to try to take to heart. I know, however, that some of the criticism was not directed toward me as a person, but I was a convenient pincushion that he could stick his pins into at that hour in the morning. He knew I was a hospital chaplain and therefore on call 24 hours a day; it was easy for him to call me. He called me simply to express his hostility, and I think I did him some good. I did not talk back— I just listened for awhile until I needed to get back to sleep. Then, in as courteous a way as I could, I broke the conversation. We are called, in our ministry of counseling, to be pincushions again and again and again, and if the hostility of people who come to us gets under our skin, then we are not good at counseling. We simply are not doing our job.

A few months ago I was talking to 500 corps men in a large army hospital down south. The corps men were mad as hops because they had been turned out at night to listen to a parson talk, and a civilian parson at that! There was a man in the front row who had evidently been having a go at the alcohol bottle on his ward because he could not attend much to what I said until I talked about being a pincushion. Then he looked up and said, "For Christ's sake, we've got to be pincushions." And I said, "Yes, for Christ's sake we have to be pincushions." That is exactly the meaning of this thing. Our vocation is to handle hostility wisely; the hospital chaplain knows this, the service chaplain knows it. Men in the service cannot kick their captain in the teeth, and patients in the hospital had better not kick their nurses or their doctors in the teeth these days, or they may find retaliation in a dull needle or the absence of a very important utensil when they ring for it. Any intelligent minister knows that he has to take hostility and it is particularly important in relation to the alcoholic.

Then, take the matter of guilt. Many times we do harm by increasing the alcoholic's sense of guilt. We do not condone what he has done. We do not say, "There, there, this isn't a problem, everything is going to be all right," because we know it is a problem, and we are not at all sure that everything is going to be all right. But most alcoholics are already eaten out with a sense of guilt, and anything we can do in a creative way to alleviate that sense of guilt and emphasize the importance of this individual to God will be helpful. This is why the use of the sacrament of penance is so useful in some churches. It is why, in the free churches, while penance is not used as a sacrament, an approximation of it, informal confession, can be used, which has some effect psychologically.

What do we do about relapses and about alcoholic fugues in our counseling? We have to accept them and we have to make use of them. At least they give us certain data to work on, and when the alcoholic comes back after his relapse we say, "What have we learned from the relapse? What do we find in your situation during the relapse which gives us new data to work on and with which we can deal creatively?"

May I point out that the alcoholic usually needs some medical attention, or some physical attention, and particularly when he is recovering from a bout. The pastoral counselor must make certain that he has the right kind of a physical examination so that he will not overlook some physical lacks and needs.

Finally, just one note about the minister himself in relation to the alcoholic. The minister must not be afraid to tackle the problem, but he must be very, very humble about what he can do for the alcoholic. Next, I believe the minister always needs to look to himself when he fails. A young psychiatrist went to study in a certain clinic in Germany some years ago, and the head of the clinic gave him four or five Bavarian patients to treat. They were not very serious psychological problems, but they all got worse. This made the young American psychiatrist very angry, so he went to the head of the clinic and said, "Doctor, this group of Bavarians are very perverse people. They just won't get well. There's something wrong with these southern Germans, they don't respond to therapy as they should." The psychiatrist waited for a moment and then said, "Doctor, I have a couple of hours free tomorrow morning, and if you will come in we will talk about your emotional problems." The trouble was not with the patients, but with the doctor. We must be very humble, and if we fail with alcoholics, or if we fail in counseling with our parishioners generally, then it is we who need counseling and not the parishioners.

All through this country there are seminars being held on pastoral counseling, not particularly of inebriates, but pastoral counseling generally. The Commission which I represent on the Federal Council of Churches of Christ in America has been responsible for many seminars throughout the country for clergy, for service chaplains, for U.S.O. directors, and for civilian clergy. These men are seeking these seminars in order to perfect their own technique in dealing with human souls. This does not mean that psychiatry or personal counseling will give the religious minister the last word. It does not mean even that it will give him a new bag of tricks which he can let loose on his parishioners. It does mean, however, that with new understanding, new insight, and new facts, the sacred minister will go forward to do his proper job, using his own tools but with better perspective than he has used them before. I believe, therefore, that this greater concern for good pastoral counseling on the part of the clergy is a sign that we as a profession are more alive to our opportunities, more alive to our deficiencies, than we have been before. And God grant to us that we can use these adjuncts to our proper work more effectively for the souls He has entrusted to our care.

DISCUSSION

Mrs. Coles: Why do you use the word "referral" to God rather than transference? Is it not transference as well?

Lecturer: If I use transference, then I get into the terminology of the psychoanalysts, and I am a little afraid of that terminology. I think transferral would perhaps be a better word.

Mrs. Coles: Is not the life experience of the average pastor an additional handicap in understanding the alcoholic and his problems?

Lecturer: Do you mean that too many pastors are too alcoholic to be objective? Or do you mean that the life experience of the average pastor is somewhat limited and somewhat circumscribed in that he has perhaps not had the opportunity to meet some of the problems of reality?

The latter, I think, has been a serious problem in the past, but I do not think it is nearly so much of a problem today. Many of the seminaries that I know about offer a rather careful period of clinical training and also have in their courses an introduction to many of these varied problems of reality. I think there are certain types of parsons who live in a world apart and who write their books about reality but have very little actual contact with reality. But I am impressed more and more with my colleagues in the ministry who are very close to reality and who have people come to them with all kinds of problems. I believe this will be one of the great values accruing from the service chaplains in the Army and Navy. I think it is true that some pastors are handicapped either because of their own home training or because of their limited experience. Most of us, of course, are terribly biased emotionally—there's no question about that. There are certain sins which, when they come to us, make us see red. We are not at all free in certain areas and we had better not try to counsel in those areas until we have had some attention ourselves. If the pastor finds he gets so terribly stirred up about sex, or about alcoholism, or about some other things, that he cannot do good pastoral counseling, then he had better go to a psychiatrist to find out what the emotional meaning is for him.

Couch: Can you illustrate for us the use of prayer in counseling inebriates?

Lecturer: I think that prayer has a number of different meanings and a number of different uses with the inebriate. We would have to go into quite a discussion of what we mean by prayer and the different types of prayer in order to cover this question at all thoroughly. I think that the prayer which brings in the reality of the doctrine of man, confessing frankly that one is a miserable sinner but asking God's help and assuming that God will give help in becoming a child of God, is the helpful kind of prayer. I think a prayer as the summary of an interview, not bringing in any technical data but frankly admitting to sinfulness that has been brought out in the interview and looking forward to further work on the problem, is a good prayer. I think a simple prayer suggesting that one is not alone but is a part of the whole church and that God is concerned with the individual, is a satisfactory kind of prayer. I think prayer for Divine guidance in interpreting data is important. Sometimes I think that the best prayer of all is a simple blessing given to the parishioner as he leaves the office of the pastoral counselor. Sometimes we can frighten patients to death in the hospital by praying in the wrong sense. For instance, in our hospital we have a Bible, a Prayer Book and a Hymnal on every bedside stand. We don't encourage some apprehensive patients to use the Prayer Book unless they are accustomed to it, because with unerring accuracy the apprehensive patient opens to the Litany for the Dying or to the Prayer for the Deceased.

Sometimes for the inebriate the repetition of a familiar prayer is important. The use of the Our Father, the Hail Mary, the use of the sign of the cross, the saying of the Rosary. These things in their context can be helpful. This is not just a matter of rote, it is important in directing the thoughts of the inebriate and in reminding him of what the pastor has said about the parishioner's importance to God.

Jackson: Is it necessarily true, or largely so, that the minister who is primarily interested in control of the liquor traffic and is the reformer type cannot be, at the same time, a good pastoral counselor of alcoholics?

Lecturer: I can answer this by saying that the minister interested in the control of alcohol is not a good counselor of the alcoholic. He is too biased and too tied up with its emotional features. I often think that some reformers and some professional prohibitionists find it a little difficult to be objective in counseling the alcoholic. One interesting thing that I may divulge to this group is that in a series of psychological analyses a number of our inebriates, and two or three of our seminarians who are the most rabid in refusing to see anything but their point of view about alcohol, showed the same psychological pattern. It is interesting that men who profess to be such terrible enemies of everything that is alcoholic should present much the same picture emotionally as the alcoholics whom we are trying to counsel. Mind you, these were not mature men, but youngsters at the beginning of their seminary course. They think it is such a nuisance to have to suffer through three years, for they are ready to go right out on the street and preach, and they do. They have no discipline, and I think their reforming tendency is quite clearly an emotional bias rather than any thought-out or God-directed position. It is always interesting to me to find that some of the obese people whom we deal with in pastoral counseling and in the hospitals present very much the same picture as the alcoholic; they are as intemperate in their eating as the alcoholic is in his drinking, and yet none of these people would touch a drop of alcohol.

Berger: How can one tell when rapport has been established?

Lecturer: That is a very good question, and a very subtle problem. The establishment of rapport shows its beginning when the parishioner is willing to relax in his chair and is willing to listen to interpretations; it shows in his frank and open facial expression toward the counselor, and in his willingness to come back. These are all on the positive side. Mind you, there can be negative rapport, and negative rapport can also be used. It is less likely to be established by most of the clergy. The negative rapport is present when the person returns but keeps sticking pins into the counselor. The parishioner says something like this: "This has been a complete waste of my time and I think you are a fool, but I want to come back tomorrow and tell you more about your foolishness." That is a negative rapport that can be used. Frequently in counseling alcoholics one goes from a positive rapport to a negative one and then back to the positive. One tells the symptoms of the negative rapport by the little criticisms of the pastor's acts outside the counseling room. It is done very subtly, usually. "You know, I once heard a good preacher preach on the text you used Sunday." "Doesn't your wife ever get enough money from you so she can wear neat-looking frocks?" "Why don't you have the walls of your office painted? I've never seen such a cracked-looking wall." These things, you see, are not direct criticisms of the pastor, but they are close enough so that he had better realize that he has a certain amount of negative rapport. I think one of the tests of the depth of the rapport is in the way in which the parishioner is willing to believe in the interpretation of certain data and yet, at the same time, asks questions about that interpretation. He is willing to differ from the counselor because he believes that the rapport is strong enough so that the differing will not break the relationship.

Evans: Do you keep records of your counseling?

Lecturer: Decidedly. The matter of records is of tremendous importance in pastoral counseling. Every pastor keeps two types of records. One is the official record which he must make to his own religious body, or to his Bishop or ecclesiastical authority, of the pastoral and sacerdotal functions which he performs in the parish. Most of us, for calling, keep a record card that has the name of the family, the number of people in it, their ecclesiastical situation, as whether they are baptized, confirmed, and so forth. And there is also a place to record the date of the call. There is not very much personal data on that card. But corresponding to it most of us keep a confidential file on which we note situations in the family—the happy events that have occurred, the advancement of the father in his business or work, or some of the negative elements, the illness of some member at a distance, the problems of one of the children, and so on. So we have a confidential record of what is happening in that family, including any indications of emotional or religious difficulty which we see on our pastoral visits. That is the second type of confidential record. Now a third record—if kept—is the record of the actual pastoral interviews. Most of us do not like to take notes while our parishioners are in the room, although some of us do, but immediately at the close of the interview it is very important for the pastor to jot down enough notes so that later in the day he can fill in the record. What is important is not alone what the parishioner said but also what the pastor said, or thinks he said. Incidentally, he probably did not say anything of the kind. Now you laugh, but for 10 years I was doing pastoral counseling and thought that I was setting down, verbatim, the conversations of the parishioners with me. Then, one summer, I worked in a clinic where the whole conversation was recorded through a microphone hidden in the desk. When I played this record back, one could see how emotionally involved I was in the situation. The tone of my voice and my interpretations were quite different from what I had reported about myself. It is a very salutary experience to go through that kind of record taking, as I'll find when this talk comes back from the recording!

Nevertheless, the written record is very important. It not only solidifies the material in the mind of the counselor, but he has it to refresh his memory before his next counsel and, furthermore, it gives him much data from which to make his interpretation. He can go back a few weeks and know that at that point the parishioner behaved in this way and said these things. Now he seems to be repeating the pattern—What does it mean? Pretty soon he has an interpretation of that behavior pattern. I don't think any pastor can do good counseling of any type unless he keeps adequate records. I think the failure on the part of many of us has been because our records have not been kept carefully.

There is a conflict here with what I said the first hour. That is, about preserving someone's confidence. Any of us who are hearing regular confessions, of course, would never think of recording anything about them and would never even reopen any of the questions raised in the confessional unless the penitent himself asks permission to do so or gives us permission to do so. Whether anyone has the right to keep, for any length of time, that third type of record I spoke about is a moral question for each pastor. I think that because of its value to the individual, and because the pastor will eventually destroy that record, he has a perfect right to keep it. Certainly each good psychiatrist and every good social worker does keep such records. It may be a question of moral theology for some of us.

Hoover: Would you please speak further on the inebriate's testing out the interpretation of the causes of his alcoholism?

Lecturer: I hope I was not misunderstood in what I said about that. I don't mean that the inebriate who believes, for example, that his alcoholism stems from his hostility toward his wife, leaves the counseling chamber and goes back and breaks her neck to see whether that relieves him of his desire for alcohol. I mean that a situation like the following may arise. The inebriate, after talking with the counselor for some time, begins to see that in almost every situation where he has used alcohol to excess he has been painting himself up, giving himself a kind of a shell. He may be a mousy little individual who never gets any attention, but when he gets drunk he gets all the attention there is, including the negative attention of his wife and children. After awhile he begins to say, "Can it be that maybe what I'm trying to do is get attention?" One pushes it further and asks why he needs attention, and then he begins to realize it is because he doesn't believe in himself enough, he doesn't find himself capable of self-belief and self-love in life situations. Then the next thing is to allow him to make the suggestion, "Why don't I try going into a group without trying to be something that

I'm not? Why don't I enter a group and just be me, see if I get by as me? See if I can test out by inquiring of my family, particularly of my parents, whether as a child I did seem to lack self-belief, whether I didn't fail to play as other children did?" Then he goes and asks his wife and family questions: "Is it possible that I'm behaving like that?" They may confirm his thoughts and say, "Yes, there is no reason for this lack of belief in yourself, but somehow you are behaving in adult life as though you are still a little boy who has not made good. Now we know that you have made good, but you won't believe it." Some such situation as that might be an illustration of what I was saying.

Or it may be that the inebriate says, "I think I just feel lonely and that's why I drink." The counselor says, "Well, why don't you record, during the day, the number of times when you feel lonely, or when you see people that you'd like to be with but don't dare be with, or when you feel self-conscious with people?" He does and brings his list back, and you run over it and ask, "What do you think, was your judgment correct?" And he answers, "Why, I think so. Tomorrow I'm going to try entering a group without thinking what effect I'll have on them. I am going to say, 'Here is a group, here is something that is interesting and amusing, and I'll just go into it on that basis.' " A few days later he comes back and says, "Yes, I tested that thing out and sometimes it works and sometimes it doesn't. I still am not free in believing in myself in a group." That's what I mean by testing out the situation. Granted, this is very dangerous for some alcoholics. Therefore we must allow him to make the suggestions, and caution him about the results. I have, in my portfolio at home, a beautiful cartoon from the *New Yorker* which shows a very masculine psychiatrist sitting high in his desk chair looking down at a little, anemic, pathetic creature in the chair in front of him, and the caption under it is, "You *should* have an inferiority complex!"

The Fellowship of Alcoholics Anonymous

W. W.

MY first task is a joyous one; it is to voice the sincere gratitude that every member of Alcoholics Anonymous present feels tonight that we can stand in the midst of such an assembly. I know that in this assembly there are many different points of view, that we have social workers, ministers, doctors and others—people we once thought did not understand us, because we did not understand them. I think right away of one of our clergyman friends. He helped start our group in St. Louis, and when Pearl Harbor came he thought to himself, "Well, this will be a hard day for the A.A.'s." He expected to see us go off like firecrackers. Well, nothing much happened and the good man was rather joyously disappointed, you might say. But he was puzzled. And then he noticed with still more wonder that the A.A.'s seemed rather less excited about Pearl Harbor than the normal people. In fact, quite a number of the so-called normal people seemed to be getting drunk and very distressed. So he went up to one of the A.A.'s and said, "Tell me, how is it that you folks hold up so well under this stress, I mean this Pearl Harbor?" The A.A. looked at him, smiled, but quite seriously said, "You know, each of us has had his own private Pearl Harbor, each of us has known the utmost of humiliation, of despair, and of defeat. So why should we, who know the resurrection, fear another Pearl Harbor?"

So you can see how grateful we are that we have found this resurrection and that so many people, not alcoholics, with so many points of view, have joined to make it a reality. I guess all of you know Marty Mann by this time. I shall always remember her story about her first A.A. meeting. She had been in a sanatorium under the care of a wonderful doctor, but how very lonely she felt! Somehow, there was a gap between that very good man and herself which could not quite be bridged. Then she went to her first A.A. meeting, wondering what she would find; and her words, when she returned to the sanatorium, in talking to her friend, another alcoholic, were: "Grenny, we are no longer alone." So we are a people who have known loneliness, but now stand here in the midst of many friends. Now I am sure you can see how very grateful for all this we must be.

I am sure that in this course you have heard that alcoholism is a malady; that something is dead wrong with us physically; that our reaction to alcohol has changed; that something has been very wrong with us emotionally; and that our alcoholic habit has become an obsession, an obsession which can no longer reckon even with death itself. Once firmly set, one is not able to turn it aside. In other words, a sort of allergy of the body which guarantees that we shall die if we drink, an obsession of the mind which guarantees that we shall go on drinking. Such has been the alcoholic's dilemma time out of mind, and it is altogether probable that even those alcoholics who did not wish to go on drinking, not more than 5 out of 100 have ever been able to stop, before A.A.

That statement always takes my mind back to a summer night at a drying-out place in New York where I lay upstairs at the end of a long trail. My wife was downstairs talking with the doctor, asking him, "Bill so badly wants to stop this thing, doctor, why can't he? He was always considered a person of enormous persistence, even obstinacy, in those things that he wished to achieve. Why can't his will power work now? It does work even yet in other areas of life, but why not in this?" And then the doctor went on to tell her something of my childhood, showing that I had grown up a rather awkward kid, how that had thrown upon me a kind of inferiority and had inspired in me a fierce desire to show other people that I could be like them; how I had become a person who abnormally craved approval, applause. He showed her the seed, planted so early, that had created me an inferiority-driven neurotic. On the surface, to be sure, very self-confident, with a certain amount of worldly success in Wall Street. But along with it this habit of getting release from myself through alcohol.

You know, as strange as it may seem to some of the clergy here who are not alcoholic, the drinking of alcohol is a sort of spiritual release. Is it not true that the great fault of all individuals is abnormal self-concern? And how well alcohol seems temporarily to expel those feelings of inferiority in us, to transport us temporarily to a better world. Yes, I was one of those people to whom drink became a necessity and then an addiction. So it was 10 years ago this summer that the good doctor told my wife I could not go on much longer; that my habit of adjusting my neurosis with alcohol had now become an obsession; how that obsession of my mind condemned me to go on drinking, and how my physical sensitivity guaranteed that I would go crazy or die, perhaps within a year. Yes, that was my dilemma. It has been the dilemma of millions of us, and still is.

Some of you wonder, "Well, he had been well instructed by a good physician, he had been told about his maladjustment, he understood himself, he knew that his increasing physical sensitivity meant that he would go out into the dark and join the endless procession. Why couldn't he stop? Why wouldn't fear hold such a man in check?"

After I left that place, fear did keep me in check for 2 or 3 months. Then came a day when I drank again. And then came a time when an old friend, a former alcoholic, called on the phone and said that he was coming over. It was perhaps right there on that very day that the Alcoholics Anonymous commenced to take shape. I remember his coming into my kitchen, where I was half drunk. I was afraid that perhaps he had come to reform me. You know, curiously enough, we alcoholics are very sensitive on this subject of reform. I could not quite make out my friend. I could see something different about him but I could not put my finger on it. So finally I said, "Ebby, what's got into you?" And he said, "Well, I've got religion." That shocked me terribly, for I was one of those people with a dandy modern education which had taught me that self-sufficiency would be enough to carry me through life, and here was a man talking a point of view which collided with mine.

Ebby did not go on colliding with me. He knew, as a former agnostic, what my prejudices were, so he said to me, blandly enough, "Well, Bill, I don't know that I'd call it religion exactly, but call it what you may, it works." I said, "What is it? What do you mean? Tell me more about this thing." He said, "Some people came and got hold of me. They said, 'Ebby, you've tried medicine, you've tried religion, you've tried change of environment, I guess you've tried love, and none of these things has been able to cure you of your liquor. Now here is an idea for you.' " And then he went on to tell me how they explained. They said, "First of all, Ebby, why don't you make a thorough appraisal of yourself? Stop finding fault with other people. Make a thoroughgoing moral appraisal of yourself. When have you been selfish, dishonest? And, especially, where have you been intolerant? Perhaps those are the things that underlie this alcoholism. And after you have made such an appraisal of yourself, why don't you sit down and talk it out with someone in full and quit this accursed business of living alone? Put an end to this Dr. Jekyll and Mr. Hyde situation into which you have fallen. And then, why don't you continue this policy of abating the disturbance in yourself? Why don't you take stock of all the people among your acquaintances that you have hurt—all of the people who annoy you, who disturb you. Why don't you go to them and make amends; set things right and talk things out, and get down these strains that exist between you and them? Then, Ebby, we have still another proposal. Why don't you try the kind of giving that demands no reward? We don't mean the mere giving of money, though you once had plenty of that. No, we mean the giving of yourself to someone who is in need. Why don't you try that? Seek out someone in need and forget your own troubles by becoming interested in his." Ebby said, "Where does the religion come in?" And his friends went on to say, "Ebby, it is our experience that no one can carry out such a program with enough thoroughness and enough continuity on pure self-sufficiency. One must have help. Now we are willing to help you, as individuals, but we think you ought to call upon a power greater than yourself, for your dilemma is well-nigh insurmountable. So, call on God as you understand God. Try prayer." Well, in effect, that was the explanation my friend made to me. Those of you who know a little of the A.A. are already able to see the basic idea.

You see, here was my friend talking to me, one alcoholic talking to another. I could no longer say, "He doesn't understand me." Sure he understood me. We had done a lot of drinking together, and gone the same route of humiliation, despair and defeat. Yes, he could understand. But now he had something. He did not shock me by calling it the resurrection, but that's what it was. He had something I did not have, and those were the terms upon which it could be obtained.

Honesty with oneself and other people, the kind of giving that demands no return, and prayer. Those were the essentials. My friend then got up and went away, but he had been very careful not to force any of his views upon me. In no sense could I have the feeling that he was moralizing with me or preaching, because I knew it was not so long ago that he was no better than I. He merely said that he was leaving these ideas with me, hoping that they would help.

Even so, I was irritated, because he had struck a blow at my pet philosophy of self-sufficiency, and was talking about dependence upon some power greater than myself. "Ah yes," I thought, as I went on drinking, "yes, it's this preacher stuff. Yes, I remember, up in the old home town where my grandfather raised me, how the deacon, who was so good, treated Ed MacDonald, the local drunk —as dirt under his feet; and more than that, the old son of a gun shortweighted my good old grandfather in his grocery store. If that's religion, I don't want any of it." Such were my prejudices. But the whole point of this is that my friend had got onto my level. He had penetrated my prejudices, although he had not yet swept them all away.

I drank on but I kept turning this thing over in my mind, and finally asked myself, "Well, how much better off am I than a cancer patient?" But a small percentage of those people recover, and the same is true with alcoholics, for by this time I knew quite a good deal about alcoholism. I knew that my chances were very, very slim. I knew that, in spite of all the vigilance in the world, this obsession would pursue me, even if I dried up temporarily. Yes, how much better off was I than a cancer patient? Then I began to say to myself, "Well, who are beggars to be choosers? Why should a man be talking about self-sufficiency when an obsession has condemned him to have none of it?" Then I became utterly willing to do anything, to try to accept any point of view, to make any sacrifice, yes, even to try to love my enemies, if I could get rid of this obsession.

First, I went up to a hospital to ask the doctor to clear me up so I could think things through clearly. And again came my friend, the second day that I was there. Again I was afraid, knowing that he had religion, that he was going to reform me. I cannot express the unreasonable prejudice that the alcoholics have against reform. That is one reason why it has been so hard to reach them. We should not be that way, but we are. And here was my friend, trying to do his best for me, but the first thought that flashed across my mind was, "I guess this is the day that he is going to try to save me. Look out! He'll bring in that high-powered sweetness and light, he'll be talking about a lot of this prayer business." But Ebby was a good general, and it's a good thing for me he was.

No, he did not collide with those prejudices of mine. He just paid me a friendly visit, and he came up there quite early in the morning. I kept waiting and waiting for him to start his reform talk, but no, he didn't. So finally I had to ask for some of it myself. I said, "Ebby, tell me once more about how you dried up." And he reviewed it again for me.

Honesty with oneself, of a kind I had never had before. Complete honesty with someone else. Straightening out all my twisted relationships as best I could. Giving of myself to help someone else in need. And prayer.

When he had gone away, I fell into a very deep depression, the blackest that I had ever known. And in that depression, I cried out, "If there is a God, will He show Himself?" Then came a sudden experience in which it seemed the room lit up. It felt as though I stood on the top of a mountain, that a great clean wind blew, that I was free. The sublime paradox of strength coming out of weakness.

So I called in the doctor and tried to tell him, as best I could, what had happened. And he said, "Yes, I have read of such experiences but I have never seen one." I said, "Well, doctor, examine me. Have I gone crazy?" And he did examine me and said, "No, boy, you're not crazy. Whatever it is, you'd better hold onto it. It's so much better than what had you just a few hours ago." Well, along with thousands of other alcoholics, I have been holding onto it ever since.

But that was only the beginning. And at the time, I actually thought that it was the end, you might say, of all my troubles. I began then, out of this sudden illumination, not only to get benefits, but to draw some serious liabilities. One of those that came immediately and most naturally was one that you might call Divine Appointment. I actually thought, I had the conceit really to believe, that God had selected me, by this sudden flash of Presence, to dry up all the drunks in the world. I really believed it. I also got another terrific liability out of the experience, and that was that it had to happen in some particular way just like mine or else it would be of no use. In other words, I conceived myself as going out, getting hold of these drunks, and producing in them just the same kind of experience that I had had. Down in New York, where they know me pretty well in the A.A., they facetiously call these sudden experiences that we sometimes have a "W. W. hot flash." I really thought that I had been endowed with the power to go out and produce a "hot flash" just like mine in every drunk.

Well, I started off. I was inspired; I knew just how to do it, as I thought then. Well, I worked like thunder for 6 months and not one alcoholic got dried up. What were the natural reactions then? I suppose some of you here, who have worked with alcoholics, have a pretty good idea. The first reaction was one of great self-pity; the other was a kind of martyrdom. I began to say, "Well, I suppose this is the kind of stuff that martyrs are made of but I will keep on at all costs." I kept on, and I kept on, until I finally got so full of self-pity and intolerance (our two greatest enemies in the A.A.) that I nearly got drunk myself. So I began to reconsider. I began to say, "Yes, I found my relief in this particular way, and glorious it was and is, for it is still the central experience of my whole life. But who am I to suppose that every other human being ought to think, act and react just as I do? Maybe we're all very much alike in a great many respects but, as individuals, we're different too."

At that juncture I was in Akron on a trip, and I got a very severe business setback. I was walking along in the corridor of the hotel, wondering how God could be so mean. After all the good I had done Him—why, I had worked here with drunks 6 months and nothing had happened—and now here was a situation that was going to set me up in business and I had been thrown out of it by dishonest people. Then I began to think, "That spiritual experience—was that real?" I began to have doubts. Then I suddenly realized that I might get drunk. But I also realized that those other times when I had had self-pity, those other times when I had had resentment and intolerance, those other times when there was that feeling of insecurity, that worry as to where the next meal would come from; yes, to talk with another alcoholic even though I failed with him, was better than to do nothing. But notice how my motivation was shifting all this time. No longer was I preaching from any moral hilltop or from the vantage point of a wonderful spiritual experience. No, this time I was looking for another alcoholic, because I felt that I needed him twice as much as he needed me. And that's when I came across Dr. "Bob" S. out in Akron. That was just 9 years ago this summer.

And Bob S. recovered. Then we two frantically set to work on alcoholics in Akron. Well, again came this tendency to preach, again this feeling that it has to be done in some particular way, again discouragement. So our progress was very slow. But little by little we were forced to analyze our experiences and say, "This approach didn't work very well with that fellow. Why not? Let's try to put ourselves in his shoes and stop this preaching. See how we might be approached if we were he." That began to lead us to the idea that the A.A. should be no set of fixed ideas, but should be a growing thing, growing out of experience. After a while, we began to reflect: "This wonderful blessing that has come to us, from what does it get its origin?" It was a spiritual awakening growing out of painful adversity. So then we began to look the harder for our mistakes, to correct them, to capitalize upon our errors. And little by little we began to grow so that there were 5 of us at the end of that first year; at the end of the second year, 15; at the end of the third year, 40; at the end of the fourth year, 100.

During those first 4 years most of us had another bad form of intolerance. As we commenced to have a little success, I am afraid our pride got the better of us and it was our tendency to forget about our friends. We were very likely to say, "Well, those doctors didn't do anything for us, and as for these sky pilots, well, they just don't know the score." And we became snobbish and patronizing.

Then we read a book by Dr. Carrel. From that book came an argument which is now a part of our system. (How much we may agree with the book in general, I don't know, but in this respect the A.A.'s think he had something.) Dr. Carrel wrote, in effect: The world is full of analysts. We have tons of ore in the mines and there are all kinds of building material above ground. Here is a man specializing in this, there another man specializing in that, and another one in something else. The modern world is full of wonderful analysts and diggers, but there are very few who deliberately synthesize, who bring together different materials, who assemble new things. We are much too shy on synthetic thinking—the kind of thinking that's willing to reach out now here and now there to see if something new cannot be evolved.

On reading that book some of us realized that that was just what we had been groping toward. We had been trying to build out of our own experiences. At this point we thought, "Let's reach into other people's experiences. Let's go back to our friends the doctors, let's go back to our friends the preachers, the social workers, all those who have been concerned with us, and again review what they have got above ground and bring that into the synthesis. And let us, where we can, bring them in where they will fit." So our process of trial and error began and, at the end of 4 years, the material was cast in the form of a book known as *Alcoholics Anonymous*. And then our friends of the press came in and they began to say nice things about us. That was not too hard for them to do because by that time we had gotten hold of the idea of not fighting anything or anyone. We began to say, "Our only motive as an organization is to help the other alcoholic. And to help him we've got to reach him. Therefore, we can't collide with his prejudices. So we aren't going to get mixed up with controversial questions, no matter what we, as individuals, think of them. We can't get concerned with prohibition, or whether to drink or not to drink. We can't get concerned with doctrine and dogma in a religious sense. We can't get into politics, because that will arouse prejudice which might keep away alcoholics who will go off and die when they might have recovered."

We began, then, to have a good press, because after all we were just a lot of very sick people trying to help those who wanted to be helped. And I am very happy to say that in all the years since, not a syllable of ridicule, or criticism, has ever been printed about us. For this we are very grateful.

That experience led us to examine some of the obscure phrases that we sometimes see in our Bibles. For a great many of us have taken to reading the Bible. It could not have been presented at first, but sooner or later in his second, third, or fourth year, the A.A. will be found reading his Bible quite as often—or more —as he will a standard psychological work. And you know, there we found a phrase which began to stick in the minds of some of us. It was this: "Resist not evil." Well, after all, what is one going to think? In the modern world, where everybody is fighting, here came someone saying, "Resist not evil." What did that mean? Did it mean anything? Was there anything in that phrase for the A.A.'s?

Well we began to have some cases on which we could try out that principle. I remember one case out of which some will get a kick, and I imagine some others here may be a little shocked, but I think there is a lesson in it, at least there was for us, a lesson in tolerance. One time, after A.A. had been going on for 3 or 4 years, an alcoholic was brought into our house over in Brooklyn where we were holding a meeting. He is the type that some of us now call the block-buster variety. He often tells the story himself. His name is Jimmy. Well, Jimmy came in and he was a man who had some very, very fixed points of view. As a class, we alcoholics are the worst possible people in that respect. I had many, many fixed points of view myself, but Jimmy eclipsed us all. Jimmy came into our little group—I guess there were then 30 or 40 of us meeting—and said, "I think you've got a pretty good idea here. This idea of straightening things out with other people is fine. Going over your own defects is all right. Working with other drunks, that's swell. But I don't like this God business." He got very emphatic about it and we thought that he would quiet down or else he would get drunk. He did neither. Time went on and Jimmy did not quiet down; he began to tell the other people in the group, "You don't need this God business. Look, I'm staying sober." Finally, he got up in the meeting at our house, the first time he was invited to speak—he had then been around for a couple of months—and he went through his usual song and dance of the desirability of being honest, straightening things out with other people, etc. Then he said, "Damn this God business." At that, people began to wince. I was deeply shocked, and we had a hurried meeting of the "elders" over in the corner. We said, "This fellow has got to be suppressed. We can't have anyone ridiculing the very idea by which we live."

We got hold of Jimmy and said, "Listen, you've just got to stop this anti-God talk if you're going to be around this section." Jimmy was cocky and he said, "Is that so? Isn't it a fact that you folks have been trying to write a book called *Alcoholics Anonymous*, and haven't you got a typewritten introduction in that book, lying over there on that shelf, and didn't we read it here about a month ago and agree to it?" And Jimmy went over and took down the introduction to *Alcoholics Anonymous* and read out of it: "The only requirement for membership in Alcoholics Anonymous is an honest desire to get over drinking." Jimmy said, "Do you mean it, or don't you?" He rather had us there. He said, "I've been honest. Didn't I get my wife back? Ain't I paying my bills? And I'm helping other drunks every day." There was nothing we could say. Then we began secretly to hope. Our intolerance caused us to hope that he would get drunk. Well, he confounded us; he did not get drunk, and louder and louder did he get with his anti-God talk. Then we used to console ourselves and say, "Well, after all, this is a very good practice in tolerance for us, trying to accommodate ourselves to Jimmy." But we never did really get accommodated.

One day Jimmy got a job that took him out on the road, out from under the old A.A. tent, you might say. And somewhere out on the road his purely psychological system of staying dry broke wide open, and sure enough he got drunk. In those days, when an alcoholic got drunk, all the brethren would come running, because we were still very afraid for ourselves and no one knew who might be next. So there was great concern about the brother who got drunk. But in Jimmy's case, there was no concern at all. He lay in a little hotel over in Providence and he began to call up long distance. He wanted money, he wanted this, and he wanted that. After a while, Jimmy hitchhiked back to New York. He put up at the house of a friend of mine, where I was staying, and I came in late that night. The next morning, Jimmy came walking downstairs where my friend and I were consuming our morning gallon of coffee. Jimmy looked at us and said, "Oh, have you people had any meditation or prayer this morning?" We thought he was being very sarcastic. But no, he meant it. We could not get very much out of Jimmy about his experience, but it appeared that over in that little second-rate hotel he had nearly died from the worst seizure he had ever had, and something in him had given way. I think it is just what gave way in me. It was his prideful obstinacy. He had thought to himself, "Maybe these fellows have got something with their God-business." His hand reached out, in the darkness, and touched something on his bureau. It was a Gideon Bible. Jimmy picked it up and he read from it. I do not know just what he read, and I have always had a queer reluctance to ask him. But Jimmy has not had a drink to this day, and that was about 5 years ago.

But there were other fruits of what little tolerance and understanding we did have. Not long ago I was in Philadelphia where we have a large and strong group. I was asked to speak, and the man who asked me was Jimmy, who was chairman of the meeting. About 400 people were there. I told this story about him and added: "Supposing that we had cast Jimmy out in the dark, supposing that our intolerance of his point of view had turned him away. Not only would Jimmy be dead, but how many of us would be together here tonight so happily secure?" So we in A.A. find that we have to carry tolerance of other people's viewpoints to really very great lengths. As someone well put it, "Honesty gets us sober but tolerance keeps us sober."

I would like to tell, in conclusion, one story about a man in a little southern community. You know, we used to think that perhaps A.A. was just for the big places; that in a small town the social ostracism of the alcoholics would be so great that they would be reluctant to get together as a group; that there would be so much unkind gossip and talk that we sensitive folk just could not be brought together.

One day our central office in New York received a little letter, and it came from a narcotic addict who was just leaving the Government hospital down in Lexington. Speaking of intolerance, it is a strange fact that we alcoholics are very, very intolerant of people who take "dope," and it is just as strange that they are very intolerant of us. I remember meeting one, one day, in the corridor of a hospital. I thought he was an alcoholic, so I stopped the man and asked him for a match. He drew himself up with great hauteur and said, "Get away from me, you damned alcoholic." At any rate, here was a letter from a narcotic addict who explained that once upon a time he had been an alcoholic, but for 12 years he had been a drug addict. He had got hold of the book *Alcoholics Anonymous* and thought the spirit of that book had got hold of him, and he wanted to go back to his own little southern town, which was Shelby, North Carolina, and start an A.A. group. We were very skeptical of the offer. The very idea of a narcotic addict starting an A.A. group, even if he had once been an alcoholic! And here he was going to try to start it in a little southern town in the midst of all this local pride and gossip.

We began to get letters from him and apparently he was doing all right. He was a medical doctor, by the way, and he told us modestly, as time went on, about getting a small crowd of alcoholics together and having his trials and tribulations. Mind you, we had never seen him all this time; he had just been writing. He said that his practice had come back somewhat. And so 3 years passed. We had a little pin on a map showing that there was an Alcoholics Anonymous group at Shelby, North Carolina. It happened that I was taking a trip south to visit one of our southern groups. By this time the movement had grown and I had gotten to be a kind of big shot, so I thought, and I wondered, "Should I stop off at Shelby? You know, after all, that's kind of a small group." It is a great thing that I did stop off at Shelby, as you will soon see.

Down the station platform came a man, followed by two others. The two in back of him were alcoholics, all right, but one looked a little bit different. I saw, as he drew near, that his lips were badly mangled, and I realized that this was the drug addict, Dr. M. In the agony of his hang-overs he had chewed his lips to pieces. Yes, it was our man, and he proved to be a wonderful person. He was really modest, and that is something you seldom see in an ex-alcoholic. He introduced me to the others, and we got into his car and went over to the town of Shelby. I soon found myself sitting at a table in one of those delightful southern ancestral homes. Here were the man's mother—and his wife. They had been married about 2 years and there was a new baby. The practice had begun to come back. Still, there was very little shop talk at that meal; and there is no such thing as an A.A. meal without shop talk. I said, "Indeed, this fellow is a very modest man, I never saw an alcoholic like him." He spoke very little of his accomplishments for the group. And then came the meeting that night. Here, next to the barber shop in the hotel, on the most prominent corner of Shelby, was the A.A. meeting room, with "A.A." looming big up over the door. I thought, "Well, this chap must be some persuader."

I went inside, and there were 40 alcoholics and their wives and friends. We had our meeting, I talked too much as I always do, and the meeting was over. I began to reflect that this was the largest Alcoholics Anonymous group in all America in proportion to the size of the town. What a wonderful accomplishment! The next morning, my telephone rang in the hotel. A man was downstairs and he said, "I'd like to come up. There are some things you ought to know about Dr. M. who got the A.A. group together in this town."

Up came this individual, and said, "You know, I, too, was once an alcoholic but for 22 years I've been on dope. I used to meet our friend Dr. M. over in Lexington, and when he got out of there and came back here, I heard he'd beaten the dope game. So when I left, I started for Shelby, but on my way I got back on morphine again. He took me into his home and took me off it. Yes, I used to be a respectable citizen of this state, I helped organize a lot of banks here, but I've heard from my family only second-hand for many years. It's my guess you don't know what this southern pride is, and you haven't any idea what this man faced when he came back to this little town to face the music. People wouldn't speak to him for months. They'd say, 'Why, this fellow, the son of our leading doctor, goes away, studies medicine, comes back, and he's a drunk, and after a while, he's on the dope.' The townspeople wouldn't have much to do with him when he first came, and I'm ashamed to say that the local drunks wouldn't either, because they said, 'We ain't going to be sobered up by a dope addict.' But you see, Dr. M. himself had once been an alcoholic, so that he could get that indispensable bond of identification across. Little by little, alcoholics began to rally around him."

My visitor continued, "Well, that was the beginning. Intolerance, misunderstanding, gossip, scandal, failure, defeat, all those things faced our friend when he came into this town. And that was 3 years ago. Well, Bill, you've seen his mother, you've seen his wife, you've seen his baby, you've seen the group. But he hasn't told you that he now has the largest medical practice in this whole town, if not in the county. And he hasn't told you that he has been made head of our local hospital. And I know you don't know this—every year in this town the citizens have a great meeting at which they cast a ballot, and last spring, at the annual casting of the ballot, the people of this town almost unanimously declared by their ballot that Dr. M. had been the town's most useful citizen during the 12 months gone by." So I thought to myself, "So you were the big shot who planned to go straight past Shelby." I looked at my visitor and said, "Indeed, 'What hath God wrought!' "

DISCUSSION

Potts: Mr. W., is it possible for someone who hasn't been drunk, or ever been an alcoholic, to do what an alcoholic has done? Have you found any possibility that laymen or preachers could begin to do such work? Is there anything in your experience that might lead to that possibility?

Lecturer: Yes, there is a great deal in our experience which leads to the idea that our friends of the nonalcoholic world can participate. While it's true that the core of our process is the transmission of these things from one alcoholic to another, it is a fact that very often a minister or a doctor can lay the groundwork for our approach. Then, too, there is a class of people that we alcoholics flatter by calling them "dry" alcoholics. In other words, they're neurotics of our description who don't drink, and we recognize them as more or less kindred spirits; sometimes they approach our group and are well received. On the other hand, sometimes people who, from their life experience, just couldn't get the pitch or couldn't make the identification would be regarded by some of the groups as complete outsiders. You know, one of our other faults is that of snobbishness. We A.A.'s have become extremely snobbish, strange as that may be. But it is true that this thing is a synthesis and we draw upon the resources of both medicine and religion. Of course, the doctor helps us on the physical side of the treatment. He can often prepare the groundwork with the potential alcoholic by pointing out that he has the symptoms of a well-nigh fatal malady. The preacher, or the friend, would do well to emphasize the idea of sickness rather than of immorality. The alcoholic knows he's a louse in most cases, even though he won't admit it, and to be told so once more by someone who never took a glass of beer seems to annoy him greatly. That is not because the other fellow is wrong; we're wrong, but we're just built that way and it's a matter of taking things as they are.

Stoneburner: What can ministers do to cooperate with A.A.?

Lecturer: Of course the approach to the alcoholic is everything. I think the preacher could do well if he does as we do. First, find out all you can about the case, how the man reacts, whether he wants to get over his drinking or not. You see, it is very difficult to make any impressions upon a man who still wants to drink. At some point in their drinking career, most alcoholics get punished enough so that they want to stop, but then it's far too late to do it alone. Sometimes, if the alcoholic can be impressed with the fact that he is a sick man, or a potentially sick man, then, in effect, you raise the bottom up to him instead of allowing him to drop down those extra hard years to reach it. I don't know any substitute for sympathy and understanding, as much as the outsider can have. No preaching, no moralizing, but the emphasis on the idea that the alcoholic is a sick man.

In other words, the minister might first say to the alcoholic, "Well, all my life I've misunderstood you people, I've taken you people to be immoral by choice and perverse and weak, but now I realize that even if there have been such factors, they really no longer count, now you're a sick man." You might win the patient by not placing yourself up on a hilltop and looking down on him, but by getting down to some level of understanding that he gets, or partially gets. Then, if you can present this thing as a fatal and a progressive malady, and you can present our group as a group of people who are not seeking to do anything against his will—we merely want to help if he wants to be helped—then sometimes you've laid the groundwork.

I think the clergyman can often do a great deal with the family. You see, we alcoholics are prone to talk too much about ourselves without sufficiently considering the collateral effects. For example, any family, wife and children, who have had to live with an alcoholic 10 or 15 years, are bound to be rather neurotic and distorted themselves. They just can't help it. After all, when you expect the old gent to come home on a shutter every night, it's wearing. Children get a very distorted point of view; so does the wife. Well, if they constantly hear it emphasized that this fellow is a terrible sinner, that he's a rotter, that he's in disgrace, and all that sort of thing, you're not improving the condition of the family at all because, as they become persuaded of it, they get highly intolerant of the alcoholic and that merely generates more intolerance in him. Therefore, the gulf which must be bridged is widened, and that is why moralizing pushes people, who might have something to offer, further away from the alcoholic. You may say that it shouldn't be so, but it's one of those things that is so.

Robinson: Would local A.A. groups be interested in preventing the development of alcoholics by giving cooperation to local option movements or other programs to that end?

Lecturer: I don't think so. That may be a very hard thing to explain. I'm sure that many people who are in the reform movement are very, very much disappointed in A.A.'s because they don't seem to want to cooperate. Now I make haste to say right away that on this question of reform, this question of prohibition or moderation or what have you, there are just as many points of view among the A.A.'s and their families as there are among the next thousand people who walk by this place. Therefore, no A.A. group can very well say, "We have a particular point of view about prohibition, or this or that degree of prohibition, or about any educational program that involves controversial issues." You see we A.A.'s are of particular and unique use to other alcoholics, therefore we have to be very careful about anything that is going to get between us and them. In other words, we can't do anything that's going to arouse prejudice. For example, if I were to make the statement here that I believe in prohibition, or that I don't believe in prohibition, and either of those points of view was quoted publicly, I would inevitably arouse prejudice. If I said, "Well I don't believe in prohibition and that's my personal view," then a great many good people who do believe in prohibition would get annoyed; they might go out and say to the alcoholic's wife, "Well, I don't like that crowd of A.A.'s because they don't believe in prohibition and look what liquor has done to your husband." So she doesn't suggest A.A. to her husband and he eventually dies because we have been foolish enough to arouse prejudice in somebody's mind.

Likewise, if we said, "Well, we believe in prohibition," and that were quoted, every alcoholic, almost without exception, reading that in the newspapers, would say, "Why, that's a bunch of reformers! and none of that for me." He shouldn't react that way, but he does. Since ours is a life and death job, you can understand why, as a group, we are very careful not to express any opinions on controversial questions. As a group we have no interest in any kind of controversy regardless of the merit of either side, because if we show such an interest, as a group, then we cut down our own peculiar usefulness.

It isn't that there aren't bonds of sympathy between us and a great many points of view. It isn't that individuals among us don't have points of view. But I wouldn't for the world, in a place like this, express my personal views about any controversial question lest my opinion be imputed publicly to the group, to A.A. Then we would be thrown into a controversy that could only prejudice our efforts and not help anybody very much. It isn't lack of understanding or lack of sympathy; it's a matter of policy about which we have to be unusually careful.

Question: How many drug addicts are there in the A.A. and in the organization similar to A.A. which operates among drug addicts?

Lecturer: We have quite a number of drug addicts who were once alcoholics. So far, I don't know of any case of pure drug addiction that we have been able to approach. In other words, we can no more approach a simon-pure addict than the outsider can usually approach us. We are in exactly the same position with them that the doctor and the clergyman have been in in respect to the alcoholic. We just don't talk that fellow's language. He always looks at us and says, "Well, these alcoholics are the scum of the earth and besides, what do they know about addiction?" Now, however, since we have a good number of addicts who were once alcoholics, those addicts in their turn are making an effort, here and there, to transfer the thing over to the straight addict. In that way we hope the bridge is going to be crossed. There may be a case here and there that has been helped. But in all, I suppose, there may be around 50 cases of real morphine addiction in former alcoholics who have been helped by A.A. Of course we have a great many barbital users, but we don't consider those people particularly difficult if they really want to do something about it; and particularly if it's associated with liquor. They seem to get out of it after a while. But where you have morphine, or some of those derivatives, then it gets very tough. Then you have to have a "dope" to talk to a "dope," and I hope that we can find, some day, a bridge to the addict.

Rogers: How many members do you have in A.A.? How many A.A. groups are there?

Lecturer: I might have made that point, although I supposed that the A.A.'s here would have advertised it from the housetops. We have, I think, about 15,000 members, and A.A. groups are in about 367 places. A.A. is showing a capacity to spread by way of literature and correspondence even outside of the United States. We have a very successful group now in Honolulu, and until recently they had had no contacts at all with us except by mail.

Question: If an alcoholic comes to an A.A. meeting under the influence of alcohol, how do you treat him or handle him during the meeting itself?

Lecturer: Groups will usually run amuck on that sort of question. At first we are likely to say that we're going to be supermen and save every drunk in town. The fact is that a great many of them just don't want to stop. They come, but they interfere very greatly with the meeting. Then, being still rather intolerant, the group will swing way over in the other direction and say, "No drunks around these meetings." We get forcible with them and put them out of the meeting, saying, "You're welcome here if you're sober." But the general rule in most places is that if a person comes for the first or second time and can sit quietly in the meeting, without creating an uproar, nobody bothers him. On the other hand, if he's a chronic "slipper" and interferes with the meetings, we lead him out gently, or maybe not so gently, on the theory that one man cannot be permitted to hold up the recovery of others. The theory is "the greatest good for the greatest number."